OFFICIAL
RUGBY UNION
CLUB DIRECTORY
1993-94

COURAGE

CLUBS CHAMPIONSHIP

OFFICIAL
RUGBY UNION
CLUB DIRECTORY
1993-94

Edited by Ross Young

Tony Williams Publications

Typeset by Interface 0395 68681

Printed and bound in Great Britain by
J H Haynes & Co Ltd. Sparkford, Somerset.

Trade Sales: Derek Searle Associates 0753 539295

Distribution: Little Red Witch Books 0823 490080

All other sales enquiries should be referred to
Little Red Witch Books on 0823 490080

ISBN 1-869833-86-4

Cover Photograph supplied by Coloursport.
Bath celebrate another Championship

PUBLISHER'S FOREWORD

by Tony Williams

The announcement that Courage were to renew their sponsorship of the massive Club Championship was certainly good news for the game. There is no doubt that the increased competitiveness of the senior national divisions provides England with players who are far better prepared for the international scene.

However as the players improve their fitness techniques and attitude to the game you only have to look at responses to our requests for information, photos and programmes for this directory, to realise that attitudes of keenness and efficiency at committee level just do not match their players progress.

Whether officials of the old school like it or not the game of Ruby Union is becoming better organised, is enjoying a wider audience and owes its public the courtesy of a reasonable public relations service.

This directory has attracted two really exciting new assets this year in the wonderful statistics of Steve McCormack and the excellent photos of Joe McCabe. These two enthusiasts are examples of the changing face of this game and Rugby Union will benefit from their much appreciated efforts.

More and more club officials are realising the importance of good public relations and hopefully the promotion of their season's details received from Rugby, Saracens and Bristol will be emulated by all senior National clubs.

Some club officials seem genuinely mystified that their supporters or even players and officials do enjoy the information and publicity given to Rugby Union through our Directory!

May we once again emphasise the fact that a huge league such as The Courage Rugby Union Club Championship deserves the very best of presentation.

This book is popular with true followers of this game so please help your supporters by sending in information when it is required next season and also introduce the Directory either by straightforward sales or through raffles (both of these methods can raise significant funds for your club).

Making this Directory available to everyone at the club on Courage League match days is surely not too much to be expected as a thank you to a very valuable sponsor.

Tony Williams

A WELCOME FROM THE RFU

by Ian Beer CBE JP

**President
The Rugby Football Union**

Over the last six years the Courage Clubs Championship has established itself as a major part of the Rugby Football Union calendar in England and, as such, has been instrumental in the leap forward in the commercial and public interest the game has seen over the past few years. That was why, when the time came, we were delighted to be able to renew the sponsorship with Courage and also that Courage felt confident enough in the future of the game of Rugby to want to extend this involvement for another four years.

Clubs and players have responded and benefited to a huge extent from the challenge of the Courage league games and we are particularly grateful to all those that administer the leagues throughout the country. The extra dedication and commitment the league structure has bought to the game is shown at every level from grass roots to the appearance of eleven Englishmen in the second and third Tests of the Lions Tour. The introduction of home and away fixtures in the National Leagues will only increase the quality of the competition still further, provided that the players and referees — for the game is for them — do not find that we as administrators have overstretched their physical and mental involvement.

It is encouraging that Courage understands the needs of the Rugby Union and I very much hope that we understand the needs of Courage Ltd. as we see the continued association as a true reflection of all that Rugby Union has to offer. We have always found Courage to be a sympathetic sponsor with a great knowledge of the game and we are deeply grateful for their support over the last six years. Many new friendships have been created through this sponsorship and that is still one of the great virtues of being associated with our game — as player, referee, coach, administrator, sponsor or spectator. We look forward to the next four years with anticipation.

Ian Beer

A WELCOME FROM COURAGE

by Andrew Simmonds

Group Manager
Courage Ales Marketing

As competitive league rugby enters its seventh year the stature and popularity of Rugby Union Football is at an all time high. The leagues give purpose and competitive edge to club rugby at every level, and the success of the English National side shows the strength and quality of player that our league structure can produce.

Courage is very proud to be the sponsor of the largest league set-up in world sport, and we are delighted to have recently announced a new package in which we are committing £7 million over the next four years. This will not only continue our association with rugby but will also expand our involvement with the game and the clubs at all levels.

If the game is to develop changes must inevitably occur. Home and away fixtures are being introduced for the first time in the National Leagues this season and these will only heighten the level of competition — but in this game of change Courage are delighted to remain a constant factor.

Best wishes for a successful 1993/94 season.

Andrew Simmonds

PRINCIPAL FIXTURES 1993-94

DATE	FIXTURE	VENUE
SEPTEMBER		
Sat 11th	**COURAGE LEAGUES' MATCHES**	
	Pilkington Cup Round 1	England
	Junior Clubs Round 1	England
Sat 18th	County Championship (1)	England
	COURAGE LEAGUES' MATCHES	
	IC Leagues all Divisions (1)	Ireland
	Swalec Cup (1)	Wales
Sat 25th	County Championship (1)	England
	COURAGE LEAGUES' MATCHES	
	IC Leagues all Divisions (2)	Ireland
Wed 29th	Wales A v Japan	Llanelli
OCTOBER		
Sat 2nd	County Championship (3)	England
	COURAGE LEAGUES' MATCHES	
	IC Leagues all Divisions (3)	Ireland
	Dunvant v Japan	Dunvant Wales
Sat 9th	**COURAGE LEAGUES' MATCHES**	
	IC Leagues all Divisions (4)	Ireland
	West Wales v Japan	Narberth
Tue 12th	3rd & 4th Divisions	
	Select v Japan	Pontypridd
Wed 13th	Wales A v North of England	Pontypool
Sat 16th	Wales v Japan	Cardiff Arms Park
	Divisional Championships	England
	South West v Midlands	Bath
	North v London & SE	Newcastle Gosforth
	Pilkington Cup (2)	England
	Junior Clubs Cup (2)	England
	Ulster v Exiles (Irish Interprovs)	Belfast
	Connacht v Munster (Irish Interprovs)	Galway
	Leinster v Scottish Exiles	Dublin
Tue 19th	Gloucester v South African Barbarians	Gloucs
Thu 21st	Leicester v South African Barbarians	Leicester
Sat 23rd	London & SE Division v New Zealand	Twickenham
	Divisional Championships	England
	South West v North	Gloucester
	COURAGE LEAGUES' MATCHES	
	Glasgow v Edinburgh	Hughenden
	South v North & Midlands	Jedburgh
	Exiles v Leinster (Irish Interprov)	Sunbury
	Connacht v Ulster (Irish Interprov)	Galway
	Swalec Cup (2)	Wales
Mon 25th	Newport v South African Barbarians	Newport
Tue 26th	Midland Division v New Zealand	Leicester
Wed 27th	Llanelli v South African Barbarians	Llanelli
	Scotland/Ireland Dist/Prov Championships	Scotland & Ireland
Sat 30th	South West v New Zealand	Redruth
	Divisional Championship	England
	Midland v London & SE	Leicester
	COURAGE LEAGUES' MATCHES	
	Scottish Inter District Finals & Play Off	Scotland
	Exiles v Connacht (Irish Interprov)	Sunbury
	Munster v Leinster (Irish Interprov)	Limerick
NOVEMBER		
Mon 1st	Bridgend v South African Barbarians	Bridgend
Tue 2nd	North Division v New Zealand	Liverpool AFC
Sat 6th	Divisional Championship	England
	London & SE v South West	Wasps prov
	Midland v North	Northampton
	COURAGE LEAGUES' MATCHES	
	Junior Clubs Cup (3)	England
	Scottish Exile v Auckland	England
Sun 7th	England A v New Zealand	Gateshead
Tue 8th	Edinburgh v Auckland	Meggetland
Wed 10th	South of Scotland v New Zealand	Gala
Sat 13th	Ireland v Romania	Dublin

8

Sat 13th Nov contd.	Scotland A V New Zealand	Hawick
	COURAGE LEAGUES' MATCHES	
Sun 14th	District Selection v Auckland	Hawick
Tue 16th	Scottish Developmen XV v New Zealand	Myreside
Sat 20th	Scotland v New Zealand	Murrayfield
	COURAGE LEAGUES' MATCHES	
	Swalec Cup (3)	Wales
	IC LEagues (5)	Ireland
Tue 23rd	England Emerging Players v New Zealand	Gloucester
Sat 27th	England v New Zealand	Twickenham
	Pilkington Cup (3)	England
	Junior Clubs Cup (4)	England
	Leinster v Ulster (Irish Interprove)	Limerick
Tue 30th	Combined Services v New Zealand	Devonport

DECEMBER

Wed 1st	Inter District Championships	Scotland
	Wanderers v Blackrock College (IC Lge Div 1)	Ireland
Sat 4th	Barbarians v New Zealand	Cardiff Arms Park
	COURAGE LEAGUES' MATCHES	
	Glasgow v Munster	Glasgow
	North & Midlands v Connacht	Dunfermline
	Ulster v South	Belfast
	Leinster v Edinbiurgh	Dublin
Tue 7th	Oxford v Cambridge	Twickenham
Wed 8th	Lansdowne v Wanderers (IC Lge Div 1)	Ireland
Sat 11th	Colts County Championship Final	Twickenham
	COURAGE LEAGUES' MATCHES	
	South Leinster	
	Edinburgh v Ulster	Melrose
	Munster v North & Midlands	Goldenacre
	Connacht v Glasgow	Cork
Sat 18th	Pilkington Cup (4)	Galway
	Junior Clubs (5)	England
	COURAGE LEAGUES' MATCHES	England
	Italy v Scotland A	Italy
	Leinster v Connacht (Irish Interprov)	Belfast
	Swalec Cup (4)	Wales
Tus 28th	Leicester v Barbarians	Leicester
	Scotland A v Ireland	Scotland

JANUARY 1994

Tue 4th	Scotland A V Spain	
Sat 8th	**COURAGE LEAGUES' MATCHES**	Murrayfield
	IC Leagues (6)	
	Newbridge v Aberavon	Ireland
Fri 14th	Wales U21 v Scotland U21	Wales
	France Students v Ireland Students	Cardiff
Sat 15th	France v Ireland	
	Wales v Scotland	Paris
	County Championship Semi Finals	Cardiff Arms Park
	COURAGE LEAGUES' MATCHES	England
Sat 22nd	Pilkington Cup (5)	
	COURAGE LEAGUES' MATCHES	England
	Junior Clubs Cup (6)	
	IC Leagues (7)	England
	Swalec Cup (5)	Ireland
Sat 29th	**COURAGE LEAGUES' MATCHES**	Wales
	IC Leagues Divs 3&4 (8)	
		Ireland

FEBRUARY

Fri 4th	Ireland A v Wales A	
	Ireland U21 v Wales U21	Dublin
	Scotland Students v England Students	
Sat 5th	Scotland v England	Edinburgh
	Ireland v Wales	Murrayfield
Sat 12th	**COURAGE LEAGUES' MATCHES**	Lansdowne Road
	IC Leagues Divs 3&4 (9)	
Fri 18th	England A v Ireland A	Ireland
	England Students v Ireland Students	England
Sat 19th	England v Ireland	Bournemouth
	Wales v France	Twickenham
Sun 20th	France A v Scotland A	Cardiff Arms Park
Sat 26th	Pilkington Cup Quarter Finals	France
	COURAGE LEAGUES' MATCHES	England
	Junior Clubs Cup Quarter Finals	
	IC Leagues Divs 1&2 (9)	England
		Ireland

Sat 26th Feb contd.	IC Leagues Divs 3&4 (10)	Ireland
	Swalec Cup (6)	Wales

MARCH

Fri 4th	France Students v England Students	France
	Ireland U21 v Scotland U21	Dublin
	Ireland Students v Scotland Students	Ireland
Sat 5th	France v England	Paris
	Ireland v Scotland	Lansdowne Road
Sat 12th	Italy Juniors v England Colts	Italy
	COURAGE LEAGUES' MATCHES	
	IC Leagues Divs 1&2 (10)	Ireland
	IC Leagues Divs 3&4 (11)	Ireland
Fri 18th	England Students v Wales Students	Oxford University
	Scotland U21 v France U21	Inverleith
	Wales A v France B	Wales
Sat 19th	England v Wales	Twickenham
	Scotland v France	Murrayfield
	IC Leagues Divs 1&2 (11)	Ireland
	IC Leagues Divs 3&4 (12)	Ireland
Wed 23rd	England v Wales 18 Group	Bournemouth
Sat 26	COURAGE LEAGUES' MATCHES	
	Royal Navy v Army	Twickenham
Sun 27	Wales Youth v England Colts	Cardiff
Wed 30	Scotland v England 18 Group	Kelso
	Ireland v Wales Schools	Ireland

APRIL

Sat 2nd	France v England 18 Group	Cahors
	Pilkington Cup Semi Finals	England
	Junior Clubs Cup Semi Finals	England
	Italy U21 v Scotland U21	Italy
	Scotland U18 v Spain U18	Rubislaw Aberdeen
	Gala Sevens	Scotland
	Swalec Cup Quarter Finals	Wales
	Cardiff v Barbarians	Cardiff
Mon 4th	Ireland v Scotland Schools	Limerick
	Swansea v Barbarians	Swansea
Sat 9th	Daily Mail Schools Cup Finals	Twickenham
	England v Wales 16 Group	Twickenham
	England Colts v Scotland U19	Waterloo
	COURAGE LEAGUES' MATCHES	
	Melrose Sevens	Scotland
	Ireland U18 v Scotland U18	Ireland
	IC Leagues Divs 1&2 (12)	Ireland
	IC Leagues Divs 3&4 (13)	Ireland
Wed 13th	Royal Navy v Royal Air Force	Twickenham
	England v Ireland 18 Groupo	Durham City
Sat 16th	County Championship Final	Twickenham
	Scotland U19 v Wales U19	Stirling
	Swalec Cup Semi Finals	Wales
Wed 20th	Army v Royal Air Force	Twickenham
Sat 23rd	England Colts v France Juinors	Moseley
	COURAGE LEAGUES' MATCHES	
	Jed Forest Sevens	Scotland
Sat 30th	COURAGE LEAGUES' MATCHES	
	Langholm Sevens	Scotland

MAY

Sat 7th	Pilkington Cup Final	Twickenham
	Swalec Cup Final	Cardiff Arms Park
Sat 14th	Middlesex Sevens Finals	Twickenham

JUNE

Sat 4th	French Championship Final	Paris

REVIEW OF THE SEASON

by Bill Mitchell

The sixth season of Courage Leagues was inevitably the most momentous and traumatic of all at least for the top three Leagues, which have now become four. Few matches at the top end of the competition were unimportant and in every case the final outcome of title and pecking order was undecided until the final day.

As a result some famous clubs will find themselves as founder members of the new third flight — Bedford, Rosslyn Park, Richmond, Blackheath, Coventry and Fylde among them along with less famous names such as Havant (who are unlucky not to be in League Two in the new season) and Redruth.

The two top leagues will consist of well-known clubs, but all must now look to their laurels in the new format since it will be easier to finish in the bottom two of a league than to attain a top two promotion position.

Our own attempts at a forecast of the composition of the new divisions were at best modest. We managed eight of the ten sides in the top league, five out of ten in League two, eight out of ten in League Three and six out of ten in League Four. Neither London Welsh nor Hereford, whom we expected to be promoted from the Fourth Leagues managed it, the latter almost stumbling to relegation out of the senior competitions, whilst "Welsh" are finding it difficult to regain their elite position in the game, mainly because promising players from the Valleys are no longer making themselves available for a variety of reasons and local lads of Welsh origin (or something like it!) look to play for bigger clubs if they are good enough.

However, as we already have stated, there were no unimportant games and all three top leagues were decided on points difference with Bath's success depending on the vital clash in late March with Wasps at the Recreation Ground, when the latter had to bow the knee after a controversial incident involving Jeremy Guscott and the Wasps and former England centre Fran Clough led to the referee dismissing the latter thus leaving the visitors to play for an hour a man short. When the dust settled it was clear that such an episode was in fact the decisive factor in Bath retaining the title.

Elsewhere in the top flight it was a hard slog, but in the end there was a clear gap between the lowest placed survivor — Orrell — and London Scottish, so there were no hard-luck stories.

Newcastle Gosforth lost their final match, but needed to do so by a huge margin at Moseley to "blow" their promotion chances and they did not, which left Waterloo with their superb cup wins over Bath and Orrell as their best memories of the season. Moseley's win in fact kept them in the second tier on points difference from Bedford, which means that two former knock-out cup winners (Coventry are the other club) will be playing third grade rugby next season.

Clifton, our tip to gain promotion to the second flight, will in fact be founder-members of League Four along with such big names as Sheffield, Liverpool St.Helens and Leeds and that competition will have two interesting newcomers in Harrogate (once a big wheel in Yorkshire rugby and the season's top points scorers in senior matches) and Sudbury from East Anglia — the only one of the senior league winners to have established daylight between themselves and the rest before the final day of the season.

So, for better or for worse, the leading four Leagues will consist of ten clubs each and there will be a full list of home and away fixtures. This will be fine for clubs which are enjoying success in the top flight but others could struggle to make ends meet. For example Redruth and Exeter must each travel to Fylde and Morley (and vice versa) in League Three, and in the new fourth grade

Plymouth Albion and Clifton must exchange visits with Sheffield, Leeds, Harrogate and Sudbury. Some club secretaries will be nervous wrecks if expenses are too high.

Another problem could arise if there is any bad weather at all during the season, since the top clubs in particular could face 18 league games plus five cup matches. The eight month season must also fit in four international matches for top players, divisional games and, probably, at least one game against the visiting All Blacks. That makes some 28 games to be crammed into 34 weeks — quite a tall order. Perhaps, the top leagues should have been smaller so as to take the pressure off the players, who are human after all.

Of course, the players themselves in an amateur game too often accept invitations to play in too many matches, which is another factor that is unhelpful, which reminds one of another problem — the demand by some that the game should go professional.

They say that this would be the only honest way to run the game — and that may well be fair comment. But we have already given reasons why certain clubs will find it difficult to survive travel costs and a full professional game with players actually being paid to play could bankrupt the top clubs as well. Some are already alleged to be paying players, but if it becomes a free-for-all the consequences for clubs, which already have problems, could become catastrophic. "Keeping up with the Joneses" will not come cheap to anyone — not even the big payers.

However, having made these strictures it would be right to point out that for junior clubs at all levels the leagues have made a massive impact — mostly for the good. They have been given a target in every case and all have the chance (in theory at least) of attaining senior status so that they can play with the big boys. Supporting competitions such as county cups add to their options and the game has become healthier for it. For example clubs like Harlow, Camberley, Stroud, Burton, Worcester, Manchester and Huddersfield are all only a step away from the big time, which has recently seen the likes of Havant and Otley flourish. The leagues also have coincided with a revival in the England national team's fortunes — if it is a coincidence — to the extent that the majority of British Lions in 1993 were English and most seasons from now onwards the national team will be pre-Five Nations favourites on a regular basis, such is the strength in depth that has been engendered by such intensive competition. There will of course be disappointing campaigns for England like the recent one, but with competition for places being so strong only poor selection and a failure to acknowledge real form can keep England down.

The one cautionary note in a good general report is that at the top level too much may be demanded of the players and there are already signs that one or two may burn themselves out before reaching a decent retiring age.

As for the new season there is no reason why we should not stick out our necks and make some forecasts:

League One: Champions — Bath. Relegation — London Irish and Orrell.

League Two: Champions — Waterloo. Promotion — Moseley. Relegation — Rugby and Otley.

League Three: Champions — Bedford. Promotion — Rosslyn Park. Relegation — Morley and Redruth

League Four: Champions — Leeds. Promotion — Sheffield. Relegation — Broughton Park and Plymouth Albion.

Division Five North: Champions — Rotherham.

Division Five South: Champions — London Welsh.

We can but try! No brickbats, please!

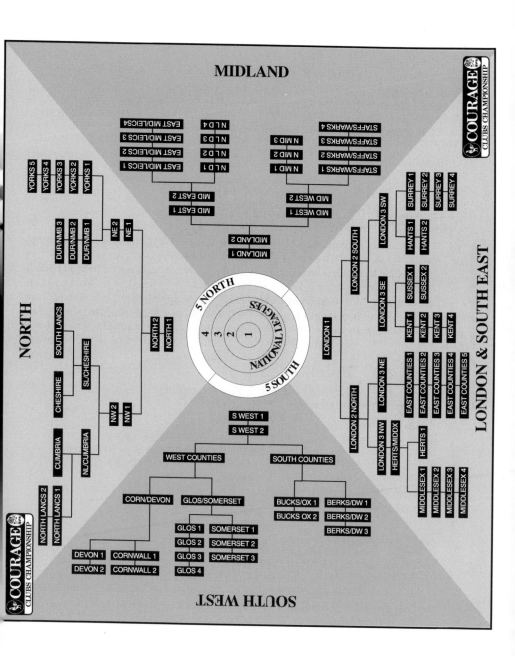

THE COURAGE CLUBS
CHAMPIONSHIP REGULATIONS 1993-94

1 **Description**

The Competition shall be called "The English Clubs Rugby Union Championship" (hereinafter referred to as "the Competition") and shall be open to Clubs in membership with the Rugby Football Union (hereinafter called "the RFU"). All matches in the Competition shall be played under the Laws of Rugby Union Football and shall comply with the Bye-Laws, Resolutions and Regulations of the RFU.

2 **Organising Committee**

The Competition will be organised by the Competition Sub-Committee of the RFU (hereinafter referred to as "the Committee") whose decision shall be binding and final on any matter not provided for in and on the interpretation of these Regulations.

3 **Delegation of Administration**

a) The Committee appoints the RFU Senior Clubs Association Committee as the Organising Committee of National Leagues 1, 2, 3 and 4 (see Appendix 1).

b) The Committee appoints the RFU Divisions as the Organising Committees of all Leagues within their Divisions.

c) The Committee will be the Organising Committee of National Leagues 5 North and South.

d) The Committee (in respect of National Leagues 5 North and South), the RFU Senior Clubs Association and the RFU Divisions shall, subject to Regulation 18(a) of these Regulations, deal with all disputes, transgressions and complaints as laid down by Regulation 19.

4 **Structure**

a) **National**

There shall be four National Leagues 1, 2, 3 and 4, comprising 10 Clubs each, unless agreed otherwise by the Committee.

b) **Areas**

(i) The Northern and Midland RFU Divisions shall combine to provide one National League 5 North and the London and South East and South West RFU Divisions shall combine to provide one National League 5 South each comprised of thirteen Clubs, unless agreed otherwise by the Committee.

(ii) Promotion from the National Leagues 5 North and South shall be to National League 4.

c) **RFU Divisions**

(i) Each of the RFU Divisions shall have a first League.

(ii) Promotion from the Northern Division League 1 and the Midland Division League 1 shall be to the National League 5 North and from the London and South East Division League 1 and the South West Division League 1 shall be to the National League 5 South.

(iii) The Divisional League structure below Division League 1 in each Division shall be such as shall, with the approval of the Committee, be determined by that Division.

(iv) Leagues shall be comprised of 13 Clubs, except that the lowest two Leagues may, with the consent of the appropriate Divisional Committee, consist of more or less, unless agreed otherwise by the Committee.

d) **General**

(i) Not more than two lower Leagues may support a higher League.

(ii) Only Club first XVs may enter the Competition.

(iii) A Club may only play in any National League 5 or Divisional League according to its RFU Constituent Body allocation.

5 Club Positions

The position of a Club in a League shall be established by awarding two points for a win and one point for a draw. In the case of equality, positions shall be determined on the basis of match points scored. A Club with a larger difference between match points for and match points against shall be placed higher in a League than a Club with a smaller difference between match points for and match points against. Should two Clubs have the same number of competition points and the same match points difference, the Club having scored more match points shall be placed higher in the League than the Club having a lesser number of match points for. In the event of the match points for still being unable to establish the position of two Clubs, and if the winning of the Competition or promotion or relegation is involved, the Club who has won the highest number of its league matches shall be placed higher. If this does not establish the position then the Club who has won the most matches, excluding its first league match of the season, then its second league match, until it can be established which is the highest placed Club.

6 Promotion and Relegation

a) Where one League supports one League, the top two Clubs from the lower League at the end of the season shall be promoted to the higher League.

b) Where two Leagues support one League the top Club in each of the supporting Leagues at the end of the season shall be promoted to the highest League.

c) After promotion has taken place according to Clauses (a) and (b) above, the requisite number of Clubs shall be relegated (upon the basis prescribed in Clause (d) below) from each League at the end of the season so that the following season there are 10 Clubs in National Leagues 1, 2, 3 and 4, and 13 Clubs in all other Leagues (or such other number of Clubs as there are to be in the lowest two Leagues in each of the RFU Divisions in accordance with Regulation 4(c)(iv) above).

d) Except in the case of relegation from National League 1 to National League 2, from National League 2 to National League 3 and from National League 3 to National League 4, Clubs shall be relegated on a geographical/Divisional/Constituent Body basis as appropriate.

Note: Given this, and the provisions of Clause (c) above, it is accordingly not possible (except in the cases of relegation from National Leagues 1, 2, 3 and 4 where two Clubs will be relegated from each League) to determine how many Clubs are to be relegated from any particular League until it has first been determined at the end of the season (i) how many Clubs are to be relegated from each (in turn) of the Leagues (both National Leagues and Divisional Leagues) higher than the League and (ii) to which League or Leagues the Clubs from those higher Leagues are to be relegated.

e) Notwithstanding the foregoing provisions of this Regulation, or the provisions of Regulation 4 above, the Committee may, as it shall in its absolute discretion think fit, at any time, (i) disapply, suspend, amend and/or vary the foregoing provisions of this Regulation and/or as to the number of Clubs comprising any League or Leagues, and/or (ii) transfer any Club from the League in which it would have been placed by virtue of the application of Clauses (a) to (d) of this Regulation to such other League (whether higher or lower) as the Committee shall think fit. Any action taken or decision made by the Committee under the powers conferred on it by the foregoing provisions of this Clause (e) shall be final and binding.

7 Fixtures

a) All League matches shall be played on fixed Saturdays as set out in the Structured Season.

b) All League matches in National Leagues 1, 2, 3 and 4 shall be played on a home and away basis.

c) All League fixture lists shall be prepared by the Organising Committee of the League concerned and submitted to the Clubs comprising the League by the 31st May in each year. A copy shall be sent to the Secretary of the RFU by the same date.

d) Every Club in all League fixtures shall play its bona fide first XV.

15

8 **Eligibility**

    a) **Clubs**

        (i) Any Club in membership with the RFU may enter the Competition subject to the approval of the Committee and of the appropriate RFU Division according to its RFU Constituent Body allocation.

        (ii) Any Club applying to join the Competition shall only be permitted to do so by being placed in the bottom League in its RFU Division.

        (iii)The Committee shall have the power to impose conditions upon the membership or continued participation of any Club or Clubs in the Competition. Any Club or Clubs failing to comply with such conditions shall not be entitled to enter the Competition or to continue to participate in it.

    b) **Players**

        (i) A Club in a Competition match may only play or select as a replacement, players who hold EFFECTIVE registration for that Club, in accordance with the RFU Registration of Players Regulations.

        (ii) A Club may only play or select as a replacement in a Competition match one player who holds EFFECTIVE registration under Regulation 9(b)(ii) of the RFU Registration of Players Regulations.

        (iii)A Club may not play or select as a replacement in a match in the Competition any player who has at any time received any material benefit (as defined in Regulation 1.3 of the IRFB Regulations Relating to Amateurism) for playing any form of rugby football.

Penalty: A Club shall be deducted two championship points on each occasion that it has been represented by an ineligible player or replacement or been in breach of Regulation 8(b)(i), 8(b)(ii) or 8(b)(iii).

9 **Players in Representative Matches**

Where an English representative match involving any National team or any match involving the Senior National Representative Team of one of the other three Home Unions is played on a date fixed for a League match, any Club which is affected by three or more players or replacements taking part in such representative match may require the League match to be rearranged for a later date. Such rearranged match will be fixed by the Clubs concerned, or failing agreement between them, by the Organising Committee of the League concerned. The Clubs concerned must notify in writing such Committee of the rearranged date within 7 days of the original match date.

10 **Replacements**

In all matches in the Competition replacements are permitted in accordance with the RFU Resolutions relating to the use of replacements.

11 **Unplayed, Postponed and Abandoned Matches**

    a) If weather conditions prevent a match being played or a match is abandoned because of such conditions with less than sixty minutes having been played, the match shall be played or replayed on a date (except Sundays) to be agreed between the two Clubs concerned (when the Clubs concerned must notify in writing the Organising Committee of the rearranged date within seven days of the original match date) or, failing agreement, as directed by the Organising Committee of the League concerned. If a match is abandoned because of weather conditions when sixty or more minutes have been played, then the score at the moment of abandonment shall stand and be deemed the final score in the match. The referee's decision as to the necessity for abandonment and the number of minutes played at the moment of abandonment shall be final.

    b) If the referee finds it necessary to abandon a match for any reason other than weather conditions, then, irrespective of the number of minutes played, the result of that match may be determined by the Organising Committee of the League concerned or that Committee may order the match to be replayed.

    c) If a match is abandoned under Clauses (a) or (b) above, the home Club shall supply the secretary of the Organising Committee of the League concerned with the match card duly signed by the referee and stating the exact time of the match abandonment, the existing match score at the time and the reason for the abandonment.

d) In the event of a Competition match not being played the Organising Committee of the League concerned shall have power to award the Competition points but no match points will be awarded to either side.

e) Any Club which is suspended by its County Constituent Body from playing Rugby Union Football for disciplinary reasons will not be permitted to rearrange any League fixtures failing to be played within the period of the suspension. The effects thereof on the non-offending Clubs in the League concerned shall be dealt with by the Organising Committee of the League concerned under Clause (f) below.

f) In the event of a Competition match not being played for whatever reason, whether or not Championship points are awarded to a Club under this Regulation, if that Club be a contender for promotion or relegation at the end of the season, the difference between the match points for and against of all Clubs (other than the offending Club) in the League shall be adjusted to exclude all match points scored in matches played against the offending Club before establishing the final position of each Club in the League in accordance with Regulation 5.

g) In the event of a Club failing to fulfil its League fixtures for reasons unacceptable to the Organising Committee of the League concerned, or if a Club voluntarily withdraws from a League, or if a Club is expelled or suspended from a League or from membership of the Competition, the results of all matches played by it shall be deleted. The final League table positions shall be established under Regulation 5 from all matches played between the remaining Clubs in such League.

12 Completion of Match Result Card

Each Club shall complete a match result card in accordance with the instructions set out in the Administrative Instructions applicable to such Club's League. The Organising Committees are empowered to impose monetary fines for failure to comply with such instructions and non-payment of fines by the due dates may lead to a deduction of two competition points for each such offence. Providing false information on players or replacements taking part in a match shall render that Club, player and/or official liable to disciplinary action in accordance with RFU Bye-Law 13(g).

13 Referees and Touch Judges

a) The referee for each match shall be appointed or provided by the Referees' Society to which the home Club pay a Referees' Society subscription, subject to any appointments made by the RFU.

b) In all matches in National Leagues 1, 2, 3, 4 and 5 North and 5 South two qualified touch judges shall be appointed by the RFU and the RFU Resolution relating to Law 6 shall apply.

c) In all other matches each Club shall provide a competent touch judge who should not be a replacement. In an emergency a replacement may act as a touch judge with the agreement of the referee.

d) If the referee appointed or provided under Regulation 13(a) has not arrived at the agreed kick-off time or if the referee is unable to officiate for the whole of the match for any reason and a replacement referee is available, the captains of the two Clubs concerned may agree that the replacement referee can officiate and the result shall count in the Competition. Such agreement shall thereafter be binding upon the Clubs. If there is no agreement then the match shall not count in the Competition and it must be replayed in accordance with the provisions of Regulation 11(a).

14 Kick-Offs and Delayed Arrivals

All Saturday matches shall start at the home Club's normal kick-off time but shall not be later than 3.00pm in any event. An earlier kick-off time may be arranged by mutual agreement between the two Clubs concerned. Any delay may be reported by the non-offending Club to the Organising Committee of the League concerned and may lead to the match being awarded to the non-offending Club.

15 Clash of Colours/Identification of Players

a) In the event of Clubs having similar or clashing colours the home Club will be responsible for changing its colours, subject to the satisfaction of the appointed referee.

b) The jerseys of teams competing in the Competition should all be numbered or lettered to ensure the correct identification of all players and replacements during a match.

16 Grounds

a) A home Club is responsible for correctly and clearly marking its pitch and it must make proper provision to ensure that (with the exception of the touch judges) all spectators, replacements and officials are kept at a reasonable distance from the field of play.

b) When a late decision as to the fitness of the ground for the playing of a match is necessary, it shall be made by the respective captains of the Clubs involved but if the captains are not able to agree, the decision shall be made by the appointed referee.

17 Finance

a) Monies provided for the1993-94 Competition and all Competitions thereafter (until otherwise agreed by Courage) shall belong to the Clubs in the Leagues for whom the monies have been provided and shall be distributed in such shares as the Committee shall decide provided always that the Committee may as it shall see fit appropriate for the benefit of Clubs whether or not participating in the Competition and Schools in membership of the ERFSU or distribute for such charitable purposes as the Committee may select not more than 15% of the said monies.

b) Any proposal involving an offer of sponsorship, financial assistance or gift for a League or combination of Leagues must be submitted to the RFU for approval.

c) Gate receipts at a match shall belong to the home Club.

d) The home Club shall be responsible for all match expenses.

e) The away Club shall be responsible for its own travelling and accommodation expenses.

f) Such membership/registration fee may be charged to each participating Club as may from time to time be determined by the Organising Committee of the League concerned with the approval of the Committee.

g) Clubs failing to register claims by the 28th February will not be eligible for payment of sponsorship monies.

18 Disciplinary Powers

a) Without prejudice to the powers of the RFU or the delegation of powers to Constituent Bodies under Bye-Law (13)(d), the Committee shall have the power to expel or suspend any Club from membership of the Competition or impose such other penalty as is considered appropriate on any Club for a breach of these Regulations.

b) The Committee shall have the right to delegate disciplinary powers (other than the power to expel or suspend from membership of the Competition) for any breach of these Regulations to an Organising Committee of a League or National League subject to the rights of appeal as hereinafter provided.

c) Specifically an Organising Committee of a League shall have power to discipline any Club participating in such League for breach of any of the Regulations of the Competition by way of loss of match or Competition points, transference of points, review of result or monetary fine, and any such Club may be liable to be placed at the bottom of the League concerned and such Club's results deleted from such League table.

19 Complaints and Appeals

a) Any complaint shall be referred to the Secretary of the League concerned by telephone within 48 hours of knowledge of the occurrence giving rise to the complaint and thereafter submitted in writing within a further 48 hours. The complaining Club shall also send a copy of such complaint in writing within such 48 hours to the other party to the complaint if applicable. The Secretary, on receipt of the written complaint, shall give a ruling within 7 days. If either party to the complaint is dissatisfied with such ruling there shall be a right of appeal to the Organising Committee of the League concerned as set out in Regulation 3 to be given in writing within 7 days of receipt of the Secretary's decision.

b) If either the complaining Club, or the other party to the complaint, or the Club against whom the complaint is made, requires an oral hearing, it shall be requested in writing and the Organising

Committee responsible for the League concerned shall, within 72 hours of receiving notice of such request, appoint a time, date and place for the hearing of such complaint.

c) Any party aggrieved at the decision of the Organising Committee may, within seven days of receipt of the decision, appeal in writing to the Secretary of the RFU restating the grounds on which the original appeal was made. The Club shall not be entitled to introduce any further grounds of objection not previously stated to the Organising Committee, nor to lodge a second objection arising from the circumstances on which the objection is based.

The Secretary of the RFU shall refer the objection to the Competition Sub-Committee of the RFU whose decision shall be final and binding. It shall be the sole discretion of the Competition Sub-Committee whether or not to grant a personal hearing.

d) (i) Any party to an appeal, (whether made under Regulation 19(b) or 19(c)) shall provide such information or evidence and within such time as the Organising Committee or the Appeal Committee (as the case may be) shall require.

(ii) Upon a party to an appeal failing to provide such information within the time required, the Organising Committee or the Appeal Committee (as the case may be) shall be entitled to refuse to hear that party when considering the appeal.

e) The Club and/or appellant may be required to pay the cost of the Appeal when a personal hearing is requested and granted.

20 Medical Safety

Whenever possible, the home team should ensure a doctor or other medically qualified person is in attendance throughout the match.

21 Terms and Conditions of Sponsorship

All Clubs participating in the Competition shall at all times comply with each and every of the obligations and requirements entered into by the RFU with the sponsors of the Competition under the terms and conditions of the sponsorship agreement, details of which obligations and requirements shall be notified by the RFU to participating Clubs as applicable.

22 Copyright

The copyright in the fixture lists of the Competition shall vest in the RFU and must not be reproduced in whole or in part except with the written consent of the RFU.

Organising Committee for National Leagues 1, 2, 3 and 4

The participating Clubs within National Leagues 1, 2, 3 and 4 of the English Club Championships within each of the four geographical divisional areas of the RFU shall nominate three members from their respective Divisional Membership who shall constitute the Organising Committee for National Leagues 1, 2, 3 and 4.

The members for 1993/94 are:

R L Ellis,
31 Russell Avenue,
Hartley,
Plymouth PL3 5RB.
Tel: 0752 771237 (H)

R Fawden,
100 Swain's Lane
Highgate,
London N6 6PL.
Tel: 081 348 4753 (H)
      081 348 4254 (B)
Fax: 081 340 2199

R Foster,
27 Carr Lane,
Sandal,
Wakefield,
West Yorkshire WF2 6HJ.
Tel: 0924 250166 (H)
      0924 371501 (B)

F M Gibbon (Chairman),
12 The Green,
Bishopton,
Stockton-on-Tees,
Cleveland TS31 1HF.
Tel: 0740 30410 (H)
      0642 602221 (B)

N G Hannah,
Gatehouse,
62 Beeston Fields Drive,
Bramcote,
Beeston,
Nottingham NG9 3DD.
Tel: 0602 254798 (H)
      0602 243243 (B)
Fax: 0509 242310

T A B Mahoney,
2 Raymend Walk,
St. John's Lane,
Bristol BS3 5AP.
Tel: 0272 664782 (H)

N R E Morris,
19 Cleveland Court,
St. Agnes Road,
Moseley,
Birmingham B13 9PR.
Tel: 021 449 4604 (H)

J W P Roberts,
Grove House,
Ashley,
Box,
Corsham,
Wilts. SN14 9AJ.
Tel: 0225 742251 (H)

D Seabrook,
29 St. Lukes Drive,
Orrell,
Nr. Wigan,
Lancs.
Tel: 0695 622648 (H)

A V H Skeats,
106 Station Road,
Chertsey,
Surrey KT16 8BN.
Tel: 0932 567573 (H)
      081 755 1177 (B)

R B Taylor,
82 Bridgwater Drive,
Abington,
Northampton
NN3 3AG.
Tel: 0604 38626 (H)

RFU REGISTRATION OF PLAYERS

Regulations and Operating Procedures — Season 1993/94

These regulations and operating procedures apply to all players making an application to be registered with a Club in membership of the RFU on or after 1st May 1993. All existing RFU player registrations and eligibility dates remain valid.

1   Definitions — for the purpose of RFU registration regulations and operating procedures —
   a)   Home Union Player is a player who has, or has the right to have, as his only or main passport either a passport of the United Kingdom of Great Britain and Northern Ireland or a passport of the Republic of Ireland or a passport issued in the Channel Islands or the Isle of Man.
   b)   Overseas Player is any player who is unable to satisfy provisions of 1(a) above.
   c)   Registrar — person appointed annually by the RFU Competition Sub-Committee for each Division/Senior Clubs Association/National Leagues 5 (North and South) responsible for the administration of computerised registration of players. The Registrars for season 1993/94 are as set out in Appendix 1.
   d)   Registration Date — the date a correctly completed application form is received by the Registrar.
   e)   EFFECTIVE Date — the date when a player's registration application becomes EFFECTIVE in accordance with the Registration Regulations.
   f)   League Level — the Courage Leagues level of the Club on the player's registration date. League levels are established on 1st September of each season.
2   All players competing in the Courage Clubs Championship, the Pilkington Cup and the Junior Clubs Knockout Competition, must be registered on the official Registration Form. Supplies of these are available from Michael Humphreys & Partners.
3   The registration application form, when fully completed, shall be submitted to the Registrar as appropriate — see Regulation 1(c). A copy should be retained by the Club. Forms may be submitted to the Registrar by fax or post. In the event of Registration Applications being sent by fax the original form must be posted to the Registrar as confirmation within 7 days. Telephone registrations cannot be accepted.
     All relevant sections of the registration form must be completed and personally signed by the player and the Club's officials.
     Registration forms from 'overseas' players must be accompanied by the completed International Rugby Football Board form endorsed by their own Union.
     Registration forms cannot be accepted for any player under the age of 18 years.
     Any incomplete forms will be returned to the sender and the registration will not be recorded until these have been resubmitted containing all the information required. Applications carrying false information or per-pro signatures are unacceptable and may render the Club, player and/or official liable to disciplinary action, under RFU Bye-Law 13(g).
4   On receipt of the registration form, the Registrar will calculate the EFFECTIVE date of registration for the RFU Club Competitions referred to in 2 above and enter this date into the computer records.
5   At any point in time a player may only be registered with two Clubs affiliated to the RFU, only one of which can be EFFECTIVE.
6   A Club wishing to register a player from another Club shall submit the pink copy of the Registration Application Form to the Registrar responsible for the player's new Club. At the same time the white copy of the form must be posted to the Secretary of the player's current Club. On receipt, this must be signed by a Club Official and then forwarded immediately to that Club's Registrar.
     The Registration date shall be the date the pink copy is received by the new Club's Registrar providing no valid objection to the registration is received from the current Club within 21 days of the Registrar's receipt of the white copy.
7   Officials of his existing Club may not refuse to sign the form. If when signing the registration form, officials of the existing Club have objections to the player moving under RFU Resolutions concerning unpaid subscriptions or RFU Bye-Law 13(g) or any of the IRFB Regulations Relating to Amateurism, these objections must be submitted in writing to the Secretary of the

Rugby Football Union stating all the grounds upon which the objection is made. The Club shall not be entitled to introduce any further grounds of objection not so stated nor to lodge a second objection arising from the circumstances upon which an objection is based.

8   On or before 7th September the Registrar will supply each Club with a complete list of registered players. This list will show Registration Date, Competition Eligibility Date and movement of players and will be updated on receipt of each new Registration Application Form. A copy of the updated list will only be forwarded to the Club if a stamped-addressed envelope has been enclosed with the new Registration Form.

9   Registration Regulations

a) Registration of Home Union Players

The registration date is the date the registration application is received by the Registrar, but the registration becomes EFFECTIVE as follows:-

(i)   On the registration date — for a player who is not registered with any other Club in membership of the RFU and who has not played, during the twelve calendar months immediately preceding his Registration Application, for any Club (other than a student Club or school) in membership of any other National Union.

(ii)   30 days — (exclusive of the period 1st May to 31st July) after the Registration Date — for a player who is applying for registration with a Club which is playing a minimum of 3 Courage League levels higher than his current Club at the time the Registration Application is received by the Registrar. Examples: from league level 5 to league level 2; from league level 8 to league level 5.

(iii)   120 days — (exclusive of the period 1st May to 31st July) after the Registration Date — for players other than in (i) or (ii) above. Players in this section (iii) may continue to play in the competition for their current Club throughout the 120 day waiting period for their new EFFECTIVE registration.

(iv)   A player in (ii) or (iii) above may within 120 days of the Registration Date, request, in writing, the Registrar to cancel his application, in which case his previous registration will be EFFECTIVE immediately upon receipt of his written request by the Registrar.

b) Registration of "Overseas" Players

(i)   A registration application cannot be made until the player arrives in the Four Home Unions and he submits, duly completed by him and endorsed by his own Union, the IRFB form of statutory declaration giving clearance for him to play outside his own Union.

(ii)   The Registration Date is the date the Registration Application is received, but the registration becomes EFFECTIVE 180 days (exclusive of the period 1st May to 31st July) after the Registration Date. Any absence from the Home Unions during this waiting period will count towards the 60 days stipulated in (b)(iv).

(iii)   When a registered player has maintained EFFECTIVE registration for a consecutive period of 730 days (2 years), he ceases to be subject to the restriction in 8(b)(ii)of the Courage Clubs Championship Regulations and 2(b)(ii) of the Pilkington Cup and Junior Clubs Knockout Competition Regulations.

(iv)   The registration of an overseas player will cease to be EFFECTIVE if the player is absent from the Four Home Unions at any time for a total of 60 days or more in any calendar year.

(v)   A player who loses his EFFECTIVE registration under 9(b)(iv) has to re-apply and is subject to 9(b)(i) and (ii).

(vi)   A player, if moving Clubs, is subject to the restrictions in 9(a)(ii) and (iii) which may run concurrently with the restriction in 9(b)(ii).

(vii)   It is the responsibility of a Club to inform the Registrar if a player is absent from the Home Unions for a total of 60 days or more in any calendar year.

c) Registration — General

(i)   Any player, however qualified, who is an employee of a Club, or of a Company which is substantially involved in any activity which is related to a Club, may not be registered with that Club unless authorised by the RFU Amateur Status Sub-Committee.

(ii)   The registration or qualifying period of any player who is ineligible to play for any other reason under the Bye-Laws, Resolutions and Regulations of the RFU, is suspended for the period of that ineligibility.

(iii)   The EFFECTIVE registration of any player, who plays in a match in a Club Competition of any other National Union during the period 1st September to 30th April inclusive, shall be discontinued. A player whose registration is discontinued under this clause must requalify under 9(a)(iii) if a Home Union player or 9(b)(ii) if an overseas player.

(iv) A Player who is registered with a Club which withdraws from an RFU competition in the season and who wishes to play for another Club in an RFU Competition, must register with that Club in accordance with these Regulations.

(v) A player may request to be deregistered or a Club may request for a player to be deregistered. On receipt of such a request, which must be in writing, the Registrar will transfer the player's existing Club registration to a lapsed registration file. On the 30th April each year, the records of all players which have remained in this file throughout the period from 1st May of the preceding year, will be deleted.

(vi) Any player whose registration has been deleted under clause 9(c)(v) may reapply for RFU registration and such registration will be EFFECTIVE on the Registration Date subject to the provision of Clause 9(a)(i).

(vii) A player who is under the age of 22 years on 1st September 1993 may request, in writing, to return to the Club which held his initial RFU registration ("his original Club"). His registration with his original Club will be EFFECTIVE immediately upon receipt of his written request by the Registrar, provided that no subsequent registration of that player shall become EFFECTIVE until the period of 120 days shall have elapsed from the date the player's registration with and upon his returning to his original Club.

(viii) A Club may not register any player who has at any time received any material benefit (as defined in Regulation 1.3 of the IRFB Regulation Relating to Amateurism) for playing any form of Rugby Football.

10 Any dispute on these Regulations and Operating Procedures must be referred in writing to the Registrar stating all the grounds on which the objection is made. If the dispute is not resolved within 7 days, the Club or player may submit the complaint in writing to the Secretary of the RFU restating the grounds upon which the objection is made. The Club shall not be entitled to introduce any further grounds of objection not previously stated to the Registrar, nor to lodge a second objection arising from the circumstances upon which an objection is based.

The Secretary of the RFU shall refer the objection to the Competition Sub-Committee of the RFU whose decision shall be final and binding.

It shall be at the sole discretion of the Competition Sub-Committee whether or not to grant a personal hearing.

11 The Competition Sub-Committee of the RFU shall have absolute and unfettered discretion to decide on any matter not provided for in and on the interpretation of these Regulations and Operating Procedures and their decision shall be final and binding.

REGISTRARS — SEASON 1993-94

Senior Clubs Association

DAE Evans
22 Brooks Road, Sutton Coldfield,
West Midlands B71 1HP
Tel: 021 354 8183 Fax: 021 321 3221

National Leagues 5 (North and South)

LCK Angel Esq
c/o Michael Humphreys & Partners Ltd,
68 South Lambeth Road, Vauxhall,
London SW1 1RL
Tel: 071 820 9911 Fax: 071 820 9259

London & South East Division

MA Ward
3 Rookery Close, Oulton Broad, Lowestoft,
Suffolk NR33 9NZ
Tel: 0502 566169 Fax: 0502 501135

Midland Division

DI Robins
c/o Russells News Agency, PO Box 183,
Leicester LE8 8BZ
Tel: 0533 872 991 Fax: 0533 320064

South West Division

JD Wooldridge
c/o The First Eleven Sports Agency,
PO Box 11, Reading, Berkshire RG6 3DT
Tel: 0734 861593 Fax: 0734 861593

Northern Division

R Archer
Brookfield House, Scotland Head, Winlaton,
Tyne & Wear NE21 6PL
Tel: 091 414 3532

THE COURAGE CLUBS CHAMPIONSHIP GENERAL CONTACTS

NATIONAL ADMINISTRATION OFFICE

Michael Humphreys & Partners Ltd.,
68 South Lambeth Road,
Vauxhall,
London SW8 1RL.
Tel: 071 820 9911
Fax: 071 820 9259

Administration Manager: Sue Wheeler
Administration Executive: Katie Bullivant

Michael Humphreys & Partners (MH&P) is responsible to the Rugby Football Union for the administration of fixtures, results and league tables for all National Leagues.

MH&P also represents the RFU in liaison with the Committee of each RFU Division of the Championship. The Company is responsible for ensuring that all necessary fixtures have been made and that all promotions and relegations are arranged.

Media Relations Director: Teresa Cash
Media Relations Manager: Sara Jones
Media Relations Executive: Julian Yeomans

MH&P is responsible to the RFU for the overall promotion and media relations with regard to the Courage Clubs Championship. All information regarding fixtures, results and tables for the National Leagues is co-ordinated from MH&P. MH&P will also hold the results and the tables for all other leagues in the Championship. All media information regarding the overall Championship is released from MH&P and all enquiries should be directed to MH&P for any regional information not available from the regional contact.

THE RUGBY FOOTBALL UNION

Roger Godfrey,
The Administrative Secretary,
The Rugby Football Union,
Rugby Road, Twickenham,
Middlesex TW1 1DZ
Tel: 081 892 8161

RFU COMPETITION SUB-COMMITTEE

The Committee will act as a final arbiter in case of all disputes.

Chairman:
John A Jeavons-Fellows,
Shrawley Wood,
Worcester WR6 6TT.
Tel: 0905 621255 (H)
Fax: 0905 621377

COURAGE LTD.

HEAD OFFICE:
Courage Ltd.,
Marketing Department,
Ashby House,
1 Bridge Street,
Staines,
Middlesex TW18 4TP
Tel: 0784 466199

EAST REGION:
Courage Ltd.,
14 Mortlake High Street,
Mortlake,
London SW14 7QX.
Tel: 081 876 3434

WEST REGION:
Courage Ltd.,
Westward House,
Stoke Gifford,
Bristol BS12 6SR.
Tel: 0272 236474

NORTH REGION:
Courage Ltd.,
John Smith's Tadcaster Brewery,
Tadcaster,
North Yorkshire
LS24 9SA.
Tel: 0937 832091

NATIONAL MEDIA CONTACTS

DAILY EXPRESS
Ludgate House, 245 Blackfriars Road,
London SE1 9UX
Tel: 071 928 8000

DAILY MAIL
Northcliffe House, 2 Derry Street,
London W8 5TT
Tel: 071 938 6000

DAILY MIRROR
Holborn Circus, London EC1P 1DQ
Tel: 071 353 0246

THE DAILY TELEGRAPH
1 Canada Square, Canary Wharf,
London E14 5DT
Tel: 071 538 5000

THE EUROPEAN
Orbit House, 5 New Fetters Lane,
London EC4A 1AR
Tel: 071 377 4903

EVENING STANDARD
Northcliffe House, 2 Derry Street,
London W8 5TT
Tel: 071 938 6000

THE GUARDIAN
119 Farringdon Road,
London EC1R 3ER
Tel: 071 278 2332

THE INDEPENDENT
40 City Road, London EC1Y 2DB
Tel: 071 253 1222

THE INDEPENDENT ON SUNDAY
40 City Road, London EC1Y 2DB
Tel: 071 253 1222

THE DAILY STAR
Ludgate House, 245 Blackfriars Road
London SE1 9UX
Tel: 071 928 8000

THE SUN
PO Box 481, Virginia Street
London E1 9BD
Tel: 071 782 4000

THE TIMES
1 Pennington Street, London E1 9XN
Tel: 071 782 5000

TODAY
1 Virginia Street, London E1 9BS
Tel: 071 782 4600

MAIL ON SUNDAY
Northcliffe House, 2 Derry Street,
London W8 5TT
Tel: 071 938 6000

NEWS OF THE WORLD
1 Virginia Street, London E1 9XR
Tel 071 782 4000

PRESS ASSOCIATION
85 Fleet Street, London EC1 9XR
Tel: 071 353 7440

NATIONAL MEDIA CONTACTS

THE OBSERVER
Chelsea Bridge House,
Queenstown Road, London SW8 4NN
Tel: 071 627 0700

ITN NEWS
200 Grays Inn Road,
London WC1X 8XZ
Tel: 071 833 3000

SUNDAY EXPRESS
Ludgate House, 245 Blackfriars Road,
London SE1 9UX
Tel: 071 928 8000

SKY NEWS
6 Centaurs Business Park, Grant Way,
Isleworth, Middlesex TW7 5QD
Tel: 071 705 3000

SUNDAY MIRROR
Holborn Circus, London, EC1 1DQ
Tel: 071 353 0246

GMTV
The London Television Centre,
Upper Ground, London SE1 9TT
Tel: 071 827 7000

SUNDAY TELEGRAPH
1 Canada Square, Canary Wharf,
London E14 5DT
Tel: 071 538 5000

CHANNEL FOUR NEWS
200 Grays Inn Road,
London WC1X 8XZ
Tel: 071 833 3000

SUNDAY TIMES
1, Pennington Street, London E1 9XW
Tel: 071 782 5000

I.R.N.
200 Grays Inn Road,
London WC1X 8XZ
Tel: 071 833 3000

THE PEOPLE
Holborn Circus, London EC1P 1DQ
Tel: 071 353 0246

SPORT ON 5
BBC Radio 5, Broadcasting House,
London W1 1AA
Tel: 071 580 4468

BBC TV NEWS
Television Centre, Wood Lane,
London W12 7RJ
Tel: 081 576 1914

BBC BREAKFAST NEWS
Room 7039, Television Centre
London W12 8QT
Tel: 081 576 7501 / 6

THE NATIONAL LEAGUES

LEAGUE 1

LEAGUE 2

LEAGUE 3

LEAGUE 4

NATIONAL LEAGUES STRUCTURE

and immediate supporting leagues

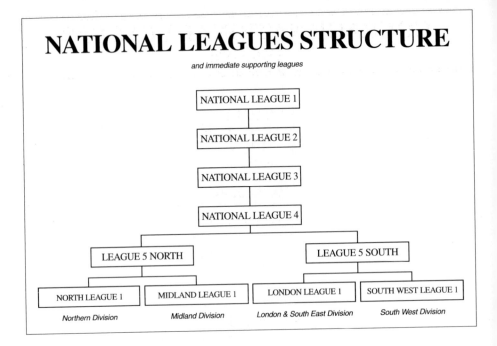

ADMINISTRATIVE INSTRUCTION
NATIONAL LEAGUES 1-4

POSTPONED MATCHES

Matches which have to be postponed must be re-scheduled for the following Saturday. The only exceptions can be when that date is:

a)   A National Club competition date

b)   Divisional Championship

c)   County Championship (not applicable to National Leagues 1 and 2)

d)   A full England International

e)   England representative matches or the Senior National Representative Team of one of the other three Home Unions where three or more players from either Club are required.

If any of the above exceptions apply then the match must be played on the first Saturday when they do not.

Where the next or next available Saturday presents another major difficulty to either side then an appeal may be made within two days of the original match date for an alternative date. This appeal should be made to the Organising Committee concerned, and their decision is final.

COURAGE NATIONAL LEAGUES 1993-94

LEAGUE 1

BATH
BRISTOL
GLOUCESTER
HARLEQUINS
LEICESTER
LONDON IRISH
NEWCASTLE GOSFORTH
NORTHAMPTON
ORRELL
WASPS

LEAGUE 2

LONDON SCOTTISH
MOSELEY
NOTTINGHAM
OTLEY
RUGBY
SALE
SARACENS
WAKEFIELD
WATERLOO
WEST HARTLEPOOL

LEAGUE 3

BEDFORD
BLACKHEATH
COVENTRY
EXETER
FYLDE
HAVANT
MORLEY
REDRUTH
RICHMOND
ROSSLYN PARK

LEAGUE 4

ASKEANS
ASPATRIA
BROUGHTON PARK
CLIFTON
HARROGATE
LEEDS
LIVERPOOL ST HELENS
PLYMOUTH ALBION
SHEFFIELD
SUDBURY

THE COURAGE CLUBS CHAMPIONSHIP 1993-94

NATIONAL LEAGUES: RFU SENIOR CLUBS ASSOCIATION (EXECUTIVE COMMITTEE)

CHAIRMAN

Frank Gibbon,
12 The Green,
Bishopton,
Stockton onTees,
Cleveland TS21 1HF.
Tel: 0740 30410 (H)
0642 602221 (B)

DEPUTY CHAIRMAN

Bob Taylor,
82 Bridgewater Drive,
Abington,
Northampton NN3 3AG.
Tel: 0604 38626 (H)

HON. SECRETARY

Alwynne Evans,
22 Brooks Road,
Wylde Green,
Sutton Coldfield,
West Midlands B72 1HP.
Tel: 021 354 8183 (H)
0675 470042 (B)
Fax: 021 321 3221 (H)
0675 470490 (B)

HON. TREASURER

Brian Baister,
The Cedars,
3 Kidderton Close,
Brindley,
Nantwich,
Cheshire CW5 8JU.
Tel: 0270 74465 (H)
0244 350000 x 2003 (B)

MEMBERS

Neil Hannah,
Gatehouse, 62 Beeston Fields Drive,
Bramcote, Beeston, Nottingham NG9 3DD.
Tel: 0602 254798 (H)
0602 243243 (B)
Fax: 0509 242310
Ray Ellis,
31 Russell Avenue, Hartley,
Plymouth PL3 5RB.
Tel: 0752 771237 (H)
Roy Fawden,
100 Swains Lane Highgate,
London N6 6PL.
Tel: 081 348 4753 (H)
081 348 4254 (B)
Fax: 081 340 2199
Tom Mahoney,
2 Raymond Walk, St. John's Lane,
Bristol BS3 5AP.
Tel: 0272 664782 (H)
0272 514134 (Club)
Nigel Morris,
19 Cleveland Court, St. Agnes Road,
Moseley, Birmingham B13 9PR.
Tel: 021 449 4604 (H)
John Roberts,
Grove House, Ashley, Box,
Corsham, Wilts. SN14 9AJ.
Tel: 0225 742251 (H)
Alan V.H. Skeats,
106 Station Road, Chertsey, Surrey KT16 8BN.
Tel: 0932 567573 (H)
081 755 1177 (B)
Des Seabrook,
29 St. Lukes Drive, Orrell, Nr. Wigan, Lancs. WM5 7AU
Tel: 0695 622648
Don Wills,
25 Woodland Gardens, Isleworth,
Middx. TW7 6LN.
Tel: 081 560 7594 (H)
Robin Foster,
27 Carr Lane, Sandal, Wakefield,
West Yorkshire WF2 6HJ.
Tel: 0924 250116 (H)
0924 371501 (B)

COURAGE LEAGUE FIXTURES

1993-94 NATIONAL LEAGUE ONE

September 11 (RFU Week 2 League Week 1)
Harlequins v London Irish
Gloucester v Wasps
Bristol v Bath
Orrell v Newcastle Gosforth
Northampton v Leicester

September 18 (RFU Week 3 League Week 2)
Wasps v Harlequins
London Irish v Bristol
Newcastle Gosforth v Gloucester
Bath v Northampton
Leicester v Orrell

September 25 (RFU Week 4 League Week 3)
Harlequins v Bristol
Wasps v Newcastle Gosforth
Northampton v London Irish
Gloucester v Leicester
Orrell v Bath

October 2 (RFU Week 5 League Week 4)
Newcastle Gosforth v Harlequins
Bristol v Northampton
Leicester v Wasps
London Irish v Orrell
Bath v Gloucester

October 9 (RFU Week 6 League Week 5)
Harlequins v Northampton
Newcastle Gosforth v Leicester
Orrell v Bristol
Wasps v Bath
Gloucester v London Irish

November 13 (RFU Week 10 League Week 6)
Leicester v Harlequins
Northampton v Orrell
Bath v Newcastle Gosforth
Bristol v Gloucester
London Irish v Wasps

November 20 (RFU Week 11 League Week 7)
Orrell v Harlequins
Leicester v Bath
Gloucester v Northampton
Newcastle Gosforth v London Irish
Wasps v Bristol

December 4 (RFU Week 13 League Week 8)
Harlequins v Bath
Orrell v Gloucester
London Irish v Leicester
Northampton v Wasps
Bristol v Newcastle Gosforth

December 11 (RFU Week 14 League Week 9)
Gloucester v Harlequins
Bath v London Irish
Wasps v Orrell
Leicester v Bristol
Newcastle Gosforth v Northampton

January 8 (RFU Week 18 League Week 10)
London Irish v Harlequins
Wasps v Gloucester
Bath v Bristol
Newcastle Gosforth v Orrell
Leicester v Northampton

January 15 (RFU Week 19 League Week 11)
Harlequins v Wasps
Bristol v London Irish
Gloucester v Newcastle Gosforth
Northampton v Bath
Orrell v Leicester

January 29 (RFU Week X5 League Week 12)
Bristol v Harlequins
Newcastle Gosforth v Wasps
London Irish v Northampton
Leicester v Gloucester
Bath v Orrell

February 12 (RFU Week 22 League Week 13)
Harlequins v Newcastle Gosforth
Northampton v Bristol
Wasps v Leicester
Orrell v London Irish
Gloucester v Bath

COURAGE LEAGUE FIXTURES

March 12 (RFU Week 26 League Week 14)

Northampton	v	Harlequins
Leicester	v	Newcastle Gosforth
Bristol	v	Orrell
Bath	v	Wasps
London Irish	v	Gloucester

March 26 (RFU Week 28 League Week 15)

Harlequins	v	Leicester
Orrell	v	Northampton
Newcastle Gosforth	v	Bath
Gloucester	v	Bristol
Wasps	v	London Irish

April 9 (RFU Week 30 League Week 16)

Harlequins	v	Orrell
Bath	v	Leicester
Northampton	v	Gloucester
London Irish	v	Newcastle Gosforth
Bristol	v	Wasps

April 23 (RFU Week 32 League Week 17)

Bath	v	Harlequins
Gloucester	v	Orrell
Leicester	v	London Irish
Wasps	v	Northampton
Newcastle Gosforth	v	Bristol

April 30 (RFU Week X8 League Week 18)

Harlequins	v	Gloucester
London Irish	v	Bath
Orrell	v	Wasps
Bristol	v	Leicester
Northampton	v	Newcastle Gosforth

COURAGE LEAGUE FIXTURES

1993-94 NATIONAL LEAGUE TWO

September 11 (RFU Week 2 League Week 1)
Saracens v Moseley
London Scottish v Sale
Wakefield v Rugby
West Hartlepool v Waterloo
Nottingham v Otley

September 18 (RFU Week 3 League Week 2)
Sale v Saracens
Moseley v Wakefield
Waterloo v London Scottish
Rugby v Nottingham
Otley v West Hartlepool

September 25 (RFU Week 4 League Week 3)
Saracens v Wakefield
Sale v Waterloo
Nottingham v Moseley
London Scottish v Otley
West Hartlepool v Rugby

October 2 (RFU Week 5 League Week 4)
Waterloo v Saracens
Wakefield v Nottingham
Otley v Sale
Moseley v West Hartlepool
Rugby v London Scottish

October 9 (RFU Week 6 League Week 5)
Saracens v Nottingham
Waterloo v Otley
West Hartlepool v Wakefield
Sale v Rugby
London Scottish v Moseley

November 13 (RFU Week 10 League Week 6)
Otley v Saracens
Nottingham v West Hartlepool
Rugby v Waterloo
Wakefield v London Scottish
Moseley v Sale

November 20 (RFU Week 11 League Week 7)
Saracens v West Hartlepool
Otley v Rugby
London Scottish v Nottingham
Waterloo v Moseley
Sale v Wakefield

December 4 (RFU Week 13 League Week 8)
Saracens v Rugby
West Hartlepool v London Scottish
Moseley v Otley
Nottingham v Sale
Wakefield v Waterloo

December 11 (RFU Week 14 League Week 9)
London Scottish v Saracens
Rugby v Moseley
Sale v West Hartlepool
Otley v Wakefield
Waterloo v Nottingham

January 8 (RFU Week 18 League Week 10)
Moseley v Saracens
Sale v London Scottish
Rugby v Wakefield
Waterloo v West Hartlepool
Otley v Nottingham

January 15 (RFU Week 19 League Week 11)
Saracens v Sale
Wakefield v Moseley
London Scottish v Waterloo
Nottingham v Rugby
West Hartlepool v Otley

January 29 (RFU Week X5 League Week 12)
Wakefield v Saracens
Waterloo v Sale
Moseley v Nottingham
Otley v London Scottish
Rugby v West Hartlepool

February 12 (RFU Week 22 League Week 13)
Saracens v Waterloo
Nottingham v Wakefield
Sale v Otley
West Hartlepool v Moseley
London Scottish v Rugby

COURAGE LEAGUE FIXTURES

March 12 (RFU Week 26 League Week 14)
Nottingham v Saracens
Otley v Waterloo
Wakefield v West Hartlepool
Rugby v Sale
Moseley v London Scottish

March 26 (RFU Week 28 League Week 15)
Saracens v Otley
West Hartlepool v Nottingham
Waterloo v Rugby
London Scottish v Wakefield
Sale v Moseley

April 9 (RFU Week 30 League Week 16)
West Hartlepool v Saracens
Rugby v Otley
Nottingham v London Scottish
Moseley v Waterloo
Wakefield v Sale

April 23 (RFU Week 32 League Week 17)
Rugby v Saracens
London Scottish v West Hartlepool
Otley v Moseley
Sale v Nottingham
Waterloo v Wakefield

April 30 (RFU Week X8 League Week 18)
Saracens v London Scottish
Moseley v Rugby
West Hartlepool v Sale
Wakefield v Otley
Nottingham v Waterloo

COURAGE LEAGUE FIXTURES

1993-94 NATIONAL LEAGUE THREE

October 23 (RFU Week 8 League Week 1)
Coventry v Exeter
Redruth v Blackheath
Rosslyn Park v Bedford
Havant v Morley
Fylde v Richmond

October 30 (RFU Week X2 League Week 2)
Blackheath v Coventry
Exeter v Rosslyn Park
Morley v Redruth
Bedford v Fylde
Richmond v Havant

November 6 (RFU Week 9 League Week 3)
Coventry v Rosslyn Park
Blackheath v Morley
Fylde v Exeter
Richmond v Redruth
Havant v Bedford

November 13 (RFU Week 10 League Week 4)
Morley v Coventry
Rosslyn Park v Fylde
Richmond v Blackheath
Exeter v Havant
Bedford v Redruth

November 20 (RFU Week 11 League Week 5)
Coventry v Fylde
Morley v Richmond
Havant v Rosslyn Park
Blackheath v Bedford
Redruth v Exeter

December 4 (RFU Week 13 League Week 6)
Richmond v Coventry
Fylde v Havant
Bedford v Morley
Rosslyn Park v Redruth
Exeter v Blackheath

December 11 (RFU Week 14 League Week 7)
Havant v Coventry
Bedford v Richmond
Redruth v Fylde
Morley v Exeter
Blackheath v Rosslyn Park

December 18 (RFU Week 15 League Week 8)
Coventry v Bedford
Havant v Redruth
Richmond v Exeter
Fylde v Blackheath
Rosslyn Park v Morley

January 8 (RFU Week 18 League Week 9)
Redruth v Coventry
Bedford v Exeter
Blackheath v Havant
Richmond v Rosslyn Park
Morley v Fylde

January 22 (RFU Week 20 League Week 10)
Exeter v Coventry
Blackheath v Redruth
Bedford v Rosslyn Park
Morley v Havant
Richmond v Fylde

January 29 (RFU Week X5 League Week 11)
Coventry v Blackheath
Rosslyn Park v Exeter
Redruth v Morley
Fylde v Bedford
Havant v Richmond

February 12 (RFU Week 22 League Week 12)
Rosslyn Park v Coventry
Morley v Blackheath
Exeter v Fylde
Redruth v Richmond
Bedford v Havant

February 26 (RFU Week 24 League Week 13)
Coventry v Morley
Fylde v Rosslyn Park
Blackheath v Richmond
Havant v Exeter
Redruth v Bedford

35

COURAGE LEAGUE FIXTURES

March 12 (RFU Week 26 League Week 14)
Fylde v Coventry
Richmond v Morley
Rosslyn Park v Havant
Bedford v Blackheath
Exeter v Redruth

March 26 (RFU Week 28 League Week 15)
Coventry v Richmond
Havant v Fylde
Morley v Bedford
Redruth v Rosslyn Park
Blackheath v Exeter

April 9 (RFU Week 30 League Week 16)
Coventry v Havant
Richmond v Bedford
Fylde v Redruth
Exeter v Morley
Rosslyn Park v Blackheath

April 23 (RFU Week 32 League Week 17)
Bedford v Coventry
Redruth v Havant
Exeter v Richmond
Blackheath v Fylde
Morley v Rosslyn Park

April 30 (RFU Week X8 League Week 18)
Coventry v Redruth
Exeter v Bedford
Havant v Blackheath
Rosslyn Park v Richmond
Fylde v Morley

COURAGE LEAGUE FIXTURES

1993-94 NATIONAL LEAGUE FOUR

October 23 (RFU Week 8 League Week 1)
Broughton Park v Liverpool St Helens
Leeds v Aspatria
Askeans v Sheffield
Harrogate v Clifton
Plymouth v Sudbury

October 30 (RFU Week X2 League Week 2)
Aspatria v Broughton Park
Liverpool St Helens v Askeans
Clifton v Leeds
Sheffield v Plymouth
Sudbury v Harrogate

November 6 (RFU Week 9 League Week 3)
Broughton Park v Askeans
Aspatria v Clifton
Plymouth v Liverpool St Helens
Leeds v Sudbury
Harrogate v Sheffield

November 13 (RFU Week 10 League Week 4)
Clifton v Broughton Park
Askeans v Plymouth
Sudbury v Aspatria
Liverpool St Helens v Harrogate
Sheffield v Leeds

November 20 (RFU Week 11 League Week 5)
Broughton Park v Plymouth
Clifton v Sudbury
Harrogate v Askeans
Aspatria v Sheffield
Leeds v Liverpool St Helens

December 4 (RFU Week 13 League Week 6)
Sudbury v Broughton Park
Plymouth v Harrogate
Sheffield v Clifton
Askeans v Leeds
Liverpool St Helens v Aspatria

December 11 (RFU Week 14 League Week 7)
Harrogate v Broughton Park
Sudbury v Sheffield
Leeds v Plymouth
Clifton v Liverpool St Helens
Aspatria v Askeans

December 18 (RFU Week 15 League Week 8)
Broughton Park v Sheffield
Harrogate v Leeds
Liverpool St Helens v Sudbury
Plymouth v Aspatria
Askeans v Clifton

January 8 (RFU Week 18 League Week 9)
Leeds v Broughton Park
Sheffield v Liverpool St Helens
Aspatria v Harrogate
Sudbury v Askeans
Clifton v Plymouth

January 22 (RFU Week 20 League Week 10)
Liverpool St Helens v Broughton Park
Aspatria v Leeds
Sheffield v Askeans
Clifton v Harrogate
Sudbury v Plymouth

January 29 (RFU Week X5 League Week 11)
Broughton Park v Aspatria
Askeans v Liverpool St Helens
Leeds v Clifton
Plymouth v Sheffield
Harrogate v Sudbury

February 12 (RFU Week 22 League Week 12)
Askeans v Broughton Park
Clifton v Aspatria
Liverpool St Helens v Plymouth
Sudbury v Leeds
Sheffield v Harrogate

February 26 (RFU Week 24 League Week 13)
Broughton Park v Clifton
Plymouth v Askeans
Aspatria v Sudbury
Harrogate v Liverpool St Helens
Leeds v Sheffield

COURAGE LEAGUE FIXTURES

March 12 (RFU Week 26 League Week 14)
Plymouth v Broughton Park
Sudbury v Clifton
Askeans v Harrogate
Sheffield v Aspatria
Liverpool St Helens v Leeds

March 26 (RFU Week 28 League Week 15)
Broughton Park v Sudbury
Harrogate v Plymouth
Clifton v Sheffield
Leeds v Askeans
Aspatria v Liverpool St Helens

April 9 (RFU Week 30 League Week 16)
Broughton Park v Harrogate
Sheffield v Sudbury
Plymouth v Leeds
Liverpool St Helens v Clifton
Askeans v Aspatria

April 23 (RFU Week 32 League Week 17)
Sheffield v Broughton Park
Leeds v Harrogate
Sudbury v Liverpool St Helens
Aspatria v Plymouth
Clifton v Askeans

April 30 (RFU Week X8 League Week 18)
Broughton Park v Leeds
Liverpool St Helens v Sheffield
Harrogate v Aspatria
Askeans v Sudbury
Plymouth v Clifton

Will Carling — an inspiration for England and Harlequins

Photo: Joe McCabe

Unisys and sport.
It's not a game, you know.

FINAL UNISYS COMPUTER RUGBY UNION STATISTICS

These statistics have been collected during the Season for players in all clubs playing first class rugby. They include representative matches, County and Divisional matches, including the Varsity Match and Barbarian Fixtures.

UNISYS TOP POINTS SCORERS

		Total	Tries	Cons	Pens	DG
1.	David Johnson (Newcastle Gos) (1)	404	4	81	71	3
2.	Andy Green (Exeter) (3)	365	8	56	67	4
3.	John Liley (Leicester) (2)	355	12	53	63	
4.	Robert Liley (Wakefield) (4)	321	5	46	62	6
5.	Steve Dyble (Sudbury) (6)	310	9	53	63	
6.	Mike Hamlin (London Welsh) (5)	307	6	68	45	2
7.	Simon Hogg (Clifton) (9)	305	9	49	50	4
8.	Martin Livesey (Richmond) (8)	304	3	47	62	3
9.	Mark Rodgers (Sheffield) (7)	297	16	38	47	
10.	Mike Corcoran (London Irish) (10)	286	13	25	57	
11.	John Stabler (West Hartlepool) (14)	279	9	48	46	
12.	Peter Rutledge (Otley) (-)	276	10	41	46	2
13.	Simon Pennington (Stourbridge) (11)	275	5	29	64	
13.	Richard Mills (Walsall) (15)	275	2	35	62	3
15.	Peter Smith (High Wycombe) (12)	274	16	49	32	
16.	Mark Tainton (Bristol) (13)	270	1	53	52	1
17.	Andy Halford (Lydney) (16)	260	7	30	54	1
18.	David Richards (Lichfield) (17)	254	2	47	50	
19.	John Bland (Durham City) (18)	251	4	39	49	2
20.	Paul Thatcher (Weston-Super-Mare) (19)	249	4	35	53	

FINAL UNISYS COMPUTER RUGBY UNION STATISTICS

UNISYS TOP TRY SCORERS

1.	Steve Titcombe (Sudbury) (1)	32
2.	Mark Sephton (liverpool St. Helens) (2)	28
3.	Dave Catchpole (Southend) (3=)	26
4.	John Hewes (High Wycombe) (3=)	23
5.	Doug Woodman (Clifton) (5)	22

UNISYS TOP KICKERS
(Tries excluded)

1.	David Johnson (Newcastle Gosforth) (1)	384
2.	Andy Green (Exeter) (2)	325
3.	Robert Liley (Wakefield) (3=)	296
4.	John Liley (Leicester) (3=)	295
5.	Martin Livesey (Richmond) (5)	289

UNISYS TOP DROP KICKERS

1.	Guy Gregory (Nottingham) (1)	11
2.	Jez Harris (Leicester) (2)	11
3.	Darren Chapman (Camborne) (3)	8

COURAGE LEAGUE STATISTICS

Compiled by Steve McCormack

COURAGE DIVISION ONE — CLUB RECORDS 1992-93

	FOR				AGAINST			
	Pts	T	C	P	DG	Pts	T	C	P	DG
Bath	355	42	23	32	1	97	7	4	14	4
Wasps	186	19	8	24	1	118	6	5	25	1
Leicester	220	21	17	23	4	116	13	3	14	1
Northampton	215	24	16	20	1	150	11	4	27	2
Gloucester	173	17	8	24	-	151	12	5	25	2
Bristol	148	13	7	23	-	169	18	11	15	4
London Irish	175	9	5	33	7	223	25	16	20	2
Harlequins	197	23	11	19	1	187	17	9	26	2
Orrell	175	20	6	21	-	183	19	11	22	-
London Scottish	192	23	10	17	2	248	31	15	21	-
Saracens	137	13	6	16	4	180	15	-	28	1
West Hartlepool	149	14	8	21	-	236	24	1	28	2
Rugby	104	10	6	11	3	368	50	2	19	3

COURAGE DIVISION TWO — CLUB RECORDS 1992-93

	FOR				AGAINST			
	Pts	T	C	P	DG	Pts	T	C	P	DG
Newcastle Gosforth	241	22	16	30	3	106	7	4	20	1
Waterloo	228	17	10	33	8	138	7	2	32	1
Wakefield	186	17	10	24	3	123	10	5	15	6
Nottingham	249	22	14	28	9	145	13	4	21	3
Sale	237	26	12	22	5	102	5	4	20	3
Moseley	184	19	7	22	3	150	10	8	23	5
Bedford	186	13	8	32	3	183	15	9	24	6
Rosslyn Park	209	17	5	36	2	199	13	7	34	6
Richmond	204	19	14	25	2	196	15	8	33	2
Blackheath	142	9	5	27	2	231	23	13	26	4
Coventry	192	19	15	16	3	236	24	13	26	4
Fylde	108	9	3	18	1	290	31	18	30	3
Morley	107	7	3	19	3	374	45	28	28	3

COURAGE DIVISION THREE — CLUB RECORDS 1992-93

	FOR				AGAINST			
	Pts	T	C	P	DG	Pts	T	C	P	DG
Otley	274	32	15	28	-	118	14	6	11	1
Havant	185	23	5	20	-	93	6	3	16	3
Exeter	247	25	10	31	3	169	16	7	24	1
Redruth	175	17	9	23	1	125	13	3	18	-
Sheffield	208	23	12	22	1	134	13	3	19	2
Leeds	228	28	17	16	2	220	24	11	24	2
Liverpool SH	203	22	12	19	4	130	13	4	18	1
Clifton	206	28	9	15	1	175	18	11	20	1
Aspatria	170	16	9	23	1	308	43	21	16	1
Askeans	132	12	6	18	2	300	36	18	26	2
Broughton Park	136	17	9	8	3	217	25	10	22	2
Plymouth Albion	130	16	4	13	1	305	38	20	22	3

MOST TRIES IN A COURAGE DIVISION ONE MATCH

4	G Hartley	Nottingham v Bedford	18-11-89
4	A Swift	Bath v Bedford	13-1-90
4	J Guscott	Bath v Bedford	13-1-90
4	P Hamer	Orell v Rugby	13-3-93
3	P Shillingford	Moseley v Wasps	5-2-88
3	M Charles	Leicester v Sale	26-3-88
3	A Harriman	Harlequins v Nottingham	1-4-88
3	S Smith	Wasps v Coventry	13-4-88
3	A Harriman	Harlequins v Sale	23-4-88
3	J Guscott	Bath v Moseley	12-11-88
3	M Bailey	Wasps v Moseley	19-11-88
3	J Liley	Leicester v Bedford	23-9-89
3	E Wedderburn	Harlequins v Bedford	14-10-89
3	M Bailey	Wasps v Gloucester	14-10-89
3	D Morgan	Gloucester v Rosslyn Park	11-11-89
3	J Callard	Bath v Bedford	13-1-90
3	C Gerard	Leicester v Moseley	31-3-90
3	P Manley	Orrell v Rosslyn Park	28-4-90
3	D Morris	Orrell v Liverpool St Helens	13-10-90
3	D Morris	Orrel v Northampton	27-10-90
3	R Underwood	Leicester v Northampton	21-1-91
3	A Harriman	Harlequins v Bristol	30-3-91
3	W Carling	Harlequins v Bristol	30-3-91
3	G Childs	Wasps v Liverpool St Helens	20-4-91
3	R Andrew	Wasps v Bristol	27-4-91
3	R Underwood	Leicester v Moseley	27-4-91
3	S Hackney	Leicester v London Irish	4-1-92
3	A Swift	Bath v Leicester	11-1-92
3	R Underwood	Leicester v Rosslyn Park	21-3-92
3	M Lloyd	Bristol v Rugby	28-3-92
3	M Pepper	Nottingham v Rosslyn Park	4-4-92
3	C Oti	Wasps v Bristol	25-4-92
3	S Barnes	Bath v Hartlepool	27-3-93
3	D Eves	Bristol v Rugby	22-3-93

MOST POINTS IN A COURAGE DIVISION ONE MATCH

31	J Liley	Leicester v Rosslyn Park	21-3-92
28	M Strett	Orrel v Rosslyn Park	28-4-90
27	D Pears	Harlequins v Bedford	14-10-89
26	J Liley	Leicester v Bedford	23-9-89
26	S Barnes	Bath v West Hartlepool	27-3-93
24	W Hare	Leicester v Rosslyn Park	19-11-88
24	S Barnes	Bath v Bedford	13-1-90
24	R Andrew	Wasps v Bristol	27-4-91
23	J Salmon	Harlequins v Waterloo	27-2-88
23	R Andrew	Wasps v Rosslyn Park	22-10-88
23	D Pears	Harlequins v Saracens	20-10-90
22	W HAre	Leicester v Sale	26-3-88
22	J Graves	Rosslyn Park v Bedford	31-3-90
22	S Thresher	Harlequins v London Irish	31-10-92
21	I Aitchison	Waterloo v Sale	2-1-88
21	D Pears	Harlequins v Rosslyn Park	7-12-91
21	B Rudling	Saracens v Harlequins	21-3-92
21	J Webb	Bath v Rugby	9-1-93
20	W Hare	Leicester v Waterloo	4-4-88
20	S Thresher	Harlequins v Sale	23-4-88
20	T Smith	Gloucester v Harlequins	12-3-90
20	J Liley	Leicester v London Irish	19-9-92
20	M Appleson	London Scottish v Rugby	31-10-92
20	P Hamer	Orrel v Rugby	13-3-93

MOST TRIES IN A COURAGE DIVISION TWO MATCH

3	J Macklin	London Scottish v Northampton	3-10-87
3	O Bluitt	Northampton v Bedford	21-11-87
3	J Roberts	Headingley v Northampton	16-4-88
3	P Rowland	Coventry v London Irish	10-9-88
3	D Kenddell	Headingley v Gosforth	14-1-89
3	L Smith	Saracens v Gosforth	22-4-89
3	N Saunders	Plymouth Albion v Blackheath	14-10-89
3	G Robbins	Coventry v Waterloo	13-1-90
3	R Saundrs	London Irish v Rugby	13-10-90
3	J Wrigley	West Hartlepool v Moseley	14-12-91
3	P Walton	Newcastle Gosforth v Blackheath	14-12-91
3	J Sleightholme	Wakefield v Blackheath	4-1-92
3	G Clark	Newcastle Gosforth v Liverpool St Helens	29-2-92
3	R Arnold	Newcastle Gosforth v Liverpool St Helens	29-2-92
3	D Spillar	Moseley v Sale	4-4-92
3	R Gee	Coventry v Morley	19-9-92
3	M Walker	Nottingham v Morley	24-10-92

MOST POINTS IN A COURAGE DIVISION TWO MATCH

28	D Johnson	Newcastle Gosforth v Morley	11-1-92
28	D Johnson	Newcastle Gosforth v Liverpool St Helens	29-2-93
26	A Mitchell	London Scottish v Northampton	3-10-87
25	C Howard	Rugby v Newcastle Gosforth	11-11-89
25	A Finnie	Bedford v Coventry	27-3-93
24	S Irving	Headingley v London Scottish	12-11-88
24	A Kennedy	Saracens v Northampton	12-11-88
24	N Grecian	London Scottish v Blackheath	16-11-91
23	S Hodgkinson	Nottingham v Blcakheath	26-9-92
23	D Johnson	Newcastle Gosforth v Nottingham	10-10-92
23	G Gregory	Nottingham v Morley	24-10-92
23	G Abraham	Rosslyn Park v Morley	27-3-93
22	G Clark	Gosforth v London Welsh	12-11-88
22	A Kennedy	Saracens v Bedford	19-11-88
22	R Liley	Wakefield v Liverpool St Helens	28-3-92
22	I Aitchison	Waterloo v Blackheath	25-4-92
22	J Graves	Rosslyn Park v Coventry	13-2-93
21	A Kennedy	Saracens v London Welsh	22-10-88
21	M Thomas	Coventry v Morley	19-9-92
21	P Turner	Sale v Fylde	19-9-92
20	N Preston	Richmond v Headingley	6-2-88
20	N Holmes	Saracens v Blackheath	23-3-88
20	A Kennedy	Saracens v Blackheath	26-11-88
20	G Hastings	London Scottish v Coventry	22-4-89
20	J Steele	Northampton v Coventry	10-3-90
20	M Livesey	Richmond v Headingley	28-4-90
20	A Atkinson	Wakefield v Coventry	17-11-90
20	M Slade	Plymouth Albion v Bedford	14-12-91
20	I Aitchison	Waterloo v Liverpool St Helens	21-12-91
20	J Eagle	Blackheath v Moseley	28-3-92
20	P Grayson	Waterloo v Sale	13-3-92

MOST TRIES IN A COURAGE DIVISION THREE MATCH

4	B Hanavan	Fylde v Exeter	3-10-87
4	S Walklin	Plymouth Albion v Birmingham	17-10-87
4	I Russell	Plymouth Albion v Fylde	31-10-87
4	B Hanavan	Fylde v Birmingham	7-11-87
4	D Cottrell	Clifton v Askeans	4-1-92
4	M Sephton	Liverpool St Helens v Aspatria	13-3-93
4	D Crompton	Liverpool St Helens v Aspatria	13-3-93
4	M Farrar	Otley v Askeans	27-3-93
3	K Norris	Plymouth Albion v Sheffield	12-9-87
3	M Preston	Fylde v Morley	17-10-87
3	S Cowling	Wakefield v Birmingham	31-10-87
3	S Cowling	Wakefield v Nuneaton	5-12-87
3	A Holloway	Wakefield v Morley	12-3-88
3	M Cathery	Exeter v Birmingham	26-3-88
3	O Evans	West Hartlepool v Nuneaton	23-4-88
3	C Howard	Rugby v Vale of Lune	10-9-88
3	M Harrison	Wakefield v Metropolitan Police	24-9-88
3	A Atkinson	Wakefield v Metropolitan Police	24-9-88
3	S Hughes	Plymouth Albion v Fylde	19-11-88
3	P Galvin	Metropolitan Police v Maidstone	14-1-89
3	M Murtagh	Wakefield v Askeans	11-11-89
3	G Hughes	London Welsh v Fylde	13-1-90
3	M Harrison	Wakefield v London Welsh	28-4-90
3	D Cottrell	Clifton v Broughton Park	13-10-90
3	A Green	Exeter v Metropolitan Police	10-11-90
3	M Spearman	Clifton v Exeter	17-11-90
3	P Robinson	West Hartlepool v Vale of Lune	2-3-91
3	G Walker	Roundhay v Askeans	6-4-91
3	M Chatterton	Exeter v Headingley	23-11-91
3	A Ireland	Fylde v Askeans	14-12-91
3	J Wrigley	West Hartlepool v Moseley	14-12-91
3	P Della-Savina	Richmond v Nuneaton	28-3-92
3	G Melville	Otley v Aspatia	24-10-92
3	C Thornton	Leeds v Exeter	13-3-93
3	H Langley	Exeter v Broughton Park	24-4-93
3	M Kelly	Broughton Park v Exeter	24-4-93

MOST POINTS IN A COURAGE DIVISION THREE MATCH

28	S Burnage	Fylde v Birmingham	7-11-87
25	D Cundy	Plymouth Albion v Metropolitan Police	26-11-89
25	M Rodgers	Sheffield v Askians	13-3-93
24	C Howard	Rugby v Maidstone	26-11-88
23	J Stabler	West Hartlepool v Broughton Park	9-3-91
22	A Atkinson	Wakefield v Metropolitan Police	24-9-88
22	S Hogg	Clifton v Lydney	28-3-92
22	K O'Brien	Broughton Park v Askeans	11-4-92
21	J Stabler	West Hartlepool v Sheffield	3-10-87
21	G Hughes	London Welsh v Fylde	13-1-90
21	P Rutledge	Otley v Askians	27-3-93
20	S Burnage	Fylde v Exeter	3-10-87
20	R Adamson	Wakefield v Vale of Lune	27-2-88
20	R Goodliffe	Sheffield v London Scottish	14-10-89
20	A Green	Exeter v Metropolitan Police	10-11-90

DIVISION ONE STATISTICS

	CHAMPIONS	RUNNERS-UP	RELEGATED
1987-88	Leicester	Wasps	Coventry Sale
1988-89	Bath	Gloucester	Waterloo Liverpool St Helens
1989-90	Wasps	Gloucester	Bedford
1990-91	Bath	Wasps	Moseley Liverpool St Helens
1991-92	Bath	Orrell	Nottingham Rosslyn Park
1992-93	Bath	Wasps	Saracens London Scottish West Hartlepool Rugby

TEAM RECORDS

Highest score: Bath 76 Bedford 0. 13-1-90
Highest aggregate: Harlequins 71 Bedford 8. 14-10-89
Highest score by a losing side: Harlequins 23 Waterloo 24. 19-11- 88
Highest Scoring draw: Leicester 22 Rugby 22. 25-4-92
Most consecutive wins: 13 Bath 1987-88 through 1988-89
Most consecutive defeats: 12 Liverpool St Helens 1990-91
Most points in a season: 355 Bath 1992-93
Most tries in a season: 44 Bath 1989-90
Most conversions in a season: 29 Bath 1989-90
Most penalties in a season: 33 Bath 1991-92, London Irish 1992-93
Most drop goals in a season: 7 Waterloo 1987-88, London Irish 1992-93

INDIVIDUAL RECORDS

Most points in a season: 129 J Liley Leicester 1991-92
Most tries in a season: 11 A Harriman Harlequins 1987-88
Most conversions in a season: 29 S Barnes Bath 1989-90
Most penalities in a season: 31 D Hare Leicester 1987-88, M Corcoran London Irish 1992-93
Most drop goals in a season: 6 S Hodgkinson Nottingham 1988-89, P Burke London Irish 1992-93
Most points in a match: 31 J Liley Leicester v Rosslyn Park 21- 3-92
Most tries in a match: 4 G Hartley Nottingham v Bedford 18-11-89, A Swift Bath v Bedford 13-1-90, J Guscott Bath v Bedford 13-1-90.
Most conversions in a match: 10 S Barnes Bath v Bedford 13-1-90
Most penalities in a match: 7 D Pears Harlequins v Rosslyn Park 7-12-91
Most drop goals in a match: 3 J Steele Northern v Wasps 23-3-91, J Harris Leicester v Wasps 23-11-91

SEASON BY SEASON LEADING SCORERS

	POINTS		TRIES	
1987-88	126	D Hare (Leicester)	11	A Harriman (Harlequins)
1988-89	103	R Andrew (Wasps)	10	J Guscott (Bath)
1989-90	126	J Liley (Leicester)	10	A Swift (Bath)
1990-91	126	R Andrew (Wasps)	9	R Underwood (Leicester) A Harriman (Harlequins)
1991-92	129	J Liley (Leicester)	9	R Underwood (Leicester)
1992-93	122	J Webb (Bath)	7	S Barnes (Bath)

47

DIVISION ONE TEAM RECORDS

MOST POINTS IN A SEASON

355	Bath	1992-93	1st
280	Bath	1990-91	1st
277	Bath	1991-92	1st
267	Harlequins	1990-91	3rd
263	Bath	1988-89	1st
262	Leicester	1991-92	6th
261	Harlequins	1987-88	3rd

BIGGEST POINTS DIFFERENCE FOR

258	Bath	1992-93	1st
176	Bath	1990-91	1st
165	Bath	1988-89	1st
154	Bath	1989-90	3rd
151	Bath	1991-92	1st
144	Wasps	1989-90	1st
142	Orrell	1990-91	5th
133	Harlequins	1987-88	3rd

LEAST NUMBER OF POINTS CONCEDED

95	Orrell	1991-92	2nd
97	Bath	1992-93	1st
98	Bath	1988-89	1st
104	Bath	1989-90	3rd
104	Bath	1990-91	1st
105	Orrell	1990-91	5th
106	Wasps	1989-90	1st

LEAST NUMBER OF TRIES CONCEDED IN A SEASON

6	Wasps	1992-93	2nd
6	Bath	1988-89	1st
7	Bath	1992-93	1st
7	Nottingham	1988-89	4th
8	Bath	1990-91	1st
8	Orrell	1991-92	2nd
8	Bath	1989-90	3rd
9	Wasps	1989-90	1st
9	Orrell	19898-90	8th
9	Gloucester	1987-88	5th

MOST TRIES SCORED IN A SEASON

44	Bath	1989-90	3rd
43	Bath	1988-89	1st
42	Bath	1992-93	1st
39	Wasps	1989-90	1st
39	Bath	1990-91	1st
38	Harlequins	1987-88	3rd
36	Leicester	1989-90	5th
35	Wasps	1990-91	2nd

LEAST NUMBER OF TRIES SCORED IN A SEASON

8	Waterloo	1988-89	11th
9	Sale	1987-88	12th
9	Liverpool St Helens	1988-89	12th
9	Bedford	1989-90	12th
9	Liverpool St Helens	1990-91	13th
9	London Irish	1992-93	
10	Nottingham	1988-89	4th
10	Rugby	1992-93	13th

MOST TRIES CONCEDED IN A SEASON

83	Bedford	1989-90	12th
60	Sale	1987-88	12th
57	Liverpool St Helens	1990-91	13th
50	Rugby	1992-93	13th
40	Rosslyn Park	1989-90	10th
38	Northampton	1990-91	9th
37	Liverpool St Helens	1988-89	12th
37	Moseley	1989-90	11th
36	Rugby	1991-92	11th
35	Coventry	1987-88	11th

LEAST NUMBER OF PENALTIES SCORED IN A SEASON

7	Bedford	1989-90	12th
8	Bath	1989-90	3rd
11	Rugby	1992-93	13th
11	Saracens	1989-90	4th
13	Liverpool St Helens	1990-91	13th
13	Bristol	1991-92	10th
14	Saracens	1990-91	10th
14	Moseley	1988-89	10th

LEAST NUMBER OF PENALTIES AGAINST IN A SEASON

11	Harlequins	1987-88	3rd
13	Gloucester	1988-89	2nd
14	Orrell	1990-91	5th
14	Leicester	1992-93	3rd
14	Bath	1992-93	1st
14	Saracens	1989-90	4th
15	Sale	1987-88	12th
15	Nottingham	1989-90	6th
15	Rosslyn Park	1989-90	10th
15	Bedford	1989-90	12th

MOST PENALTIES SCORED AGAINST IN A SEASON

31	Rosslyn Park	1991-92	13th
30	Rosslyn Park	1988-89	9th
28	Leicester	1991-92	6th
28	West Hartlepool	1992-93	12th
28	Saracens	1992-93	11th
28	Orrell	1989-90	8th

DIVISION TWO STATISTICS

	CHAMPIONS	RUNNERS-UP	RELEGATED
1987-88	Rosslyn Park	Liverpoool St Helens	None
1988-89	Saracens	Bedford	London Welsh London Scottish
1989-90	Northampton	Liverpool St Helens	None
1990-91	Rugby	London Irish	Richmond Headingley
1991-92	London Scottish	West Hartlepool	Plymouth Albion Liverpool St Helens
1992-93	Newcastle Gosforth	Waterloo	Bedford Rosslyn Park Richmond Blackheath Coventry Fylde Morley

TEAM RECORDS

Highest score: Richmond 86 Headingley 8 28-4-90
Highest aggregate: 94 points as above
Highest score by a losing side: 28 Waterloo 28 Plymouth 33 31-3- 90
Highest scoring draw: 24-24 London Scottish v London Welsh 13-4- 88
Most consecutive wins: 15 Saracens 1987-88 through 1988-89
Most consecutive defeats: 12 Liverpool St Helens 1991-92
Most points in a season: 371 Newcastle Gosforth 1991-92
Most tries in a season: 57 Newcastle Gosforth 1991-92
Most conversions in a season: 31 Newcastle Gosforth 1991-92
Most penalties in a season: 33 Saracens 1988-89
Most drop goals in a season: 9 Nottingham 1992-93

INDIVIDUAL RECORDS

Most points in a season: 147 D Johnson Newcastle Gosforth 1991-92
Most tries in a season: 11 N Grecian London Scottish 1991-92
Most conversions in a season: 31 D Johnson Newcastle Gosforth 1991-92
Most penalities in a season: 30 A Kennedy Saracens 1988-89
Most drop goals in a season: 9 G Gregory Nottingham 1992-93
Most points in a match: 28 D Johnson Newcastle Gosforth v Morley, 11-1-92, Newcastle Gosforth v Liverpool St Helens 29-2-92
Most tries in a match: 3 15 Players have achieved this feat
Most conversions in a match: 9 D Johnson Newcastle Gosforth v Liverpool St Helens 29-2-92
Most penalities in a match: 6 9 players have achieved this feat
Most drop goals in a match: 3 M Livesey (Richmond v Northampton) 19-11-88

SEASON BY SEASON LEADING SCORES

	POINTS	TRIES
1987-88	75 A Finnie (Bedford)	10 D McLagan (Saracens)
1988-89	138 A Kennedy (Saracens)	7 D McLagan (Saracens)
1989-90	107 I Aitchison (London Irish)	7 J Fallon (Richmond)
1990-91	117 B Mullen (London Irish)	9 L Renwick (London Scottish)
1991-92	147 D Johnson (Newcastle Gosforth)	11 N Grecian (London Scottish)
1992-93	136 D Johnson (Newcastle Gosforth)	7 J Sleightholme (Wakefield)

DIVISION TWO TEAM RECORDS

MOST POINTS IN A SEASON

371	Newcastle Gosforth	1991-92	4th
280	London Scottish	1991-92	1st
277	Saracens	1988-89	1st
282	Richmond	1988-89	3rd
242	Rugby	1990-91	1st
249	Nottingham	1992-93	4th
244	West Hartlepool	1991-92	2nd

BIGGEST POINTS DIFFERENCE FOR

221	Newcastle Gosforth	1991-92	4th
208	Saracens	1988-89	1st
174	London Scottish	1991-92	1st
155	West Hartlepool	1991-92	2nd
147	Richmond	1989-90	3rd
142	Saracens	1987-88	3rd
135	Newcastle Gosforth	1992-93	1st
135	Sale	1992-93	5th

LEAST NUMBER OF POINT CONCEDED

80	Saracens	1988-89	1st
83	Rosslyn Park	1987-88	1st
86	Saracens	1987-88	3rd
89	West Hartlepool	1991-92	2nd
97	Liverpool St Helens	1987-88	2nd
102	Sale	1992-93	5th
104	Headingley	1987-88	4th

LEAST NUMBER OF TRIES CONCEDED IN A SEASON

5	Sale	1992-93	5th
7	Newcsatle Gosforth	1992-93	1st
7	Waterloo	1992-93	2nd
8	Wakefield	1990-91	3rd
8	Rosslyn Park	1987-88	1st
9	Saracens	1988-89	1st
10	Liverpool St Helens	1987-88	2nd
11	Saracens	1987-88	3rd
12	Northampton	1988-89	3rd
12	West Hartlepool	1991-92	2nd

MOST TRIES SCORED IN A SEASON

57	Newcastle Gosforth	1991-92	4th
45	London Scottish	1991-92	1st
41	Richmond	1989-90	3rd
39	Rugby	1990-91	1st
38	Saracens	1987-88	3rd
37	Saracens	1988-89	1st
36	London Scottish	1990-91	5th
34	Rugby	1989-90	6th

LEAST NUMBER OF TRIES SCORED IN A SEASON

7	Morley	1992-93	13th
8	Richmond	1988-89	9th
9	Blackheath	1992-93	10th
9	Fylde	1992-93	12th
9	Plymouth Albion	1990-91	11th
10	Northampton	1987-88	12th
11	Newcastle Gosforth	1989-90	12th
12	Blackheath	1990-91	10th
12	Blackheath	1991-92	11th

MOST TRIES CONCEDED IN A SEASON

65	Liverpool St Helens	1991-92	13th
45	Morley	1992-93	13th
41	Newcastle Gosforth	1988-89	10th
39	Newcastle Gosforth	1989-90	12th
37	Blackheath	1991-92	11th
35	Headingley	1990-91	13th
33	London Irish	1989-90	5th
33	Northampton	1987-88	12th
32	London Welsh	1988-89	12th
32	Headingley	1989-90	8th

LEAST NUMBER OF PENALTIES SCORED IN A SEASON

6	Newcastle Gosforth	1987-88	12th
7	Liverpool St Helens	1991-92	13th
9	Northampton	1987-88	12th
10	Northampton	1988-89	13th
11	Blackheath	1987-88	11th
12	Coventry	1988-89	5th
13	Saracens	1987-88	3rd
13	London Welsh	1988-89	12th
13	Headingley	1988-89	7th
13	Headingley	1989-90	13th
13	Wakefield	1991-92	5th

LEAST NUMBER OF PENALTIES AGAINST IN A SEASON

8	Saracens	1987-88	3rd
8	Sale	1990-91	5th
10	Headingley	1987-88	4th
20	Coventry	1990-91	4th
11	Saracens	1988-89	1st
11	Headingley	1990-91	13th
11	West Hartlepool	1991-92	2nd
12	Newcastle Gosforth	1988-89	9th
13	Liverpool St Helens	1987-88	2nd
13	Rugby	1990-91	1st

MOST PENALTIES SCORED AGAINST IN A SEASON

34	Rosslyn Park	1992-93	8th
33	Richmond	1992-93	9th
32	Waterloo	1992-93	2nd
31	Richmond	1990-91	12th
30	Fylde	1992-93	12th
29	Morley	1991-92	9th
29	London Irish	1988-89	6th
28	Morley	1992-93	13th

DIVISION THREE STATISTICS

	CHAMPIONS	RUNNERS-UP	RELEGATED
1987-88	Wakefield	West Hartlepool	Morley Birmingham
1988-89	Plymouth Albion	Rugby	Maidstone Metropolitan Police
1989-90	London Scottish	Wakefield	London Welsh
1990-91	West Hartlepool	Morley	Metropolitan Police Vale of Lune
1991-92	Richmond	Fylde	Lydney Nuneaton
1992-93	Otley	Havant	Sheffield Leeds Liverpool St Helens Clifton Aspatria Askeans Broughton Park Plymouth

TEAM RECORDS

Highest score: Liverpool St Helens 77 Aspatria 5 13-3-93
Highest aggregate: 82 points as above
Highest score by a losing side: 32 Leeds 42 Clifton 32 24-4-93
Highest scoring draw: 18-18 Exeter v West Hartlepool 22-9-90
Most consecutive wins: 11 London Scottish 1989-90
Most consecutive defeats: 11 Maidstone 1988-89
Most points in a season: 311 Plymouth Albion 1988-89
Most tries in a season: 46 Wakefield 1988-89,
Most conversions in a season: 31 Fylde 1987-88
Most penalties in a season: 31 Exeter 1992-93
Most drop goals in a season: 6 Vale of Lune 1989-90, Broughton Park 1990-91 & 1991-92

INDIVIDUAL RECORDS

Most points in a season: 123 C Howard Rugby 1988-89
Most tries in a season: 10 B Hanavan Fylde 1987-88
Most conversions in a season: 30 S Burnage Fylde 1987-88
Most penalities in a season: 31 A Green Exeter 1992-93,
Most drop goals in a season: 6 A Higgin Vale of Lune 1989-90, A Rimmer Broughton Park 1990-91
Most points in a match: 28, S Burnage Fylde v Birmingahm 7-11-87
Most tries in a match: B Hanavan Fylde v Exeter 3-10-87 & v Birmingham 7-11-87, S Walklin Plymouth v Birmingham 17-10-87, I Russell Plymouth Albion v Fylde 31-10-87, D Cottrell Clifton v Askeans 13-10-87, M Sephton Liverpool St Helens v Aspatria 13-3- 90, D Crompton Liverpool St Helens v Aspatria 13-3-90, M Farrar Otley v Askeans 27-3-90
Most conversions in a match: 9 S Burnage Fylde v Birmingham 7-11- 87
Most penalities in a match: 6 J Stabler West Hartlepool v Metropolitan Police 2-1-88, R Adamson Wakefield v Vale of Lune 27-2-88, C Howard Rugby v Nuneaton 22-10-88, R Goodliffe Sheffield v London Scottish 14-10-89, Mark Rodgers Sheffield v Morley 23-2-91, J Clark Richmond v Lydney 14-3-92
Most drop goals in a match: 4 A Rimmer Broughton Park v Sheffield 17-11-90

SEASON BY SEASON LEADING SCORES

	POINTS	TRIES
1987-88	121 S Burnage (Fylde)	10 B Hanavan (Fylde)
1988-89	123 C Howard (Rugby)	8 S Walklin (Plymouth Albion) D Scully (Wakefield)
1989-90	102 A Higgin (Vale of Lune)	7 M Harrison (Wakefield) B Hananan (Fylde)
1990-91	108 M Rodgers (Sheffield)	9 J Wrigley (West Hartlepool)
1991-92	106 M Jackson (Fylde)	8 M Brain (Clifton)
1992-93	122 A Green (Exeter)	8 M Kelly (Broughton Park) M Sephton (Liverpool)

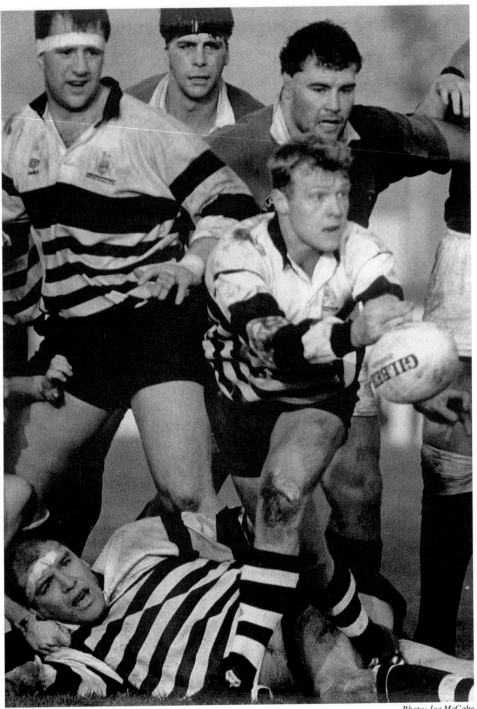

Action from 'Quins v Bristol

Photo: Joe McCabe

NATIONAL LEAGUE ONE

RESULTS AND LEAGUE TABLES
1987-1993
Pages 56-58

MEMBER CLUBS
1993-94

NATIONAL LEAGUE ONE RESULTS

1987-88

	1	2	3	4	5	6	7	8	9	10	11	12
1 Bath		15-9			21-9		14.0		23-18			10-17
2 Bristol				16-21			21-10				12-12	N/P
3 Coventry	9-9				12-15			15-20	11-24	24-19		15- 10
4 Gloucester	9-16	39-3			18-12	17-9			61-7	13-24		
5 Harlequins		28-22		9-9		9-12		34-8	6-12	66-0		37- 4
6 Leicester	24-13	15-10	32-16	N/P						42-15	12-9	39-15
7 Moseley			26-3		11-32	3-21			28-10		19-12	27-3
8 Nottingham	25-15	3-16				13-22	21-12		12-12			
9 Orrell		13-25		9-13		30-6				19-0		30-6
10 Sale	17-46						15-19	3-17			6-14	
11 Wasps	19-15		20-4		17-16			17-9	23-15			
12 Waterloo				16-6				10-9		29-13	13-22	

1988-89

	1	2	3	4	5	6	7	8	9	10	11	12
1 Bath		16-9	19-9					22-16	36-12		16-6	38-9
2 Bristol				18-6		50-14	18-0		13-7			14-3
3 Gloucester		10-11			28-0		37-9	13-6			19-3	
4 Harlequins	9-26		26-11			15-6	38-15					23- 24
5 Leicester	15-12	13-12		21-31					15-27	28-15	15-6	
6 Liverpool St. Helens	7-21		9-31			15-22		12-32				
7 Moseley	0-38				22-13	18-15			10-12	7-13		13- 6
8 Nottingham	10-6		12-0	12-12		13-9			9-15			
9 Orrell			6-16	16-15		20-24		12-6			9-9	15-12
10 Rosslyn Park	6-19	18-16	8-26	12-16				9-18	17-13			
11 Wasps		21-19		23-15		16-10	39-10			39-16		
12 Waterloo		15-15			23-34	6-12		9-18		14-24	0-29	

1989-90

	1	2	3	4	5	6	7	8	9	10	11	12
1 Bath		76-0			32-12	26-15	27-9			34-6		
2 Bedford			6-16		8-71		0-24		7-25		3-22	9-44
3 Bristol	13-14			6-13		11-13		13-9		6-15		21- 22
4 Gloucester	13-6	37-6			24-9				16-10	41-12	21- 21	
5 Harlequins			13-7			15-12		22-27	15-9	19-15		12-9
6 Leicester		60-3		16-26			38-20	18-6		34-6		
7 Moseley			10-16	12-16	22-21			6-22				0-42
8 Nottingham	12-9	47-16		12-3					9-25	6-11	25-12	
9 Orrell	6-9		12-15			33-10	25-13			64-14		
10 Rosslyn Park	45-12				9-23	18-19					13-15	6-14
11 Saracens	9-7		17-12		15-9		33-13		12-6			
12 Wasps	9-18			29-4		29-12		16-12	12-6		24-6	

56

1990-91

		1	2	3	4	5	6	7	8	9	10	11	12	13
1	Bath				23-3		46-3	11-6			17-9	45-21		15-16
2	Bristol	3-10		15-12		10-6				6-22	3-36		25-6	
3	Gloucester	15-17			38-19			30-12		22-6	9-16		21-16	
4	Harlequins	,38-16				41-12	33-6	21-6			18-6		12-18	
5	Leicester	3-9		18-6	12-15					25-9	15-12	29-6		
6	Liverpool St. Helens		6-7	7-26		7-28			13-23	12-13			3-17	
7	Moseley		9-9			19-43	20-12		10-16			9-19	,9-22	
8	Northampton	10-16	12-9	6-7		18-28				22-15			15-6	
9	Nottingham	9-22			6-19			12-7			16-12		3-28	12-10
10	Orrell			12-9		38-0	16-0		60-0			12-3		12-14
11	Rosslyn Park		16-13	17-12		17-15	39-9		48-0	9-15				
12	Saracens	6-49			7-39			21-6			19-12	13-11		6-15
13	Wasps		46-19	14-9		12-22	51-4		21-21		13-10			

1991-92

		1	2	3	4	5	6	7	8	9	10	11	12	13
1	Bath		9-4	29-9		37-6		15-6	25-15				32-12	
2	Bristol			16-0		14-19	9-15			22-4	48-4			10-33
3	Gloucester		29-15			21-3	22-15	10-17		12-9				15-10
4	Harlequins	18-18		21-18		20-13		23-6	7-10			21-37		
5	Leicester		25-9				36-13	19-22		51-16	22-22			31-12
6	London Irish	21-26			3-39				7-21	12-12	6-6			18-13
7	Northampton				24-14		12-12		12-3	21-12	29-0			28-15
8	Nottingham		0-32	3-14		14-27	9-12	18-9		34-9				
9	Orrell	10-9	23-9	18-12		21-9			20-6			23-0		
10	Rosslyn Park	13-21		12-24					4-22		7-15	6-10	7-15	
11	Rugby	0-32		16-19	29-20				9-9	7-21			6-22	
12	Saracens		13-4	12-12		9-20	27-9	9-14	13-12					
13	Wasps	12-24			20-6				11-7	13-12		17-10	6-12	

1992-93

		1	2	3	4	5	6	7	8	9	10	11	12	13
1	Bath				22-6	13-3	42-19	40-6		39-3	16-7		22-11	
2	Bristol	8-13		9-22		15-0				23-11		12-7		19-11
3	Gloucester	0-20			25-5					8-13	21-12	19-5		6-21
4	Harlequins		16-0				47-24	22-22	7-12		35-14		13-15	
5	Leicester			22-21	23-0					9-0		30-3		21-8
6	London Irish		9-7	9-18		14-30			12-3			10-9		25-13
7	London Scottish		8-11	8-3		11-28	28-21		21-34					10-15
8	Northampton	11-8	16-6	16-21		12-13						21-17		55-9
9	Orrell				18-16		8-12	13-10	9-10		66-0		10-11	
10	Rugby		21-32			5-28	1-14	20-45	7-13				3-34	
11	Saracens	13-19			3-18			41-17		6-9	14-9		9-13	
12	Wasps		7-6	19-9		14-13	18-9	10-6	20-12					
13	West Hartlepool	10-38			9-12					39-15	5-6	3-10	6-19	

NATIONAL LEAGUE ONE TABLES

1987-88

	P	W	D	L	F	A	Pts
Leicester	10	9	0	1	225	133	37
Wasps	11	8	1	2	218	136	36
Harlequins	11	6	1	4	261	128	30
Bath	11	6	1	4	197	156	30
Gloucester	10	6	1	3	206	121	29
Orrell	11	5	1	5	192	153	27
Moseley	11	5	0	6	167	170	26
Nottingham	11	4	1	6	146	170	24
Bristol	10	4	1	5	171	145	23
Waterloo	10	4	0	6	123	208	22
Coventry	11	3	1	7	133	246	21
Sale	11	0	0	11	95	374	0

1988-89

	P	W	D	L	F	A	Pts
Bath	11	10	0	1	263	98	20
Gloucester	11	7	1	3	215	112	15
Wasps	11	7	1	3	206	138	15
Nottingham	11	6	1	4	142	122	13
Orrell	11	6	1	4	148	157	13
Leicester	11	6	1	4	189	199	13
Bristol	11	6	0	5	188	117	12
Harlequins	11	5	0	6	194	184	10
Rosslyn Park	11	5	0	6	172	208	10
Moseley	11	3	0	8	113	242	6
Waterloo	11	1	1	9	120	235	3
Liverpool St. H.	11	1	0	10	116	254	2

1989-90

	P	W	D	L	F	A	Pts
Wasps	11	9	0	2	250	106	18
Gloucester	11	8	1	2	214	139	17
Bath	11	8	0	3	258	104	16
Saracens	11	7	1	3	168	167	15
Leicester	11	6	0	5	248	184	12
Nottingham	11	6	0	5	187	148	12
Harlequins	11	6	0	5	218	180	12
Orrell	11	5	0	6	221	132	10
Bristol	11	4	0	7	136	144	8
Rosslyn Park	11	4	0	7	164	243	8
Moseley	11	2	0	9	138	258	4
Bedford	11	0	0	11	70	467	0

1990-91

	P	W	D	L	F	A	Pts
Bath	12	11	0	1	280	104	22
Wasps	12	9	1	2	252	151	19
Harlequins	12	8	0	4	267	162	16
Leicester	12	8	0	4	244	140	16
Orrell	12	7	0	5	247	105	14
Gloucester	12	6	0	6	207	163	12
Rosslyn Park	12	6	0	6	216	174	12
Nottingham	12	6	0	6	138	194	12
Northampton	12	5	1	6	149	254	11
Saracens	12	5	0	7	151	228	10
Bristol	12	4	1	7	135	219	9
Moseley	12	1	1	10	113	244	3
Liverpool St. H.	12	0	0	12	88	349	0

1991-92

	P	W	D	L	F	A	PD	Pts
Bath	12	10	1	1	277	126	151	20
Orrell	12	10	0	2	204	95	109	20
Northampton	12	9	1	2	209	136	73	19
Gloucester	12	7	1	4	193	168	11	15
Saracens	12	7	1	4	176	165	11	15
Leicester	12	6	1	5	262	216	46	13
Wasps	12	6	0	6	177	180	-3	12
Harlequins	12	5	1	6	213	207	6	11
London Irish	12	3	3	6	147	237	-90	9
Bristol	12	4	0	8	192	174	18	8
Rugby	12	2	3	7	124	252	-128	7
Nottingham	12	2	1	9	133	204	-71	5
Rosslyn Park	12	0	1	11	111	258	-147	1

1992-93

	P	W	D	L	F	A	PD	Pts
Bath	12	11	0	1	355	97	258	22
Wasps	12	11	0	1	186	118	118	68
Leicester	12	9	0	3	220	116	104	18
Northampton	12	8	0	4	215	150	65	16
Gloucester	12	6	0	6	173	151	22	12
Bristol	12	6	0	6	148	169	-21	12
London Irish	12	6	0	6	175	223	-48	12
Harlequins	12	5	1	6	197	187	10	11
Orrell	12	5	0	7	175	183	-8	10
London Scottish	12	3	1	8	192	248	-56	7
Saracens	12	3	0	9	137	180	-43	6
West Hartlepool	12	3	0	9	149	236	-87	6
Rugby	12	1	0	11	104	368	-264	2

1992-93 WEEK BY WEEK POSITION IN LEAGUE ONE

	26/9	3/10	10/10	24/10	31/10	21/11	9/1	13/2	13/3	27/3	3/4	24/4
Bath	1	2	5	3	3	2	2	2	1	1	1	1
Bristol	8	6	4	5	6	5	5	6	5	4	5	6
Gloucester	10	7	10	10	10	9	8	8	9	9	9	5
Harlequins	11	10	9	7	5	7	7	5	7	8	7	8
Leicester	2	3	2	2	1	3	3	3	3	3	3	3
London Irish	13	11	7	6	7	6	6	7	6	7	6	7
London Scottish	6	8	8	9	8	8	10	10	11	10	10	10
Northampton	4	5	3	4	4	4	4	4	4	5	4	4
Orrell	5	4	6	8	9	10	9	9	8	6	8	9
Rugby	9	12	13	12	13	13	13	13	13	13	13	13
Saracns	7	9	11	11	12	12	12	12	10	11	11	11
Wasps	3	1	1	1	2	1	1	1	2	2	2	2
W Hartlepool	12	13	12	13	11	11	11	11	12	12	12	12

Caption please — A free copy of next year's Directory will be sent to the writer of the best caption for the picture above!

THE BEST PACK IN THE CHAMPIONSHIP.

BATH RFC

President: G W Hancock
Chairman: J M Gaynor
Club Secretary: Major J W Quin (Acting until AGM)
Fixtures Secretary: T D Martland, 22 Gainsborough Gardens, Weston lane, Bath, BA1 4AJ. Tel: (H) 0225 317801 (W) 0272 674481
Press Officer: K Johnstone, 10 St Michaels Court, Monkton Combe, Bath, BA2 7HA.
1993/94 1XV Captain: Jon Hall
1993/94 1XV Coach: Jack Rowell
Treasurer: C S Gale
Marketing: D G Ryder

Review of the Season

No side adapted better to the new laws than Bath.

The westcountrymen could justly claim to be head and shoulders above the rest after smashing their own points scoring record on their way to a third successive Courage League Championship.

Only two sides came close to halting Bath's surge. Wasps stayed neck and neck with Bath in terms of wins but trailed dismally — a difference of 190 — in the points stakes.

And brave Saracens had Jack Rowell contemplating a bungee jump before the coach's nerves were soothed by Jon Callard's second try of the match in the final minutes of the campaign.

Yet the Bath success went so much further than a fourth league title. Four players — Ben Clarke, Victor Ubogu, Andy Reed and Phil de Glanville won their first caps with Reed and Clarke going on to gain selection for the British Lions.

Another Lion, Stuart Barnes stole the headlines with his pulsating England comeback.

John Hall, who succeeds Andy Robinson as club captain for the new season, made a comeback of a different kind, leading England A and playing a huge part in Bath's championship roll soon after injury had threatened his career.

It was a season when the up and comers up and came. At half-back Ian Sanders, Mike Catt and Craig Raymond showed that Bath need not panic when Barnes and Richard Hill are missing.

And there were farewells. Jon Webb retired after a glorious three year resurrection and Richard Lee moved on to Wellington after 363 first team games. The nadir was a third round Pilkington Cup exit at Waterloo. As outgoing skipper Andy Robinson said: "The Waterloo defeat ruined my Pilkington Cup Saturdays". The cup final lacked the Bath fans and the Bath charisma.

The champions won 27 of their 32 games, scoring over 3O pts on 17 occasions. Five times they scored over 6O.

Jon Callard emerged as the outstanding points scorer. The full-back scored a remarkable 18 tries in 16 games to finish top try scorer ahead of winger Tony Swift (15). Callard's improved goal-kicking helped give him 2O9 points at an average of 13 a game.

In all 51 players represented the first team, ten of them for the first time. There were 36 different scorers, testament to Bath's multi-pronged attack.

Bath's first team weren't the only champions. The club won county titles at under-15, under-17, under-19 and Youth level while the under-21s enjoyed a magnificent first season.

BATH RFC

COURAGE CLUBS CHAMPIONSHIP
NATIONAL DIVISION ONE 1992-93

No	Date	Opponents	Venue	Result	Point Scorers
1	Sep 19	Harlequins	H	W22-6	Guscott (1T) Webb (1C)(5P)
2	Sep 26	L Irish	H	W42-19	Ubogu (2T) Degranvill (1T) Clarke (1T) Barnes (1T) Webb (4C)(3P)
3	Oct 3	Free	Free	Free	Free
4	Oct 10	Northampton	A	L8-211	B Clarke (1T) S Barnes (1P)
5	Oct 24	Orrell	H	W39-3	J Hall (2T) Hill (T) Redman (T) Webb (T)(4C)(2P)
6	Oct 31	Bristol	A	W31-8	Swift (2T) Clarke (1T) Webb (1T)(4C)(1P)
7	Nov 21	Leicester	H	W13-3	Adebayo (1T) Redman (1T) Webb (1P)
8	Jan 9	Rugby	H	W61-7	Barnes (2T) Adebayo (2T) O'Leary (1T) Robinson (1T) Redman (1T) Guscott (1T) Webb (1T)(5C)(2P)
9	Feb 13	Gloucester	A	W20-0	Swift (1T) Webb (5P)
10	Mar 13	Wasps	H	W22-11	Guscott (T) Webb (C)(4P) Barnes (DG)
11	Mar 27	West Hartlepool	A	W38-10	Callard (2T)(C) Barnes (3T)(3P)(C)
12	Apr 3	L Scottish	H	W40-6	Swift (T) Barnes (T)(C)(2P) Ubogu (T) Clarke (T) Callard (T)(C) De Galnville (T)
13	Apr 24	Saracens	A	W19-13	Callard (2T) Barnes (3P)

ADDITIONAL RESULTS 1992-93

No	Date	Opponents	Venue	Result
1	Sep 9	Record Cucine Casale		W62-15
2	Sep 12	Benetton Treviso		W18-15
3	Sep 19	Harlequins		W22-6
4	Sep 26	London Irish		W42-19
5	Oct 3	Blackheath		W51-0
6	Oct 10	Northampton		L8-11
7	Oct 17	Coventy		W63-6
8	Oct 24	Orrell		W39-3
9	Oct 31	Bristol		W31-8
10	Nov 7	Cardiff		W31-22
11	Nov 21	Leicester		W13-3
12	Nov 28	Waterloo		W9-8
13	Dec 5	Nottingham		W24-17
14	Dec 12	Richmond		W38-22
15	Dec 19	London Welsh		W37-7
16	Dec 26	Clifton		W28-0
17	Jan 2	Sale		W26-6
18	Jan 9	Rugby		W61-7
19	Jan 15	Clifton		W43-3
20	Jan 23	London Irish		W47-5
21	Jan 30	Plymouth		W63-13
22	Feb 13	Gloucester		W20-0
23	Feb 19	Swansea		W79-3
24	Feb 27	Cardiff		L27-17
25	Mar 5	Newbridge		L19-13
26	Mar 13	Wasps		W22-11
27	Mar 19	Pontypool		W12-10
28	Mar 27	West Hartlepool		W38-10
29	Apr 3	London Scottish		W40-6
30	Apr 10	Newbury		W81-8
31	Apr 17	Gloucester		L16-17
32	Apr 24	Saracens		W19-13

CLUB PLAYING RECORD 1992-93 SEASON

National Division: One
Final League Position at end 1992/93 Season: 1st
League Playing Record: P 12, W 11, D 0, L 1,
Pts F 355, Pts A 97

COMPETITIONS WON DURING SEASON 1992-93

Courage League 1st Division title 3rd year in succession

SPECIAL OCCASSIONS IN 1993-94

Visit of Toulouse (Opening Game) Summer Canada Tour

BATH RFC

MATCH BY MATCH PLAYERS BY POSITION

Webb	Swift	Guscott	De Glanville	Adebayo	Barnes	Hill	Chilcott	Dawe	Mallett	Redman	O'Leary	Hall	Ojomoh	Clarke	Lewis	Obogu	Haag	Robinson	Reed	Hilton	Atkins	Sanders	Egerton
16	15	14	12	11	10	9	1	2	3	4	5	6	7	8									
16	12		12	11	10	9	1,2	R		4	5	6	7	8	14	13							
		F	R	E	E		F	R	E	E		F	R	E	E			F	R	E	E		
16	15	12	14	11	10	9	1	2			5		7	8		3	4	6					
16	15	12	14	11	10	9	1	2		4			7	8		3		6	5				
16	15	12	14	11	10	9	1	2		4			8	7		3		6	5				
16	15	14	12	11	10	9	1	2		4			7	8		3		6	5				
16	15	14	12	11				2		4	5		7			3		6		1	R	R	8
16	15	14	12	11				2		4			7	8		3		6	5	1		9	
16	15	12	14	11	10	9	1	2			5		7	8		3		6	4				
14			13	11	10	9	1	2			5	6	7		10	3		8	4				
14	12	13		11	10	9	1	2			5		7	8		3		6	4				
16	15	12	14		10	9	1	2			5		7	8		3		6	4				

PLAYING SQUAD 1992-93

Full back: J Callard, A Lumsden, J Webb
Wing: A Adebayo, P Blackett, D Cottrell, T Swift
Centre: A Webber, J Bamsey, P de Glanville, J Guscott, I Lewis
Outside Half: S Barnes, M Catt, C Raymond
Scrum Half: R Hill, I Sanders
Prop: G Chilcott, M Crane, D Crompton, D Hilton, J Mallett, V Ubogu
Hooker: T Beddow, C Atkins, G Dawe
Lock: M Haag, P McCoy, S O'Leary, N Redman, A Reed
Flanker: G Adams, J Hall, N Maslen, S Ojomoh, A Robinson
No 8: B Clarke, D Eggerton

LEADING APPEARANCES FOR CLUB 1992-93

T Swift, 21
A Adebayo, 19
N Redman, 19
A Robinson, 18
R Hill, 17
G Dawe, 17
J hall, 17
P de Glanville, 17

LEADING SCORERS 1992-93

J Callard, Full Back, 209
J Webb, Full Back, 150
T Swift, Wing, 75
S Barnes, Fly Half, 69
C Raymond, Fly Half, 67
M Catt, Fly Half, 49

BATH FC

COURAGE LEAGUE RECORDS

Highest score: 76 v Bedford (76-0) 13-1-90 Home CL1
Largest winning margin: 43 as above
Highest score against: 25 v Nottingham (15-25) 10-10-87 Away CL1
Largest losing margin: 11 v Leicester (13-24) 12-9-87 Away CL1
Drawn Matches: 2
Clean Sheets: 5
Failed to score: 0

INDIVIDUAL SCORING RECORDS
IN A MATCH

Most points: 26 Stuart Barnes v W Hartlepool 27-3-93 Away CL1
Most tries: 4 Jeremy Guscott & Tony Swift v Bedford 13-1-90 Home CL1
Most conversions: 10 Stuart Barnes v Bedford 13-1-90 Home CL1
Most penalities: 5 Jon Webb v Northampton 7-12-91 Home CL1, v Harlequins 19-9-92 Home CL1, v, Gloucester 13-2-93 Away CL1
Most drop goals: 1 on 10 occassions by 4 players. Stuart Barnes 7, Phil Cue 1, Jonathan Palmer 1, Jeremy Guscott 1.

IN A SEASON

Most points: 122 Jon Webb 1992-93 CL1
Most tries: 10 Jeremy Guscott 1988-89 CL1, Tony Swift 1989-90 CL1
Most conversions: 29 Stuart Barnes 1989-90 CL1
Most penalties: 23 Jon Webb 1992-93 CL1 CL2
Most drop goals: 2 Stuart Barnes 1987-88, 1988-89, 1990-91

IN A CAREER

Most points: 446 Stuart Barnes 1987-93
Most tries: 35 Tony Swift 1987-93
Most conversions: 65 Stuart Barnes 1987-93
Most penalties: 65 Stuart Barnes 1987-93
Most drop goals: 8 Stuart Barnes 1987-93

SEASON BY SEASON LEADING SCORERS

	Most Points			Most Tries	
1987-88	40	Phil Cue	4	Tony Swift	
1988-89	83	Stuart Barnes	10	Jeremy Guscott	
1989-90	103	Stuart Barnes	10	Tony Swift	
1990-91	98	Stuart Barnes	6	Tony Swift	
1991-92	95	Stuart Barnes	8	Tony Swift	
1992-93	122	Jon Webb	7	Stuart Barnes	

Jeremy Guscot evades a tackle during Bath's 22-6 victory over Harlequins.   *Photo: Joe McCabe*

BATH FC

Club Details

Colours: Blue, white & black
Change of Colours: White & thin blue/black hoops
Date Founded: 1865
Membership: Total 3,500
Membership Fees: Full £40 ground, Junior/Youth/Minis £5
Number of Teams: Senior 3, Junior 12
Programme Advertising Rates: On application

Ground Details

Ground Address: Recreation Ground, Bath, BA2 6PW
Telephone: 0225 425192/465328 **Fax:** 0225 443253
Directions: City Centre, Bath
Capacity: Total 8,500
Ticket Prices: Adults £5, Student/Junior/U16/OAP £2
Clubhouse Facilities: Three bars and sponsors area with own bar
Training Nights: Mondays & Wednesdays

Craig Luxton tackles Richard Hill as Ben Clarke supports his scrum half   Photo: Joe McCabe

66

BRISTOL RFC

President: A J Holmes
Chairman: B W Redwood
Club Secretary: T Wynne Jones, 31 Bromley Heath Road, Downend, Bristol, BS16 4HY. Tel: 0272 569161
Fixtures Secretary: K T Gerrish, 52 West Town Lane, Brislington, Bristol, BS4 5DB. Tel: (H) 0272 777009
Press Officer: D G Tyler, Memorial Ground, Filton Avenue, Horsfield, Bristol, BS7 0AQ.
1993/94 Coaching Panel: D Alred, P Johnson, D Robson, R Sellars.
Club Administrator: D G Tyler

Review of the Season

Bristol achieved their best ever placing in Division One by finishing the season in sixth place through winning six of their games.

After promising pre-season results the League programme started badly as Northampton continued their unbeaten League record over Bristol with a 16pts-6 victory at Franklins Gardens. Fly-half Andy May kicking two penalties for Bristol on his league debut.then Bristol settled down into winning form as first they beat West Hartlepool 19pts-11 on their first visit to the Memorial Ground then an 11pts-8 win at London Scottish was followed by a 12pts-0 scoreline against Saracens. This game marked the 200th 1st XV game for lucky Andy Blackmore and the 50th league game for centre Ralph Knibbs.

Bristol suffered a double setback at London Irish with lock Phil Adams suffering an ankle injury, which ruled him out for the remainder of the season, and secondly, the exiles recording a narrow 9pts-7 victory.

Over ten thousand people crammed into the Ground for the 200th local derby game against Bath but Bristol were to suffer their biggest defeat by their neighbours since 1912. To add salt to the wound former Bristol player Jonathan Webb scored 10pts for Bath in the 31pts-8 victory.

Despite Ralph Knibbs and full back Paul Hull being delayed on their return with the England side from the Dubai Sevens. Bristol were able to record their fourth league win of the season as the best the 1991-92 Champions Orrell by 23pts-11, fly half Mark Tainton firmly back in the line-up, kicking two conversions and three penalties.

After a break of twelve weeks from league rugby it was to the Stoop to take on the Harlequins. After the game the only celebrations for Bristol were to mark the 250th 1st XV appearance for hooker David Palmer and the league debut for Paul Bullridge following the 16pts-Nil win by the Quins.

Bristol, down to 14 men for the last quarter, held on to beat Leicester by 15pts-10. The early bath for prop Guttridge meant that lock Simon Shaw had to squeeze his 6ft 9in frame into the front row on his league debut. Three second half tries from captain Derek Eves gave Bristol their sixth league victory of the season as the best rugby 32pts-21 on only their second visit to Webb Ellis Road.

The local derby jinx struck again as Gloucester ran out 22pts & Victors with Bristol points coming from the boot of Tainton and then Bristol suffered a disappointing one point defeat as Wasps won 7pts-6 in the last game of the season.

Like West Country neighbours Bath, Gloucester and Clifton, Round Three saw Bristol make their exit from the Pilkington Cup. The Sarries secured their victory with two excellent tries in the first half but Bristol had to rely on the boot of Tainton for 5 penalties.

Besides the six defeats in the league and the Cup defeat in Round Three Bristol lost only two other games in their 36 outings during the season. These were at Gloucester (18pts-11) and at Llanelli (36pts-10).

67

BRISTOL FC

COURAGE CLUBS CHAMPIONSHIP
NATIONAL DIVISION ONE 1992-93

No	Date	Opponents	Venue	Result	Point Scorers
1	Sep 19	Northampton	A	L6-16	May (2P)
2	Sep 26	W. Hartlepool	H	W19-11	Knibbs (T) Hull (T) May (3P)
3	Oct 3	L. Scottish	A	W11-8	Lloud (T) Tainton (2P)
4	Oct 10	Saracens	H	W12-7	Tainton (4P)
5	Oct 24	L. Irish	A	L7-9	Lloyd (T) Tainton (C)
6	Oct 31	Bath	H	L8-31	Johnson (T) Tainton (P)
7	Nov 21	Orrell	H	W23-11	Wring (PT) Tainton (2C)(3P)
8	Jan 9	Free	Free	Free	Free
9	Feb 13	Harlequins	A	L0-16	
10	Mar 13	Leicester	H	W15-10	Barrow (T) Bracken (T) Tainton (C)(P)
11	Mar 27	Rugby	A	W32-21	Eves (3T) Waghorn (T) Tainton (3C)(2P)
12	Apr 3	Gloucester	H	L9-22	Tainton (3P)
13	Apr 24	Wasps	A	L6-7	Tainton (3P)

ADDITIONAL RESULTS 1992-93

No	Date	Opponents	Venue	Result
1	Sep 2	Salisbury	H	W72-0
2	Sep 5	Plymouth Albion	A	W41-11
3	Sep 6	Devon (at Cullompton)	A	W39-10
4	Sep 12	Rugby	H	W35-13
5	Oct 17	Gloucester	A	11-38
6	Nov 6	Llanelli	A	L10-36
7	Nov 13	Wasps	H	W32-6
8	Nov 28	Saracens (Cup 3rd Rd)	A	L15-20
9	Dec 5	Clifton	A	W28-15
10	Dec 12	Moseley	H	26-7
11	Dec 26	Newport	H	W21-16
12	Dec 28	Glamorgan Wanderers	A	W25-12
13	Jan 2	Nottingham	H	W45-6
14	Jan 9	Loughborough Students	H	W54-10
15	Jan 15	Exeter	H	Cancelled
16	Jan 23	Bedford	A	W41-6
17	Jan 30	Orrell	A	W10-6
18	Feb 5	Bridgend	H	W31-7
19	Feb 17	Aberavon	A	W17-10
20	Feb 27	L. Irish	H	W28-17
21	Mar 5	Pontypridd	H	W61-7
22	Mar 16	Cardiff	A	W23-19
23	Apr 10	Bridgend	A	W36-8
24	Apr 12	Glamorgan Wanderers	H	W41-14
25	Apr 17	Waterloo	A	W22-6

CLUB PLAYING RECORD 1992-93 SEASON

National Division: One

Final League Position at end 1992/93 Season: 6th

League Playing Record: P 12, W 6, D 0, L 6, Pts F 148, Pts A 169

Season Playing Record (including League matches/Pilkington cup etc): P 36, W 27, D 0, L 9, Pts F 912, P A 479

Special congratulations to Bristol on their splendid match day programme. We enjoyed reading the complete set which were kindly sent to us. Bristol supporters must be very appreciative of this publication.

BRISTOL FC

MATCH BY MATCH PLAYERS BY POSITION

Hull	Morgan	Wring	Knibbs	Lloyd	May	Bracken	Sharp	Reagan	Hinkins	Adams	Blackmore	Armstrong	Eves	Barrow	Tainton	Palmer	Patton	Taylor	Becconsall	Johnson	Stiff	Duggan	Waghorn
A	B	C	D	E	F	G	H	I	J	K	L	M	N	O									
A	B	D	C	E	F	G	H	I	J	K	L	M	N	O									
A	B	D	C	E		G	H		J	K	L		N	O	F	I		M			R		
A	B	D	C	E			H		J	K	L		N	O		I		M		F	G		
A	B	D	C	E		G	H		J	K	L		N	O	F	I		M			R		
A		D	C	E		G	H		J		L	M	O	N	F	I			B	K			
	B		D	E			H		J		L	M	N	O	F	I				K	A	C	
	F	R	E	E			F	R	E	E			F	R	E	E			F	R	E	E	
A		C		E			H				L	M	N	O	F	I			G	B	K		D
A	E	C				G		I	H		L		N	O	F			M					D
A	E	C				G		I	J		L		N	O	F			M					D
A	E	C				G		I	J		L	M		O	F			N					D
A	E	C				G		I	J		L			O	F			N					D

Also Played: Kitchen G Match 7, Gutteridge J Match 8, John B Match 10, Gutteridge J Match 10 (Sent Off), Shaw k Match 10, John B Match 11, Hickey H Match 11, Saw K Match 11, John b Match 12, Hickey H Match 12, Shaw K Match 12, Griffin replaced by Blackmore Match 12, John B Match 13, Gutteridge H Match 13, Shaw K Match 13, Griffin M Match 13.

MOST CAPPED PLAYERS
including British Lions Appearances

J V Pullin, 42 - 1966-76
J S Tucker, 27 - 1922-31
M Rafter, 17 - 1977-81
L J Corbett, 16 - 1921-27
W R Johnston, 16 - 1910-14
G G Gregory, 13 - 1931-34

LEADING APPEARANCES FOR CLUB

R Gribbs, 383 - 87/82 92/93
P Stiff, 350 - 78/79 92/93
D Palmer, 252 - 80/81 92/93
H Duggan, 224 - 80/81 92/93
A Blackmore, 215 - 84/85 92/93
D Eves, 209 - 85/86 92/93

LEADING SCORERS

M Taunton, Out/Half, 270
R Gribbs, Centre, 61
M Lloyd, Wing/3Qtr, 55
J Johnstone, Wing/3Qtr, 50
A May, Out/Half, 46
D John, Wing/3Qtr, 40

APPEARANCES AND POINT SCORERS

33 Eves, Hinkins
29 Knibbs
27 Tainton
25 Barrow, Morgan (3)
23 Hull
21 Armstrong (1)
20 Lloyd
19 Blackmore, Stiff
18 Waghorn
16 Palmer, Patten, Regan, Wring
14 Guttridge, John, Sharp, Shaw
12 Bracken
11 Kitchin
10 Dugan (1), Johnston
9 Adams
8 Becconsall (1)
7 Griffin (1)
6 May, Morrison, Saverimutto
5 Hickey, Newall (2)
4 Bennett, Crossland
3 Gunningham, Lathrope (1), Moore
2 Bullstrode, Pearson, Williams
1 Allnutt, Collins, Davies, Doubleday, Ford, Fountain (1), Kerley, Matthews, Powell, Whitingham, Willett

TRIES

11 Lloyd
10 Johnston, Knibbs
8 John
7 Eves
6 Barrow, Stiff
5 Morgan
4 Armstrong, Bracken, Hull, Patten, Sharp, Waghorn, Wring
3 Kitchin, Newall
2 Crossland, Griffin, Moore, Regan, Shaw
1 Duggan, Guttridge, Lathrope, Tainton

CONVERSIONS

53 Tainton
8 May
3 Willett
1 Duggan, Knibbs, Saverimutto

PENALTIES

52 Tainton
10 Matthews
3 Knibbs

DROPPED GOALS

1 Tainton

Bristol FC (RFU). Back Row (L to R) Mark Tainton, Huw Duggan, David Palmer, Peter Stiff, Craig Barrow, Ian Patten, Darryl Hickey, Dean Wring, Chris Moore. Front Row (L to R) Will Waghorn, Rob Kitchen, Ralph Knibbs, Mark Regan, Derek Eves (capt.), Paul Hull (v, capt.), David Hinkins, Kevin Morgan, Andy Lathrope.
Photo: Neil Elston

BRISTOL FC

COURAGE LEAGUE RECORDS

Highest score: 50 v Liverpool St Helens (50-14) 22-4-89 Home CL1
Largest winning margin: 44 v Rugby (48-4) 28-3-92 Home CL1
Highest score against: 46 v Wasps (19-46) 27-4-91 Away CL1
Largest losing margin: 33 v Orrell (3-36) 17-11-90 Home CL1
Drawn Matches: 2
Clean Sheets: 3
Failed to score: 1

INDIVIDUAL SCORING RECORDS
IN A MATCH
Most points: 17 Jon Webb v Sale 24-10-87 Home CL1, Mark Tainton v Wasps 31-3-90 Home CL1
Most tries: 3, Mike Lloyd v Rugby 28-3-92 Home CL1, Drek Eves v Rugby 27-3-93 Home CL1
Most conversions: 5 Jon Webb, v, Sale 24-10-87 Home CL1
Most penalities: 5 Jon Webb v Orrell 9-9-89 Away CL1, Mark Tainton v Wasps 31-3-90 Home CL1
Most drop goals: 2 Simon Hogg v Leicester 9-3-91 Home CL1

IN A SEASON
Most points: 68 Mark Tainton 1992-93 CL1
Most tries: 5 Pete Stiff 1991-92 CL1
Most conversions: 12 Jon Webb 1987-88 CL1
Most penalties: 18 Mark Tainton 1992-93 CL1
Most drop goals: 3 Simon Hogg 1988-89 CL1

IN A CAREER
Most points: 155 Jon Webb 1987-90
Most tries: 10 John Davis 1988-92
Most conversions: 17 Mark Tainton 1987-93
Most penalties: 37 Jon Webb 1987-90
Most drop goals: 5 Simon Hogg 1987-91

SEASON BY SEASON LEADING SCORES

	Most Points			Most Tries
1987-88	58	Jon Webb	3	Andy Dun
1988-89	50	Jon Webb	2	8 players
1989-90	47	Jon Webb	2	Paul Hull Paul Collings J Davis
1990-91	35	Simon Hogg	4	Julian Horrobin
1991-92	29	Mark Tainton	5	Pete Stiff
1992-93	68	Mark Tainton	3	Derek Eves

BRISTOL FC

Club Details

Colours: Blue & white.
Change of Colours: White.
Date Founded: 1888.
Membership: Total 1550, Full 1,350, Social 200.
Membership Fees: Full - Stand £20, Enclosure £50,
Ground £40, Junior/Youth/Minis - Stand £40 &
Enclosure £25, Ground £20.
Number of Teams: Senior 3 + Colts, Junior 3, Mini 4.
Programme Advertising Rates: On application.

Ground Details

Ground Address: Memorial Ground, Filton Avenue,
Horfield, Bristol, VS7 0AQ.
Telephone: 0272 514448.
Fax: 0272 514226.
Capacity: Total 8,500.
Ticket Prices: Adults: Division 1 Stand £7, Ground
£5; Other matches Stand £6.00, Ground £4.00. OAP:
Stand £4, Enclosure £3.50, Ground £3.
Clubhouse Facilities: Public/members bar,
hospitality areas, social club.
Training Nights: 1st team Mon & Wed, U21/Colts
Tues & Thurs.

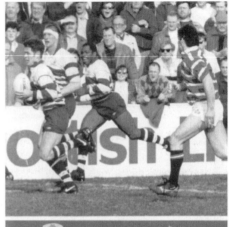

Bristol's K Bracken breaks through the London Irish defence
Photo: Neil Elston

GLOUCESTER RFC

President: H Hughes
Chairman: Peter Ford
Club Secretary: A D Wadley,
"Byeways", Belmont Avenue,
Hucclecote, Gloucester, GL3 3SF. Tel:
(H) 0452 617202 (W) 0452 381087 Fax:
(W) 0452 383321.
Fixtures Secretary: Mike Nicholls, 90
Kingsholm Road, Gloucester. Tel: (H)
0452 301879.
Press Officer: Peter Ford, "Rivermead",
Sandhurst Lane, Gloucester, GL2 9AB.
1993/94 1XV Captain: Ian Smith
1993/94 1XV Coach: Keith Richardson
Commercial Manager: Mike Burton
Director of Rugby: Barry Corless.

All's well that ends well

In the end, all came right for Gloucester in 1992/3. Fnishing in fifth place in Division One of the Courage League was a creditable achievement in a season in which relegation was a very real possibility for much of the time.

Things were never going to be easy. No fewer than twelve players had departed for pastures new, and pre-season injuries had left the club without a recognised scrum half. Against that background it is arguable that few sides could have retained their First Division status in a season when four teams were to be relegated.

The positive side was that new players, including England Under-21 selection Paul Beech, and wingers Holford and Nicholson, were able to make their mark. There were excellent victories against the otherwise undefeated Transvaal side, Bath, Northampton, Bristol and Harlequins. The United side won their Second XV Championship for an amazing third successive season. To top it all, against all predictions, Gloucester won the first National Tens Tournament at the end of the season.

But perhaps the stars of 1992/3 were the supporters. Many clubs would have seen their support melt away during the early-season adversities. Not so the Kingsholm faithful. They were there to roar the side home in vital away games, when it really mattered.

Gloucester RFC Committee & 1st XV Players. Back Row: Jim Holder, Mervyn Elway, Cecil Pope, Brian Howells, Terry Close, Jim Jarrett, Keith Richardson (Coach), John Beaman, Allan Townsend, Eric Stephens, (Team Secretary), Paul Williams. Middle Row: Andy Mitchell, Trevor Pritchard, Doug Wadley (Secretary), Paul Holford, Tony Windo, Andy Deacon, Martyn Roberts, Simon Devereux, Dave Sims, Bobby Fowke, Paul Ashmead, Andrew Stanley, Pete Jones, Jerry Perrins, Alan Brinn, Roy Morris. Front Row: Damian Cummins, Bob Phillips, Derrick Morgan, Marcus Hannaford, Canon M Hughes (President), Ian Smith (Capt.), Peter Ford (Chairman), Tim Smith, Don Caskie, Dave Kearsey, Ian Morgan.   *Photo: The Gloucester Citizen*

GLOUCESTER RFC

COURAGE CLUBS CHAMPIONSHIP
NATIONAL DIVISION ONE 1992-93

No	Date	Opponents	Venue	Result	Point Scorers
1	Sep 19	L. Scottish	A	L3-8	T Smith (P)
2	Sep 26	Leicester	A	L21-22	Morgan (T) Hannaford (T) T Smith (C)(P)
3	Oct 3	Rugby	H	L21-12	Morgan (PT) T Smith (C)(3P)
4	Oct 10	Free	Free	Free	Free
5	oct 24	Wasps	A	L9-19	T Smith (3P)
6	Oct 31	W. Hartlepool	H	L6-21	T Smith (P) Matthews (P)
7	Nov 21	Saracens	H	W19-5	West (T) Morgan (T) Roberts (3P)
8	Jan 9	L. Irish	A	W18-6	Roberts (PT)(2P)(C)(T)
9	Feb 13	Bath	H	L0-20	
10	Mar 13	Northampton	A	W21-16	Holford (T) Morris (T) Beech (C)(P) Smith (2P)
11	Mar 27	orrell	H	L8-13	Smith (T)(P)
12	Apr 3	Bristol	A	W22-9	Caskie (T) Smith (T) Philips (T) Beech (2C)(P)
13	Apr 24	Harlequins	H	W25-5	Morris (T) Fowke(T) T Smith (T)(2C)(2P)

CLUB PLAYING RECORD
1992-93 SEASON

National Division: One
Final League Position at end 1992/93 Season: 5th
League Playing Record: P 11, W 5, D 0, L 6,
Pts F 156, Pts A 117
Season Playing Record (including League
matches/Pilkington cup etc): P 38, W 28, D 0, L 10,
Pts F 851, Pts A 428

COMPETITIONS WON
DURING SEASON 1992-93

Worthington National Tens Tournament

Line-out action against Bath
Photo: Gloucester Citizen

GLOUCESTER RFC

MATCH BY MATCH PLAYERS BY POSITION

Roberts	Morgan	Morris	Caskie	Perrins	T. Smith	Hannaford	Jones	Hawker	Phillips	Sims	West	Knox	I. Smith	Fowke	Cummins	Ashmead	Kearsey	Glanville	Matthews	Windo	Deacon	Ashmead	Miles
15	14	13	12	11	10	9	1	2	3	4	5	6	7	8									
15	14	13	12	11	10	9	1	2	3	4	5	6	7	8									
11	12	13	14	15		9	1	2	3,4	5		8	7		10	6	R						
11	12	13	14	15		9	1	2	3,4	5			7	8	10	6							
F	R	E	E				F	R	E	E			F	R	E	E			F	R	E	E	
	14	11	13		15	9	1	2	3	4	5		7	8	12			6	10				
	14	12	13	11	15	9	1	2	3	4	5		7	8	R			6	10				
15	14	11	13	R		9				4	5		7		12		2		10	1	3	6	8
15		14	12	11		9		2		4	5		7		13	8		6	10	1	3		
15	11	13	12	14		9	1			4	5		7		10	8	2	6			3		
	11	13		15			1			4	5		7	8	12	6	2				3		
	11	13		15			1			4	5		8	7	12	6	2				3		
	11	13		15		9	1		3	4	5		8	7	12	6	2						
		13	12	15		9	1		3	4			7	8		6	2						

Also Played: Holford 14 Match 10, Beech 10 March 10, Beck 9 Match 10, Holford 14 Match 11, Beech 10 March 11, Beck 9 Match 11, Holford 14 Match 12, Beech 10 March 12, Holford 14 Match 13, Nicholson 11 Match 13, Merchant 10, Devereux 5 Match 13.

PLAYING SQUAD 1992-93

15 - Tim Smith, Martyn Roberts
14 - Paul Holford, Jerry Perrins
13 - Don Caskie, Ian Morgan
12 - Damian Cummins, Jason Merchant
11 - Simon Morris, Chris Dee
10 - Paul Beech
9 - Marcus Hannaford, Julian Davis, Laurie Beck
1 - Pete Jones, Andy Deacon
2 - John Hawker, Dave Kearsey, Glyn Mann
3 - Bob Phillips, Anthony windo
4 - Pete Miles, Shaun Bryan
5 - Dave Sims, Richard West, Simon Devereux
6 - Paul Ashmead, Peter Glanville
7 - Ian Smith (Capt), Andrew Stanley
8 - Bobby Fowke

MOST CAPPED PLAYERS
including British Lions Appearances
Tom Voyce, 29
Mike Teague, 29
Don Rutherford, 15

LEADING SCORERS
Martyn Roberts, Full back, 157
Tim Smith, Full back, 102
Paul Beech, Stand Off Half, 60

LEADING APPEARANCES FOR CLUB DURING SEASON 1992-93
Dave Sims, 27
Don Caskie, 26
Simon Morris, 25
Richard West, 23
Tim Smith, 23

Richard West sets up a Gloucester attack against Sale

GLOUCESTER RFC

COURAGE LEAGUE RECORDS

Highest score: 61 v Sale (61-7) 16-4-88 Home CL1
Largest winning margin: 54 as above
Highest score against: 29 v Wasps (4-39) 14-10-89 Away CL1
Largest losing margin: 25 as above

INDIVIDUAL SCORING RECORDS

IN A MATCH

Most points: 20 Tim Smith v Harlequins 12-3-90 Home CL1
Most tries: 3 Derek Morgan v Rosslyn Park 11-11-89 Home CL1
Most conversions: 6 Paul Mansell v Sale 16-4-88 Home CL1
Most penalities: 6 Tim Smith v Harlequins 12-3-90 Home CL1
Most drop goals: 1 Mike Hamlin v Moseley 9-9-89 Away CL1, v, London Irish, Home CL1, Neil Matthew v Bath 29-2-92 Away CL1

IN A SEASON

Most points: 85 Tim Smith 1988-89 CL1
Most tries: 6 Jim Breeze 1987-88 CL1, Mike Hamlin 1988-89 CL1, Derek Morgan 1989-90 CL1
Most conversions: 12 Tim Smith 1988-89 CL1, 1990-91 CL1
Most penalties: 21 Tim Smith 1991-92 CL1
Most drop goals: 1 Mike Hamlin 1989-90 CL1 & 1991-92 CL1, Neil Matthews 1991-92 CL1

IN A CAREER

Most points: 408 Tim Smith 1987-93
Most tries: 15 Derek Morgan 1988-93
Most conversions: 45 Tim Smith 1987-93
Most penalties: 97 Tim Smith 1987-93
Most drop goals: 2 Mike Hamlin 1987-92

SEASON BY SEASON LEADING SCORES

	Most Points			Most Tries
1987-88	42	Nick Marment	6	Jim Breeze
1988-89	85	Tim Smith	6	Mike Hamlin
1989-90	75	Tim Smith	6	Derek Morgan
1990-91	75	Tim Smith	3	Ian Smith Derek Morgan Paul Ashmead Chris Dee
1991-92	81	Tim Smith	5	Simon Morris
1992-93	71	Tim Smith	3	Tim Smith Derek Morgan

GLOUCESTER RFC

Club Details

Colours: Red & white.
Change of Colours: Black & white.
Nickname: Elver Eaters/Cherry & Whites.
Date Founded: 1873.
Membership: Total 1,888, Full 1,366,
Junior/Youth/Minis 522.
Membership Fees: Full £80/£40, Junior/Youth/Minis
£40/£20.
Number of Teams: Senior 2.
Programme Advertising Rates: Various rates from
£300.

Ground Details

Ground Address: Kingsholm, Kingsholm Road,
Gloucester, GL1 3AX.
Telephone: 0452 381087.
Fax: 0452 383321.
Directions: M5 Jcn 11 towards Gloucester, first
roundabout right towards Gloucester/Wales, next
roundabout left, next roundabout straight over.
Ground 300 yds on right.
Capacity: Total 12,000, Seated 1,250, Standing
10,750.
Ticket Prices: Adults: Stand £6.50, Ground £4.00,
Juniors £2, Students £3.
Clubhouse Facilities: Lounge bar, hospitality boxes
with restaurant & sponsorship facilities.
Training Nights: Monday & Thursday.

Special Occassions in 1993-94

N2 v Emerging England Players - Div S.W. v North,
Gloucester v S.A. Barbarians.

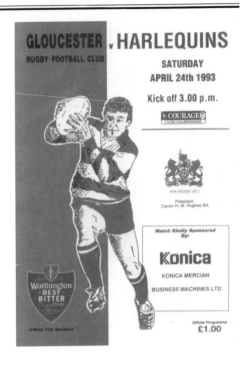

HARLEQUIN FC

18 66

President: D K Brooks
Chairman: R F Looker
Club Secretary: C M Herridge,
Ridgewood, 29 Blackhills, Esher, Surrey,
KT10 9JP. Tel: 0372 469925 Fax: 0372
469488
Fixtures Secretary: R F Reed,
Brookside, Lodge Lane, Salfords,
Redhill, Surrey, RH1 5DH. Tel: (H) 0293
783711 (W) 081 770 5204
Press Officer: G A D Saward, 152
Woodseer Street, London, E1 5HQ. Tel:
071 377 1151
1993/94 1XV Captain: Andy Millins
1993/94 1XV Coach: Bob Templeton,
Andy Keast
1st XV Manager: Jamie Salmon

Review of the Season

The new democracy in rugby football, created by the league structure, has serious implications for any club which fails to maintain its playing standards. Our ability to produce a winning team to compete consistently at the top level is the only standard by which we can be fairly judged. Thus we can gauge our true playing standard by our eighth position in League Division One, which can only be described as disappointing. Despite reaching the Pilkington Cup Final for the fourth time in six seasons, by the most demanding yardstick of league football, we had a relatively unsuccessful season. League and cup matches are now the only ones which matter, and with eighteen league matches (nine home and nine away) in the 1993-94 season, the pressures will be even greater. However, with an enlarged squad of high quality and a combination of youth and experience we can look forward to next season in a very positive frame of mind.

COURAGE LEAGUE

It is interesting to note that the 1991/92 report began "we once again got off to a bad start..." Well, we did exactly the same this year by losing both our opening games, struggling to beat West Hartlepool and then only achieving a draw at home to London Scottish. So, by October 10th our chances of success in the League were gone and with four teams to be relegated survival in the top flight became a growing concern. Victories over Saracens (18-6) and London Irish (47-24) repaired some of the damage but it was not until the penultimate game when we beat Rugby (35-14) at home that our place in the 1st Division was secured.

Unbelievably we used over thirty players in twelve league games and long term injuries to Neil Edwards and David Pears certainly did not help. Everything hinges on how we start next season and we have changed our pre-season planning with everybody now on a summer fitness programme, together with a short tour to Ireland in early September. For too long we have not been adequately prepared or indeed fit enough and this has now, we hope, been rectified.

Certain players made significant progress during the Season, notably Gavin Thompson, Paul Challinor and Jeff Alexander in the backs, whilst Alex Snow did exceptionally well at lock in his first season. Certain young players have considerable potential, Simon Brown (in the England U21 tour to Australia), Paul Simmonds at hooker and Rob Leach at blindside.

COURAGE CLUBS CHAMPIONSHIP

HARLEQUIN FC

COURAGE CLUBS CHAMPIONSHIP
NATIONAL DIVISION ONE 1992-93

No	Date	Opponents	Venue	Result	Point Scorers
1	Sept 19	Bath	A	L6-22	Pears (P) Challinor (P)
2	Sep 26	Wasps	H	L13-15	Evans (T) Thresher (C)(2P)
3	Oct 3	W. Hartlepool	A	W12-9	Challinor (4P)
4	Oct 10	L Scottish	H	D22-22	Carling (T) Sheasby (T) Wedderburn (T) Thresher (2C)(P)
5	Oct 24	Saracens	A	W18-3	Thresher (T)(C)(2P) Glennister (T)
6	Oct 31	L Irish	H	W47-24	Glenister (2T) Thresher (T)(4C) Challinor (T) Carung (T) Harriman (T)
7	Nov 21	Northampton	H	L7-12	Challinor (T) Thresher (C)
8	Jan 9	Orrell	A	L16-18	Thresher (T) Wedderburn (T) Challinor (2P)
9	Feb 13	Bristol	H	W16-0	Carling (T) Sheasby (T) Challinor (DG)(P)
10	Mar 13	Free	Free	Free	Free
11	Mar 27	Leicester	A	L0-23	
12	Apr 3	Rugby	H	W35-14	Alexander (2T) Winterbottom (2T) Challinor (T)(2C)(2P)
13	Apr 24	Gloucester	A	L5-25	Wedderburn (T)

ADDITIONAL RESULTS 1992-93

No	Date	Opponents	Venue	Result
1	Sep 5	Northampton	A	L16-21
2	Sep 9	Askeans	H	W85-12
3	Sep 12	Plymouth Albion	A	W64-6
4	Oct 17	Bedford	H	L27-30
5	Nov 7	Cambridge University	H	W41-11
6	Nov 14	Nottingham	H	W27-16
7	Nov 28	Blackheath	A	W72-3
8	Dec 28	Richmond	H	W34-30
9	Jan 2	Rugby	A	Cancelled
10	Jan 16	Saracens	H	D17-17
11	Jan 23	Wakefield	H	W47-18
12	Jan 30	London Irish	A	W14-6
13	Feb 6	Blackheath	A	W22-17
14	Feb 20	Leeds	H	W83-12
15	Feb 27	Waterloo	H	W21-14
16	Mar 20	Coventry	H	W54-18
17	Apr 17	Rosslyn Park	A	W23-22

CLUB PLAYING RECORD 1992-93 SEASON

National Division: One
Final League Position at end 1992/93 Season: 8th
League Playing Record: P 12, W 5, D 1, L 6,
Pts F 197, Pts A 187
Season Playing Record (including League
matches/Pilkington cup etc): P 32, W 20, D 2, L 10,
Pts F 902, Pts A 521

MOST CAPPED PLAYERS

including British Lions Appearances
P J Winterbottom (England), 60, 1982-93
Brian Moore (England), 48, 1987-93
W D C Carling (England), 42, 1988-93
I G Milne (Scotland), 41, 1979-90
A M Hayden (New Zealand), 41, 1977-85
W W Wakefield (England), 31, 1926-27

LEADING APPEARANCES FOR CLUB DURING SEASON 1992-93

M P Russell, 26
A P Challinor, 25
R J Glenister, 25
G J Thompson, 25
A R Mullins, 23
A C W Snow, 22

LEADING SCORERS

S E Thresher, Full Back, 168 (5T 43C 19P)
A P Challinor, Fly Half, 166 (9T 11C 29P 4DG)
A T Harriman, Wing, 65 (13T)
M A Wedderburn, Wing, 55 (11T)
G J Thompson, Centre, 48 (9T 1DG)
K A Bray, Fly Half, 42 (3T 6C 5P)

HARLEQUIN FC

MATCH BY MATCH PLAYERS BY POSITION

Pears	Harriman	Carling	Evans	Wedderburn	Challinor	Glenister	Hobley	Moore	Mullins	Dear	Snow	Fox	Russell	Langhorn	Short	Thresher	Killick	Challis	Sheasby	Winterbottom	Thompson	Leonard	Brown
15	14	13	12	11	10	9	1	2	3	4	5	6	7	8	R								
	14	13	12	11	10	9	1		3	4	5		6		R	15	2	R	7	8			
	14			11	10	9	R	2			5		6		12	15			8	7	13	1	
	14	13	12	11	10	9	R		3		5		6			15	2		8	7		1	
	14	13			10	9			3	4	5		6	8		15	2			7	12	1	
	14	13	12		10	9		2	3	4	5		6	8		15				7		1	
	14	13	12		10	9			3	5	4		6	8		15	2			7		1	
		13		14	10	9		2	3	5	4		6	8		15	R			7	12	1	
		13	12	14	10	9		2	3		4		6	5					8	7	11	1	
F	R	E	E				F	R	E	E			F	R	E	E				F	R	E	E
		13		14	10	9		2	3	5	4	8	6							7	12	1	
		13			10	9		2	3	5	4		6		R				8	7	12	1	
			12	11	10				3	5	4		6	8		15	2				13		1

Also played: Mullins 3 March 3, Edwards 4 Match 3, 4 Match 4, Davies 11 Match 5, 11 Match 6, Parton 11 Match 7, Bray replaced Carling Match 8, Molineux 11 Match 8, Bray 15 Match 9, Match 11, Alexander 11 Match 11, Bray 15 Match 12, Davis 14 Match 12, Alexander 11 Match 12, Simmonds replaced Winterbottom Match 12, Madderson 14 Match 13, Goodwin 9 Match 13, Desmond 7 Match 13

PLAYING SQUAD 1992-93

Jeff Alexander
Kent Bray
Simon Brown
Will Carling (OBE)
Paul Challinor
Andy Challis
Everton Davis
Simon Dear
Neil Edwards
Mark Evans
Alan Fox
Rob Glenister
Andrew Harriman
Martin Hobley
Richard Langhorn
Jason Leonard
Chris Madderson

Mike Molyneux
Brian Moore
Andy Mullins
Andy Parton
David Pears
Johan Roux
Mark Russell
Chris Sheasby
Ben Short
Cameron Short
Paul Simmonds
Alex Snow
Gavin Thompson
Steve Thompson
Stuart Thresher
Mike Wedderburn
Peter Winterbottom

Harlequin FC 1992-93

Photo: Action Plus

HARLEQUIN FC

COURAGE LEAGUE RECORDS

Highest score: 71 v Bedford (71-8) 14-10-89 Away CL1
Largest winning margin: 66 v Sale (66-0) 23-4-88 Home CL1
Highest score against: 37 v Saracens (21-37) 14-3-92 Home CL1
Largest losing margin: 23 v Leicester (13-24) 23-3-93 Away CL1
Drawn Matches: 3
Clean Sheets: 3
Failed to score: 4

INDIVIDUAL SCORING RECORDS
IN A MATCH

Most points: 27 David Pears v Bedford 14-10-89 Home CL1
Most tries: 3 Andrew Harriman v Nottingham 1-4-88 Home CL1, v Sale 23-4-88 Home CL1, Mike Wedderburn v Bedford 14-10-89 Away CL1, Andrew Harriman v Bristol 30-3-91 Home CL1, Will Carling v Bristol 30-30-91 Home CL1
Most conversions: 8 David Pears v Bedford 14-10-89 Away CL1
Most penalities: 7 David Pears v Rosslyn Park 7-12-91 Away CL1
Most drop goals: 2 David Pears v Rosslyn Park 13-10-92Home CL1, v Leicester 23-3-91 Away CL1

IN A SEASON

Most points: 120 David Pears 1990-91 CL1
Most tries: 11 Andrew Harriman 1987-88 CL1
Most conversions: 16 David Pears 1990-91 CL1
Most penalties: 24 David Pears 1989-90 CL1
Most drop goals: 5 David Pears 1990-91 CL1

IN A CAREER

Most points: 354 David Pears 1989-93
Most tries: 22 Andrew Harriman 1987-93
Most conversions: 46 David Pears 1989-93
Most penalties: 71 David Pears 1989-93
Most drop goals: 7 David Pears 1989-93

SEASON BY SEASON LEADING SCORES

	Most Points			**Most Tries**	
1987-88	58	Stuart Thresher	11	Andrew Harriman	
1988-89	71	Stuart Thresher	4	Mickey Skinner Jon Eagle	
1989-90	114	David Pears	5	Craig Luxton	
1990-91	120	David Pears	9	Andrew Harriman	
1991-92	109	David Pears	4	David Pears	
1992-93	57	Stuart Thresher	3	Will Carling Rob Glenister Paul Challinor Stuart Thresher	

HARLEQUIN FC

Club Details

Colours: Light blue, magenta, chocolate, French grey, light green and black
Nickname: Quins
Date Founded: 1866
Membership: Total 2,016, Social 850
Membership Fees: Full £50, Junior/Youth £15
Number of Teams: Senior 2, Junior, U21, U19
Programme Advertising Rates: £700 colour, £500 b/w

Ground Details

Ground Address: RFU Ground Twickenha, TW1 1DZ. Stoop Memorial Ground, Craneford Way, Twickenahm TW2 7SQ.
Telephone: 081 892 0822 081 892 1222
Fax: 081 744 2764
Capacity: Total 7,000, 3,000 seated, 4,000 standing
Ticket Prices: Adults £6, Student/Junior/OAP/Child £2
Clubhouse Facilities: 3 bars and sponsors room, 4 changing rooms and weights room.
Training Nights: Tuesday & Thursday

Peter Winterbottom receives a silver plate on his last
appearance at Stoop Memorial Ground
Photo: Joe McCabe

LEICESTER FC

President: J T Tjomas
Chairman: K P Andrews
Club Secretary: J A Allen, The Clubhouse, Aylestone Road, Leicester, LG2 7LF Tel: (H) 0533 858407 (W) 0533 471234 Fax: (W) 0533 471434
Fixtures Secretary: J W Berry, Hall Lane, Knoulton, Nottinghamshire. Tel: (W) 0949 81428
Press Officer: J A Allen (address as above)
1993/94 1XV Captain: D Richards
1993/94 1XV Coach: I R Smith
Director of Rugby: A O Russ

Review of the Season

For the Leicester "Tigers" the best was reserved for the season's last day, when they found themselves at Twickenham in the final of the Pilkington Cup against knock-out specialists Harlequins and turned round a 13-10 half-time deficit to win 23-16 thanks to an early second-half try through a determined forward effort culminating in the final thrust coming from lock Martin Johnson, for whom it was far from being a sign-off game, but rather the start of a series of events which mean that he starts the new season having been "capped" by the British Lions more than by England!

That Twickenham success meant that it was a superb season rather than just a good one. They had won the old John Player Cup in successive years from 1979 to 1981 and were beaten finalists in 1983, but their name was being inscribed on the new Pilkington version for the first time and their progress towards success was impressive. A visit to London Scottish is never easy, but in the Third Round they emerged 20-11 winners and then won at another none too easy venue — Nottingham — in the fourth sortie by a decisive 28-3. The last eight was embarrassing with visitors Exeter on the receiving end of a 76-0 hammering, whilst in the semis Northampton felt no happier after a 28-6 thrashing at Welford Road.

And so to HQ. The truth is that it was a moderate match but Leicester were the better side and deserved to win. Johnson apart there were other fine performances with a first half try from centre Stuart Potter, a neat dropped-goal from the under-rated fly-half Jezz Harris and the usual contributions from fullback John Liley — two penalties and conversions of both tries. Against all this a fine third place in the top division, with defeats at the hands of only Wasps, Bath and Bristol, pales by comparison.

There is an abundance of talent at Welford Road apart from those already mentioned. What about the Underwood brothers, scrum half Aadel Kardooni and a young pack with its sprinkling of experience provided by heavily capped no. 8 Dean Richards and inspired by the soon-to-be honoured Neil Back? They could just take that title from Bath this coming season.

Leicester's Pilkington Cup Winners

Photo: Joe McCabe

LEICESTER FC

COURAGE CLUBS CHAMPIONSHIP
NATIONAL DIVISION ONE 1992-93

No	Date	Opponents	Venue	Result	Point Scorers
1	Sep 19	L Irish	A	W30-14	Liley (T)(3C)(3P) Underwood (T) Richardson (T)
2	Sep 26	Gloucester	H	W22-21	Hackney (T) Kardooni (T) Richardson (T) Liley (2C)(P)
3	Oct 3	Wasps	A	L13-14	Potter (T) Liley (C)(2P)
4	Oct 10	W Hartlepool	H	W21-8	Potter (T) Liley (T)(3P)
5	Oct 24	L Scottish	A	W18-11	T Underwood (T) Liley (C)(2P)
6	Oct 31	Saracens	H	W30-3	Cockerill (T) Underwood (T) Liley (3C)(2P) Harris (DG)
7	Nov 21	Bath	A	L3-13	Liley (P)
8	Jan 9	Northampton	A	W13-12	Back (T) Liley (C)(2P)
9	Feb 13	Orrell	H	W9-0	Liley (3P)
10	Mar 13	Bristol	A	W15-10	Kardooni (T)Liley (P)(C)
11	Mar 27	Harlequins	H	W23-0	Richardson (T) Provos (T) Harris (DG) Liley (2P)(2C)
12	Apr 3	Free	Free	Free	Free
13	Apr 24	Rugby	A	W28-5	A Underwood (T) R Underwood (T) Grewcock (T) Harris (2C)(2DG) Kilford (P)

ADDITIONAL RESULTS 1992-93

No	Date	Opponents	Venue	Result
1		Sheffield	A	W27-7
2		England XV	H	L11-18
3		Leicestershire	H	W40-20
4		Mediolanum	H	W40-24
5		Oxford University	H	W27-15
6		Moseley	A	L14-20
7		Cambridge Univ	A	L18-23
8		Orrell	A	W33-18
9		Northampton	H	W28-3
10		London Scottish	A	W20-11
11		Gloucester	A	L13-36
12		Barbarians	H	W41-23
13		Bedford	A	W16-13
14		Nottingham	A	W28-3
15		Coventry	A	W37-17
16		Rosslyn Park	H	w52-10
17		Nuneaton	A	W61-18
18		Exeter	H	W76-0
19		Moseley	H	W25-5
20		Nottingham	A	W27-7
21		Richmond	A	W29-15
22		Northampton	H	W28-6
23		Wasps	H	W14-13
24		Sale	H	W43-8
25		Harlequins		W23-16

COMPETITIONS WON DURING SEASON 1992-93
Pilkington Cup Winners

CLUB PLAYING RECORD 1992-93 SEASON

National Division: One
Final League Position at end 1992/93 Season: 3rd
League Playing Record: P 12, W 9, D -. L 3
Season Playing Record (including League matches/Pilkington cup etc): P 37, W 30, D -, L 7

MOST CAPPED PLAYERS
including British Lions Appearances
R Underwood, 60 + 4 Lions
D Richards, 34 + 4 Lions
P J Wheeler, 41 + 7 Lions
P W Dodge, 32 + 2 Lions

LEADING APPEARANCES FOR CLUB (1992/93 SEASON)
J Harris, G Rowntree, 32
D Garforth, 31
M Poole, 29
J Liley, S Potter, 28
I Bates, 27
R Cockerill, 26
A Kardooni, J Wells, 25
D Richards, 24
S Povoas, 22
M Johnson, 21
S Hackney, R Underwood, n Back, 18
L Boyle, 15
T Underwood, P Sandford, 14

86

LEICESTER FC

MATCH BY MATCH PLAYERS BY POSITION

Liley	A Underwood	Potter	Bates	R Underwood	HArris	Kardooni	Rowntree	Cockerill	Gardforth	Richards	Poole	Wells	Richardson	Povoas	Hackney	Back	Boyle	Johnson	Grant	Kilford	Grewcock	Jelly	Grimsdell
O	N	M	L	K	J	I	A	B	C	D	E	F	G	H									
O		M	L	K	J	I	A	B	C	D	E	F	H	G	N								
O		K	M	L	J	I	A	B	C	D	E	F		H	N	G							
O		K	M	L	J	I	A	B	C	D	E	F		H	N	G							
O		K	M	N	J	I	A	B	C	H	E	F			G		L	D					
O		M	L	K	J	I	A	B	C	G	E			F	N	H		D					
O		M	L	K	J	I	A	B	C		E			F	N	G		D	H				
O	N	M	L	K	J	I	A	B	C	H	E	F			G			D					
O		M		K	J	I	A	B	C	G		F			N	H	L	D	E				
O	L	M		K	J	I	A	B	C	H		F		R	N	G		D	E				
O		M	L	K	J	I	A	B	C		E	F	H	G		R		D		N			
	F	R	E	E				F	R	E	E			F	R	E	E			F	R	E	E
N		M	L	K	J			B	C	H	E	F	G			R		D		O	I	A	R

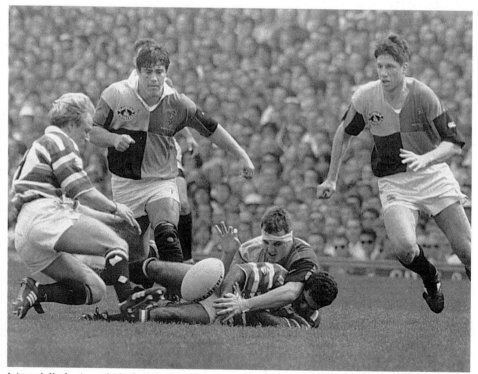

Leicester's Kardooni grapples for the ball with Alex Snow. Neil Back waits to collect and Harlequin's Andy Mullins and Simon Longhorn are in support during the Pilkington Cup Final

Photo: Joe McCabe

Harlequin's Martin Johnson beats Leicester's Chris Sheesby to the ball in this line-out as Winterbottom waits in the Pilkington
Cup Final   Photo: Joe McCabe

LEICESTER FC

COURAGE LEAGUE RECORDS

Highest score: 60 v Bedford (60-3) 23-9-89 Home CL1
Largest winning margin: 57 as above
Highest score against: 37 v Bath (21-37) 11-1-92 Away CL1
Largest losing margin: 31 as above
Drawn Matches: 2
Clean Sheets: 1
Failed to score: 1

INDIVIDUAL SCORING RECORDS

IN A MATCH

Most points: 31 John Liley v Rosslyn Park 21-03-92 Home CL1
Most tries: 3 M Charles v Sale 26-3-88 Home CL1, John Liley v Bedford 23-9-89 Home CL1, C Gerard v Moseley 31-3-90 Home CL1, Rory underwood v Moseley 27-4-91 Away CL1, Steve Hackney v London irish 9-1-92 Home CL1 & v Rosslyn Park 21-3-92 Home CL1
Most conversions: 7 John Liley v Rosslyn Park 21-03-92 Home CL1
Most penalities: 6 Dusty Hare v Rosslyn Park 19-11-88 Home CL1
Most drop goals: 3 Jez Harris v Wasps 23-11-91 Home CL1

IN A SEASON

Most points: 129 John Liley 1991-92 CL1
Most tries: 9 Rory Underwood 1990-91 & 1991-92 CL1
Most conversions: 19 John Liley 1991-92 CL1
Most penalties: 31 Dusty Hare 1987-88 CL1
Most drop goals: 5 Les Cusworth 1987-88 CL1

IN A CAREER

Most points: 480 John Liley 1988-93
Most tries: 28 Rory Underwood 1987-93
Most conversions: 68 John Liley 1988-93
Most penalties: 9 John Liley 1988-93
Most drop goals: 9 Jez Harris 1987-93

SEASON BY SEASON LEADING SCORES

	Most Points			Most Tries	
1987-88	126	Dusty Hare	5	Barry Evans	
1988-89	97	Dusty Hare	3	Barry Evans D Richards R Underwood	
1989-90	126	John Liley	7	John Liley	
1990-91	110	John Liley	9	Rory Underwood	
1991-92	129	John Liley	7	Rory Underwood	
1992-93	106	John Liley	3	Tony Underwood Nigel Richardson	

LEICESTER FC

Club Details

Colours: Scarlet, Green & White hoops
Change of Colours: Red with green and white band
Nickname: Tigers
Date Founded: 1880
Membership: Total 8,150, Full 6,590,
Junior/Youth/Minis 660, S/C 900
Membership Fees: Full £32, Junior/Youth/Minis £17
Number of Teams: Senior 2, Junior 2
Programme Advertising Rates: Full £600

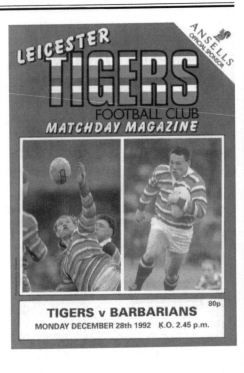

Ground Details

Ground Address: the Clubhouse, Aylestone Road,
Leicester, LE2 7LE.
Telephone: 0533 541607
Directions: Leave M1 (Jnc M69), taking main signs
for Leicester. After second roundabout onto dual
carriageway take outside lane to 1st lights, turn right
leaving Post House Hotel on left to approx 2.5 miles
after large Vauxhall Garage on right. Ground can be
found on right hand side.
Capacity: 13,800
Ticket Prices: Adults £5, OAP/Child £3
Clubhouse Facilities: Two large bars. Upstairs bvar
serves food to general public before and after games.
Training Nights: Tuesday & Thursday

LONDON IRISH RFC

President: Dr H Condon
Chairman: Patrick Barragry
Club Secretary: Kieran McCarthy, 28 lichfield Court, Sheen Road, Richmond, Surrey TW9 1AW. Tel: (H) 081 940 4999 (W) 0732 783034 Fax: 0932 784462
Fixtures Secretary: Bill Gingles, 55 Pimlico Road, London, SW1 Tel: 071 730 0704 (W) 071 480 5516
Press Officer: Michael Flatley, 65 Esher Road, East Molesey, Surrey, KT8 1AQ
1993/94 1XV Captain: Paul Collins
1993/94 1XV Coach: Hika Reid
Director of Coaching: Dean Shelford

Review of the Season

London Irish finished in seventh position of the Courage League Division One (or sharing 5th position with Gloucester & Bristol on League points!). Being mindful of the formidable task of survival with four teams being relegated, the plan was further consolidated in the premier division and this was achieved. The 'Irish' now find themselves sharing a berth with Wasps and Harlequins as the trio of London Clubs represented in the top flight. The safety net for the season was constituted of wins over Northampton, Bristol, Orrell, Rugby, West Hartlepool and Saracens. The nadir of the season was the exit at Round 3 (again!) of the Pilkington cup against West Hartlepool.

Several leading players enjoyed further representative honours with Ireland at Student, U21's and full international level, the most notable being Simon Geoghegan's and Brian Robinson's part in victories over Wales and England.

The tranquil meadows of Sunbury were again hosts of ever-increasing crowds and the fine facilities were more than a match for the demand. The club flourishes with the availability of rugby enjoyment opportunity to some 4OO playing members, fielding 1O adult teams each Saturday and 15 under-age sides on Sundays.

As in last season, London Irish will again be seeking to consolidate further and to improve their league position in 1993/94.

Part of the London Irish front row

Photo: Joe McCabe

LONDON IRISH RFC

COURAGE CLUBS CHAMPIONSHIP
NATIONAL DIVISION ONE 1992-93

No	Date	Opponents	Venue	Result	Point Scorers
1	Sep 19	Leicester	H	L14-30	Corcoran (T)(3P)
2	Sep 26	Bath	A	L19-42	Geoghegan (T) Corcoran (C)(2P) Burke (DG) Hennessy (DG)
3	Oct 3	Northampton	H	W12-3	Corcoran (4P)
4	Oct 10	Orrell	A	W12-8	Corcoran (4P)
5	Oct 24	Bristol	H	W9-7	Corcoran (T) Burke (2DG)
6	Oct 31	Harlequins	A	L24-47	Young (T) Curtis (T) Corcoran (C)(4P)
7	Nov 21	Rugby	A	W14-0	Geoghegan (T) Corcoran (2P) Burke (DG)
8	Jan 9	Gloucester	H	L6-18	Corcoran (P) Burke (DG)
9	Feb 13	Wasps	A	L9-18	Corcoran (3P)
10	Mar 13	W Hartlepool	H	W25-13	Collins (T) Corcoran (T)(2C)(P) Geoghegan (T) Burke (DG)
11	Mar 27	L Scottish	A	L21-28	Corcoran (6P) Burke (P)
12	Apr 3	Saracens	H	W10-9	Halpin (T) Burke (P)(C)
13	Apr 24	Free	Free	Free	Free

CLUB PLAYING RECORD 1992-93 SEASON

National Division: One
Final League Position at end 1992/93 Season: 7th
League Playing Record: P 12, W 6, D -, L 6,
Pts F 175, Pts A 223
Season Playing Record (including League
matches/Pilkington cup etc): P 36, W 18, D 1, L 17,
Pts F 820, Pts A 667

Simon Geoghegan
Photo: Joe McCabe

92

LONDON IRISH RFC

MATCH BY MATCH PLAYERS BY POSITION

Staples	Geoghegan	Curtis	Corcoran	Cobbe	Saunders	Donovan	McFarland	Halpin	Hall	Keenan	Collins	Pegler	Robinson	Hennessey	Burke	Mooney	Byrne	Verling	Leonard	Higgins	Cowhaig	Young
15	14	13	12	11	10	9	1	2	3	4	5	6	7	8								
15	14		12	11		9	1	2	3,4	5	6	7	8		13	10	R					
15	14		12	11		9	1	2	3	4	5		7	8	13	10		R		6		
15	14		12	11		9	1	2	3	4	5		7	8	13	10		6				
15	14		12	11		9	1	2	3	4		6	7		13	10	8	R		5		
			12	11	10		1	2		4		8	7	13		9	6		5	15	14	
15	14		12	11			1	2	3	4	5		7	8	13	10	9	6				
	14		12	11	15	9	1	2	3	4	5	6	7		13	10	8					
	14	13		11		9	1			4	5	6	7	8	15	10						
	14		12	11		9	1	2	3	4		6	7	8	15	10						
	14		12	11		9	1	2	3	4			7	8	15	10	R					
	14		12			11	9	1	2	3	4	5		8		10			6			
				F	R	E	E	F	R	E	E		F	R	E	E		F	R	E	E	

Also played: McCormick 3 Match 6, Patton replaced Halpen Match 8, Smith 12 Match 9, Patton 2 Match 9, Hayes 3 Match 9, Burns 13 March 10, Buss 5 Match 10, Hayes replaced Collins Match 10, Burns 13 Match 11, Buss 5 March 11, Bird 6 Match 11, Malone 15 Match 12, Burns 13, Match 12, Bird 7 Match 12

PLAYING SQUAD 1992-93

15: J Staples, O Cobbe
14: S Geogheran, V Roland
13: R Hennessy, R Henderson
12: D Curtis, S Burns
11: M Corcoran, J Harley
10: P Burke, N Malone
9: R Saunders, J Byrne
1: N Donovan, L Mooney
2: J McFarland, M Leonard
3: G Halpin, M McCormack
4: C Hall, A Higgins
5: M Keenan, C Buss
6: P Collins, P Neary
7: D Pegler, C Bird
8: B Robinson, A Verling

MOST CAPPED PLAYERS

including British Lions Appearances
Ken Kennedy, 45 + 4 Lions

LEADING APPEARANCES FOR CLUB DURING SEASON 1992-93

Neil Donovan, 28
Colin Hall, 28

LEADING SCORERS

Micahel Corcoran, Winger, 287

Michael Corcoran of London Irish goes over for a tyr against West Hartlepool in the Courage League relegation battle
Photo: Joe McCabe

LONDON IRISH RFC

COURAGE LEAGUE RECORDS

Highest score: 39 v Waterloo (39-0) 27-10-89 Home CL2
Largest winning margin: 39 as above
Highest score against: 48 v Headingley (9-48) 12-11-88 Away CL2
Largest losing margin: 39 as above
Drawn Matches: 7
Clean Sheets: 2
Failed to score: 1

INDIVIDUAL SCORING RECORDS
IN A MATCH

Most points: 18 Brian Mullen v Richmond 8-4-89 Away CL2, Michael Corcoran v London Scottish 27-3-93 Away CL1
Most tries: 3 Rob Saunders v Rugby 13-10-90 Home CL2
Most conversions: 4 Brian Mullen
Most penalities: 6 Michael Corcoran v London Scottish 27-3-93 Away CL1
Most drop goals: Ralph Kuhn v London Scottish 14-1-89 Away CL2, Brian Mullen v Richmond 8-4-89 Away CL2, Ian Aitchison v Plymouth 13-1-90 Home CL2, Paul Burke v Bristol 24-1-92 Home CL2

IN A SEASON

Most points: 117 Brian Mullen 1990-91 CL2
Most tries: 6 Shaun Brown 1989-90 CL2, Rob Saunders 1990-91 CL2
Most conversions: 16 Ian Aitchison 1989-90 CL2, Brian Mullen 1990-91 CL2
Most penalties: 31 Michael Corcoran 1992-93 CL1
Most drop goals: 6 Paul Burke 1992-93 CL1

IN A CAREER

Most points: 263 Brian Mullen 1988-92
Most tries: 13 Jim Staples 1987-93
Most conversions: 27 Brian Mullen 1988-92
Most penalties: 57 Brian Mullen 1988-92
Most drop goals: 10 Brian Mullen 1988-92

SEASON BY SEASON LEADING SCORES

	Most Points			Most Tries
1987-88	27	Paul Bell	4	Harry Harbison
1988-89	100	Brian Mullen	5	Simon Geoghegan
1989-90	107	Ian Aitchison	6	Shaun Brown
1990-91	117	Brian Mullen	6	Rob Saunders
1991-92	71	Michael Corcoran	4	Michael Corcoran
1992-93	111	Michael Corcoran	3	Simon Geoghegan

LONDON IRISH RFC

Club Details

Colours: Green shirts, white shorts, green socks
Change of Colours: All white
Nickname: The Irish
Date Founded: 1898
Membership: Total 2,000, Full 1,500, Social 100, Junior/Youth/Minis 400
Membership Fees: Full £60, Junior/Youth/Minis £10
Number of Teams: Snior 10, Junior 15
Programme Advertising Rates: Full £500, Half £300

Ground Details

Ground Address: The Avenue, Sunbury on Thames, Middlesex, TW16 5EQ
Telephone: 0932 783034
Fax: 0932 784462
Capacity: Total 6,000, Seated 1,400, Standing 4,600
Ticket Prices: Adult £3, OAP/Child £2
Clubhouse Facilities: Three bars, Dining/Function Room
Training Nights: Tues & Thurs

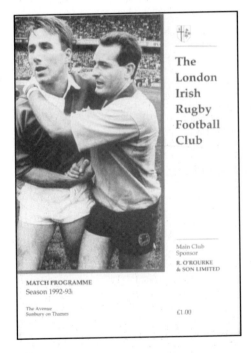

Rob Saunders in action against Harlequin
Photo: Joe McCabe

NEWCASTLE GOSFORTH RFC

President: C Morgan
Chairman: G Brown
Club Secretary: G McMurchie, c/o Newcastle Gosforth RFC, Kingston Park, Brunton Road, Kenton Bank Foot, Newcastle Upon Tyne, NE13 8AF. Tel: (W) 091 214 0422 Fax: 091 214 0488.
Fixtures Secretary: J H Addison, Mycliffe Mills, High Church Street, New Bosford, Nottingham, NG7 7JP. Tel: (H) 06077 4780 (W) 0602 785466.
Press Officer: M W Mahoney, 2 Holly Haven, East Rainton, Houghton Le-Spring, Co. Durham, DHJ 9SB.
1993/94 1XV Coach: S Gustard.
Director of Rugby: M W Mahoney.

Review of the Season

Three seasons ago league re-structuring saved Newcastle Gosforth from Division Three and probable oblivion. Re-born as Newcastle Gosforth and rehoused in spanking new facilities the upward progress since under Mike Mahoney's directorship has been steady but relentless culminating in promotion to Division One. Promotion was won in the autumn when early pace setters Sale, Waterloo and Nottingham were beaten. The levels of performance achieved in these games could not be maintained but the side overcame injuries to key forwards to reach Christmas unbeaten. A disastrous defeat at home to Wakefield when a 17-O lead was turned into a 17-2O deficit in the last 15 minutes threatened to upset the apple cart but the side steadied its nerves and didn't slip up again until the final Saturday at Moseley when promotion was already secure. Success was founded on a rock solid defence — one try conceded in the first six league games and just seven in all league games.

In the cup, Newcastle saw off Towcestrians before displaying their First Division credentials with a 13-1O victory over Gloucester. A rude awakening followed at Northampton but useful lessons will have been learnt.

Away from competitive rugby only one defeat was suffered and that on a pre-season tour in Ulster. The scoring feats of the previous season were not quite matched although the side topped 5O points on five occasions.

Individually, David Johnson was once again the country's leading scorer whilst Steve Douglas, despite a disappointing season by his own standards, won a call up for the England tour to Canada. Newcastle now re-join the elite with a side short of stars but boasting an array of youthful talent. If survival can be achieved this time around the club and the First Division should enjoy a long relationship.

Newcastle Gosforth 1992-93. Back row: K Hyland (Team Secretary), G Clark, D Johnson, A Hetherington, R Fuller, A Meadows, S Bainbridge, J Curry, S Gibbs, R Arnold, B Chick, MmMahoney (Director of Rugby), S Gustard (Coach) Front row: I Chandler, N Robinson, R Wilkinson, M White, N Frankland (Capt.), J Whisker, S Douglas, J Mray, M Laing (physio) Photo: Chris Roberts

NEWCASTLE GOSFORTH RFC

APPEARANCES AND POINT SCORERS

Name	Apps	Tries	Conv	Pens	Drops	Points
D Johnson	34	4	79	69	3	394
R Wilkinson	34	11				65
G Clark	31	13				65
N Frankland	31	4				20
S Douglas	28	9				45
R Fuller	28	3				15
I Chandler	26	9		1		48
R Arnold	25	3				15
A Meadows	24	5				25
J Murray	23	5	2	1		32
M White	23	9				45
A Campbell	20	1				5
T Roberts	19	3				15
S Gibbs	18	1				5
T Penn	18	7				35
J Curry	16	7				35
P Thompson	16					
S Bainbridge	14					
E Jobling-Purser	14	3				15
F Mitchell	14					
N Robinson	11					
B Chick	9	1				5
P Vanzandvliet	8	1				5
D Walker	8	5				25
M Beattie	7					
S Cassidy	7	4				20
P Smith	7	2				10
I williams	7	3				15
A Hetherington	6	1				5
G Sinton	6	3				15
M Walker	6	1				5
M Wardle	6					
J Whisker	6	2		2		16
N Winn	6	2				10
D Briggs	4	2				10
D Hayes	4					
D Taylorson	4					
A Durkin	3					
N Hannah	3	3				15
E Metcalf	3					
A Robertson	3					
G Doar	2					
J Scales	2	2				10
I Shanks	2	3				15
R Wharton	2					
M Corrie	1					
C Dew	1					
A Gair	1					
A Jackson	1					
P Jenkinson	1					
P Jobson	1					
J Miller	1					
A Redpath	1	1				5

CLUB PLAYING RECORD

1992-93 SEASON
National Division: One
Final League Position at end 1992/93 Season: 1st
League Playing Record: P 12, W 10, D 0, L 2,
Pts F 241 Pts A 106
Season Playing Record (including League matches/Pilkington cup etc): P 38, W 32, D 2, L 4,
Pts F 1085, Pts A 355

COMPETITIONS WON DURING SEASON 1992-93

Courage League Division Two
Shared Northumberland Senior Cup

MOST CAPPED PLAYERS

including British Lions Appearances
R J McCoughlin (Ireland), 40
A Smith (Scotland), 33
R J Uttley (England), 23
P J Dixon (England), 22
S Bainbridge (England), 16
D F Madren (Scotland), 14

LEADING SCORERS

D Johnson, Fly Half, 394 (4T 79C 69P 30G)
G Clarke, Flanker, 65 (13T)
R Wilkinson, Centre, 55 (11T)
I Chandler, Centre, 48 (9T 1P)
S Douglas, Scrum half 45 (9T)
M White, Wing 45 (9T)

NEWCASTLE GOSFORTH RFC

PLAYING SQUAD 1992-93

Full Backs: J Murray, J Whisker, J Miller
Wings: M White, T Penn, I Williams, G Sinton, D Briggs, N Hannah, G Doar, J Scales, R Wharton
Centres: R Wilkinson, I Chandler, A Campbell, N Robinson, M Beattie, A Robertson, A Gair, A Redpath
Fly Half: D Johnson
Scrum Half: S Douglas, D Walker, A Durkin, C Dew
Props: R Fuller, J Curry, P Thompson, P Vanzandvliet, M Wardle, N Winn, I Shanks, A Jackson
Hookers: N Frankland, A Hetherington, D Hayes, P Jenkinson
Flankers: G Clark, E Jobling-Purser, B Chick, S Cassidy, P Smith, D Taylorson, M Corrie, P Jobson
No. 8: R Arnold
Lock: A Meadows, T Roberts, S Gibbs, S Bainbridge, F Mitchell, M Walker, R Metcalf

Compensation —Ross Wilkinson goes over for Newcastle Gosforth's only try of the game against Moseley
Photo: Paul Dodds, Newcastle Chronicle & Journal

Photo: Paul Dodds

Division Champions — Newcastle Gosforth and the Trophy in their dressing room after their match against Moseley

NEWCASTLE GOSFORTH RFC

COURAGE LEAGUE RECORDS

Highest score: 76 v Liverpool St Helens (76-4) 29-2-92 Home CL2
Largest winning margin: 72 as above
Highest score against: 49 v Rugby (9-49) 11-11-89 Away CL2
Largest losing margin: 40 as above
Drawn Matches: 2
Clean Sheets: 1
Failed to score: 1

INDIVIDUAL SCORING RECORDS
IN A MATCH

Most points: 28 David Johnson v Morley 11-1-92 Home CL2, v Liverpool St Helens 24-2-92 Home CL2
Most tries: 3 Peter Walton v Blackheath 14-12-91 Home CL2, Graham CLark v Liverpool St Helemns 29-2-92 Home CL2, Richard
Most conversions: 9 David Johnson v Liverpool St Helens 29-2-92 Home CL2
Most penalities: 6 David Johnson v Morley 11-1-92 Home CL2, v Nottingham 10-10-92 Home CL2
Most drop goals: 2 David Johnson v Bedford 5-12-87 AwayCL2

IN A SEASON

Most points: 147 David Jonson 1991-92 CL2
Most tries: 10 Peter Walton 1991-92 CL2
Most conversions: 31 David Johnson 1991-92 CL2
Most penalties: 30 David Johnson 1992-93 CL2
Most drop goals: 4 David Johnson 1987-88

IN A CAREER

Most points: 405 David Johnson 1987-93
Most tries: 12 David Walker
Most conversions: 60 David Johnson 1987-93
Most penalties: 83 David Johnson 1987-93
Most drop goals: 9 David Johnson 1987-93

SEASON BY SEASON LEADING SCORES

	Most Points			Most Tries	
1987-88	57	David Johnson	4		David Walker
1988-89	57	Peter Clark	3		David Walker
1989-90	62	Graham Spearman	1		by 11 players
1990-91	66	David Johnson	5		Steve Douglas
1991-92	147	David Johnson	10		Peter Walton
1992-93	136	David Johnson	7		Ross Wilkinson

NEWCASTLE GOSFORTH RFC

Club Details

Colours: Black, green & white hoops
Change of Colours: Green & white hoops - black
Date Founded: 1877
Membership: Total 3,000, Full 600, Social 2,100, Junior/Youth/Minis 200, Other 100.
Number of Teams: Senior 7

Ground Details

Ground Address: Kingston Park, Brunton Road, Kenton Bank Foot, Newcastle Upon Tyne, NE13 8AF
Telephone: 091 2140422
Fax: 091 2140488
Directions: Follow airport signs north of Newcastle - Kingston Park - Kenton Bank Foot.
Capacity: 10,000
Ticket Prices: Adult £4 (+£2 for seat). OAP/Child £2 (+ £2 for seat).
Clubhouse Facilities: :Lounge bar, players bar, function suite, weight training room, squash courts, sports injuries cliniec.
Training Nights: Tues & Thurs

Special Occassions in 1993-94

October 16 - North v London Division.

NEWCASTLE GOSFORTH R·F·C

FORTH TO THE FIELD

PROGRAMME 1992-93

Main Sponsor

REED PRINT & DESIGN

Steve Douglas gets the ball away even though Rosslyn Park's scrum half Moon has a hold of his leg   Photo: David Hewitson

NORTHAMPTON FC

President: R B Taylor
Chairman: M Holmes
Club Secretary: R Horwood, c/o
Northampton FC, Franklins Gardens,
Weedon Road, Northampton. Tel: (H)
0604 410326 Fax: (H) 0604 414131.
Fixtures Secretary: R B Taylor, c/o
Northampton FC, Franklins Gardens,
Weedon Road, Northampton. Tel: (H)
0604 38626 Fax: (Club) 0604 750061.
Press Officer: R Horwood, c/o
Northampton FC, Franklins Gardens,
Weedon Road, Northampton.
1993/94 1XV Captain: John Oliver
1993/94 1XV Coach: Glenn Ross
Commercial Manager: John Shurvinton

Review of the Season

After a relatively successful Courage League campaign in 1991-92, where the Saints finished in third position just one point behind champions Bath and runners up Orrell, much was expected of the Saints in 1992-93. However a semi-final Pilkington Cup place and fourth position in the Courage League was all we could manage. The season did however prove to be a real learning experience, for the first time in many years the players and the Club had to cope with the pressure of expectation and the disruption of National and International commitments. We hope that lessons we have learned will place us in a better position to challenge seriously in the forthcoming season.

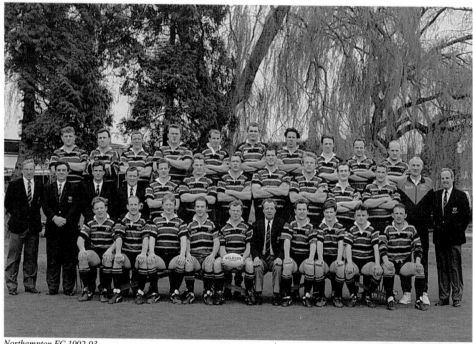

Northampton FC 1992-93

Photo: Beedle & Cooper

NORTHAMPTON FC

COURAGE CLUBS CHAMPIONSHIP
NATIONAL DIVISION ONE 1992-93

No	Date	Opponents	Venue	Result	Point Scorers
1	Sep 19	Bristol	H	W16-6	Rodber (T) Steel (C)(3P)
2	Sep 26	Saracens	H	W21-17	Thorneycroft (T) Packman (T) Steele (C)(3P)
3	Oct 3	L. Irish	A	L3-12	Steele (P)
4	Oct 10	Bath	H	W11-8	Beal (T) Steele (2P)
5	Oct 24	Free	Free	Free	Free
6	Oct 31	Orrell	A	W10-9	Hunter (T) Tubb (C)(P)
7	Nov 21	Harlequins	A	W12-7	Steele (3P) Dawson (DG)
8	Jan 9	Leicester	H	L12-13	Packman (T) Thorneycroft (T) Steele (C)
9	Feb 13	Rugby	A	W13-7	Torneycroft (T) Tubb (C)(P) Steele (P)
10	Mar 13	Gloucester	H	L16-21	Packman (T) Steele (C)(P) Tubb (2P)
11	Mar 27	Wasps	A	L12-20	Macnaughton (T) Ward (T) Beale (C)
12	Apr 3	W Hartlepool	H	W55-9	Rodber (2T) Baldwin (T) Daswson (T) Shelford (T) Thorneycroft (T) Packman (T) Ward (T) Beal (6C)(P)
13	Apr 24	L. Scottish	A	W34-21	Thorneycroft (2T) Ward (T) Pask (T) Rees (T) Tubb (3C)(1P)

ADDITIONAL RESULTS 1992-93

No	Date	Opponents	Venue	Result
1	Sep 1	Rugby	H	W76-0
2	Sep 5	Harlequins	H	W21-6
3	Sep 8	Richmond	H	L14-30
4	Sep 12	Coventry	A	L7-10
5	Sep 19	Bristol	H (L)	W16-6
6	Sep 26	Saracens	H (L)	W21-17
7	Oct 3	L. Irish	A (L)	L3-12
8	Oct 10	Bath	H (L)	W11-8
9	Oct 17	Nottingham	A	W46-17
10	Oct 24	Camb. Uni.	H	W46-15
11	Oct 31	Orrill	A (L)	W10-9
12	Nov 7	Aberavon	A	L12-20
13	Nov 13	Leicester	A	L3-128
14	Nov 21	Harlequins	A (L)	W12-7
15	Nov 28	labard (PC3)	A	W50-13
16	Dec 5	Bedford	H	W33-16
17	Dec 12	London W.	A	W37-3
18	Dec 19	Moseley	A	W13-10
19	Jan 9	Leicester	H (L)	L12-13
20	Jan 15	Harrogate	H	W36-14
21	Jan 23	Newcastle (PC4)	H	W33-3
22	Jan 30	Moseley	H	W8-6
23	Feb 13	Rugby	A (L)	W13-7
24	Feb 20	Cobentry	H	L21-26
25	Feb 21	New Zealand XV	H	L27-71
26	Feb 27	Moseley (PCQF)	H	W37-15
27	Mar 5	Gala	H	W41-17
28	Mar 13	Gloucester	H (L)	L16-21
29	Mar 16	RAF	H	W33-30
30	Mar 19	Bective R.	A	W37-15
31	Mar 27	Wasps	A (L)	L12-20
32	Apr 3	W Hartlepool	H (L)	W55-9
33	Apr 6	Met. Police	H	W35-10
34	Apr 10	Leicester (PCSF)	A	L6-28
35	Apr 24	L. Scottish	A (L)	W34-21.

CLUB PLAYING RECORD 1992-93 SEASON

National Division: One
Final League Position at end 1992/93 Season: 4th
League Playing Record: P 12, W 8, D 0, L 4,
Pts F 225, Pts A 141
Season Playing Record (including League
matches/Pilkington cup etc): P 34, W 24, D 0, L 10,
Pts F 860, Pts A 487

COMPETITIONS WON DURING SEASON 1992-93
Semi finalists Pilkington Cup
Finalists Middlesex 7s
Youth Whitbread Team of the Year

104

NORTHAMPTON FC

MATCH BY MATCH PLAYERS BY POSITION

Beal	Packman	Dawson	MacNaughton	Thorneycroft	Steele	Elkington	Baldwin	Olver	Pearce	Bayfield	Etheridge	Rodber	Tebbutt	Shelford	Foale	Griffiths	Baker	Walton	Hunter	Allen	Tubb	Merlin	B. Ward
15	14	13	12	11	10	9	1	2	3	4	5	6	7	8									
15	14	13	12	11	10	9	1	2	3	4	5	6	7	8	R								
15	13	9	12	11	10		1	2		4	5		7	8		14	3	6					
14	13	9	12	11	10	R	1	2		5	4		7	8				6	15	3			
F	R	E	E				F	R	E	E				F	R	E	E		F	R	E	E	
14	13	12		11	9		1	2	3	5	4		7	8				6	15		10		
14	13	12		11	15	9	1	2	3	4	5	6		8				7			10		
13	12	9		11	15		1	2	3	5	4	7		8		14		6			10	R	
14	13	9	12	11	15		1	2	3	5	4		7	8				6			10		
13	12			11	15	9	1	2	3	5	4		7	8				6			10		14
14	13	9	12	11,10			1	2	3	5	4	7		8				6	15			R	
10	12	9	13	11			1	2	3	5	4	7	R	8	R			6					14
	13		12	11			1	2	3		4		7						15		10	8	

Also played: Ward 15 Match 12, Ward 14 Match 13, Rees 9 Match 13, Phillips 5 Match 13, Pask 6 Match 13

PLAYING SQUAD 1992-93

Full Backs: N Beal, J Steele, J Griffiths, J Ward, I Hunter

Wings: F Packman, N Beal, H Thorneycroft, B Ward, N Wood, J Moffat, S Reed

Centres: F Packman, N Beal, R McNaughton, M Dawson, M Fielden, R Glenn, A Warwood, A Beales, J Fletcher, J Moffat, N Ward

Flankers: P Walton, R Tebbutt, T Rodber, S Foale, P Pask, M Steffert, M Ord, C Millhouse, B Robinson

Scrum Half: M Dawson, D Elkington, B Taylor, M Douglas, Phil Miles, R Rees

Props: G Baldwin, G Pearce, C Allen, M Lewis, L Baker

Hookers: J Olver, P Roworth, S Carter

Outside Half: S Tubb, J Steele, C Waggett

No. 8: W Shelford, T Rodber, D Merlin

Locks: J Etheridge, M Bayfield, J Phillips, S Foale, G Webster, D Jones

MOST CAPPED PLAYERS
including British Lions Appearances
Gary Pearle, 35

LEADING APPEARANCES FOR CLUB
R Jacobs, 470 - 1949-65
D F White, 448 - 1945-60
V Cannon, 437 - 1973-86

LEADING SCORERS
John Steele, Fly Half/Full back, 130
Seb Tubb, Fly Half, 120
Frank Packman, Centre/Wing, 13 Tries
Harvey Thorneycroft, Wing, 13 Tries

HONOURS
British Lions: Bayfield, Hunter

England: Bayfield, Hunter, Olver, Ropdber, Beal, Dawson

Scotland: McNaughton

England Seven: Rodber, Beal, Dawson

England U21: Merlin, Phillips

England B: Dawson, Thorneycroft, Beal

Ireland B: Etheridge

NORTHAMPTON FC

APPEARANCES AND POINT SCORERS

F Packman, 27, 65pts (13T)
G Baldwin, 26
J Etheridge, 24
W Shelford, 24
N Beal, 23, 60 pts (7T)
S Tubb, 22, 120 pts
H Thorneycroft, 22, 65 pts (13T)
P Walton, 22
R McNaughton, 20
G Pearce, 20
J Steele, 20, 130 pts
M Dawson, 19
J Oliver, 19
R Tebbutt, 17
J Griffiths, 16
B Ward, 16, 45 pts (9T)
C Allen, 15
M Bayfield, 15
D Elkington, 15
T Rodber, 14, 30 pts (6T)
P Roworth, 14
J Phillips, 12
S Foale, 9
D Merlin, 9
M Ord, 9

J Ward, 8
P Pask, 7, 35 pts
I Hunter, 6, 42 pts (5T)
M Fielden, 5
M Steffert, 5
B Taylor, 5
G Webster, 5
M Lewis, 4
N Wood, 4
L Baker, 3
M Douglas, 3
D Jones, 3
R Glenn, 2
P Miles, 2
A Warwood, 2
A Beales, 1
S Carter, 1
J Fletcher, 1
C Millhouse, 1
J Moffatt, 1
S Reed, 1
R Rees, 1
B Robinson, 1
C Wagget, 1
N Ward, 1

Saracens are in possession but John Etheridge, Tim Rodber & Wayne Shelford are on hand for 'The Saints'

Photo: Damian McFadden

NORTHAMPTON FC

COURAGE LEAGUE RECORDS

Highest score: 55 v West Hartlepool (55-9) 3-4-93 Home CL1
Largest winning margin: 46 as above
Highest score against: 60 v Orrel (60-0) 27-10-90 Away CL1
Largest losing margin: 60 as above
Drawn Matches: 4
Clean Sheets: 2
Failed to score: 3

INDIVIDUAL SCORING RECORDS
IN A MATCH

Most points: 20 John Steele v Coventry 10-3-90 Home CL2
Most tries: 3 Orson Bluitt v Bedford 21-11-88 Away CL2
Most conversions: 6 Nick Beal v West Hartlepool 3-4-93 Home CL1
Most penalities: 5 John Steele v Coventry 10-3-90 Home CL2, v Rugby 29-2-92 Home CL1
Most drop goals: 3 John Steele v Wasps 23-9-91 Away CL1

IN A SEASON

Most points: 110 John Steele 1991-92 CL1
Most tries: 6 Frank Packman 1988-89 CL2, Harvey Thorneycroft 1992-93 CL1
Most conversions: 11 John Steele 1989-90 CL2
Most penalties: 28 John Steele 1991-92 CL1
Most drop goals: 3 John Steel 1989-90 CL2 & 1990-91 CL1

IN A CAREER

Most points: 393 John Steele 1988-93
Most tries: 18 Frank Packman 1987-93
Most conversions: 40 John Steele 1988-93
Most penalties: 88 John Steele 1988-93
Most drop goals: 9 John Steele 1988-93

SEASON BY SEASON LEADING SCORES

	Most Points			Most Tries	
1987-88	27	Phil Larkin	4	Paul Alston	
1988-89	43	John Steele	6	Frank Packman	
1989-90	105	John Steele	4	John Thame Frank Packman	
1990-91	83	John Steele	3	Wayne Shelford	
1991-92	110	John Steele	5	Harvey Thorneycroft	
1992-93	52	John Steele	6	Harvey Thorneycroft	

NORTHAMPTON FC

Club Details

Colours: Black, green & gold hoops
Change of Colours: White with black, green & gold bands
Nickname: the Saints
Date Founded: 1880
Membership: Total 2,500
Membership Fees: Full £90
Number of Teams: Senior 2.

Ground Details

Ground Address: Franklins Gardens, Weedon Road, Northampton, NN5 5BG.
Telephone: 0604 751543/755149
Fax: 0604 750061
Capacity: Total 8,500, seated 2,500.
Ticket Prices: Adult £10 League £6 other, OAP/Child half price
Clubhouse Facilities: Members bar, public bar x2, 8 hospitality boxes, sponsors suite.
Training Nights: Tuesday & Thursday

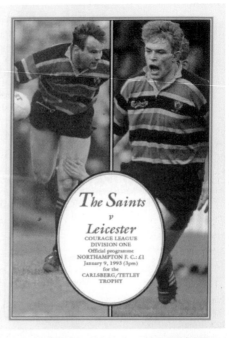

The Saints
v
Leicester
COURAGE LEAGUE
DIVISION ONE
Official programme
NORTHAMPTON F. C.: £1
January 9, 1993 (3pm)
for the
CARLSBERG/TETLEY
TROPHY

Smart Saints 1992-93   *Photo: Beedle & Cooper*

ORRELL RUFC

Review of the Season

The 1992-93 Season will be best remembered at Orrell when they made themselves 'safe' against relegation with a tremendous victory at Gloucester in March. After losing the title in 1991-92 only on points difference but, what happened? Law changes, unavailability of key players, defections to Rugby League and player movement are but a few reasons but when it mattered the team came good and if they had won their last league game at West Hartlepool would have finished fifth.

Again Orrell provided the majority of the Lancashire County Championship winning side and in reaching the semi final played three difficult games against strong opposition with new emerging players, winning all three — in style — showing that there is strength in depth.

Dewi Morris again represented England whilst big Bob (Kinnins) still kept the sportswriters asking "why has he never been selected for England". Orrell look forward to 1993-94 in Division One, home and away because "9 out of 1O players questioned stated that Edgehall Road was the ground they least expected to win on".

President: Bill Huxley
Chairman: Ron Pimblett
Club Secretary: J Arrowsmith, 1 Fisher Drive, Orrell, Wigan, WN5 8QX. Tel: (H) 0942 216879
Fixtures Secretary: N Fairclough, 123 Walton Road, Lower Walton, Warrington. Tel: 0925 225077
Press Officer: c/o Hon Secretary
1993/94 1XV Captain: Steven Taberner
1993/94 1XV Coach: Bill Lyon

Club Details

Colours: Black or amber shirts with red & white facings
Change of Colours: Amber & black
Date Founded: 1927
Membership: Total 1,150, Full 600, Associate 100, Junior/Youth/Minis 350
Membership Fees: Full £45
Number of Teams: Senior 6 Junior/Youth/Minis 7
Programme Advertising Rates: Contact Commercial Manager

Ground Details

Ground Address: Edgehall Raod, Orrell, WN5 8TL
Telephone: 0695 623193
Fax: 0695 632116
Directions: Leave M6 at Jcn 26. Follow signs for Up Holland until Orrell RUFC is signposted - approx 2 miles from M6.
Capacity: Total 9,999, Seated 400, Standing 9,599
Ticket Prices: TBA
Clubhouse Facilities: Members Lounge, Clubroom, 3 Sponsor Suites, Restaurant, Medical Room, Shop, President's Lounge
Training Nights: Mon, Tues, Thurs

ORRELL RUFC

COURAGE CLUBS CHAMPIONSHIP
NATIONAL DIVISION ONE 1992-93

No	Date	Opponents	Venue	Result	Point Scorers
1	Sep 19	Free	Free	Free	Free
2	Sep 26	L Scottish	H	W13-10	Ashurst (T) Halsall (T) Ainscough (P)
3	Oct 3	Saracens	A	W9-6	Ainscough (3P)
4	Oct 10	L Irish	H	L8-12	Morris (T) Ainscough (P)
5	Oct 24	Bath	A	L3-39	Ainscough (P)
6	Oct 31	Northampton	H	L9-10	Ainscough (3P)
7	Nov 21	Bristol	A	L11-23	Morris (T) Ainscough (2P)
8	Jan 9	Harlequins	H	W18-16	Taberner (T) Cleary (T) Hamer (T) Ainscough (P)
9	Feb 13	Leicester	A	L0-9	
10	Mar 13	Rugby	H	W66-0	Hamer (4T) Ashurst (2T) Kimmins (T) Halsall (T) Horrocks (T) Taberner (T) Manley (T) Ainscough (4C)(P)
11	Mar 27	Gloucester	A	W13-8	Morris (T) Ainscough (2P)(C)
12	Apr 3	Wasps	H	L10-11	Hamer (T) Ainscough (C)(P)
13	Apr 24	W Hartlepool	A	L15-39	Langford (4P) Ainscough (P)

ADDITIONAL RESULTS 1992-93

No	Date	Opponents	Venue	Result
1	Sep 1	Kendal	A	45-16
2	Sep 5	Sale	H	8-14
3	Sep 12	Moseley	A	9-18
4	Oct 17	Fylde	H	25-3
5	Nov 7	Leicester	H	18-33
6	Nov 28	Sale	H	20-3
7	Dec 5	Liverpool St Helens	A	22-5
8	Dec 12	Harrogate	A	24-10
9	Dec 19	Broughton Park	H	11-0
10	Dec 26	Wigan	H	Cancelled
11	Jan 2	Coventry	A	Cancelled
12	Jan 16	Sale	A	10-24
13	Jan 17	LSH	A	0-11
14	Jan 23	Waterloo	A	3-8
15	Jan 30	Bristol	H	6-10
16	Feb 6	Bedford	H	20-3
17	Feb 27	Morley	A	19-16
18	Mar 6	Wakefield	A	39-28
19	Mar 20	Saracens	H	31-3

CLUB PLAYING RECORD 1992-93 SEASON

National Division: One

Final League Position at end 1992/93 Season: 9th

COMPETITIONS WON DURING SEASON 1992-93

Pilkington Glass Roses Challenge Trophy

MOST CAPPED PLAYERS

including British Lions Appearances

J Carlton, 26
D Morris, 12
N Heslop, 6
P Williams, 5
F Clough, 3
D Cusan, 1

LEADING APPEARANCES FOR CLUB

D V Southern, 600, (He won't say how many seasons!)

110

ORRELL RUFC

MATCH BY MATCH PLAYERS BY POSITION

Taberner	Heslop	Langford	Fielden	Halsall	Ainscough	Morris	Hynes	Hitchin	Ridenaugh	Gallagher	Bibby	Ashurst	Mancey	Hamer	Birerley	Wellens	Taylor	Southern	Wellens	Cusani	Cleary	Kimmins
F	R	E	E				F	R	E	E			F	R	E	E			F	R	E	E
15	14	13	12	11	10	9	1	2	3	4	5	6	7	8								
15	14	13	12		10	9	1	2	3	7	4	6		8	11	5						
15	14	13		11	10	9	1			8	4	6		7			5	12	2	3		
15	11	13	14		10	9	1	2		8				7		5			3	12	4	6
15	14	13		11	10	9	1	2		8				7	R	5			3	12	6	4
	14	15		11	12	9	1	2		7		R		8		5			3	13	6	4
15		13		11	12	9	1	2		8		6	,R	14		10			3	5	7	4
15		13			12	9	1	2		7	14	6		8	11	10			3	5		4
15		13		11	10	9	1	2		8		6		7	14				3	5		4
15		13		11	10	9	1	2		7		8		6	14				3	5		4
15		13		11	10	9	1	2		8		7		6	14				3	5		4
15		13		11	10		1	2			12	6		8	14	5			3			

Also Played: Strett 10 Match 7, Wynn replaced Wellens Match 8, Horrocks 12 Match 10, Horrocks 12 Match 11, Horrocks 12 Match 12, Ellis 9 Match 13, Jackson 4 Match 13, Parr replaced Hamer Match 13, Clayton 7 Match 13.

ORRELL RUFC

COURAGE LEAGUE RECORDS

Highest score: 66 v Rugby (66-0) 13-3-93 Home CL1
Largest winning margin: 66 as above
Highest score against: 39 v Bath (3-39) 24-10-92 Away CL1, v West Hartlepool (15-39) 24-4-93 Away CL1
Largest losing margin: 36 v Bath (3-39) 24-10-92 Away CL1
Drawn Matches: 2
Clean Sheets: 6
Failed to score: 1

INDIVIDUAL SCORING RECORDS

IN A MATCH

Most points: 28 Martin Street v Rosslyn Park 28-4-90 Home CL1
Most tries: 4 Paul Hamer v Rugby 13-3-93 Home CL1
Most conversions: 8 Martin Strett v Rosslyn Park 28-4-90 Home CL1
Most penalities: 6 Martin Strett v Gloucester 28-3-92 Home CL1
Most drop goals: 1 on 6 occasions by2 players. Martin Strett 4, Gerry Ainscough 2

IN A SEASON

Most points: 109 Martin strett 1990-91 CL1
Most tries: 7 Phil Halsall 1990-91 CL1, Dewi Morris 1990-91 & 1991-92
Most conversions: 21 Martin Strett 1990-91 CL1
Most penalties: 26 Martin Strett 1991-92 CL1
Most drop goals: 2 Martin Strett 1991-92 CL1

IN A CAREER

Most points: 323 Martin Strett 1988-93
Most tries: 19 Phil Halsall 1987-93
Most conversions: 43 Martin Strett 1988-93
Most penalties: 67 Martin Strett 1988-93
Most drop goals: 4 Martin Strett 1988-93

SEASON BY SEASON LEADING SCORES

	Most Points			Most Tries
1987-88	72	Gerry Ainscough	6	Gerry Ainscough
1988-89	54	Gerry Ainscough	3	Nigel Heslop
1989-90	104	Martin Strett	5	Paul Manley Nigel Heslop
1990-91	109	Martin Strett	7	Phil Halsall Dewi Morris
1991-92	104	Martin Street	7	Dewi Morris
1992-93	63	Gerry Ainscough	6	Paul Hamer

WASPS FC

President: John Kemp
Chairman: Sir Patrick Lowry (Executive Committee)
Club Secretary: Ivor Mountlake, c/o Wasps FC, Repton Avenue, Sudbury, Middlesex, HA0 3DW. Tel: 0892 511348
Fixtures Secretary: Don Wills, 25 Woodland Gardens, Isleworth, Middlesex TW7 6LN. Tel: 081 560 7594.
Press Officer: John Gasson, The Manor, Willington, Bedfordshire, MK44 3PX.
Tel: (H) 0234 838735 (W) 071 409 3455.
1993/94 1XV Captain: Dean Ryan
1993/94 1XV Coach: Rob Smith
Marketing Manager: Sara Rigby
Club Steward: Louis O'Meara
Medical Officer (Sports Injury Clinic): Dr Ben Gilfeather
Club Treasurer: Malcolm Evans
Chairman of Club Council: Sir Peter Yarranton
Chairman of Playing Alex Finch

Review of the Season

Following 1991-92's season, where for the first time we were not in the 1st three in the First Division, under new Captain Dean Ryan, everything turned round and a really magnificent season resulted, albeit just missing out by a whisker from our ambitious target of winning the League and the Cup.

In the League, we were joint Top with Bath who took first place on their superior points difference. Had we not lost to Bath in certain unfortunate circumstances, we would have been outright Champions.

In the Cup, we were to lose at the Semi-Final stage, but were compensated by an incredibly exciting win in the Middlesex Sevens, putting out Wellington (NZ), & Western Samoa en route. As the Press observed, "when last did Wasps play in front of 45000 delirious supporters?".

Our under 21's point the way to an exciting future by winning the National U21. 15-a-side Championship and also the National U21 Sevens.

In addition to many, many representative honours that included both Rob Andrew and Jeff Probyn breaking the record number of Caps in their positions, our proudest moment was perhaps the magnificent efforts of two of our young Players, Lawrence Dallaglio and Damian Hopley in England's glorious win of the World Cup sevens at Murrayfield.

From this position of strength, we approach 1993-94 with tremendous confidence, supported by a new Sponsor, the major US Airline, United Airlines (who are twice the size of B.A.). Surprisingly a major Tour is in hand for next summer!

Wasps FC 1992-93

113

WASPS FC

COURAGE CLUBS CHAMPIONSHIP
NATIONAL DIVISION ONE 1992-93

No	Date	Opponents	Venue	Result	Point Scorers
1	Sep 19	W.Hartlepool	A	W19-6	White (T) Buzza (C)(4P)
2	Sep 26	Harlequins	A	W15-13	Childs (T) Emeruwa (T) Buzza (C)(P)
3	Oct 3	Leicester	H	W14-13	Dunn (T) Buzza (3P)
4	Oct 10	Rugby	A	W34-3	Buzza (2T) White (T) Oti (T) Ryan (T) Buzza (2C)(IP) Pilgrim (C)
5	Oct 24	Gloucester	H	W19-9	Oti (T) Pilgrim (3P)
6	Oct 31	Free	Free	Free	Free
7	Nov 21	L. Scottish	H	W10-6	Davies (T) Pilgrim (C)(P)
8	Jan 9	Saracens	A	W13-9	Oti (T) Buzza (C)(2P)
9	Feb 13	L. Irish	H	W18-9	Hopley (2T) Bates (T) Hopley (P)
10	Mar 13	Bath	A	L11-22	Hopley (T) Andrew (2P)
11	Nar 27	Northampton	H	W20-12	Davies (T) Andrew (4P)(DG)
12	Apr 3	Orrell	A	W11-10	Oti (T) Andrew (2P)
13	Apr 24	Bristol	H	W7-6	Hopley (T) Andrew (C)

ADDITIONAL RESULTS 1992-93

No	Date	Opponents	Venue	Result
1	Sep 6	Mosley	A	W25-18
2	Sep 8	Ealing	H	W56-13
3	Sep 12	Newcastle Gosforth	A	D3-3
4	Sep 19	W. Hartlepool (League)	A	W19-6
5	Sep 26	Harlequins (League)	A	W15-13
6	Oct 3	Leicester (League)	H	W14-13
7	Oct 10	Rugby (League)	A	W34-3
8	Oct 17	Liverpool St Helens	H	Cancelled
9	Oct 24	Gloucester (League)	H	W14-9
10	Oct 31	Cambridge University	H	W19-16
11	Nov 7	Swansea	A	L17-25
12	Nov 10	Oxford University	H	W16-7
13	Nov 13	Bristol	A	L6-32
14	Nov 21	L. Scottish (League)	H	W10-6
15	Nov 28	Rosslyn Park (Cup)	A	W37-10
16	Dec 5	L. Welsh	A	D16-16
17	Dec 12	Bedford	A	L9-13
18	Dec 19	Wakefield	H	L5-6
19	Jan 2	Plymouth Albion	A	W11-9
20	Jan 9	Saracens (League)	A	W13-9
21	Jan 17	Racing Club de France	H	W48-23
22	Jan 23	Saracens (Pilkington Cup)	H	W18-17
23	Jan 30	Rosslyn Park	H	W32-11
24	Feb 13	L. Irish (League)	H	W18-9
25	Feb 20	Sale	H	W48-10
26	Feb 27	W. Hartlepool (Cup Qtr Final)	A	W15-9
27	Mar 5	Melrose	H	L11-16
28	Mar 13	Bath (League)	A	L11-22
29	Mar 20	Wanderers Dublin	A	W36-21
30	Mar 27	Northampton (League)	H	W20-12
31	Apr 3	Orrell (League)	A	W11-10
32	Apr 10	Harlequins (Cup Semi final)	H	L13-14
33	Apr 12	Leicester	A	L13-14
34	Apr 25	Bristol (League)	H	W7-6

CLUB PLAYING RECORD 1992-93 SEASON

National Division: One
Final League Position at end 1992/93 Season:
Runners up (Joint Top)
League Playing Record: P 12, W 11, d 0, l 1, Pts F 186, Pts A 118
Season Playing Record (including League matches/Pilkington cup etc): P 31, W 21, D 2, L 8, Pts F 707, Pts A 407

COMPETITIONS WON DURING SEASON 1992-93

Middlesex Sevens Cup Semi-Finalists
National U21s 15 A side
National U21 Sevens

WASPS FC

MATCH BY MATCH PLAYERS BY POSITION

Buzza	Hopley	Clough	Childs	Oti	Thompson	Bates	Holmes	Dunn	Probyn	Kinsey	Ryan	Emeruwa	White	Greenwood	Abadom	Pilgrim	Maddock	Davies	Delaney	Scrace	Andrew	Shortland
15	14	13	12	11	10	9	1	2	3	4	5	6	7	8								
15		13	12	11	10	9	1	2	3	4	5	6	8	7	14							
15		13	12	11	10	9	1	2	3	4	5	6	7	8	14							
154			12	11	10	9	1	2	3	4	5	6	8	7	14	13						
15		13	12	11	10	9	1	2	3	4	5	6	7	8	14							
	F	R	E	E		F	R	E	E			F	R	E	E				F	R	E	E
15	11	13	12			9	1	2	3	4	5	6	7	8	14			10	R			
15		13	12	11	10	9	1	2	3	4	5	6	7	8				14				
15	14	13	12	11		9	1	2	3	4	5	6	7	8			R	10				
15	14	13	12	11		9	1	2	3	4	5	6	7	8				10				
	14	13	12	11		9	1	2	3	4	5	6	7	8			15	10				
	14	13	12	11		9	1	2	3	4	5	6	7	8			15	10				
	14	13	12	11		9	1	2	3	4		6	7	8			15	10		5		

PLAYING SQUAD 1992-93

Hookers: P Delaney, K Dunn, P Green
Scrum Halves: S Bates, C Wright
Locks: R Kinsey, D Ryan, S Shortland
Wings: J Abadom, P Hopley, C Oti, L Scrase
Full Backs: A Buzza, H Davies, A Maddock
Centres: G Childs, F Clough, D Hopley, A Maddock, L Scrase
Fly half: R Andrew, H Davies, A Thompson
No 8: M Greenwood, D Ryan, C Wilkins
Props: I Dunston, G Holmes, D Molloy, J Probyn
Flankers: L Dallaglio, F Emeruwa, P Green, M Greenwood, S Holmes, M White, C Wilkins

MOST CAPPED PLAYERS

including British Lions Appearances
Rob Andrew - 42 + 3 Lions, 1985 to date
Jeff Probyn - 37, 1988 to date
Paul Rendall - 28, 1984-91
Maurice Colclough - 25 + 8 Lions, 1978-86
Roger Uttley - 23 + 4 Lions, 1973-80
Huw Davies - 21, 1981 to date

LEADING SCORERS

Steve Pilgrim, Full Back, Wing - 101 Points
Philip Hopely, Wing - 72
Alan Buzza, Full Back - 68
Rob Andrew, Fly Half - 64
Chris Oti, Wing - 35
Graham Childs, Centre - 25

LEADING APPEARANCES FOR CLUB DURING SEASON 1992-93

Steve Bates - 16
Francis Emeruwa - 16
Matt Greenwood - 16
Richard Kinsey - 16
Mike White - 16
Kevin Dunn - 16

Wasps' scrum half Steve Bates

WASPS FC

COURAGE LEAGUE RECORDS

Highest score: 51 v Liverpool St Helens (51-4) 20-4-91 Home CL1
Largest winning margin: 43 as above
Highest score against: 28 v Northampton (15-28) 20-3-92 Away CL1
Largest losing margin: 16 v Gloucester (3-19) 8-19-88 Away CL1
Drawn Matches: 3
Clean Sheets: 2
Failed to score: 0

INDIVIDUAL SCORING RECORDS
IN A MATCH

Most points: 24 Rob Andrew v Bristol 27-4-91 Home CL1
Most tries: 3 Simon Smith v Coventry 13-4-88 Home CL1, Mark Bailey v Moseley 19-11-88 Home CL1 & v Gloucester 14-10-89 Home CL1, Graham Childs v Liverpool St Helens 20-4-91 Home CL1, Rob Andrew v Bristol 27-4-91 Home CL1, Chris Oti v Bristol 25-4-92 Away CL1
Most conversions: 6 Rob Andrew v Liverpool St Helens 20-4-91 Home CL1, & v Bristol 27-4-91 Home CL1
Most penalities: 5 Nick Stringer v Orrel 23-4-88 Home CL1, Rob Andrew v Nottingham 12-11-88 Away CL1 & v Leicester 9-9-89 Home CL1, Steve Pilgrim v Rosslyn park 11-1-92 Away CL1 & v Bristol 25-4-92 Away CL1
Most drop goals: 1 on 6 occasions by 2 players. Rob Andrew 4, Huw Davies 2

IN A SEASON

Most points: 126 Rob Andrew 1990-91 CL1
Most tries: 7 Mark Bailey 1989-90 CL1, Chris Oti 1990-91 CL1
Most conversions: 16 Rob Andrew 1990-91 CL1
Most penalties: 27 Steve Pilgrim 1991-92 CL1
Most drop goals: 2 Rob Andrew 1988-89 CL1

IN A CAREER

Most points: 387 Rob Andrew 1987-93
Most tries: 19 Chris Oti 1988-93
Most conversions: 42 Rob Andrew 1987-93
Most penalties: 81 Rob Andrew 1987-93
Most drop goals: 4 Rob Andrew 1987-93

SEASON BY SEASON LEADING SCORES

	Most Points			Most Tries
1987-88	57	Nick Stringer	5	Mark Bailey Simon Smith
1988-89	103	Rob Andrew	4	Mark Bailey
1989-90	90	Rob Andrew	7	Mark Bailey
1990-91	126	Rob Andrew	7	Chris Oti
1991-92	101	Steve Pilgrim	5	Chris Oti
1992-93	53	Alan Buzza	4	Phil Hopley Chris Oti

WASPS FC

Club Details

Colours: Black with gold wasp on left breast
Change of Colours: Black and gold hoops
Date Founded: 1867
Membership: Total 1600, Full 1,550, Junior/Youth/Minis 50.
Membership Fees: Full £25, Junir/Youth/Minis £12.
Number of Teams: Senior 6 + 2 ladies XVs, Junior Colts U19s & U21s
Programme Advertising Rates: For the season, approx. 20 games (Courage League, Pilkington cup and friendlies) 1 page B/W (A5) £575 + VAT, 1/2 page B/W £330 + VAT, 1/4 page B/W £165 + VAT, Back page £660 + VAT, Inside Back Page £600 + VAT, Centre Page Strip £360 + VAT, 1 page B/W "one-off" £55 + VAT.

Ground Details

Ground Address: Repton Avenue, Sudbury, Nr Wembley, Middlesex, HA0 3DW
Telephone: 081 902 4220
Fax: 081 900 2659
Capacity: 4,000(seated 1,200, standing 2,800).
Ticket Prices: Adult £8. OAP/Child £2.
Clubhouse Facilities: Bars, Trophy room, Dining room, Sponsorship suites (4), Press office, Medical suite, Gym, Changing rooms, Toilet for disabled.
Training Nights: Tuesday, Wednesday, Thursday

Club Sponsors
DTZ Debenham Thorpe
International Property Advisers

WASPS
FOOTBALL
CLUB
Founded in 1867

WASPS
V
BRISTOL

COURAGE CLUBS CHAMPIONSHIP

Saturday, 24th April, 1993. Kick-off 3.00 p.m.

£1.00

'Just like that' —Richard Kinsey of Wasps and Mark Russell of Quins in the Pilkington Cup Semi-Final   Photo: Joe McCabe

118

Jeff Probin, whose illustrious England career came to an end last year

Photo: Joe McCabe

LEAGUE TWO PROGRAMMES

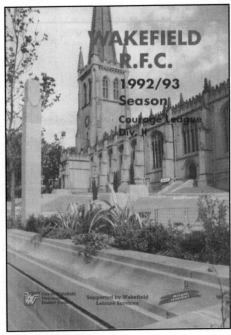

NATIONAL LEAGUE TWO

RESULTS AND LEAGUE TABLES
1987-1993
Pages 122-124

MEMBER CLUBS
1993-94

NATIONAL LEAGUE TWO RESULTS

1987-88

	1	2	3	4	5	6	7	8	9	10	11	12
1 Bedford		6-0	16-25		33-25		21-9	6-6	17-16		15-3	
2 Blackheath						12-16		22-7	19-12	3-4		12-48
3 Gosforth		26-8				14-22		12-14	N/P	12-10		
4 Headingley	7-13	21-9	26-7						38-3		12-12	3-12
5 Liverpool St. Helens		15-0	15-12	6-6		14-0	10-3				3-13	
6 London Irish	12-12			12-32			3-6			17-15		9-27
7 London Scottish		18-9	13-8	6-22					50-3			
8 London Welsh				10-18	10-27	6-13	24-24			22-26		
9 Northampton					9-13	15-13		14-16		3-16	0-22	
10 Richmond	28-25			14-13		9-6					3-22	
11 Rosslyn Park			14-8	14-3			20-3	15-6	16-15		20-12	
12 Saracens	33-4			7-7	10-13		34-0	7-25	22-6		6-6	

1988-89

	1	2	3	4	5	6	7	8	9	10	11	12
1 Bedford			19-99			15-2	9-6	16-6		15-3		
2 Blackheath	12-13			34-10	21-3					31-3	12-6	12-24
3 Coventry		18-2		19-12	7-18				22-10		7-3	
4 Gosforth	16-17				29-14		16-14	34-26		16-4		9-27
5 Headingley	7-7					48-9	22-10	24-0		9-12		3-7
6 London Irish			21-6	6-29	32-7		24-19	18-10		18-8		
7 London Scottish			6-3			16-21			3-3	16-17		
8 London Welsh			15-15	14-21			29-10		0-22	9-16		
9 Northampton	42-3	15-7		13-12	19-7					15-12		4-32
10 Richmond			12-3			18-18	12-32	14-3	15-12			10-27
11 Sale	15-15		23-15	15-24					50-9		10-12	
12 Saracens	50-10		13-6			20-3	19-9	37-4				

1989-90

	1	2	3	4	5	6	7	8	9	10	11	12
1 Blackheath		16-21				28-18	9-10	9-37		0-21		
2 Coventry					13-13	18-25		15-13	21-18	18-10		22-12
3 Gosforth	12-12	0-16				6-27	15-22			22-18		
4 Headingley	31-12	30-22	17-10				15-3			3-9		
5 Liverpool St. Helens	16-3		16-11	10-4			13-13			22-15	10-3	
6 London Irish			25-19	12-23				27-19	12-36			24-33
7 Northampton		24-18				33-21		6-4	12-6	41-25		
8 Plymouth Albion			28-13	9-20	20-3				11-12	21-16		33-28
9 Richmond	15-15		36-3	86-8	6-17					16-28	16-7	
10 Rugby			49-9	31-8	6-11	23-10			16-28			28-6
11 Sale	14-18	24-22				19-27	3-16	15-11		20-13		
12 Waterloo	10-19		25-7	9-6			6-12		13-23		12-9	

1990-91

	1	2	3	4	5	6	7	8	9	10	11	12	13
1 Bedford			7-9	16-10	18-19	21-16		10-9			10-10		
2 Blackheath	12-16					13-19	9-19		12-9		14-12	12-7	
3 Coventry		16-4		11-3	20-4			21-9		9-13			26-15
4 Headingley		16-15			9-10		7-18	31-6		11-20			16-13
5 London Irish		21-18					24-16	19-18		29-17		15-9	39-0
6 London Scottish			9-12	30-7	13-17			32-0		27-19			22-16
7 Newcastle/Gosforth	22-7		10-9			12-13			38-3		7-6	6-13	
8 Plymouth	13-3					12-3		19-13	6-28		15-9	13-21	
9 Richmond	28-17		0-13	17-6	18-18	15-40				10-9			
10 Rugby	28-3	18-7					25-8		25-8		28-9		
11 Sale			23-16	42-0	36-24	25-10		20-9		18-26			
12 Wakefield	27-0		32-10	17-9		21-9			20-3		13-10		
13 Waterloo	13-13	3-15					12-10			25-9	17-13	6-14	

1991-92

	1	2	3	4	5	6	7	8	9	10	11	12	13
1 Bedford		52-10					8-9	9-4		6-25	25-4	6-30	
2 Blackheath			21-13	9-6		3-9	31-6		16-20			6-34	
3 Coventry	19-13				15-32			6-30		19-12	21-20		18-24
4 Liverpoool St. H.	6-22		0-19		4-41	6-49				11-38			0-32
5 London Scottish	38-0	36-16						16-11		40-13	31-4		7-6
6 Morley	19-12		12-16		12-13					12-13	9-13		13-21
7 Moseley			12-22	33-3	18-25	19-3			15-10	47-15			
8 Newcastle-Gosforth		30-0		76-4		60-12	20-26		54-21			37-6	
9 Plymouth Alb.	24-9		10-13	25-10	9-10	10-12				10-15			
10 Sale	16,6	10-14						19-15			37-3	3-17	13-15
11 Wakefield		20-6		34-25			14-9	8-18	22-7			24-18	
12 Waterloo			10-6	40-12	22-15	16-9	18-17		12-3				
13 West Hartlepool		21-8					27-4	13-7	21-4	7-0	27-9		

1992-93

	1	2	3	4	5	6	7	8	9	10	11	12	13
1 Bedford			30-156	24-12	25-10			15-9	22-16		9-9	9-9	
2 Blackheath	16-12						9-12	5-46		18-14	3-20		
3 Coventry		38-15		37-10	41-3	19-22			13-18				6-32
4 Fylde		9-9				15-15	5-32			9-22		7-27	14-15
5 Morley		8-23		10-10		6-13	13-36		6-28				12-27
6 Moseley	9-9	23-6					19-16			32-10		3-14	9-12
7 Newcastle/Gosforth	19-13		26-3						28-6	16-3	7-3	17-20	
8 Nottingham			16-10	19-8	78-0	9-5			17-12				19-9
9 Richmond		13-23		29-6		28-21	9-21				11-6	12-16	
10 Rosslyn Park	13-16	,32-10		43-24			6-18	24-18		18-8			
11 Sale			24-3	51-3	34-0	6-13		25-8	21-10				
12 Wakefield	27-3		8-0		16-15			22-9		20-15	6-12		
13 Waterloo	28-8	27-6					3-13			12-9	25-24	22-11	

NATIONAL LEAGUE TWO TABLES

1987-88

	P	W	D	L	F	A	Pts
Rosslyn Park	11	8	2	1	155	83	18
Liverpool St. H.	11	8	1	2	154	97	17
Saracens	11	7	2	2	228	86	16
Headingley	11	6	2	3	202	104	14
Bedford	11	6	2	3	152	139	14
Richmond	11	6	0	5	140	156	12
London Scottish	11	4	1	6	141	158	9
London Irish	11	4	1	6	120	177	9
London Welsh	11	3	2	6	153	185	8
Gosforth	10	2	1	7	99	129	5
Blackheath	11	2	0	9	102	187	4
Northampton	11	1	0	9	81	226	2

1988-89

	P	W	D	L	F	A	Pts
Saracens	11	11	0	0	288	80	22
Bedford	11	6	2	3	141	187	14
Northampton	11	5	2	4	195	152	12
Sale	11	6	0	5	150	143	12
Coventry	11	6	0	5	150	143	12
London Irish	11	5	2	4	194	222	12
Headingley	11	5	1	5	179	136	11
Blackheath	11	4	11	6	181	144	9
Richmond	11	4	1	6	112	216	9
Gosforth	11	4	0	7	176	246	8
London Scottish	11	3	1	7	146	160	7
London Welsh	11	1	1	9	125	235	3

1989-90

	P	W	D	L	F	A	Pts
Northampton	11	9	1	1	192	135	19
Liverpool St. H.	11	8	2	1	154	106	18
Richmond	11	7	1	3	282	135	15
Coventry	11	6	1	4	206	185	13
London Irish	11	6	0	5	228	247	12
Rugby	11	5	0	6	238	172	10
Plymouth Albion	11	5	0	6	206	164	10
Headingley	11	5	0	6	161	226	10
Sale	11	4	0	7	153	182	8
Blackheath	11	3	2	6	141	205	8
Waterloo	11	3	0	8	147	193	6
Gosforth	11	1	1	9	108	266	3

1990-91

	P	W	D	L	F	A	Pts
Rugby	12	10	0	2	252	146	20
London Irish	12	9	1	2	239	192	19
Wakefield	12	8	0	4	188	109	16
Coventry	12	8	0	4	172	129	16
London Scottish	12	7	0	5	240	178	14
Gosforth	12	6	0	6	169	140	12
Sale	12	5	1	6	224	156	11
Bedford	12	4	2	6	138	203	10
Waterloo	12	4	0	8	134	169	8
Blackheath	12	4	0	8	134	169	8
Plymouth Albion	12	4	0	8	129	210	8
Richmond	12	3	1	8	134	245	7
Headingley	12	3	0	9	125	215	6

1991-92

	P	W	D	L	F	A	PD	Pts
London Scottish	12	11	0	1	304	130	174	22
West Hartlepool	12	11	0	1	244	89	155	22
Waterloo	12	8	0	4	206	184	22	16
Newcastle Gosf'th	12	7	0	5	371	371	140	231
Wakefield	12	7	0	5	187	194	-7	14
Coventry	12	7	0	5	187	196	-9	14
Moseley	12	6	0	6	215	196	19	12
Sale	12	6	0	6	204	209	-5	12
Morley	12	4	0	8	171	202	-31	8
Bedford	12	4	0	8	168	204	-36	8
Blackheath	12	4	0	8	140	266	-126	8
Plymouth	12	3	0	9	153	209	-56	6
Liverpool St. H.	12	0	0	12	87	418	-331	0

1992-93

	P	W	D	L	F	A	PD	Pts
Newcastle Gosf'th	12	10	0	2	241	106	135	20
Waterloo	12	10	0	2	228	138	90	20
Wakefield	12	8	1	3	186	123	63	17
Nottingham	12	8	0	4	249	154	104	16
Sale	12	7	1	4	237	102	135	15
Moseley	12	6	2	4	184	150	34	14
Bedford	12	6	2	4	186	183	3	14
Rosslyn Park	12	5	0	7	209	199	10	10
Richmond	12	5	0	7	204	196	8	10
Blackheath	12	4	2	6	142	231	-89	10
Coventry	12	3	0	9	192	236	-44	6
Fylde	12	0	3	9	108	290	-182	3
Morley	12	0	1	11	107	374	-267	1

LONDON SCOTTISH FC

President: A C W Boyle
Club Secretary: J J Smith, Richmond Athletic Ground, Kew Foot Road, Richmond, Surrey, TW9 2SS. Tel: (H) 0784 459463 (W) 081 332 2473 Fax: (W) 081 332 6775.
Fixtures Secretary: A l Rhodes, 19 St Peter Street, Winchester, Hants SO23 8BU. Tel: (H) 0962 75539 (W) 0962 844440.
Press Officer: J J Smith, Richmond Athletic Ground, Kew Foot Road, Richmond, Surrey, TW9 2SS.
1993/94 1XV Captain: D B Milland
1993/94 1XV Coach: TBA

Review of the Season

No one can pretend that the season was anything but a disappointment with relegation to Division Two after only one season in the top echelon. However, in a normal season with two up and two down, finishing fourth from bottom in our first season in the top would have been considered a success. At least we have the satisfaction that, unlike most relegated clubs, we are retaining our players. Surely they are good enough to bounce straight back up.

We started the season with a good win against Gloucester but then lost two games against Orrell and Bristol which we could have won. Our hopes were raised again by an excellent draw against Quins after being 22-3 down at half time. Then followed two defeats by Leicester in the league and cup, but a 45-2O win against Rugby seemed to put us back on track only to suffer another set back with a 6-1O defeat at Wasps. In the long lull between the end of November and the beginning of January the Scottish District Championship took place and our players became strangers to the Athletic Ground and we were poorly prepared for the game against West Hartlepool. The result of this game 1O-15 will be etched on the hearts of members for a long time and from then on, despite, a good win against London Irish it was a rearguard action for the rest of the season to try and avoid relegation.

CLUB PLAYING RECORD 1992-93 SEASON

National Division: One
Final League Position at end 1992/93 Season: Tenth
League Playing Record: P 12, W 3, D 1, L 8, Pts F 192, Pts A, 248
Season Playing Record (including League matches/Pilkington cup etc): P 29, W 7, D 1, L 21, Pts F 525, Pts A 721

London Scottish FC 1992-93

LONDON SCOTTISH FC

COURAGE CLUBS CHAMPIONSHIP
NATIONAL DIVISION ONE 1992-93

No	Date	Opponents	Venue	Result	Point Scorers
1	Sep 19	Gloucester	H	W8-3	Erikson (T) Appleson (P)
2	Sep 26	Orrell	A	L10-13	Mair (T) Appleson (C)(P)
3	Oct 3	Bristol	H	L8-11	Morrison (T) Appleson (P)
4	Oct 10	Harlequins	A	D22-22	Cronin (T) White (T) Grecian (3P) Appleson (P)
5	Oct 24	Leicester	H	L11-18	White (T) Appleson (P) Cramb (DG)
6	Oct 31	Rugby	A	W45-20	Appleson (2T)
7	Nov 21	Wasps	A	L6-10	Grecian (2P)
8	Jan 9	W Hartlepool	H	L10-15	Wichary (T)(C)(P)
9	Feb 13	Free	Free	Free	Free
10	Mar 13	Saracens	A	L17-41	Millard (2T) Wichery (2C) Grecian (P)
11	Mar 27	L Irish	H	W28-21	Renwick (2T) Leckie (T) Grecian (2C)(2P) Cramb (DG)
12	Apr 3	Bath	A	L6-40	Grecian (2P)
13	Apr 24	Northampton	H	L21-34	Renwick (T) Scott (T) Appleson (T) Grecian (2P)

ADDITIONAL RESULTS 1992-93

No	Date	Opponents	Venue	Result
1	Sep 5	Heriots F. P.	A	W51-8
2	Sep 12	Nottingham	H	W29-20
3	Oct 17	Richmond	H	L13-48
4	Nov 7	Newport	A	L14-22
5	Nov 14	Rosslyn Park	H	W20-15
6	Nov 29	Leicester (P.C.)	H	L11-20
7	Dec 12	Nottingham	A	L3-14
8	Dec 19	Richmond	A	L15-31
9	Jan 2	L. Welsh	A	L24-25
10	Jan 23	Blackheath	A	W34-16
11	Jan 30	Havant	A	L15-25
12	Feb 6	Hawick	H	L28-30
13	Feb 13	Sale	A	L17-55
14	Feb 20	Rugby	H	L25-37
15	Mar 6	Edinburgh Academicals	H	L12-25
16	Mar 19	Bedford	A	L15-35
17	Apr 17	Saracens	H	L7-47

MOST CAPPED PLAYERS

including British Lions Appearances

A G Hastings, 45 + 3

A F McHarg, 44

D B White, 41 + 1

I H P Laughland, 31

A P Burnell, 29

D F Cronin, 28

LEADING APPEARANCES FOR CLUB DURING SEASON 1992-93

R Cramb, 26

M Sly, D Denham, L Renwick, 23

L Mair, 20

LEADING SCORERS

M Appleson, Full Back, 91

S Wichary, Wing & Full Back, 81

N Grecian, Wing, 54

D White, No 8, 37

L Renwick, Wing, 30

R Cramb, Fly Half, 28

PLAYING SQUAD 1992-93

Full Backs: M Appleson, S Wichary

Wings: L Renwick, N Grecian, C Henderson

Centres: M Sly, F Harrold, G Dingwall, R Erikson

Fly Half: R Cramb

Scrum Half: K Troup, D Millard

Props: D Denham, P Burnell, D Signorini, B Hillicks

Hookers: L Mair, B Gilchrist

Second Row: R Scott, D Cronin, D Johnston

Back Row: N Provan, I Dixon, I Morrison, I Macleod

No. 8: D White, C Brown, D Leckie

LONDON SCOTTISH FC

MATCH BY MATCH PLAYERS BY POSITION

Appleson	Grecian	Sly	Eriksson	Renwick	Cramb	Millard	Denham	Mair	Burnell	Scott	Cronin	Provan	Morrison	White	Macleod	Gilchrist	Harrold	Troup	Pearson	Dixon	Johnston	Wichary	Nisbet
15	14	13	12	11	10	9	1	2	3	4	5	6	7	8									
15	14	13	12	11	10	9	1	2	3	4	5	6		8	7								
15	14	13	12	11	10	9	1	2	3	4	5	6	7	8									
15	14	13	12	11	10	9	1		3	4	5	6	7	8		2							
15	14	12		11	10		1		3	4	5	6	7	8		2	13	9					
15	14	12		11	10		1		3	5	4	6	7	8		2	13	9					
15	14	12		11	10		1		3	5	4	6		8		2	13	9	R	7			
15		13		14	10	9	1	2	3		4	6	7	8			12					11	5
	F	R	E	E					F	R	E	E		F	R	E	E		F	R	E	E	
	14	13	12		10	9		2	3	5	4	6		8							15		
	15	13		11	10	9	1	2	3	5	4		8							7	14		
15	14			11	10	9	1	2		5	4									7	13		
15	14		13	11	10		1	2		4			7					9			5		

Also played: Henderson 11 Match 10, Signorini 1 Match 10, Leckie 7 Match 10, Dingwall 12 Match 11, Leckie 6 Match 11, Dingwall 12 Match 12, Hillicks 3 Match 12, McBain 6 Match 12, Brown 8 Match 12, Dingwall 12 Match 13, Hillicks 3 Match 13, Brown 6 Match 13, McBain 8 Match 13

Club Details

Colours: Blue.
Change of Colours: White.
Nickname: Scottish.
Date Founded: 1878.
Membership: Total 1476, Full 1270, Junior/Youth/Minis 206.
Membership Fees: Full £40, Junior/Youth/Minis £15.
Number of Teams: Senior 9, Youth 2, Mini 7.
Programme Advertising Rates: £600.

Ground Details

Ground Address: Richmond Athletic Ground, Kew Foot Road, Richmond, Surrey TW9 2SS.
Telephone: 081 332 2473.
Fax: 081 332 6775.
Directions: From Richmond 100 yards on right on A316, or 2 mins walk from station (BR or tube).
Capacity: Total 6,200, Seated 1,200, Standing 5,000.
Ticket Prices: Adults £5, OAP/Child £3.
Clubhouse Facilities: Two bars, lunch rooms, club shop.
Training Nights: Tuesday & Thursday.

London Scottish Football Club

Founded 1878

Saturday, 24th April, 93

London Scottish v Northampton

THE FAMOUS GROUSE FINEST SCOTCH WHISKY

OFFICIAL CLUB SPONSOR

LONDON SCOTTISH FC

COURAGE LEAGUE RECORDS

HIGHEST SCORE : 5O v Northampton (5O-3) 3-1O-87 Home CL2
LARGEST WINNING MARGIN : 47 As above
HIGHEST SCORE AGAINST : 41 v Saracens (17-41) 13-3-93 Away CL1
LARGEST LOSING MARGIN : 36 v Bath (6-4O) 3-4-93 Away CL1
DRAWN MATCHES : 3
CLEAN SHEETS : 3
FAILED TO SCORE : 1

INDIVIDUAL SCORING RECORDS
IN A MATCH

Most Points: 26 Andy Mitchell v Northampton 3-1O-87 Home CL2
Most Tries: 3 Jerry Macklin v Northampton 3-1O-87 Home CL2
Most Conversions: 5 Andy Mitchell v Northampton 3-1O-87 Home CL2, Gavin Hastings v Vale of Lune 23-9-89 Home CL3, Mark Appleson v Rugby 31-1O-92 Away CL1
Most Penalties: 4 Gavin Hastings v Sale 12-11-88 Home CL2, v Coventry 22-4-89 Home CL2, Cameron Glasgow v London Iris 14-1-89 Home CL2, Nick Grecian v Blackheath 16-11-91 Home CL2
Most Drop Goals: 2 Richard Cramb v London Welsh 11-11-89 CL3, v Richmond 17-11-9O Away CL2

IN A SEASON

Most Points: 124 Nick Grecian 1991-92 CL2
Most Tries: 11 Nick Grecian 1991-92 CL2
Most Conversions: 16 Nick Grecian 199O-91 CL2
Most Penalties: 18 Nick Grecian 1991-92 CL2
Most Drop Goals: 4 Richard Cramb 1989-9O CL3

IN A CAREER

Most Points: 318 Nick Grecian 11988-93
Most Tries: 23 Lindsey Renwick 1987-93
Most Conversions: 39 Nick Grecian 1988-93
Most Penalties: 51 Nick Grecian 1988-93
Most Drop Goals: 8 Richard Cramb 1989-93

SEASON BY SEASON LEADING SCORERS

	Most Points			Most Tries	
1987-88	38	Andy Mitchell	4	Lindsay Renwick	
1988-89	49	Gavin Hastings	3	Nick Grecian	
1989-9O	64	Gavin Hsastings	4	Tim Exeter	
199O-91	89	Nick Grecian	9	Lindsey Renwick	
1991-92	124	Nick Grecian	11	Nick Grecian	
1992-93	4O	Nick Gecian	4	Derek White	

MOSELEY FC

President: Joe Jordan
Chairman: Bernard Hampson
Club Secretary: Peter Veitch, c/o
Moseley FC, The Reddings, Reddings
Road, Moseley, Birmingham, B13 8LW.
Tel: (H) 0527 32660 (W) 021 428 3076
Fax: 021 442 4147.
Fixtures Secretary: Alnynne Evans, c/o
Moseley FC, The Reddings, Reddings
Road, Moseley, Birmingham, B13 8LW.
Tel: (H) 021 354 8183 (W) 0675 470042
Fax: 021 354 8183.
Press Officer: Alex Keay, c/o Moseley
FC, The Redding, Reddings Road,
Moseley, Birmingham, B13 8LW.
1993/94 1XV Captain: Peter Shillingford
1993/94 1XV Coach: Derek Nutt
Director of Rugby: Alex Keay
Bar & Catering Manager: Kevin Ryan
Administration Secretary: Jean
Shepherd
Commercial Manager: Greville Edwards

Review of the Season

A place in the Pilkington Cup Quarter Final and their status preserved in the Second Division, left Moseley feeling what might have been, had they not had a couple of hiccups early in the season.

Disappointing league results against Fylde, Richmond and Seaford in the early part of the season, left Moseley with a lot of ground to make up despite excellent victories against 1st Division opposition in the form of Orrell (twice), Leicester, Rugby, Saracens and London Irish.

Nevertheless it was a satisfactory season and improvement was there to be seen following an unbeaten run of eight matches at the end of the season, including the last three league matches and only four defeats since Christmas, Moseley with an average team age of only 23 can look forward positively to next season with promise of success.

CLUB PLAYING RECORD 1992-93 SEASON

National Division: Two
Final League Position at end 1992/93 Season: Sixth
League Playing Record: P 12, W 6, D 2, L 4, Pts F 184, Pts A 150
Season Playing Record (including League matches/Pilkington cup etc):
P 42, W 26, D 2, L 14, Pts F 888, Pts A 662

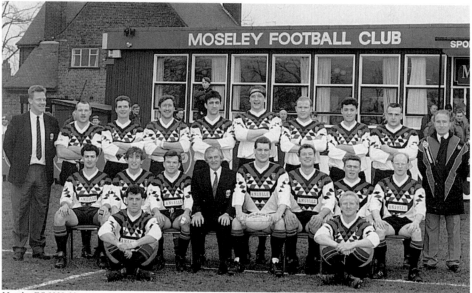

Moseley FC 1992-93

Photo: Arthur Hind

MOSELEY FC

COMPETITIONS WON DURING SEASON 1992-93
Pilkington Cup Quarter Final
Variety Club 7s winners
North Midlands County Colts Winners

PLAYING SQUAD 1992-93
Full Backs: S Purdy, J Reed-Daunter, C Dossett, L Corbett
Wings: D Spiller, L McKenzie, A James, L Sherriffe, D Hanson, G Bartlett
Centres: R Massey, J Bonney, I Bancroft, S Badock, D Wilson
Fly Half: A Houston, M Hardcastle, M Drane, A Kerr
Scrum Half: B Fenley, N Parry, M Chudleigh
Props: M Linnett, N Lyman, M Whiteley, N Webber, L Baker, R Harvey
Hookers: D Ball, R Hampton, N Horton, A Holden
Locks: S Lloyd, C Raymond, M Bright, G Watson, M Proctor
B Row: P Shillingford, M Teague, J Morris, W H Art, D Parry, M Burley, R Barr, R Harknett, N Topping.

MOST CAPPED PLAYERS
including British Lions Appearances
M Teague, 34
N Norton, 20
P Robbins, 19
P Crammer, 16
N Jeavons, 14
J Finlan, 13

LEADING SCORERS
J Reed-Daunter, Full Back, 91
A Kerr, Fly Half, 68
R Massey, Centre, 50
N Parry, Scrum Half, 44
M Deane, Fly Half, 34
M Hardcastle, Fly Half, 34

REPRESENTATIVE SELECTIONS 1992-93
British Lions: M Teague
England: M Teaqgue
Midlands v South Africa: M Linnett, P Shillingford
Barbarians: M Linnett, S Lloyd
Midlands: Steve Lloyd
Midlands B: C Raymond, D Ball, A Kerr
England Under 21s reserve: M Whiteley
England Colts: M Chudleigh

MOSELEY FC

Club Details

Colours: Red & black hoops.
Change of Colours: White.
Nickname: The Eagles.
Date Founded: 1873.
Membership: Total 1,600, Full 1,200, Junior/Youth/Minis 400.
Membership Fees: Full £42, Junior/Youth/Minis £10.
Number of Teams: Senior 3, U21s 1, Colts 1, Junior 10.
Programme Advertising Rates: From £150.

Ground Details

Ground Address: The Reddings, Reddings Road, Moseley, Birmingham, B13 8LW.
Telephone: 021 449 2149. Clubline 0891 884537.
Fax: 021 442 4147.
Directions: South Birmingham A38 take Priory Road traffic lights. County cricket ground on left, island right into Moorcroft Road, then into Reddings Road.
Capacity: Total 9,999.
Ticket Prices: Adults £5, OAP/Child £2.
Clubhouse Facilities: Two members bars, public bar, two players bars, club shop, hospitality rooms, sports treatment clinic.
Training Nights: Monday, Tuesday, Thursday.

Moseley in possession at 'The Reddings'

MOSELEY FC

COURAGE LEAGUE RECORDS

HIGHEST SCORE : 47 v Sale (47-15) 4-4-92 Home CL2
LARGEST WINNING MARGIN : 32 as above
HIGHEST SCORE AGAINST : 43 v Leicester (19-43) 27-4-91 Home CL1
LARGEST LOSING MARGIN : 42 v Wasps (O-42) 18-11-89 Home CL1
DRAWN MATCHES : 3
CLEAN SHEETS : 1
FAILED TO SCORE : 5

INDIVIDUAL SCORING RECORDS
IN A MATCH

Most Points: 15 Simon Pennington v Morley 16-11-91 Home CL2
Most Tries: 3 Peter Shillingford v Wasps 5-2-88 Home CL1, Dave Spillar v Sale 4-4-92
Most Conversions: 4 Alistair Kerr v Sale 4-4-92 Home CL2
Most Penalties: 5 Simon Pennington v Morley 16-11-91 Home CL2
Most Drop Goals: 2 Alistair Kerr v Plymouth 21-12-92 Home CL2

IN A SEASON

Most Points: 68 Carl Arntzen 199O-91 CL1
Most Tries: 8 Peter Shillingford 1987-88 CL1
Most Conversions: 13 Alistair Kerr 1991-92 CL2
Most Penalties: 15 Carl Arntzen 199O-91 CL1
Most Drop Goals: 2 Paul Roblin 1991-92 CL1

IN A CAREER

Most Points: 176 Carl Arntzen 1987-91
Most Tries: 15 Peter Shillingford 1987-93
Most Conversions: 21 Carl Arntzen 1987-91
Most Penalties: 41 Carl Arntzen 1987-91
Most Drop Goals: 2 Alistair Kerr 1991-93, Matt Hardcastle 1989-93

SEASON BY SEASON LEADING SCORERS

	Most Points			Most Tries	
1987-88	48	John Goodwin	8	Peter Shillingford	
1988-89	46	Carl Arntzen	4	Peter Shillingford	
1989-9O	52	Carl Arntzen	6	Simon Robson	
199O-91	68	Carl Arntzen	3	Carl Arntzen	
1991-92	62	Alistair Kerr	2	Dave Spillar	
1992-93	4O	Bob Massey	3	Nick Parry Bob Massey	

NOTTINGHAM RFC

President: Ian Smellie
Chairman: Tony Butcher
Club Secretary: David Roberts, 91 Loughborough Road, West Bridgford, Nottingham, NG2 7JX. Tel: (H) 0662 816384 (W) 0602 418159
Fixtures Secretary: Jim Farquahar, 29 Welbeck Gardens, Toton, Beeston, Nottingham, NG9 6JD. Tel: (H) 0602 733374 (W) 0602 784676
Press Officer: Andi Starr, 7 Cavendish Court, Woodborough Road, Mapperley, Nottingham, NG3 5RA.
1993/94 1XV Captain: Chris Gray
1993/94 1XV Coach: Peter Stone
Director of Coaching: D Hare
Club House Manager: Ruth Cross

Review of the Season

When Dusty Hare returned to his former club as Director of Rugby, the situation he inherited was far from promising: the side had been relegated to Division Two, and several key players had left. Furthermore, league restructuring meant that Nottingham had to finish in the top six to avoid a second successive relegation. But the shrewd Hare refused to panic, and recognised the need to rebuild from grass-roots level. To that end, he set up a development squad and attracted many talented youngsters to the club.

At first team level, wins in their opening three league games relieved the early season pressure. But for disappointing performances at Bedford and Sale, Nottingham could well have been challenging for the title in the closing weeks. As it was, they saved one of their best displays of the season for their final league game to end Waterloo's title aspirations, and finish a very satisfactory fourth in the table.

The progress made by youngsters such as Andy Jackson, Russell Brackenbury, David Roberts, Andy Furley and Richard Bygrave, fully justified Hare's commitment to youth, and home grown talent. But in order to blossom fully young talent needs to be balanced with experience. In that respect, Chris Gray, Martin Freer, Richard Byrom — voted the "Supporters player of the Year" — Clifton Jones and Simon Hodgkinson, all once again gave invaluable service.

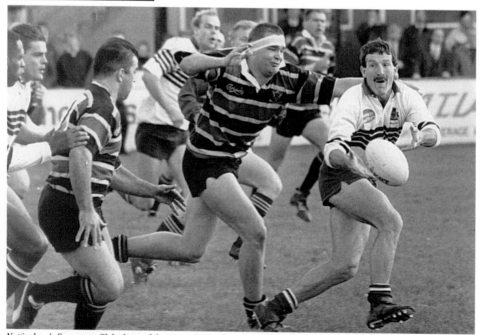

Nottingham's Supporters Club player of the season. Richard Byron, gets his pass away against Northampton
Photo: P Bailey,Forman Newspapers

NOTTINGHAM RFC

Club Details

Colours: Green & white
Change of Colours: White with narrow green hoops
Nickname: Green & white
Date Founded: 1877
Membership: Total 1,024, Full 869, Junior/Youth/Minis 250
Membership Fees: Full £40, Junior/Youth/Minis £5
Number of Teams: Senior 3, Junior 7
Programme Advertising Rates: Full £225

Ground Details

Ground Address: Ireland Avenue, Dovecote Lane, Beeston, Nottingham, NG9 1JD
Telephone: 0602 254238
Fax: 0602 254238
Directions:From M1: Leave M1 at Jcn 25, follow A52 to Nottingham, at 1st roundabout take third exit (B6003), through 1st set traffic lights to T-junction. take A6005 (Nottingham - Long Eaton Rd) turn L direction to Nottingham, pass through duel carriageway, pass Chilwell Golf Club on Right, over traffic lights, pass Barton's Buss depot and Nottingham RFC stand is half a mile on the right. **From A1:** Leave A1 at Jcn with M18, follow M18 to junction with M1, leave M1 at junction 25 and proceed as above.
Capacity: 4,900, Seated 590, Standing 4,400
Ticket Prices: Adult £4, OAP/Child £2
Clubhouse Facilities: Two club houses with bars, hospitality suites, 3 squash courts
Training Nights: Mon & Thurs 7.00pm

CLUB PLAYING RECORD 1992-93 SEASON

National Division: Two
Final League Position at end 1992/93 Season: 4th
League Playing Record: P 12, W 8, D -, L 4, Pts F 249, Pts A 145
Season Playing Record (including League matches/Pilkington cup etc): P 35, W 21, D -, L 14, Pts F 823, Pts A 611

PLAYING SQUAD 1992-93

Full Backs: S Hodgkinson, B Ryan, S Willis,
Wings: R Byrom, M Walker, S Summons, J Flint, A Blore
Centres: A Furley, C Jones, R Bygrave
Fly Half: G Gregory, A Sutton, N Marval
Scrum Half: B Gabriel, M Nadin, D Roberts, D Wright, J Hughes, D Wright
Props: A Jackson, M Freer, M Ireland, M Hallam, S Carbutt, M Feathers, K Fenton
Hookers: D West, J Prince, A Hall, J Hudson
Lock: C Gray, D Hindmarch, B Langley, G Callan, M Howells, I Grant, J Isherwood
Flankers: M Bradley, M Pepper, R Brackenbury, P Cook, G Rees, D Bourne
No. 8: D Saxelby

MOST CAPPED PLAYERS

including British Lions Appearances
Brian Moore, 24
Gary Rees, 23
Chris Gray (Scotland),22
V H Cartwright, Simon Hodgkinson, 14
Rob Andrew, 9

LEADING APPEARANCES

Peter Cook, 344
Garry Rees, 260
Simon Hodgkinson, 259
Richard Byron, 212
Clifton Jones, 182
Chris Gray, 179

LEADING SCORERS

Guy Gregory, Fly half, 246
Simon Hodgkinson, Full Back, 96
Malcolm Walker, Wing, 53
Brian Gabriel, Scrum Half, 51
Spence Summons, Wing, 40
Richard Byrom, Wing, 35

Scottish international Chris Grey — giving a captain's example

Photo: R Bailey, Forman Newspapers

NOTTINGHAM RFC

COURAGE LEAGUE RECORDS
HIGHEST SCORE : 78-O v Morley (78-O) 24-1O-92 Home CL2
LARGEST WINNING MARGIN : 78 As above
HIGHEST SCORE AGAINST : 34 v Harlequins (8-34) 1-4-88 CL1
LARGEST LOSING MARGIN : 32 v Bristol (O-32) 16-11-91 Home CL1
DRAWN MATCHES : 3
CLEAN SHEETS : 3
FAILED TO SCORE : 1

INDIVIDUAL SCORING RECORDS
IN A MATCH
Most Points: 23 Guy Gregory v Morley 24-1O-92 Home CL2
Most Tries: 4 Gary Hartley v Bedford 18-11-9O Home CL1
Most Conversions: 9 Guy Gregory v Morley 24-1O-92 Home CL2
Most Penalties: 5 Simon Hodgkinson v Waterloo 8-1O-88 Away CL1, v Blackheath 26-9-92 Away CL2,
Guy Gregory v Bath 28-3-92 Away CL1
Most Drop Goals: 2 Andy Sutton v Harlequins 31-3-9O Away CL1, Guy Gregory v Rosslyn Park 4-4-92
Home CL1, v Rosslyn Park 21-11-92 Away CL2, v Fylde 9-1-93 Home CL2, v Bedford 13-2-93 Away CL2

IN A SEASON
Most Points: 1O6 Guy Gregory 1992-939 CL2
Most Tries: 5 Clifton Jones 1987-88 CL1, Gary Hartley 1989-9O CL1
Most Conversions: 13 Simon Hodgkinson 1989-9O CL1
Most Penalties: 22 Simon Hodgkinson 1988-89 CL1 & 199O-91 CL1
Most Drop Goals: 9 Guy Gregory 1992-93 CL2

IN A CAREER
Most Points: 416 Simon Hodgkinson 1987-93
Most Tries: 11 Richard Byrom 1987-93
Most Conversions: 35 Simon Hodgkinson 1987-93
Most Penalties: 1OO Simon Hodgkinson 1987-93
Most Drop Goals: 14 Guy Gregory 1991-93

SEASON BY SEASON LEADING SCORERS

	Most Points			Most Tries
1987-88	86	Simon Hodgkinson	5	Clifton Jones
1988-89	98	Simon Hodgkinson	2	Lee Johnson
1989-9O	82	Simon Hodgkinson	5	Gary Hartley
199O-91	8O	Simon Hodgkinson	3	Richard Byrom
1991-92	48	Mark Mapletoft	4	Martin Pepper
1992-93	1O6	Guy Gregoryoft	3	Richard Byrom

OTLEY RUFC

President: M H E Dracup
Chairman: K Thompson
Club Secretary: G Highcliffe, 22 Cyprus Drive, Thackley, Bradford, BD10 0AJ. Tel: (H) 0274 615543 (W) 0272 724282.
Fixtures Secretary: C Wright, Wrenberry, 2 St Clair Road, Otley. Tel: 0943 465889.
Press Officer: J Finch, 9 Glen Mount, Menston, LS29 6DJ.
1993/94 1XV Captain: M Winterbottom
Chairman of Rugby Committee: M Wright
Chairman of Selectors: D W S Malir

Review of the Season

Otley's meteoric rise has taken them from Division North 1, where they were champions in 1989-9O, straight through Division 1 North the following year when they were once again Champions and after one settling season in League 3 they emerged Champions once again last term to move into League 2.

It was an unsettling time with injuries, centre Bob Booth unable to shake of a persistant thigh strain and fellow county centre Adrian Scott missed half of the League games. In addition scrum-half Nigel Melville had to call it a day after damaging ligaments when playing for Yorkshire in December but Mark Farrar proved to be an able deputy, scoring 17 tries in the remainder of the season.

Losing narrowly away at Havant and Exeter, Otley compounded the error by letting Redruth come back from being 15-3 down at Cross Green and were eventually happy to scramble a 19-19 draw.

Good wins against Askeans, 61-6 and Aspatria, 47-8 ensured the points advantage required when on the final day, having disposed of Liverpool St. Helens, the news came through that leaders Havant had been defeated up in Cumbria.

The icing was put on the cake when they went on to win the Yorkshire Cup for the 9th time, the first being in 1889.

With Nigel Melville now installed as Director of Rugby and Mike Winterbottom once again leading the side expectations are high in the Dales Market Town of 14,OOO inhabitants.

Skipper Mike Winterbottom holds aloft the Yorkshire Cup

Photo: Kevin Bumby, New Image

137

OTLEY RUFC

PLAYING SQUAD 1992-93

Full Backs: I Colquhona, P Rutledge, R Sharp
Wings: S Atkinson, A Booth, A Edson, G Melville, J Opara, J Shinwell, M Gray, J Scales
Centres: A Ballance, A Booth, R Booth, A Edson, W Holdsworth, D Lester, Ad Scott, A Scott
Fly Half: R Petyt, I Whitehurst, R Lake
Scrum Half: Rich Booth, M Farrar, N Melville
Props: C Baldwin, J Chappell, M Leason, N Marklew, R Nolan, A Rayner, S Rice, J Nightingale, N Blenskinsop
Hookers: M Barnett, D Finlay, M Peel
Second Row: S Henry, S Hudson, F Thompson, S Wilson, M Gilson
Back Row: J Chapman, D George, A Hargreaves, R Midgeley, B Strachan, S Tippine, M Winterbottom, I Spence

LEADING APPEARANCES FOR CLUB DURING SEASON 1992-93

A Hargreaves, 385, 1981/82 — 1992/93
M Barnett, 315, 1981/82 — 1992/93
D Lester, 231, 1981/82 — 1992/93
M Marklen, 265, 1983/84 — 1992/93
G Melville, 185, 1983/84 — 1992/93
S Rice, 183, 1986/87 — 1992/93

LEADING SCORERS

P Rutledge, Full Back, 276
M Farrar, Scrum Half, 85
R Petyt, Fly Half, 66
G Melville, Wing, 55

PLAYER OF THE YEAR

Peter Rutledge, Full Back

YOUNG PLAYER OF THE YEAR

Christ Baldkin, Prop

ADDITIONAL RESULTS 1992-93

No	Date	Opponents	Venue	Result
1	Sep 5	West Hartlepool	A	L16-34
2	Sep 12	Halifax	A	W46-10
3	Sep 19	Vale-of-Lune	A	W46-3
4	Oct 17	Wharfedale	H	W21-10
5	Nov 21	Moseley	A	L17-38
6	Nov 28	Northern	H	W24-8
7	Dec 5	Wakefield	A	L11-21
8	Dec 12	Sale	A	L11-15
9	Dec 19	Bradford & Bingley	H	L15-17
10	Jan 16	Vale-of-Lune	A	W42-5
11	Jan 23	West Park Bramhope	H	W15-0
12	Jan 30	Waterloo	H	W46-11
13	Feb 6	Huddersfield	A	W42-8
14	Feb 20	Hartlepool Rovers	H	W20-8
15	Feb 27	Redcar	H	W45-3
16	Mar 6	Middlesbrough	H	L11-14
17	Mar 13	Rotherham	A	L15-32
18	Mar 20	Pontefract	H	W12-8
19	Apr 6	Sandal	H	W24-0
20	Apr 10	Hull Ionians	H	W31-17
21	Apr 13	Sheffield	· H	W22-7
22	Apr 27	Rotherham		W22-5

CLUB PLAYING RECORD 1992-93 SEASON

National Division: Three
Final League Position at end 1992/93 Season: 1st
League Playing Record:
P 11, W 8, D 1, L 2, Pts F 274, Pts A 118
Season Playing Record (including League matches/Pilkington cup etc):
P 34, W 23, D 1, L 10, Pts F 836, Pts A 413

COMPETITIONS WON DURING SEASON 1992-93

National Division 3 Champions
Yorkshire Cup
Aire/Wharfe Cup
West Park Sevens

OTLEY RUFC

Club Details

Colours: Black & white hoops.
Change of Colours: Red.
Date Founded: 1865.
Membership: Total 750, Full 500, Social 250, Junior/Youth/Minis 120.
Membership Fees: Full £45.
Number of Teams: Senior 5, Colts, Under 21s, Junior 11.
Programme Advertising Rates: Full £200.

Ground Details

Ground Address: Cross Green, Otley, LS21 1HE.
Telephone: 0943 461180.
Directions: Take Harrogate Road from centre of Otley about half a mile on left.
Capacity: Total 7,000, Seated 852, Standing 6,148.
Ticket Prices: £4 league £3 others, OAP/Child Half price.
Clubhouse Facilities: Sponsors room overlooking ground, 2 other sponsors rooms, excellent bar & refreshment facilities.
Training Nights: Seniors Tues & Thurs, Colts & U21s Weds.

Open side flanker Andy Hargreaves runs around front of line with support from No 6 Simon Tipping   *Photo Kevin Bumby*

OTLEY RUFC

COURAGE LEAGUE RECORDS

HIGHEST SCORE : 61 v Askeans (61-O) 27-3-93 Home CL3
LARGEST WINNING MARGIN : 61 As above
HIGHEST SCORE AGAINST : 33 v Nuneaton (8-33) 7-3-93 Away CL3
LARGEST LOSING MARGIN : 25 As above
DRAWN MATCHES : 2
CLEAN SHEETS : 6
FAILED TO SCORE : O

INDIVIDUAL SCORING RECORDS

IN A MATCH

Most Points: 25 Jon Howarth v Lichfield 13-1O-9O Away D4N
Most Tries: 4 Glyn Melville v Wigton 12-3-88 Home ND1, John Walker v Harrogate 22-9-9O Away D4N, Mark Farrar v Askeans 27-3- 93 Home CL3
Most Conversions: 7 Ian Colquhuon v Birmingham 27-4-91 Home CL3
Most Penalties: 5 Jon Howarth v Lichfield 13-1O-9O Away D4N
Most Drop Goals: 1 David Lester v Middlesborough 28-4-9O Away N1, v Harrogate 22-9-9O Away D4N, v Walsall 1O-11-9O Home D4N, Richard Petyt v Clifton 23-11-91 Away CL3, v Redruth 29-2-92 Away CL3

IN A SEASON

Most Points: 121 Peter Rutledge 1992-93 CL3
Most Tries: 16 John Walker 199O-91 D4N
Most Conversions: 17 Jon Howarth 199O-91 D4N
Most Penalties: 26 Peter Rutledge 1992-93 CL3
Most Drop Goals: 2 David Lester 199O-91 D4N & Richard Petyt 1991- 92

IN A CAREER

Most Points: 146 Glyn Melville 1987-93
Most Tries: 35 Glyn Melville 1987-93
Most Conversions: 22 Robert Sharp 1987-92
Most Penalties: 26 Peter Rutledge 1992-93
Most Drop Goals: 3 David Lester 1987-93

SEASON BY SEASON LEADING SCORERS

	Most Points			Most Tries	
1987-88	34	Ian Colquhuon	8	Glyn Merlville	
1988-89	59	robert Sharp	3	Robert Sharp	
1989-9O	31	David Lester	3	John Walker	
199O-91	73	David Lester	16	John Walker Jon Howarth	
1991-92	62	Richard Petyt	4	Mark Farrar	
1992-93	121	Peter Rutledge	6	Glyn Melville	

RUGBY FC

President: John W Llewellyn
Chairman: David Rees
Club Secretary: Ivan Cawood, Stanford House, Stanford-on-Avon, Northamptonshire, NN6 7JR. Tel: (H) 0788 860409 (W) 0788 573444
Fixtures Secretary: Malcolm Palmer, The cottage, Knuston Home Farm, Irchester, Nr Wellingborough, Northamptonshire. Tel: (H) 0933 57297 (W) 0536 401344 Fax: (W) 0536 206133.
Press Officer: Roy W Batchelor, 36 Barton Road, Rugby, Warks, CV22 7PT. Tel: (H) 0788 810573.
1993/94 1XV Captain: David Bishop
1993/94 1XV Coach: John Cubitt
Commercial Manager: Mrs Terri Short
Playing Adminstrator: Neal Mapletoft
Playing Committee Chairman: Roger Large
Team Manager 1st XV: Guy Steele-Bodger

Review of the Season

Following five years of well chronicled Courage League success, season 1992-93 for the Lions proved a disappointing watershed, especially after hard won Division One status had been retained a year earlier to give them a second change in the top flight.

But last season they suffered relegation as the bottom club and by the lessons of a somewhat inadequately prepared start had been learned the Lions approached the second half of the season with just one win, by the narrowest of margins, over West Hartlepool by 6-5 although points were on offer against Saracens and Gloucester but for costly unforced errors in each of the two games.

There was then a mountain to climb during the post Christmas period. A heavy defeat to a full strength Bath by 61-7 was not the humiliation the score suggests and a strong performance against Northampton saw a somewhat unlucky defeat by 13-7 but the 66-0 defeat against Orrell, who fielded their strongest side for perhaps the first time of last season's campaign, was painful.

Further reverses followed to Bristol 32-21, Harlequins 35-14 and finally to Pilkington Cup winners, Leicester by 28-5 but in these games the Lions showed that they were on the way back and they can confidently look forward to life in Division Two, spurred by a determination to recapture top status in the shortest possible time.

CLUB PLAYING RECORD 1992-93 SEASON

National Division: One
Final League Position at end 1992/93 Season: 13th
League Playing Record: P 12, W 1, D 0, L 11, Pts F 104, Pts A, 368
Season Playing Record (including League matches/Pilkington cup etc): P 36, W 14, D 0, L 22, Pts F 720, Pts A 844

Caption — see page 143

141

RUGBY FC

COURAGE CLUBS CHAMPIONSHIP
NATIONAL DIVISION ONE 1992-93

No	Date	Opponents	Venue	Result	Point Scorers
1	Sep 19	Saracens	A	L9-14	Mapletoft (3P)
2	Sep 26	Free	Free	Free	Free
3	Oct 3	Gloucester	A	L12-21	Mapletoft (3P) Pell (DG)
4	Oct 10	Wasps	H	L3-34	Mapletoft (P)
5	Oct 24	W Hartlepool	A	W6-5	Mapletoft (P) Pell (DG)
6	Oct 31	L Scottish	H	L20-45	Bromley (T) Pell (TC) Suanders (T) Tomlinson (P)
7	Nov 21	L Irish	H	L0-14	
8	Jan 9	Bath	A	L7-61	Riley (T) Pell (C)
9	Feb 13	Northampton	H	L7-13	Bromley (T) Maplecroft (C)
10	Mar 13	Orrell	A	L0-66	
11	Mar 27	Bristol	H	L21-32	Saunders (T) Cockerill (T) Macleod (C)(2P)(DG)
12	Apr 3	Harlequins	A	L14-35	Saunders (T) Cockerill (T) Macleod (2C)
13	Apr 24	Leicester	H	L5-28	Bishop (T)

ADDITIONAL RESULTS 1992-93

No	Date	Opponents	Venue	Result
1	Sep 1	Northampton	A	L0-76
2	Sep 5	Nottingham	A	L6-23
3	Sep 9	Coventry	H	W21-18
4	Sep 12	Bristol	A	L13-35
5	Sep 26	Aspatria	H	W60-19
6	Oct 17	L. Welsh	A	L14-15
7	Nov 7	Preston G	H	W94-5
8	Nov 14	Morley	A	L17-24
9	Dec 12	Fylde	A	L8-13
10	Dec 19	Bedford	H	W12-10
11	Dec 28	Nottingham	H	H34-10
12	Jan 16	Blackheath	H	W11-8
13	Jan 30	Newcastle Gosforth	A	L10-47
14	Feb 3	Nuneaton	A	W103-3
15	Feb 5	Moseley	A	L3-29
16	Feb 20	L. Scottish	A	W37-25
17	Feb 27	Wakefield	H	W15-3
18	Mar 5	Jedforset	H	W42-15
19	Mar 19	Greystones	A	L24-25
20	Apr 7	Nuneaton	H	W48-0
21	Apr 10	Plymouth	A	W12-8
22	Apr 12	Redruth	A	L0-40

COMPETITIONS WON DURING SEASON 1992-93

Warwickshire Colts Cup

MOST CAPPED PLAYERS

including British Lions Appearances

S E Brain, 13, 1984-86, G S Conway, 11, 1922-24
S J Pirdy, 1, 1962, L J Percival, 1, 1893

PLAYING SQUAD 1992-93

Full Backs: Mark Mapletoft, J Quantrill, W Morgan
Wings: E Saunders, D Watson, K Mills, A Gillooly,
S Rush, J Barrows, J Cockerill
Centres: S Bromley, R Tomlinson, S Glover,
G Fletcher, L Turnell, S Holley, M Palmer, S House,
K Devgun
Fly Half: R Pell, J MacLeod
Scrum Half: D Bishop, M Broomhall, P Dewey,
R Cox.
Props: T Revan, G Tregilgas, N Riley, R Mee,
D Manders
Hookers: D Fry, J Aldwinckle, R Milner, S Brain
Locks: S Smith, P Bowman, N Underhill, C Hunt
Flankers: J Gardner, M J Ellis, M R Ellis, J Darragh,
S Lewis, T Simms, N Leeming, D Perkins,
A Ruddlesdin
No. 8: J Jenkins, M Charles, R Huges, C Gubbins

LEADING APPEARANCES FOR CLUB DURING SEASON 1992-93

S Smith, D Bishop, 29
P Bowman, T Revan, 26
R Pell, G Tregilgas, E Saunders 25

LEADING SCORERS

M Mapletoft, Full Back, 108 (5T 22C 13P)
E Saunders, Right Wing, 85 (17T)
R Pell, Fly Half, 83 (3T 13C 11P 3DG)
D Bishop, Scrum Half, 40 (8T)
S Bromley, Left Wing, 40 (8T)
D Watson, Left Wing, 35 (7T)

RUGBY FC

MATCH BY MATCH PLAYERS BY POSITION

Mapletoft	Saunders	Turnell	Glover	Bromley	Pell	Bishop	Tregilgas	Brain	Revan	Smith	Bowman	M R Ellis	Simms	M J Ellis	Quantrill	Charces	Fry	Tomlinson	Lewis	Riley	Aldwinckle	Leeming	Jenkins
15	14	13	12	11	10	9	1	2	3	4,5	6	7	8										
			F	R	E	E		F	R	E	E		F	R	E	E		F	R	E	E		
15	14	13	12		10	9	1	2	3	5	4	6	7	8	11								
15	14	13	12	11	10	9	1	2	3	4	5	6	7	8									
15	14		12	11	10	9	1		3	4	5	6	7		13	8	2						
	14		12	11	10	9	1		3	4	5	6	7		13	8	2	15	R				
	14		12	11	10	9			3	4	5		7		13	8	15		1	2	6		
15	14	13		11	10	9			3	5	4	7			6	12	2		1				8
15	14		12	11		9	1		3	4	5	6			13			R					8
	14	13		11	15	9	1		3,4			6			2	12	7	R					
	14		13			9	1		3	8	5			15		2	12	6					
	14	13	12			9	1		3	5	4		8		2	15	6						
	14	13	12			9	1		3	4	5				2	15							8

Also played: Macleod 10 Match 9, Miller 2 Match 9, Gardner 7 Match 9, Macleod 9 Match 10, Underhill 5 Match 10, Hughes 8 Match 10, Cox replaced Hughes Match 10, Broomhall replaced Quantrill Match 11, Cockerill 11 Match 11, Macleod 10 March 11, Underhill 4 Match 11, Gardner 7 Match 11, Cockerill 11 Match 12, Macleod 10 Match 12, Gardner 7 Match 12, Broomhall Rep Bromley Match 13, Cockerill 11 Match 13, Macleod 10 Match 13, Gardner 6 Match 13, Hughes 7 Match 13

Club Details

Colours: Orange, black & white.
Change of Colours: Red & white.
Nickname: Lions.
Date Founded: 1873.
Membership: Total 850, Full 700, Junior/Youth/Minis 150.
Membership Fees: Senior Playing Member £25, U/21 Member £10, Colt Playing Member £5, Vice President £50, Family Vice President £75, Corporate Vice president £125 + VAT, Senior Member £15, Season Ticket Member £45, Junior Season Ticket Member £10.
Number of Teams: Senior 3, plus U/21. Junior Colts + 16 Mini Groups.
Programme Advertising Rates: Details on request.

Ground Details

Ground Address: Webb Ellis Road, Off Bilton Road, Rugby.
Telephone: 0788 542252.
Directions: Second turning right half mile south west of town centre on A4071 (Bilton Road).
Capacity: Total 4,200, Seated 200, Standing 4,000.
Ticket Prices: Adults: Club games £4 League & Cup £4.50, Student/Junior U16/OAP £2, Programme £1, Entry to Stand £1, Car Parking £1.
Clubhouse Facilities: Large bar and function room, ground floor, Three first floor hospitality suites with balcony overlooking the pitch. Players bar (Lions Den). Club shop. Sports injury clinic. Fitness Room. Four large changing rooms, showers, toilets and toiled facities for disabled.
Training Nights: Tuesday & Thursday.

Photo, page 141— Rugby FC 1st XV Squad, 1992-93

Insets, top: Jason Aldwinckle, Dean Watson, Neil Riley, Eddie Saunders, Phil Bowman, Richard Tomlinson, Neil Underhill, Jim Quantrill.

Back row: Stewart Martin (Former Playing Committee Chairman), Mike Tarrant (Former Club Chairman), Dave McDonough (Team Manager), David Fry, Steve Smith, Trevor Revan, Mark J Ellis, Mark Charles, Steve Brain, Tony Simms, Luke Turnell, John Cubitt (Coach), Allen Foster (Former Chief Coach), Neal Mapletoft (Playing Administrator)

Front row: Spencer Glover, Stuart Bromley, Mark Mapletoft, Mark R Ellis, David Bishop (Captain), Richard Pell, Peter Dewey.

Insets, bottom: Neal Leeming, Steve Smith, Richard Mee, Kevin Mills.

Photo: Derek Warren, Coventry Evening Telegraph

Missing from photo: John Gardner, John Jenkins, John Macleod, John Cockerill, Adrian Gillooly, Richard Hughes, Rob Milner, Gary Fletcher

RUGBY FC

COURAGE LEAGUE RECORDS
HIGHEST SCORE : 49 v Gosforth (49-9) 11-11-89 Home CL2
LARGEST WINNING MARGIN : 41 v Maidstone (44-3) 26-11-88 Home CL3
HIGHEST SCORE AGAINST : 66 v Orrell (O-66) 13-3-93) Away CL1
LARGEST LOSING MARGIN :66 As above
DRAWN MATCHES : 3
CLEAN SHEETS : 2
FAILED TO SCORE : 4

INDIVIDUAL SCORING RECORDS
IN A MATCH
Most Points: 25 Chris Howard v Gosforth 11-11-89 Home CL2
Most Tries: 3 Chris Howard v Vale of lune 1O-9-88 Home CL3
Most Conversions: 6 Chris Howard v Gosforth 11-11-89 Home CL2
Most Penalties: 6 Chris Howard v Nneaton 22-1O-88 Away CL3,
Russell Hensley v Leicester 25-4-92 Away CL1
Most Drop Goals: 1 On 16 occasions R Pell 16, S Vaudin 3, C Howard 1, M Mapletoft 1, J McLeod 1

IN A SEASON
Most Points: 123 Chris Howard 1988-89 CL3
Most Tries: 9 David Bishop 199O-91 CL2
Most Conversions: 19 Chris Howard 1988-89 CL3
Most Penalties: 19 Chris Howard 1988-89 CL3
Most Drop Goals: 4 Richard Pell 1987-88

IN A CAREER
Most Points: 3O6 Chris Howard 1987-91
Most Tries: 31 Eddie Saunders 1987-93
Most Conversions: 52 Chris Howard 1987-91
Most Penalties: 52 Chris Howard 1987-91
Most Drop Goals: 1O Richard Pell 1987-93

SEASON BY SEASON LEADING SCORERS

	Most Points			Most Tries	
1987-88	69	Chris Howard	7	Eddie Saunders	
1988-89	123	Chris Howard	3	Chris Howard	
1989-9O	1OO	Chris Howard	7	Eddie Saunders	
199O-91	68	Stuart Vaudin	5	Steve Douglas	
1991-92	6O	Mark Mapletoft	2	Eddie Saunders	
1992-93	26	Mark Mapletoft	3	Eddie Saunders	

SALE FC

President: John Gardiner
Chairman: Tom Barker
Club Secretary: Laura Murrell, 41 Lawrence Road, Altrincham, Cheshire, WA14 4EL. Tel: (H) 061 926 9223 (W) 061 905 6318.
Fixtures Secretary: Tony Dolan, 9 Greenway Road, Timperley, Cheshire. Tel: (H) 061 973 4799 (W) 061 795 0711.
Press Officer: Christine Kenrick, 41 Lawrence Road, Altrincham, Cheshire, WA14 4EL.
1993/94 1XV Captain: Mike Kenrick
1993/94 1XV Coach: Paul Turner
Director of Coaching: Steve Smith
Director of Rugby: Brian Wilkinson
Financial Controller: Doug Baden
Match Programme Editor: Ken Brooks
Membership Secretary: Eric Tootill
Player Registration: Peter Tasker

Review of the Season

Maintaining Division 2 status was uppermost in Sale's mind and instrumental in achieving a place in the top six was new recruit ex Welsh International, Paul Turner — who was inspirational in his role as player/coach.

It all went pretty well up until Christmas but went horribly wrong when Sale had a disastrous defeat at home to Moseley (6-13). A win at Waterloo would have relieved the pressure but the see-sawing score ended 24-25 in Waterloo's favour and second division rugby in 1993/94 began to look somewhat in the balance. But, the team rallied and made a spirited comeback although nothing was definite until all the results from the last match of the season had been taken into account. It was good news for Sale, a 24-O victory over Coventry, 5th position, the best defensive record in the division and joint best points difference with leaders Newcastle Gosforth.

With sights set on divisional success Sale's run in the Pilkington Cup was brought to an unceremonious end by Orrell in the 3rd round. But outside divisional and competition matches, Sale managed to slot up victories over a number of First Division teams — Orrell (twice), Gloucester, London Scottish and Saracens.

Sale were proud to have three representatives in the North team who took on South Africa at Elland Road — Martin Whitcombe, Jim Mallinder and Andrew Macfarlane. It was unfortunate that Macfarlane sustained a head injury that kept him out for some time, but this, and other injuries, actually paved the way for promising young talent to emerge. Sale intends to capitalise on such talent to maintain a position in the top half of the newly arranged Courage League Division 2.

Sale FC 1992-93

Photo: Peter Barton

SALE FC

PLAYING SQUAD 1992-93

Full Backs: J Mallinder, C Gunning
Wings: J Powell, K Young, C Park, R Brice, R Harper, C Birch
Centres: P Stansfield, R Davis, M Burt, G Stocks, J Brennand, D Pollard
Fly Half: P Turner, P Gee, P Harrison
Scrum Half: H Fitton, M Warr, P Turner
Props: M Whitcombe, N Wheeler, A Smith, P Smith, R Kelly
Hookers: S Diamon, L Hewson
Lock: D Baldwin, D Erskine, B Finney, N Finney
Flankers: D Rowlands, D O'Grady, M Dobson, M Kenrick, L Bannon, H Greenwood
No. 8: A Macfarlane, A Gallagher

MOST CAPPED PLAYERS

including British Lions Appearances
E Evans, Captain, 30
S Smith, Captain, 28
C Davy, Wales Captain & 2 Lions Tours, 28
P Stagg, Scotland, 26
J Roberts, 1 Lions Tour, 19
W Wooler, Wales Captain, 18

LEADING APPEARANCES FOR CLUB DURING SEASON 1992-93

S Diamond, 30
D Erskine, 29
K Young, 28
M Whitcombe, 27

LEADING SCORERS

P Jee, Fly Half 166
P Turner, Fly Half, 116
K Young, Wing, 55 (11T)
J Malinder, Full Back, 40 (8T)

ADDITIONAL RESULTS 1992-93

No	Date	Opponents	Venue	Result
1	Sep 5	Orrell	A	W14-8
2	Sep 12	Gloucester	A	L11-17
3	Oct 17	Saracens	H	W19-13
4	Dec 2	Loughborough Uni	H	W38-12
5	Dec 5	Kendal	H	W37-6
6	Dec 19	Sheffield	H	W34-10
7	Jan 2	Bath	A	L6-26
8	Jan 16	Orrell	H	W24-10
9	Jan 23	Leeds	A	W24-5
10	Jan 30	Gloucester	H	W19-17
11	Feb 6	Vale-of-Lune	A	W63-5
12	Feb 13	L. Scottish	H	W55-17
13	Feb 20	Wasps	A	L10-48
14	Feb 27	Fylde	H	W40-18
15	Mar 6	W. Hartlepool	A	W27-23
16	Mar 20	Harwick	A	W21-0
17	Apr 10	Liverpool	H	W35-0
18	Apr 17	Leicester	A	L8-43

CLUB PLAYING RECORD 1992-93 SEASON

National Division: Two
Final League Position at end 1992/93 Season: 5th
League Playing Record: P 12, W 7, D 1, L 4,
Pts F 237, Pts A 102
Season Playing Record (including League matches/Pilkington cup etc): P 33, W 23, D 1, L 9, Pts F 754, Pts A 419

SALE FC

Club Details
Colours: Royal blue & white hoops.
Change of Colours: Red & white hoops.
Date Founded: 1861.
Membership: Total 680, Full 680, Junior/Youth/Minis 30.
Membership Fees: Full £26.50, Junior/Youth/Minis £13.
Number of Teams: Senior 4.
Programme Advertising Rates: Full £180, Half £90.

Ground Details
Ground Address: Hewyood Road, Brooklands, Sale, Cheshire, M33 3WB.
Telephone: 061 993 6348.
Directions: Brooklands Railway Station Manchester/Altrincham line, 500 yards.
Capacity: 4,000 (restricted to 3,000), Seated 500, Standing 3,500.
Ticket Prices: Adults £4, OAP/Child/Student £1.50.
Clubhouse Facilities: Two bars, large function room, 3 committee rooms.
Training Nights: Tuesday & Thursday.

Phil Jee takes on the LSH full back (April '93)   *Photo: Peter Barton*

SALE FC

COURAGE LEAGUE RECORDS

HIGHEST SCORE : 51 V Fylde (51-3) 19-9-92 home CL2
LARGEST WINNING MARGIN : 48 As above
HIGHEST SCORE AGAINST : 66 v Harlequins (6-66) 23-4-88 Away CL1
LARGEST LOSING MARGIN : 6O As above
DRAWN MATCHES : 4
CLEAN SHEETS : 3
FAILED TO SCORE : 3

INDIVIDUAL SCORING RECORDS

IN A MATCH

Most Points: 21 Paul Turner v Fylde 19-9=92 Home CL2
Most Tries: 2 On 15 occasions by 9 players-most Jime Mallinder 4
Most Conversions: 6 Graham Jenion v Richmond 1O-9-88 Home CL2
Most Penalties: 5 David Pears v Headingley 19-11-88 Home CL2, v Gosforth
Most Drop Goals: 2 David Pears v Bedford 22-2-89 Home CL2

IN A SEASON

Most Points: 1O2 David Pears 1988-89 CL2
Most Tries: 5 Jeff Powell 199O-91 CL2 & Jim Mallinder 199O-91 & 1991-92
Most Conversions: 14 Richard Booth 199O-91 CL2
Most Penalties: 26 David Pears 1988-89 CL2
Most Drop Goals: 3 David Shufflebottom 199O-91 CL2

IN A CAREER

Most Points: 137 Richard Booth 1987-92
Most Tries: 14 Jim Mallinder1988-93
Most Conversions: 17 Richard Booth 1987-92
Most Penalties: 31 Richard Booth 1987-92
Most Drop Goals: 3 David Shufflebottom

SEASON BY SEASON LEADING SCORERS

	Most Points			Most Tries	
1987-88	49	Graham Jenion	3	Howard Fitto	
1988-89	1O2	David Pears	3	David Pears	
1989-9O	29	Graham Jension	4	Phil Stansfield	
199O-91	92	Richard Booth	5	Jeff Powell	
1991-92	79	Matthew Alexander	5	Jim Mallinder	
1992-93	63	Phil Jee	7	Mark Warr	

SARACENS FC

President: John Heggadon
Chairman: Bruce Claridge
Club Secretary: Barney Richards, 36 Stone Hall Road, Winchmore Hill, London N21 1LP. Tel: (H) 081 360 4061 Fax: (Club) 081 449 9101.
Fixtures Secretary: David Grammer, 75 Roundwood Lane, Harpenden, Herts, AL5 3EX. Tel: (H) 0582 762356.
Press Officer: Bill Edwards, 15 Brachore Court, 119 cockfosters Road, Barnet, Herts EN4 0AE.
1993/94 1XV Captain: Brian Davies
1993/94 1XV Coach: John Davies, Mark Evans (1st XV)

Review of the Season

Unfortunately the season was not as successful as the previous year, a single score being the difference between victory and defeat in at least four games and the final result relegation to the Second Division.

The first league match was at home to Rugby and although won 14-9 the scoreline should have been much more decisive. The following week the club travelled to Northampton and showed vastly improved form coming strongly from behind only to lose 17-21. A similar trend of narrow defeats continued with losses to Orrell and Bristol both by single scores when both matches could have been won.

Further defeats followed from Harlequins, Leicester and Gloucester. The New Year failed to reverse the trend losing 9-13 to Wasps. Better results followed however with victories away to West Hartlepool 1O-3 and at home to London Scottish 41-7. However the game which could have meant survival in the First Division against London Irish was lost 9-1O, prop Stuart Wilson being held-up on the line in what was literally the last second.

The ability of the club to play fine rugby in the best company was amply demonstrated when they led the champions Bath 13-11 before finally losing 13-19 in the last match.

Despite relegation to the Second Division, it is hoped that the continued coaching of John Davies and Mark Evans, the captaincy of Brian Davies and the skills of John Buckton at centre allied to their strong youth development policy will enable this apparently unfashionable yet successful club to regain their status as well as the new ground and facilities so desperately needed and deserved.

Saracens FC 1992-93 Insets: Anthony Diprose, Steve Ravenscroft, Chris Tarbuck, Andy Lee, Darren O'Leary, Ben Rudling, Eric Peters. Back row: Bruce Millar (Chair of Selection), Dan Dooley, Gary Clarke, Barry Crawley, Lee Adamson, John Buckton, Mark Langley, Gregg Botterman, Martin Cass, Mark Burrows, Lee Bywater. Front row: John Davies (Club Coach), Steve Reed, Justyn Cassell, Brian Davies (Capt.), Richard Andrews, Stuart Wilson, Andy Tunningley, Gareth Hughes, Mark Evans (1st XV Coach) Bim Downes (Team Manager)
Photo: John Townsend

SARACENS FC

COURAGE CLUBS CHAMPIONSHIP
NATIONAL DIVISION ONE 1992-93

No	Date	Opponents	Venue	Result	Point Scorers
1	Sep 19	Rugby	H	W14-9	Crawley (T) Rudling (3P)
2	Sep 26	Northampton	A	L17-21	Reed (T) Rudling (3P)(DG)
3	Oct 3	Orrell	H	L6-9	Rudling (2P)
4	Oct 10	Bristol	A	L7-12	Cassell (T) Rudling (C)
5	Oct 24	Harlequins	H	L3-18	Rudling (P)
6	Oct 31	Leicester	A	L3-13	Rudling (P)
7	Nov 21	Gloucester	A	L5-19	O'Leary (T)
8	Jan 9	Wasps	H	L9-13	Rudling (3P)
9	Feb 13	W Hartlepool	A	W10-3	O'Leary (T) Crawley (T)
10	Mar 13	L Scottish	H	W41-17	Wilson (T) Adamson (T) Dooley (T) Crawley (T) O'Leary (T) Buckton (T) Tunningley (4C)(P)
11	Mar 27	Free	Free	Free	Free
12	Apr 3	L Irish	A	L9-10	Tunningley (2P) Hughes (DG)
13	Apr 24	Bath	H	L13-19	Davies (T) Tunningley (C) Hughes (2DG)

ADDITIONAL RESULTS 1992-93

No	Date	Opponents	Venue	Result
1	Sep 1	Munster	A	D13-13
2	Sep 5	Cork Constitution	A	L3-9
3	Sep 12	Wakefield	H	W10-8
4	Sep 30	Loughborough Stds	H	W38-3
5	Oct 14	West London Inst	A	L16-26
6	Oct 17	Sale	A	L13-19
7	Nov 7	Maesteg	H	W27-3
8	Nov 28	Bristol (PC3)	H	W20-15
9	Dec 5	Exeter	H	W34-17
10	Dec 12	Rosslyn Park	H	W20-3
11	Dec 19	Morley	H	W36-7
12	Jan 2	Richmond	A	L5-14
13	Jan 16	Harlequins	A	D17-17
14	Jan 23	Wasps (PC4)	A	L17-18
15	Jan 30	L Welsh	H	W36-22
16	Feb 7	Met. Police	A	W42-0
17	Feb 20	Mosel;ey	H	L24-41
18	Feb 27	Bedford	H	W20-11
19	Mar 7	Blackheath	A	W49-15
20	Mar 20	Orrell	A	L3-31
21	Mar 27	Waterloo	A	W32-27
22	Apr 10	Bedford	A	L23-55
23	Apr 17	L. Scottish	A	W47-7

MOST CAPPED PLAYERS
including British Lions Appearances
V S J Harding, 6, J H Steeds, 5
G A Sherriff, J Buckton, 3
J Leonard, 2

LEADING APPEARANCES FOR CLUB DURING SEASON 1992-93
M Langley, 29
R Andrews, B Davies, 28
S Wilson, 27
L Adamson, D Dooley, 26

LEADING SCORERS
G Hughes, Fly Half, 104
B Rudcing, Fly Half, 92
A Tunningley, Full Back, 61
S Ravenscroft, Centre, 45
B Davies, Scrum Half, 35
S Reed, Wing, 35

PLAYING SQUAD 1992-93
Full Backs: C Doseet, A Tunningley
Wings: P Butler, M Cass, M Gregory, P Hughes, M Kemp
Centres: J Buckton, D Dooley, S Ravenscroft
Fly Half: G Hughes, B Rudling, A Lee
Scrum Half: B Davies, J Jenkins
Props: R Andrews, R James, S Wilson, C Wright
Hookers: G Botterman, A Clark, J Locke
Second Row: L Adamson, S Kimberley, M Langley, M Burrow
Flankers: J Cassell, G Clark, A Mcphersn, C Tarbuck, J Green
No. 8: B Crawley, A Diprose, E Peters

150

SARACENS FC

MATCH BY MATCH PLAYERS BY POSITION

Dossett	Gregory	Buckton	Dooley	Reed	Rudling	Davies	Andrews	Botterman	Wilson	Langley	Adamson	Tarbuck	Cassell	Crawley	O'Leary	Diprose	Ravenscroft	Tunningley	Locke	Hughes	Clark	Dooley
15	14	13	12	11	10	9	1	2	3	4	5	6	7	8								
15		13	12	11	10	9	1	2	3	4	5	6	7	8	14							
15	11	13	12		10	9	1	2	3	4	5	6	7		14	8						
15	14	13	12	11	10	9	1	2	3	4	5	6	7			8						
15			12	11	10	9	1	2	3	4	5	6	7		14	8	13					
15			12	11	10	9	1	2	3	4	5	6	8	7	14		13					
		13	12	11	10	9	1		3	4	5	6	7	8	14				15	2		
		13	12	11	10	9	1	2	3	4	5	6	7	8	14				15			
		13	12	11		9	3	2	1	4	5	6	7	8	14				15	10		
		13	12	11		9	1	2	3	4	5	6	7	8	14				15	10		
	F	R	E	E			F	R	E	E			F	R	E	E			F	R	E	E
				12	14	9	1	2	3	4	5	6	7	8	11			13	15	10	R	
				11		9	1	2	3	4	5	6	7	8	14	R		13	15	10		12

CLUB PLAYING RECORD 1992-93 SEASON

National Division: One

League Playing Record: P 12, W 3, D 0, L 9, Pts F 137, Pts A 180

Season Playing Record (including League matches/Pilkington cup etc): P 36, W 17, D 2, L 17, Pts F 719, Pts A 580

REPRESENTATIVE HONOURS 1992/93

England Students: C Tarbuck, D O'Leary, E Peters, A Diprose, A Lee

England Universities: A Dalwood

England Under 21s: A Diprose, A O'Leary

England Colts: A Bailey

England Under 18s: W Smith

Barbarians: L Adamson (3)

Cambridge Blue: E Peters (Captain)

London Division: G Botterman, J Cassell, J Buckton, D O'Leary

London Under 21s: M Kemp, T Ellis, E O'Herlihy

Irish Exiles: D Dooley

Anglo Scottish Under 21s: M Kemp

Anglo Welsh Under 21s: J Edwards, G Crispin

Middlesex County: L Adamson, G Botterman, A Lee, C Tarbuch, S Wilson

Hertfordshire County: A Dalwood

Kent County: A Clark, G Hughes

Surrey County: R Castleton

England Womens: Karen Almond (Capt), Annie Cole, Emma Mitchell, Jane Mitchell, Janis Ross, Genevieve Shore

Scotland Womens: Michelle Cave

Wales Womens: Liza Burgess (Capt)

Club Details

Colours: Black shirts, black shorts, red socks.

Change of Colours: Black, white & red striped shirts, black shorts, red socks.

Nickname: Sarries.

Date Founded: 1876.

Membership: Total 1,500, Full 1,200, Junior/Youth/Minis 300.

Membership Fees: Full £24, Junior/Youth/Minis £15.

Number of Teams: Senior 7, Junior 11.

Programme Advertising Rates: Full £400, Half £250, Qtr £150.

Ground Details

Ground Address: Bramley Sports Ground, Chase Side, Southgate, London N14 4AB.

Telephone: 081 449 3770/8662.

Fax: 081 449 9101.

Directions: Junction 24 of M25, A111 to Cockfosters. Ground on left past first roundabout.

Capacity: Total 2,300, Seated 300, Standing 2,000.

Ticket Prices: Adults £6, Junior/Youth/Minis Nil.

Clubhouse Facilities: Bar, tea bar.

Training Nights: Every night 7.00pm.

SARACENS FC

COURAGE LEAGUE RECORDS

HIGHEST SCORE : 50 v Bedford (50-10) 19-11-88 Home CL2
LARGEST WINNING MARGIN : 40 As above
HIGHEST SCORE AGAINST : 49 v Bath (6-49) 27-4-91 Home CL1
LARGEST LOSING MARGIN : 43 As above
DRAWN MATCHES : 4
CLEAN SHEETS : 1
FAILED TO SCORE : 1

INDIVIDUAL SCORING RECORDS
IN A MATCH

Most Points: 24 Andy Kennedy v Northampton 12-11-88 Away CL2
Most Tries: 3 Laurie Smith v Gosforth 22-4-89 Away CL2
Most Conversions: 5 Nick Holmes v Blackheath 23-3-88 Away CL2, v London Scot 23-4-88 Home CL2,
Andy Kennedy v Bedford 19-11-88 Home CL2 v Moseley 28-10-89 Home CL1
Most Penalties: 5 Andy Kennedy v Richmond 11-3-89 Home CL2, v London Scot 8-4-89 Home CL2
Most Drop Goals: 2 Andy Lee v Wasps 22-2-92 Away CL1, Ben Rudling v London Irish 11-4-92 Home CL1,
Gareth Hughes v Bath 24-4-93 Home CL1

IN A SEASON

Most Points: 138 Andy Kennedy 1988-89 CL2
Most Tries: 10 Dave McLagen 1987-88 CL2
Most Conversions: 14 Andy Kennedy 1988-89 CL2
Most Penalties: 30 Andy Kennedy 1988-89 CL2
Most Drop Goals: 4 Ben Rudling 1991-92 CL1

IN A CAREER

Most Points: 213 Ben Rudling 1987-93
Most Tries: 17 Dave McLagen 1987-89
Most Conversions: 27 Andy Kennedy 1987-90
Most Penalties: 45 Ben Rudling 1987-93
Most Drop Goals: 6 Ben Rudling 1987-93

SEASON BY SEASON LEADING SCORERS

	Most Points			Most Tries
1987-88	46	Nick Holmes	10	Dave McLagen
1988-89	138	Andy Kennedy	7	Dave McLagen
1989-90	50	Andy Kennedy	4	Ben Clarke
1990-91	36	Ben Rudling	4	Ben Clarke
1991-92	91	Ben Rudling	4	Martin Gregory
1992-93	43	Ben Rudling	3	Barry Crawley

WAKEFIELD RFC

President: John Waind
Chairman: Nigel Foster
Club Secretary: Jim Coulson, 39 Melbourne Road, St Johns, Wakefield, WF1 2RL. Tel (H) 0924 373586 (W) 0924 374801 Fax: (W) 0924 374801.
Fixtures Secretary: W E Halstead, 84 Whitcliffe Road, Cleckheaton, West Yorkshire, BD19 3DR. Tel: 0274 872710.
Press Officer: Jim Coulson, 39 Melbourne Road, St Johns, Wakefield, WF1 2RL.
1993/94 1XV Captain: Dave Scully
1993/94 1XV Coach: Jim Kilfoyle
Commercial Manager: Steve Bladen
Coaching Administrator: Mich Dearman
Colts Secretary: Cyril Edge

Review of the Season

With 7 clubs out of 13 to be relegated, 1992-93 was always going to be a difficult season. When you add to this, 27 different players used in league games of which 7 were playing at this level for the first time, an even more perilous season could be envisaged. With 5 of this squad being 21 or under, confidence was high for the future if membership of Division 2 could be secured. Therefore 3rd place represented an excellent base for our continuing ascent towards Division 1.

Without doubt the highlights of our league campaign were 14-3 victory at Moseley and the astonishing 20-17 win at eventual league winners Newcastle Gosforth. This result was made more remarkable by the fact we were 17-0 down with 20 minutes to go. One other notable result was our 6-5 win at Wasps, to take their unbeaten home record on a day when both sides were hit by Division and County Calls.

There is undoubted talent at College Grove, nowhere more in evidence than the 9 players in Yorkshire's Squad throughout the County season culminating in the final at Twickenham. The club were well represented at North level with Dave Scully and Bryan Barley playing and Mich Dearman Asst. Coach.

For Dave Scully, his season was completed by his magnificent performances for England in winning the World sevens at Murrayfield and the award of "Famous Grouse Moment of the Tournament".

Our strength in depth with young players is evidenced by the selection of Richard Bramley (Capt), Diccon Edwards, Jonathan Griffiths, Johnathon Sleightholme and Tim Stimpson to go to Australia in June/July with England U21. We are the only club in the country to have more than 2 players in the 30 man squad.

Bryan Barley's contribution to the game at both club and representative level is enormous and his efforts have brought prestige and honour to both him and Wakefield RFC. The end of the season saw Bryan decide to step aside to allow the many promising youngster their opportunity to progress. His experience, skills and knowledge are to be helping out at Sandal next season and everybody at Wakefield R F C wishes him will for the future.

With such accomplished senior players, very exciting youngsters and one of the best coaching set-ups in the North the future of rugby at Wakefield is an exciting one.

Wakefield RFC 1992-93

WAKEFIELD RFC

ADDITIONAL RESULTS 1992-93

No	Date	Opponents	Venue	Result
1	Sep 5	Boroughmuir	H	W42-9
2	Sep 8	Ionian	H	W19-0
3	Sep 12	Saracens	A	L8-10
4	Sep 19	Blackheath	A	D9-9
5	Sep 26	Bedford	H	W27-3
6	SDOct 3	Moseley	A	W14-3
7	Oct 10	Sale	H	L6-12
8	Oct 17	Sheffield	H	W30-8
9	Oct 24	Waterloo	A	L11-22
10	Oct 31	Nottingham	H	W22-9
11	Nov 7	Bradford & Bingley	H	W31-9
12	Nov 9	Griqualand West	H	W54-3
13	Nov 14	W Hartlepool	A	L15-48
14	Nov 21	Coventry	H	W8-0
15	Nov 28	Richmond	A	W25-22
16	Dec 5	Otley	H	W21-11
17	Dec 12	L St Helens	H	W50-17
18	Dec 19	Wasps	A	W6-5
19	Jan 2	Vale of Lune	A	W65-0
20	Jan 9	New/Gosforth	A	W20-17
21	Jan 16	Coventry	A	L13-19
22	Jan 23	Harlequins	A	L18-47
23	Jan 30	Boroughmuir	H	W28-22
24	Feb 6	Bradford & Bingley	H	W26-13
25	Feb 13	Morley	H	W16-15
26	Feb 27	Rugby	A	L3-15
27	Mar 6	Orrell	H	L28-39
28	Mar 20	Gala	H	W49-31
29	Mar 27	Richmond	A	L6-11
30	Apr 3	Rosslyn Park	H	W20-15
31	Apr 10	Morley	A	W34-17
32	Apr 24	Fylde	A	W27-7

CLUB PLAYING RECORD 1992-93 SEASON

National Division: Two
Final League Position at end 1992/93 Season: 3rd
League Playing Record:
P 12, W 8, D 1, L 3, Pts F 186, Pts A 123
Season Playing Record (including League matches/Pilkington cup etc):
P 32, W 22, D 1, L 9, Pts F 751, Pts A 468

COMPETITIONS WON DURING SEASON 1992-93

Scarborough 7s winners

PLAYING SQUAD 1992-93

Full Backs: R Thompson, T Stimpson, S Cowling
Wings: J Sleightholm, K Morley, M Harrison,
    D Edge, D Holdsworth, T Stimpson
Centres: A Atkinson, B Barley, D Edwards,
    A Metcalfe, C Harris, P Maynard
Fly Half: R Liley, S Townend, S Cowling
Scrum Half: D Scully, M Cawthorne
Props: D Allott, R Burman, A Day, M Vincent
Hookers: T Garnett, S Cruise, S Pennington
Second Row: I Carroll, P Stewart, P Bramley,
    A Rawes, J Mortimer
Flankers: D Cooper, J Griffiths, M Price,
    M Sowerby, M Rawnsley, I Hill
No. 8: M Rawnsley, M Sowerby, R Bramley, M Price

MOST CAPPED PLAYERS

including British Lions Appearances)
M Harrison, 15 (7 as England Captain), 1985-88
B Barley, 7, 1984,1986,1988

LEADING APPEARANCES FOR CLUB

S Townend, 416, M Rawnsley, 335
B Barley, 306, M Harrison, 294
D Scully, 193, A Atkinson, 151

LEADING SCORERS

R Liley, Fly Half, 321
K Morley, Winger, 70 (14T Top tryscorer)
A Atkinson, Centre, 65
R Thompson, Full Back, 60
J Slightholm, Winger, 50 (10T in 14 appearances)

REPRESENTATIVE HONOURS 1992-93

England 7s: D Scully
England "B" Tour to New Zealand: D Scully
England XV: R F Oakes, T Garnet
England U21: R Bramley (capt), D Edwards,
J Sleightholme, T Stimpson, J Griffiths
England Students: D Edwards, J Sleightholme,
T Stimpson
England Students to World Cup in Italy:
R Bramley, D Edwards, J Sleightholme, S Whiteside
Barbarians: J Sleightholme
North Division: D Scully, B Barley, J Sleightholme
North Tour to Zimbabwe/Namibia: R Bramley,
B Barley, J Sleightholme
North U21: R Bramley, J Sleightholme
Yorkshire: A Atkinson, I Carroll, D Edwards,
T Garnett, R Liley, J Sleightholme, R Thompson,
M Vincent, D Scully
Yorkshire U21: J Griffiths, M Cawthorne
Yorkshire U17: N Barratt

WAKEFIELD RFC

Club Details

Colours: Black & gold.
Change of Colours: All black or red.
Nickname: Field.
Date Founded: 1901.
Membership: Total 376, Full 290, Junior/Youth/Minis 20.
Membership Fees: Full £50, Junior/Youth/Minis £10/£8/£5, Playing £25, Ladies £22.50.
Number of Teams: Senior 4, Junior 1.
Programme Advertising Rates: Full £160, Half £90.

Ground Details

Ground Address: College Grove, Eastmoor Road, Wakefield, WF1 3RR.
Telephone: 0924 374801. **Fax:** 0924 374801.
Directions: From M1 (north or south) Exit 41, A650 into Wakefield (city centre sign). Turn left at Queen Elizabeth Grammar School, Westfield Road, ground in front 250 yds. From M62 (east or west) Exit 30, A642 into Waefield. Turn right at traffic lights immediately after Pinderfields Hospital. Ground on left.
Capacity: Total 4,000, Seated 500, Standing 3,500.
Ticket Prices: Adults £4, OAP/Child £2.
Clubhouse Facilities: Lounge & large sports room, both with bars and after-match dining. New Sponsors Pavilion.
Training Nights: Mon & Thur, Colts Wed nights.

Wakefield Front Row

Photo: Joe McCabe

WAKEFIELD RFC

COURAGE LEAGUE RECORDS

HIGHEST SCORE : 70 v Metropolitan Police (70-0) 24-9-98 Home CL3
LARGEST WINNING MARGIN : 70 As above
HIGHEST SCORE AGAINST : 37 v Sale (37-3) 7-12-91 Away CL2
LARGEST LOSING MARGIN : 34 As above
DRAWN MATCHES : 2
CLEAN SHEETS : 4
FAILED TO SCORE : 1

INDIVIDUAL SCORING RECORDS
IN A MATCH
Most Points: 22 Andy Atkinson v Met Police 24-9-88 Home CL3
Most Tries: 3 Simon Cowling v Birmingham 31-10-87 Away CL3, v Nuneaton 5-12-87 Home CL3, Andy Holloway v Morley 12-3-88 Away CL3, Mike Harrison v Met Police 24-9-88 Home CL3, v London Irish 28-4-90 Home CL3, Andy Atkinson v Met Police 24-9-88 Home CL3, Mike Murtagh v Askeans 11-11-89 Home CL3, Jon Sleightholme v Blackheath 4-1-92 Home CL2
Most Conversions: 7 Ray Adamson v Birmingham 31-10-87 Away CL3
Most Penalties: 6 Ray Adamson v Vale of Lune 27-2-88 CL2
Most Drop Goals: 1 Steve Townend v Nuneaton 18-11-89 Away CL3, v Rugby 6-10-90 Away CL3, Robert Liley v Bedford 26-9-92 Home CL2, v Rosslyn Park 3-4-93 Home CL2

IN A SEASON
Most Points: 105 Ray Adamson 1987-88 CL3
Most Tries: 8 Simon Cowling 1987-88 CL3, Dave Scully 1988-89 CL3, Jon Sleightholme 1991-92 CL2
Most Conversions: 19 Ray Adamson 1987-88 CL3
Most Penalties: 24 Robert Liley 1992-93 CL2
Most Drop Goals: 2 Robert Liley 1992-93 CL2

IN A CAREER
Most Points: 223 Andy Atkinson 1987-93
Most Tries: 25 David Scully 1987-93
Most Conversions: 36 Ray Adamson 1987-90
Most Penalties: 39 Andy Atkinson 1987-93
Most Drop Goals: 2 Steve Townend 1987-93, Robert Liley 1991-93

SEASON BY SEASON LEADING SCORERS

	Most Points			Most Tries
1987-88	105	Ray Adamson	8	Simon Cowling
1988-89	69	Andy Atkinson	8	David Scully
1989-90	31	Ray Adamson	7	Mike Murtagh Mike Harrison
1990-91	89	Andy Atkinson	4	Raz Bowers David Scully
1991-92	32	Robert Liley Jon Sleightholme	8	Jon Sleigholme
1992-93	101	Robert Liley	7	Jon Sleightholme

156

WATERLOO FC

President: Coplin Brennand
Chairman: Ray Wilson
Club Secretary: Keith Alderson, 66 St Michaels Road, Blundell Sands, Liverpool, L23 7UW, Tel: (H) 051 924 1168 (W) 051 924 1168
Fixtures Secretary: John Rimmer, 2 Chapel Meadow, Longton, Preston, PR4 5NR. Tel: 0772 614277
Press Officer: A Cove, 1 Wicks Green, Formby, Liverpool
1993/94 1XV Captain: P Hackett
1993/94 1XV Coach: M Briers
Director of Coaching: M Briers
Senior Coach: J Mostyn, G Jackson, J Hogan

Review of the Season

Having finished Third in Division Two last season and with the acquisition of several young promising newcomers such as Paul Grayson from Preston Grasshoppers, Steve Swindells and Stuart Beeley from Manchester and England Colt Tony Handley from De La Salle, the 1992-93 season offered to be full of potential and so it turned out. The highlight of the season was an impressive Pilkington Cup campaign which took the Club to the quarter finals. Although eventually losing to Harlequins, Waterloo produced impressive performances to defeat Bath 9-8 and Orrell 8-3.

Waterloo's cup exploits were not limited to the national competition. In their home county the team won the Lancashire Cup winning a close fought final against Liverpool St Helens.

In the League Division Two campaign Waterloo improved on last season's performance. Winning twelve and losing only two games the team finished at the top of the Second Division with the same points as Newcastle Gosforth, but unfortunately with an inferior points difference.

In terms of representative honours, Paul Grayson played for England "A" and Grayson. Austin Healey and Tony Handley all played for England Under 21. Gavin Fraser represented Scotland Under 21.

Waterloo FC 1992-93

WATERLOO FC

Club Details

Colours: Myrtle/Scarlet/White hoops
Change of Colours: Green
Date Founded: 1882
Membership: Total 500, Junior/Youth/Minis 150
Membership Fees: Full £47, Junior/Youth/Minis £13
Number of Teams: Senior 4, Junior 6
Programme Advertising Rates: £200 per page

Ground Details

Ground Address: The Pavilion, St Anthonys Road, Blundell Sands, Liverpool
Telephone: 051 924 4552
Directions: End of M57, follow signs for Crosby, Waterloo FC signposted to ground.
Capacity: Total 9,000, Seated 900, Standing 8,100.
Ticket Prices: Adult £2.50, Student/Junior/OAP/Child £1
Clubhouse Facilities: 2 bars, 2 hospitality lounges, gym, dining room
Training Nights: Monday, Tuesday & Thursday

CLUB PLAYING RECORD 1992-93 SEASON

National Division: Two
Final League Position at end 1992/93 Season: 2nd
League Playing Record: P 12, W 10, D -, L 2
Season Playing Record (including League matches/Pilkington cup etc): P 33, W 22, D -, L 11

COMPETITIONS WON DURING SEASON 1992-93
Lancashire Cup Winners

MOST CAPPED PLAYERS
including British Lions Appearances
Joe Periton, 14
H (Bert) Toft
Jack Heaton
Gordon Rimmer
Alan Ashcroft
Watcyn Thomas

LEADING APPEARANCES FOR CLUB DURING SEASON 1992-93
Nick Allott (Capt)
Paul Hackett
Steve Swindells

LEADING SCORERS 1992-93
Paul Grayson, Fly Half, 189

WATERLOO FC

COURAGE LEAGUE RECORDS

HIGHEST SCORE : 40 v Liverpool St H (40-12) 21-12-91 Home CL2
LARGEST WINNING MARGIN : 28 As above & v Blackheath (6-34) 25-4- 92
HIGHEST SCORE AGAINST : 39 v Leicester (15-39) 4-4-88 Away CL1,
London Irish (O-39) 27-10-90 Away CL2
LARGEST LOSING MARGIN : 39 As above
DRAWN MATCHES : 2
CLEAN SHEETS :
FAILED TO SCORE : 2

INDIVIDUAL SCORING RECORDS
IN A MATCH

Most Points: 22 Ian Aitchison v Blackheath 25-4-92 Away CL2
Most Tries: 2 Maurice Cotter v Sale 2-1-88 Home CL1, Ian Gibbons v Plymo 31-3-90 Away CL2,
Steve Bracegirdle v Rugby 23-2-91 Away, v Liverpool SH 21-12-91 Home CL2,
Austin Healey v Richmond 31-10- 92 CL2
Most Conversions: 4 Ian Aitchison v Liverpool SH 21-12-91 Home CL2
Most Penalties: 6 Ian Aitchison v Blackheath 25-4-92 Away CL2
Most Drop Goals: 2 Ian Aitchison v Gloucester 31-10-87 Home CL1, v Sale 2-1-88 Home CL1,
Ian Cropper v Sale 9-3-91 Home CL2, Paul Grayson v 13-3-93 Home CL2

IN A SEASON

Most Points: 126 Paul Grayson 1992-93 CL2
Most Tries: 8 Steve Bracegirdle 190-91 CL2
Most Conversions: 10 Ian Aitchison 1991-92 CL2
Most Penalties: 29 Paul Grayson 1992-93 CL2
Most Drop Goals: 6 Paul Grayson 1992-93 CL2

IN A CAREER

Most Points: 301 Ian Aitchison 1987-93
Most Tries: 14 Steve Bracegirdle 1990-93
Most Conversions: 22 Ian Aitchison 1987-93
Most Penalties: 76 Ian Aitchison 1987-93
Most Drop Goals: 7 Ian Aitchison 1987-93

SEASON BY SEASON LEADING SCORERS

	Most Points			**Most Tries**
1987-88	66	Ian Aitchison	4	Peter Cooley
1988-89	77	Ian Aitchison	4	Peter Cooley
1989-90	43	Richard Angell	5	Peter Cooley
1990-91	57	Ian Aitchison	8	Steve Bracegirdle
1991-92	92	Ian Aitchison	4	Gary Meredith
1992-93	126	Paul Grayson	3	Austin Healey

Austin Healey scores the only try of the match against Orrell — Pilkington Cup 4th Round, 22/1/93

Paul Hackett No 2 the 1992-93 Captain fights for the ball against Bath aided by the 1991-92 Captain Nick Allott, with Jason Ashcroft and Chris Saverimutto on hand, whilst Mark Beckett restrains Gareth Chilcott. Pilkington Cup 3rd Round, 28/11/92

WEST HARTLEPOOL RFC

President: Nev Brown
Chairman: Bob Bateman
Club Secretary: Tony Savage, 17 Greenbank Court, Hartlepool, Cleveland, TS26 0HH. Tel: (H) 0429 273187 (W) 0836 709652 Fax: (W) 0429 231263.
Fixtures Secretary: David Butcher, 55 Arncliffs Gardens, Hartlepool, Cleveland. Tel: (H) 0429 236886 (W) 0325 300616 Fax: (W) 0325 316007.
Press Officer: Ken Williams, 47 The Oval, Hartlepool, Cleveland. Tel: 0429 260572.
1993/94 1XV Captain: Paul Hodder
1993/94 1XV Coach: Dave Stubbs
Treasurer: Peter Olsen
Promotions and Sponsorship Officer: John Dixon-Barber

Reflections on the Season

Success in 1992-93 was never going to be easy in Division 1, particularly for a newly promoted club, which due to its own successful good rugby had spent but one season only in Division 2. In the end, survival into the newly constituted First Division proved to be just two great a task.

However, disappointing as that is, the season was not all gloom and despair. Good league wins at Gloucester and against Orrell were very satisfying — would that there had been fewer missed opportunities in other games, and thus more league victories to savour along with the many successes in non-league games. A creditable Pilkington Cup run to the Quarter-Final also brought its rewards.

Furthermore, we like to think that both individually and collectively we learned a good deal from our albeit brief First Division experience — we liked the taste and are hungry and determined to return early for more of it.

CLUB PLAYING RECORD 1992-93 SEASON

National Division: One
Final League Position at end 1992/93 Season: 12th
League Playing Record: P 12, W 3, D 0, L 9, Pts F 149, Pts A 263
Season Playing Record (including League matches/Pilkington cup etc): P 32, W 21, D 0, L 11, Pts F 851, Pts A 454

Craig Lee with ball, supported by Alan Brown, Paul Hodder, Shaun Cassidy, Paul Evans, John Dixon

WEST HARTLEPOOL RFC

COURAGE CLUBS CHAMPIONSHIP
NATIONAL DIVISION ONE 1992-93

No	Date	Opponents	Venue	Result	Point Scorers
1	Sep 19	Wasps	H	L6-19	Stabler (2P)
2	Sep 26	Bristol	A	L11-19	Brown (T) Stabler (2P)
3	Oct 3	Harlequins	H	L9-12	Stabler (3P)
4	Oct 10	Leicester	A	L8-21	O Evans (T) Stabler (P)
5	Oct 24	Rugby	H	L5-6	Stabler (T)
6	Oct 31	Gloucester	A	W21-6	Brown (T) Lee (T) Stabler (C)(3P)
7	Nov 21	Free	Free	Free	Free
8	Jan 9	L Scottish	A	W15-10	Cook (T) Whitelock (T) Stabler (P)(T)
9	Feb 13	Saracens	A	L3-10	Stabler (P)
10	Mar 13	L Irish	A	L13-25	Mitchell (T) Stabler (C)(2P)
11	Mar 27	Bath	H	L10-38	Havery (T) Stabler (P)(C)
12	Apr 3	Northampton	H	L9-55	Stabler (3P)
13	Apr 24	Orrell	H	W39-15	Evans (T) Cooke (T) Stabler (T) Brown (PT) Stabler (4C)(2P)

ADDITIONAL RESULTS 1992-93

No	Date	Opponents	Venue	Result
1	Sep 2	Middlesbrough	H	W31-0
2	Sep 5	Otley	H	W34-16
3	Sep 5	Hartlepool	A	W45-3
4	Sep 9	Gateshead Fell	H	W66-0
5	Sep 12	Liverpool St Helens	H	W56-0
6	Oct 17	Durham City	A	W36-29
7	Nov 14	Wakefield	H	W48-15
8	Nov 21	Northern	A	W41-5
9	Nov 28	L Irish	H	W13-8
10	Dec 5	Preston Grasshoppers	H	W25-0
11	Dec 26	Hartlepool Rovers	A	W49-5
12	Dec 28	Stockton	H	W24,13
13	Jan 23	Morley	H	W21-3
14	Jan 30	Rotherham	A	W42028
15	Feb 6	Fylde	H	W29-13
16	Feb 20	Bedford	H	W27-14
17	Feb 27	Wasps	H	L9-15
18	Mar 6	Sale	H	L23-27
19	Mar 20	Boroughmuir	H	W55-15
20	Apr 10	Leeds	A	W28-9

COMPETITIONS WON DURING SEASON 1992-93

Pilkington Cup Qtr Finals
Secon XV & Colts Durham County Cup winners

MOST CAPPED PLAYERS

including British Lions Appearances
C D Arnold, 16
J T Taylor, 11

LEADING SCORERS

J Stabler, Stand Off, 279
D Cooke, Winger, G Evans, Winger, 60
A Brown, Flanker, 55
M Watson, No 8, 55
C Lee, Centre, 40

PLAYING SQUAD 1992-93

Full Backs: K Oliphant
Wings: O Evans, D Cooke, G Evans, B Ridley
Centres: C Lee, P Hoddes, A Elwine
Fly Half: J Stables
Scrum Half: J Wrigley, S Havery
Props: P Lancaster, P Whitelock, D Rusby, A Jackson
Hookers: S Mitchell, S Whitehead
Lock: J Dixon, K Westgarth, D Ince
Flankers: D Blyth, A Brown, D Mitchell
No. 8: P Evans, M Watson

WEST HARTLEPOOL RFC

MATCH BY MATCH PLAYERS BY POSITION

Ouphant	O Evans	Hodder	Lee	Cooke Stabler	Wrigley	Lancaster	S Mitchell	Whitelock	Dixon	Westgarth	Blythe	Brown	P Evans	D Mitchell	Harvery	Lancaster	Watson	Peacock	Rusby	Havery	D Mitchell	Westgarth
15	14	13	12	11	10	9	1	2	3	4	5	6	7	8								
15	14	12	13	11	10	9	1	2	3	4	5	6	7	8								
15	14	13	12	11	10	9	1	2	3	4	5	6	7	8								
15	14	12	13	11	10	9	1	2	3	4	5	6	7	8								
15	14	12	13	11	10	9	1	2	3	4	5	6	8	7	R							
15	14	12	13	11	10	9	1	2	3	4	5	6	7	8								
F	R	E	E				F	R	E	E		F	R	E	E			F	R	E	E	
15	11	12	13	14	10		1	2	3	4	5	6	7	8	9							
15	14	12	13	11	10	9	1	2	3	4	5	6	7	8								
15	14	12	13	11	10			2	3	4	5	6	7	8	9	1						
15	14	12	13	11	10			2	3	4	5	8	6		9	1	7					
15	14	12	13	11	10		1		3	4	5	7	6		9		8	2	R			
15	14	12	13	11	10		1		3	4		7	6				8	2		9	R	5

Club Details

Colours: Green/red/white hoop shirts, white shorts, green socks.
Change of Colours: Red shirts.
Nickname: West.
Date Founded: 1981.
Membership: Total 2,600, Full 700, Social 1,500, Junior/Youth/Minis 280.
Membership Fees: Full £17, Junior/Youth/Minis £7.
Number of Teams: Senior 4 + U21 Junior 7 + Minis.

Ground Details

Ground Address: Brierton Lane, Hartlepool, Cleveland TS25 5DR.
Telephone: 0429 272640 (Clubhouse) 0429 233149.
Fax: 0429 231263.
Directions: From A1 or A19 take the A689 to Hartlepool. Within a mile of first houses turn left into Brierton Lane. Ground 800 yds on left, immediately after hospital.
Capacity: Total 6,100, Seated 600, Standing 5,500.
Ticket Prices: Adults £4 league games.
Clubhouse Facilities: Lounge, Lounge Bar, Sponsors Lounges, Two Committee Rooms.
Training Nights: Tues & Thurs (Senior), Mon 7 Wed (Colts), Sunday (Minis).

WEST HARTLEPOOL RFC

COURAGE LEAGUE RECORDS

HIGHEST SCORE : 47 v Broughton Park (47-4) 09-03-91 Home CL3
LARGEST WINNING MARGIN : 43 As above
HIGHEST SCORE AGAINST : 55 v Northampton (9-55) 03-04-93 Away CL1
LARGEST LOSING MARGIN : 46 As above
DRAWN MATCHES : 4
CLEAN SHEETS : 3
FAILED TO SCORE : O
MOST LEAGUE APPEARANCES:
BY A FORWARD : 57 Phil Lancaster
BY A BACK : 61 John Stabler

INDIVIDUAL SCORING RECORDS

IN A MATCH

Most Points: 23 John Stabler v Broughton Park 09-03-91 Home CL3
Most Tries: 3 Owain Evans v Nuneaton 23-04-88 Home CL3,
Peter Robinson v Vale of Lune 02-03-91 Away CL3, John Wrigley v Moseley 14-12-91 Home CL2
Most Conversions: 6 John Stabler v Broughton Park 09-03-91 Away CL3
Most Penalties: 6 John Stabler v Met Police 06-01-88 Away CL3
Most Drop Goals: 2 Kevin Oliphant v Vale of Lune 07-11-88 Away CL3,
John Stabler v Sheffield 19-11-88 Home CL3

IN A SEASON

Most Points: 118 John Stabler 1991-92 CL3
Most Tries: 9 John Wrigley 1990-91 CL3
Most Conversions: 19 John Stabler 1990-91 CL3
Most Penalties: 26 John Stabler 1991-92 CL2
Most Drop Goals: 3 John Stabler 1988-89 CL3

IN A CAREER

Most Points: 466 John Stabler 1987-93
Most Tries: 22 Dave Cooke 1987-93
Most Conversions: 63 John Stabler 1987-93
Most Penalties: 98 John Stabler 1987-93
Most Drop Goals: 6 John Stabler 1987-93

SEASON BY SEASON LEADING SCORERS

	Most Points			**Most Tries**
1987-88	83	John Stabler	6	Owain Evans
1988-89	6O	John Stabler	8	Dave Cooke
1989-9O	65	Gary Armstrong	5	Dave Cooke
199O-91	87	John Stabler	9	John Wrighley
1991-92	118	John Stabler	7	John Wrighley
1992-93	89	John Stabler	3	Alan Brown

NATIONAL LEAGUE THREE

RESULTS AND LEAGUE TABLES
1987-1993
Pages 166-168

MEMBER CLUBS
1993-94

NATIONAL LEAGUE THREE RESULTS

1987-88

		1	2	3	4	5	6	7	8	9	10	11	12
1	Birmingham					3-22		3-3	3-46	,15-42	3-50	6-43	
2	Exeter	32-0				4-3			9-18	12-12		19-29	6-18
3	Fylde	68-7	48-13								12-14	3-23	12-17
4	Maldston	18-3	23-9	16-18		15-0	9-3				14-16		
5	Metropolitan Police		9-23	9-6		26-12			25-18			6-7	6-22
6	Morley	23-3	10-10	12-38						7-12		7-38	
7	Nuneaton		9-11	13-18		7-12	21-6		9-7				
8	Plymouth Albion			33-17	45-11		24-0			43-7		16- 12	
9	Sheffield	34-0		13-12	10-3	13-6		15-9			8-3		
10	Vale of Lune		27-3			13-6	25-19	6-3	13-16				12-21
11	Wakefield				27-9			33-3		41-0	32-12		16-12
12	West Hartlepool				12-10		23-3	37-14	19-10	25-10			

1988-89

		1	2	3	4	5	6	7	8	9	10	11	12
1	Askeans		6-20			21-10		12-28				10-23	10-10
2	Exeter					14-6	12-25	6-21		19-12	12-26		
3	Fylde	13-6	16-14		34-7				12-17	9-24			18-13
4	Maidstone	12-15	0-21			10-27	11-28					6-23	
5	Metropolitan Police			17-15			32-13		6-36		13-7		10-25
6	Nuneaton	12-19		24-10				3-21	15-18		16-6		22-18
7	Plymouth Albion				43-6	20-6	57-3			34-13		21-12	20-12
8	Rugby	41-3	23-3		44-3			10-26			28-9	14-13	
9	Sheffield	17-27			28-3	10-6	25-16		6-22		9-9		
10	Vale of Lune	29-12		6-0	12-7			6-20				4-19	
11	Wakefield		29-18	10-6		70-0	42-4			25-22			
12	West Hartleypool		16-3		37-9				3-15	12-4	9-6	9- 16	

1989-90

		1	2	3	4	5	6	7	8	9	10	11	12
1	Askeans		19-11			29-28		12-19	20-9	16-26	25-21		
2	Exeter	30-3		22-17		15-7			9-7			18-13	15-15
3	Fylde				12-26		18-13	17-14			19-18	15-11	
4	London	31-6	16-7			18-14		36-0		34-3			
5	London Welsh		29-9				3-22	9-10					17-15
6	Lydney	7-10	16-6		16-0				18-13	7-9		7-9	
7	Nuneaton		27-14				19-15		11-18	16-14	7-9		
8	Roundbay			27-21	3-30				22-10	20-0			12-15
9	Sheffield		7-3	33-18	24-28							12-27	13- 10
10	Vale of Lune		25-10			9-0	21-20	24-10		7-28			6-16
11	Wakefield	40-14			4-10	24-10		,26-3		37-20		10-10	
12	West Hartlepool	25-6		10-12	3-9		28-6	28-4					

1990-91

		1	2	3	4	5	6	7	8	9	10	11	12	13
1	Askeans		29-6	9-10		19-7			9-9	22-10		9-9		
2	Broughton Park				10-4		9-12	3-0	11-15		13-11		6-7	
3	Clifton		25-6		28-3			9-4	9-15	17-22		18-16		
4	Exeter	13-7					9-3	28-3			13-3		14-12	18-18
5	Fylde		6-14	25-6	11-11				16-6	20-3		29-12		
6	Lydney	31-6		10-10		4-20					12-10		9-14	3-19
7	Metropolitan Police	3-21				6-20	13-15				17-12		24-18	8-12
8	Morley				22-6		19-7	11-17			30-3		33-3	10-9
9	Nuneaton		16-6		6-13		35-3	23-12	10-17			14-23		
10	Roundhay	23-4		34-7		7-7				10-6			22-13	9-21
11	Sheffield		13-21		16-28		24-16	16-23	18-23		23-3			
12	Vale of Lune	16-6		14-7		9-18				18-27		9-13		0-32
13	West Hartleypool	w/o	47-4	36-16		18-4				39-8		29-10		

1991-92

		1	2	3	4	5	6	7	8	9	10	11	12	13
1	Askeans				3-12			36-0		12-8	10-8	6-17	9-6	
2	Broughton Park	42-15		20-15		9-10			27-3		3-20			22-7
3	Clifton	48-7			21-3		42-3		26-9	16-10		29-9		
4	Exeter		13-0	16-10		9-16	26-13		25-18					15-15
5	Fylde	34-4						17-0		16-13	9-9	12-13	29-12	
6	Headingley	0-25	19-13	11-38		6-12			10-9					18-3
7	Lydney		3-17		21-15		9-16		22-4			7-18		13-19
8	Nuneaton	16-16		12-15		9-18				33-8	9-15		25-25	
9	Otley		23-16		3-9		19-12	34-4			119-9	15-10		
10	Redruth				10-16		13-6	15-6		21-16		6-9	13-3	
11	Richmond		20-18	16-15	16-16		28-13		43-6					57-3
12	Roundhay		9-9		13-31		25-12	28-3				3-50		18-5
13	Sheffield	12-6		16-23		4-22			13-9	22-10	17-15			

1992-93

		1	2	3	4	5	6	7	8	9	10	11	12
1	Askeans		23-16	6-18	6-24				8-6				8-45
2	Aspatria			24-8		16-21	13-12	10			42-20		15-32
3	Broughton Park					19-33	3-22	10-30		10-21	31-3		
4	Clifton	10-10		35-24		13-13					24-8		35-6
5	Exeter	P					21-18	28-33	16-11	15-8	20-9		
6	Havant	10-3			17-6			35-11	9-6	20-16		3-3	
7	Leeds	24-23	34-15		43-32				16-10	0-16		10-17	
8	Liverpool St. Helens		77-5	21-3	21-8	19-26							13-3
9	Otley	61-6	47-8		14-9				20-7			19-19	21-7
10	Plymouth Albion	20-23					3-35	22-27	6-12	16-28		13-20	
11	Redruth	23-13	24-6	10-5	13-5				26-11				11-20
12	Sheffield			12-5		15-6	8-9	12-0			48-11		

NATIONAL LEAGUE THREE TABLES

1987-88

	P	W	D	L	F	A	Pts
Wakefield	11	10	0	1	308	90	20
West Hartlepool	11	10	0	1	249	105	20
Plymouth A.	11	8	0	3	276	125	16
Sheffield	11	7	1	3	134	161	15
Vale of Lune	11	7	0	4	183	149	14
Fylde	11	6	0	5	269	170	142
Met. Police	11	5	0	6	130	128	10
Maidstone	11	4	0	7	134	162	8
Exeter	11	3	2	6	128	197	8
Nuneaton	11	2	1	8	94	157	5
Morley	11	1	1	9	109	235	3
Birmingham	11	0	1	10	46	381	1

1990-91

	P	W	D	L	F	A	Pts
West Hartlepool	12	10	1	1	282	90	21
Morley	12	9	1	2	210	118	19
Fylde	12	7	2	3	183	115	16
Exeter	12	7	2	3	160	139	16
Clifton	12	6	1	5	172	186	13
Askeans	12	4	2	6	141	137	10
Nuneaton	12	5	0	7	180	200	10
Broughton Park	12	5	0	7	109	185	10
Roundhay	12	4	1	7	147	166	9
Sheffield	12	4	1	7	193	222	9
Lydney	12	4	1	7	125	188	9
Met. Police	12	4	0	8	130	188	8
Vale of Lune	12	3	0	9	123	221	6

1998-89

	P	W	D	L	F	A	Pts
Plymouth A.	11	11	0	0	311	89	22
Rugby	11	10	0	1	268	99	20
Wakefield	11	9	0	2	282	114	18
West Hartlepool	11	5	1	5	164	133	11
Nuneaton	11	5	0	6	178	214	10
Sheffield	11	4	1	6	170	182	9
Vale of Lune	11	4	1	6	120	145	9
Askeans	11	4	1	6	141	215	9
Exeter	11	4	0	7	142	180	8
Fylde	11	4	0	7	136	181	8
Met. Police	11	4	0	7	130	275	8
Maidstone	11	0	0	11	74	289	0

1991-92

	P	W	D	L	F	A	PD	Pts
Richmond	12	10	1	1	296	124	172	21
Fylde	12	9	1	2	198	109	89	19
Clifton	12	9	0	3	298	132	166	18
Exeter	12	8	2	2	203	138	65	18
Redruth	12	6	1	5	155	123	32	13
Broughton Park	12	5	1	69	196	157	39	11
Askeans	12	5	1	6	149	203	-54	11
Sheffield	12	5	1	6	146	228	-82	11
Otley	12	5	0	7	177	190	-13	10
Roundhay	12	3	2	7	161	240	-79	8
Headingley	12	4	0	8	139	220	-81	8
Nuneaton	12	1	2	9	153	237	-84	4
Lydney	12	2	0	10	91	261	-170	4

1989-90

	P	W	D	L	F	A	Pts
Lon. Scottish	11	11	0	0	258	92	22
Wakefield	11	7	1	3	310	126	15
West Hartlepool	11	5	2	4	175	110	12
Sheffield	11	6	0	5	176	174	12
Askeans	11	6	0	5	170	235	12
Exeter	11	5	1	5	149	153	11
Roundhay	11	5	0	6	156	166	10
Fylde	11	5	0	6	169	222	10
Vale of Lune	11	4	0	7	154	219	8
Nuneaton	11	4	0	7	127	196	8
Lydney	11	3	0	8	153	166	6
Lon. Welsh	11	3	0	8	141	179	6

1992-93

	P	W	D	L	F	A	PD	Pts
Otley	11	8	1	2	274	118	156	17
Havant	11	8	1	2	185	93	92	17
Exeter	11	8	1	2	247	169	78	17
Redruth	11	7	2	2	175	125	50	16
Sheffield	11	7	0	4	208	134	74	14
Leeds	11	7	0	4	228	220	8	14
Liverpool St. H.	11	5	0	6	203	130	73	10
Clifton	11	4	2	5	206	175	31	10
Aspatria	11	3	1	7	170	308	-138	7
Askeans	11	3	0	8	132	300	-168	6
Broughton Park	11	2	0	9	136	217	-81	4
Plymouth Albion	11	0	0	11	130	305	-175	0

BEDFORD RUFC

Review of the Season

Two words could be used to sum up the 1992-93 season — frustrating and positive. We now find ourselves in the Third Division but as we reflect, this season has been the best for too long. Our improvements have been outstanding both on and off the pitch. Dedicated people have worked tirelessly, none more than Ian Bullerwell. The coaching staff have worked tremendously well together, from the U21s to the 1st team. The future of the Club of course relies heavily on a successful youth policy, coupled with player strength in depth, which brings healthy competition and is now very evident at the Club. This shows our recruitment platform has been and is working.

Our record shows only two home losses and four league games. This meagre amount of defeats shows an inspiring support around the ground and is a credit to the whole town. To lose four league games and to be relegated I feel is ludicrous and then the promotion of a team having lost two league games shows the stark contrast.

The players all season have showed great commitment and talent. Mark Rennell (Eddie) has perhaps been one of the leading lights in this. His selection for the full England squad shows everybody that Bedford are not only on the map but are actually achieving things.

President: G B Willey
Chairman: I M Butterwell
Club Secretary: A D Mills, 1 Newbury House, Kimbolton Road, Bedford, MK40 2PD. Tel: (H) 02334 212524 (W) 0234 364351 Fax: (W) 0234 268843.
Fixtures Secretary: D Saunders, College Farm, Oakley, Glos. MK43 7RX. Tel: (H) 02302 2328.
Press Officer: H Travis, 17 Furzefiled, Putney, Bedford, MK41 9DS. Tel: 0234 213808.
1993/94 1XV Captain: P Alston
1993/94 1XV Coach: M Rafter

Bedford RUFC 1992-93

BEDFORD RUFC

ADDITIONAL RESULTS 1992-93

No	Date	Opponents	Venue	Result
1	Sep 5	Harrogate	A	W35-11
2	Sep 12	L Welsh	H	W39-3
3	Oct 17	Harlequins	A	W30-27
4	Oct 31	Loughborough	A	L13-22
5	Nov 7	Askeans	H	W21-12
6	Nov 13	Cambridge U	A	L11-17
7	Nov 28	Rugby	AW	L14-27
8	Dec 5	Northampton	A	L16-33
9	Dec 12	Wasps	H	W13-9
10	Dec 16	RAF	H	W17-10
11	Dec 19	Rugby	A	L10-12
12	Jan 2	Rosslyn Park	A	W20-9
13	Jan 15	Leicester	H	L13-16
14	Jan 23	Bristol	H	L6-41
15	Jan 27	Bedfordshire	H	W25-16
16	Jan 30	Askeans	A	W20-12
17	Feb 6	Orrell	A	L3-20
18	Feb 20	W Hartlepool	A	L14-27
19	Feb 27	Saracens	A	L11-20
20	Mar 3	Selkirk	H	W23-19
21	Mar 19	L Scottish	H	W25-15
22	Apr 10	Saracens	H	W52-23
23	Apr 17	Sheffield	H	W57-17

CLUB PLAYING RECORD 1992-93 SEASON

National Division: Two
Final League Position at end 1992/93 Season: 7th
League Playing Record:
P 12, W 6, D 2, L 4, Pts F 186, Pts A 183
Season Playing Record (including League matches/Pilkington cup etc):
P 35, W 19, D 2, L 14, Pts F 687, Pts A 601

MOST CAPPED PLAYERS
including British Lions Appearances
D Rogers, 34, D Perry, 15, W Steele, 13
J Janion, 9, R Hearn, 6, R Wilkinson, 6

LEADING APPEARANCES FOR CLUB
D Rogers, 485, 1956-76, M Howe, 441, 1976
R Eidsforth, 374, 1924-49, R Willsher, 354, 1928-49
F Barker, 347, 1966-67, J Smith 343, 1953-68

LEADING SCORERS
A Finnie, Fly Half, 188
N Marment, Full Back, 77
P Moss, Full Back/Centre, 68
M Rennell, Flanker/No 8, 45

Mark Denney makes a break

170

BEDFORD RUFC

Club Details

Colours: Wide hoops in Oxford & Cambridge blues.
Change of Colours: Two shades of blue & cerise squares.
Nickname: The Blues.
Date Founded: 1886.
Membership: Total 700, Full 600, Social 100, Junior/Youth/Minis 250.
Membership Fees: Full £55, Junior/Youth/Minis £12.
Number of Teams: Senior 5 (First team, Wanderers, U21, Colts) Junior (all ages U8 to U17).

Ground Details

Ground Address: Goldington Road, Bedford.
Telephone: 0234 354619/347511.
Fax: 0234 268843 (I.B. Bullerwell)
Directions: Near Jcn A428 Bedford-Cambridge & B660 Bedford- Bimbolton.
Capacity: Total 6,000, Seated 900, Standing 5,100.
Ticket Prices: Adults £4 Ground, OAP/Child/Student £2.
Clubhouse Facilities: Two bars, players tea room, hospitality suites, committee room available to sponsors, meals available match days & Wed to Fri.
Training Nights: Mon, Wed, Thurs. First Team Squad Mon & Thurs.

'Let's get at 'em' —Leigh Mansell, David McGavin & Pete Garrett prepare for battle

BEDFORD RUFC

COURAGE LEAGUE RECORDS

HIGHEST SCORE: 52 V Blackheath (52-1O) 14-3-92 Home CL2
LARGEST WINNING MARGIN: 42 As above
HIGHEST SCORE AGAINST: 76 v Bath (O-76) 13-1-9O Away CL1
LARGEST LOSING MARGIN: 76 as above
DRAWN MATCHES: 8
CLEAN SHEETS: 1
FAILED TO SCORE: 4

INDIVIDUAL SCORING RECORDS
IN A MATCH

Most Points: 25 Andy Finnie v Coventry 27-3-93 Home CL2
Most Tries: 2 On 8 occasions by 6 players, Most B Gabriel 2
Most Conversions: 5 Steve Batty v Liverpool SH 3O-4-88 Home CL2,
Andy Finnie v Blackheath 14.3.92 Home CL2
Most Penalties: 5 Andy Finnie v London Irish 22-1O-88 CL2, v Waterloo 4-4-92 Home CL2,
v Nottingham 13-2-93 Home CL2, Nick Marment v Richmond 3-1O-92 Home
Most Drop Goals: 2 Andy Finnie v Coventry 27-3-93 Home CL2

IN A SEASON

Most Points: 92 Andy Finnie 1991-92 CL2
Most Tries: 5 Mark Rennell 1991-92 CL2
Most Conversions:: 11 Andy Finnie 1991-92 CL2
Most Penalties: 19 Andy Finnie 1987-88 CL2 & 1991-92 CL2
Most Drop Goals: 4 Andy Finnie 199O-91 CL2

IN A CAREER

Most Points: 382 Andy Finnie 1987-93
Most Tries: 1O Mark Rennell 199O-93
Most Conversions: 33 Andy Finnie 1987-93
Most Penalties: 88 Andy Finnie 1987-93
Most Drop Goals: 13 Andy Finnie 1987-93

SEASON BY SEASON LEADING SCORERS

	Most Points			Most Tries	
1987-88	75	Andy Finnie	3	Steve Harris Brian Gabriel Steve Batty	
1988-89	56	Andy Finnie	2	Steve Harris Garry Colleran	
1989-9O	13	Richard Greed	3	Mark Howe	
199O-91	78	Andy Finnie	3	Tim Young	
1991-92	92	Andy Fnnie	5	Mark Rennell	
1992-93	75	Andy Finnie	3	Mark Rennell	

BLACKHEATH FC

President: M F Turner
Chairman: F J McCarthy
Club Secretary: Roger Pearce, Garden Cottage, Church Street, Eastbury, Berks, RG16 7JZ. Tel: (H) 0488 71588 (W) 0235 433477 Fax: (W) 0235 433899.
Fixtures Secretary: Jim Collett, 8 Vanbrugh Fields, Blackheath, London, SE3 7TZ. Tel: (H) 081 858 7591 (W) 081 539 3348.
Press Officer: Mic Thomas, c/o Rectory Field, Charlton Road, Blackheath, London, SE3. Tel: (W) 071 691 3087.
1993/94 1XV Captain: Owen Coyne
1993/94 1XV Coach: Danny Vaughan
Director of Rugby: Alan Davies

Review of the Season

Blackheath commenced the season at Kingsholm. Eight players making their 1st class debuts at Gloucester!! That the game was only lost 1O-7 with a last minute home try gave grounds for optimism for the season ahead. Over the next 6 matches this feeling was dispelled, the first win of the season did not arrive until the last day of October with a league victory at Morley; this win helped to dispel the doubts with 9 out of a possible 1O points being won. Then came disaster; the 1st XV fly-half Andy Mercer incurred a triple fracture of his right leg and second choice Neil Munn tore his medial ligament — a direct result in the final 3 matches being lost. The curtain had finally come down on the "Houdini" act.

In the Pilkington Cup Blackheath, minus Mick Skinner who played for the Barbarians against Australia on the Saturday, had a Sunday fixture against Harlequins. Unfortunately any hopes of catching them on the hop were finished by Bath's defeat at Waterloo the previous day. A resounding defeat ensued.

Hope for the future is high; the squad is probably the youngest ever; all have last year's experience behind them; only one player has defected to another club; of the sides relegated the only defeat was at the hands of Coventry; a pre-season tour of South Africa should sharpen them. Blackheath should be a prime contender for promotion this season.

Blackheath FC 1992-93

Photo: Tom Morris

BLACKHEATH FC

ADDITIONAL RESULTS 1992-93

No	Date	Opponents	Result
1	Sep 5	Gloucester	L10-7
2	Sep 19	Wakefield	D9-9
3	Sep 26	Nottingham	L46-5
4	Oct 3	Bath	L51-0
5	Oct 10	Coventry	L38-15
6	Oct 11	Gordon	L18-17
7	Oct 17	Loughborough Students	L35-3
8	Oct 24	Newcastle Gosforth	L12-9
9	Nov 3	Morley	W23-8
10	Nov 7	Old Blues	W27-3
11	Nov 13	Griqualand West	L17-15
12	Nov 21	Richmond	W23-13
13	Nov 29	Harlequins	L72-3
14	Dec 13	Lydney	L12-9
15	Dec 19	Met Police	W28-3
16	Jan 2	L Irish	W27-20
17	Jan 9	Rosslyn Park	W18-14
18	Jan 16	Rugby	L11-8
19	Jan 23	L Scottish	W34-16
20	Jan 30	Nuneaton	W37-9
21	Feb 6	Harlequins	L22-17
22	Feb 13	Fylde	D9-9
23	Feb 17	Los Tordos (Argentina)	W47-3
24	Feb 20	Askeans	L20-13
25	Feb 24	Regattas (Argentina)	L27-10
26	Mar 7	Saracens	L15-49
27	Mar 13	Bedford	W16-12
28	Mar 20	Rosslyn Park	L31-17
29	Mar 27	Moseley	L23-6
30	Apr 3	Sale	L20-3
31	Apr 10	Maidston	W76-7
32	Apr 17	Clifton	W15-12
33	Apr 24	Waterloo	L27-6

CLUB PLAYING RECORD 1992-93 SEASON

National Division: Two
Final League Position at end 1992/93 Season: 10th
League Playing Record:
P 12, W 4, D 2, L 6, Pts F 142, Pts A 231
Season Playing Record (including League matches/Pilkington cup etc):
P 32, W 11, D 2, L 19, Pts F 523, Pts A 655

PLAYING SQUAD 1992-93

Full Backs: Burns, Connolly, Eagle, Maxted
Wings: Aldridge, Batthews, Campbell, Griffiths, Jones, Mitchell, Walton, Ward
Centres: Barlow, Bennett, Caroll, Coyne, McIntyre, Neil-Dwyer
Fly Half: Mercer, Munn, Mycroft
Scrum Half: Greenway, Hails, Simmons, Springhall
Props: Burfield, Cousins, Curry Keohane, Reece, Standen, Stewart, Taylor, Tierney, Webster
Hookers: Brown, Howe, Nicholson
Second Row: Begley, Furneaux, Hursey, Lloyd, O'Sullivan, Patrick, Williams
Flankers: Barham, Booth, Preston, Skinner, Smith, Walton
No. 8: Slack, Urwin, Vaughan

LEADING SCORERS

G Eagle, Full Back, 233
J McIntyre, Centre, 35
M Griffiths, Wing, 35
P Mitchell, Wing, 30
J Aldridge, Wing, 25
A Merser, Fly Half, 21

BLACKHEATH FC

COURAGE LEAGUE RECORDS

HIGHEST SCORE: 34 V Gosforth (34-10) 24-9-88 Home CL2
LARGEST WINNING MARGIN: 28 v Richmond (32-3) 2-11-88 Home CL2
HIGHEST SCORE AGAINST: 52 v Bedford (10-52) 14-3-92 Away CL2
LARGEST LOSING MARGIN: 42 As above
DRAWN MATCHES: 5
CLEAN SHEETS: 4
FAILED TO SCORE: 0

INDIVIDUAL SCORING RECORDS

IN A MATCH

Most Points: 20 Grant Eagle v Moseley 28-3-92 Home CL2
Most Tries: 2 Joe McIntyre v Morley 31-10-92 Away CL2, v Bedford 13-3-93 Home CL2
Most Conversions: 3 Colin Parker v Richmond 12-11-88 Home CL2, v London Irish 28-4-90 Home CL2
Most Penalties: 6 Grant Eagle v Moseley 28-3-92 Home CL2, v Rosslyn Park 9-1-93 Home CL2
Most Drop Goals: 2 Jon King v Coventry 19-11-88 Away CL2, v London Irish 22-4-89 Away CL2,
v London Irish 28-4-90 Home CL2

IN A SEASON

Most Points: 97 Grant Eagle 1992-93 CL3
Most Tries: 5 Joe McIntyre 1992-93 CL2
Most Conversions: 10 Colin Parker 1987-88 CL2 & 1989-90 CL2
Most Penalties: 26 Grant Eagle 1992-93 CL2
Most Drop Goals: 8 Jon King 1988-89 CL2

IN A CAREER

Most Points: 175 Colin Parker 1987-91
Most Tries: 9 Pat Jones 1987-93
Most Conversions: 23 Colin Parker 1987-91
Most Penalties: 38 Colin Parker 1987-91
Most Drop Goals: 16 Jon King 1987-91

SEASON BY SEASON LEADING SCORERS

	Most Points			Most Tries
1987-88	30	Nick Colyer	2	Pat Jones Giles Marshall Martin Holcombe
1988-89	70	Colin Parker	3	Peter Vaughan Mickey Scott
1989-90	57	Colin Parker	3	Jon King
1990-91	48	Colin Parker	3	Pat Jones
1991-92	61	Neil Munn	2	Andy Mercer
1992-93	97	Grant Eagle	5	Joe McIntyre

BLACKHEATH FC

Club Details

Colours: Red & black hoops.
Change of Colours: Black.
Nickname: Club.
Date Founded: 1858.
Membership: Total 1,000, Full 750, Junior/Youth/Minis 250.
Membership Fees: £30, Junior/Youth/Minis £5-£15.
Number of Teams: Senior 6.
Programme Advertising Rates: Full £800, Half £450, Qtr £250.

Ground Details

Ground Address: Rectory Field, Charlton Road, Blackheath, London SE3.
Telephone: 081 858 1578.
Directions: Charlton Road is B210 off A2 between Blackheath and Charlton. Access from London Blackwall Tunnel or M25.
Capacity: Seated 500, Standing ample.
Ticket Prices: Adults £3.
Clubhouse Facilities: Bar, hospitality suite etc.
Training Nights: Mon & Thurs.

Matt Griffiths breaks, supported by Joe McIntyre against London Scottish   *Photo: Lightbox Photographics*

COVENTRY FC

President: Peter Bell
Chairman: Gerry Sugrue
Club Secretary: Peter Jackson, 147 Chester Road, Castle Bromwich, Birmingham, B36 0AE. Tel: (H) 021 747 2498.
Fixtures Secretary: John Butler, 62 Spring Lane, Whittington, Nr Lichfield, Staffs, WS14 9NA. Tel: (H) 0543 432654 (W) 0827 289999.
Press Officer: Rob Wilkinson, c/o Coventry FC, Barkers Butts Lane, Coundon, Coventry.
1993/94 1XV Captain: Barry Evans
1993/94 1XV Coach: Ian Darnell
Commercial Manager: Rob Wilkinson
Director of Coaching: Andy Johnson

Review of the Season

Without doubt the season will rate as one of the worst in the 119 year history of the club. The side never remotely challenged for the one promotion place and after a big win over Morley in the opening league match, disaster followed disaster, notably against Waterloo, Richmond and Moseley.

In club matches, a notable double was achieved over 1st Division Midland rivals Northampton, another high being the Boxing Day win at Moseley.

The club have however reacted swiftly in an attempt to arrest the decline and make a swift return to Division 2 by appointing Andy Johnson, the former Northampton and Midlands hooker as their first full time playing administrator. News on the recruitment front has also been encouraging. Mark Douglas the former Welsh International scrum half, having played three club matches at the end of the season should be available regularly, whilst Doug Woodman ex Clifton & Bristol and Julian Horrobin ex Berry Hill have both signed. In addition, top points scorer Richard Angell has reversed his decision to join rivals Moseley, a route however taken by Leroy McKenzie, the only significant departure.

Only time will tell whether the guarded optimism that the clubs decline has bottomed out is true.

Coventry FC 1992-93. Back row: John Burgun, Ron Jones, Mark Bennett, Warwick Bullock, Julian Hyde, Dave Addleton, Tony Gulliver, Jim Wingham, Rob Field, Lee Jones, Norman Smith, Kevin Hickey, Ernie Boxall, Jackie Mahon. Front row: Mick Curtis, Richard Turner, Richard Gee, Richard Angell, Steve Chapman, Steve Carter, Leroy McKenzie, Greg Harwood.

COVENTRY FC

CLUB PLAYING RECORD 1992-93 SEASON

National Division: Two
Final League Position at end 1992/93 Season: 11th
League Playing Record: P 12, W 3, D 0, L 9, Pts F 192, Pts A 236
Season Playing Record (including League matches/Pilkington cup etc): P 37, W 14, D 0, L 23, Pts F 687, Pts A 759

PLAYING SQUAD 1992-93

Full Backs: R Gee, R Angell, M Thomas, N Stainton
Wings: L McKenzie, B Evans, K Shaw, M Bennett, B Shepherd
Centres: S Chapman, J Minshull, R Rowan, M Curtis, K Street, S Barden
Fly Half: R Angell, M Lakey, G Harwood
Scrum Half: R Turner, S Thomas, D Butler, M Elridge, M Douglas, B Sylvester
Props: C Phillips, W Bulluck, P Butler, J Wingham
Hookers: D Addleton, A Farrington
Locks: J Hude, R Field, A gulliver, R Mackie, D Andreou
Flankers: K Hickey, S Carter, p Thomas, P Staveley, M Pearson, P Stone, C Gardner, G Caswell
No. 8: S Carter, J Hyde, R Field, L Jones

MOST CAPPED PLAYERS including British Lions Appearances

D Duckham, 36, 1969
F Cotton, 31, 1971
P Jackson, 20, 1956
P Robbins, 19, 1956
J Owen, 14, 1963
S Brain, 14, 1984

LEADING APPEARANCES FOR CLUB DURING SEASON 1992-93

D Addleton, 36, Hooker
S Chapman, 34, Centre
C Phillips, 33, Prop
W Bulluck, 33, Prop
J Hyde, 33, Lock
B Evans, 31, Wing

LEADING SCORERS

R Angell, Full Back/Fly Half, 166
B Evans, Wing, 70
M Thomas, Full Back 64
K Hickey, Flanker, 45
M Lakey, Fly Half, 37

COVENTRY FC

COURAGE LEAGUE RECORDS

HIGHEST SCORE : 41 v Morley (41-3) 19-9-92 Home CL2
LARGEST WINNING MARGIN : 38 as above
HIGHEST SCORE AGAINST : 49 v Wasps (6-49) 13-4-88 Away CL1
LARGEST LOSING MARGIN : 43 As above
DRAWN MATCHES : 2
CLEAN SHEETS : 3
FAILED TO SCORE : 2

INDIVIDUAL SCORING RECORDS

IN A MATCH

Most Points: 21 Marc Thomas v Morley 19.9.92 Home CL2
Most Tries: 3 Pete Rowlands v London Irish 10-9-98 Away CL2, Graham Robbins v Waterloo 13-1-90 Home CL2, Richard Gee v Morley 19-9-92 Home CL2
Most Conversions: 5 Marc Thomas v Morley 19-9-92 Home CL2
Most Penalties: 6 Steve Thomas v Sale 23-9-89 Away CL2
Most Drop Goals: 2 Mark Lakey v Moseley 3-4-93 Home CL2

IN A SEASON

Most Points: 79 Steve Thomas 1989-90 CL2
Most Tries: 6 Steve Thomas 1989-90 CL2
Most Conversions: 8 Steve Thomas 1989-90 CL2
Most Penalties: 19 Steve Thomas 1991-91 CL2
Most Drop Goals: 4 Mark Lakey 1988-89 CL2

IN A CAREER

Most Points: 228 Steve Thomas 1987-93
Most Tries: 11 Kevin Hickey 1988-93
Most Conversions: 21 Steve Thomas 1987-93
Most Penalties: 50 Steve Thomas 1987-93
Most Drop Goals: 7 Mark Lakey 1987-93

SEASON BY SEASON LEADING SCORERS

	Most Points			Most Tries
1987-88	28	Martin Fairn	3	Paul Suckling
1988-89	36	Martin Fairn	4	Dick Travers
1989-90	79	Steve Thomas	6	Steve Thomas
1990-91	37	Richard Angell	4	Richard Angell
1991-92	73	Steve Thomas	4	Kevin Hickey Jason Minshull
1992-93	53	Richard Angell	4	Barry Evans

COVENTRY FC

Club Details

Colours: Navy blue & white hoops.
Change of Colours: Dark blue.
Nickname: Cov.
Date Founded: 1874.
Membership: Total 900.
Membership Fees: Full £60.
Number of Teams: Senior 3, Junior 4.
Programme Advertising Rates: Full £390, Half £205, Qtr £110.

Ground Details

Ground Address: Barkers Butts Lane, Coundon, Coventry.
Telephone: 0203 591274/593399.
Capacity: Total 10,000, Seated 1,100, Standing 8,900.
Ticket Prices: Adults £4.
Clubhouse Facilities: Main bar & lounge, sponsors hospitality suite, cocktail bar, restaurant room.
Training Nights: Monday & Thursday.

Coventry scrum-half Harwood clears his lines agains Harlequin   *Photo: Joe McCabe*

EXETER FC

President: R J Roach
Chairman: W J Baxter
Club Secretary: B P (Tug) Wilson, 11
Washbrook View, Ottery St Mary, EX11
1EP. Tel: 0404 813316 (W) 0884 243200
Fax: (W) 0884 257303.
Fixtures Secretary: T Turner, April
House, Sandford, Crediton, Devon. Tel:
(H) 0363 772044 (W) 0392 210344.
Press Officer: Dave Wiggings, Bullers
Arms, Strand, Brixham, Devon. Tel: (H)
0803 853329.
1993/94 1XV Captain: A Maunder
1993/94 1XV Coach: D Wiggins
Commercial Manager: M Dolton
Hon Treasurer: S L Williams
Club Administrator: R Huxtable

Club Details

Colours: Black with white collars.
Change of Colours: White.
Date Founded: 1872.
Membership: Total 630, Full 400, Social 18, Junior/Youth/Minis 120.
Membership Fees: Full £32, Junior/Youth/Minis £3.
Number of Teams: Senior 6, Junior 8.
Programme Advertising Rates: Full £400 + VAT, Half £200 + VAT.

Ground Details

Ground Address: The County Ground Stadium, Church Road, St Thomas, Exeter, Devon, EX2 9BQ.
Telephone: 0392 78759.
Directions: Jcn 30 M5 head on A377 to Town centre, Sainsbury's turn left, under railway bridge turn left, then right.
Capacity: Total 5,750.
Ticket Prices: Adults £3.50, OAP/Child £1.75.
Clubhouse Facilities: With bar etc.
Training Nights: Tuesday & Thursday.

Special Occasions in 1993-94

100 years of rugby at County Ground.

Competitions won during Season 1992-93

Devon Cup Winners

CLUB PLAYING RECORD 1992-93 SEASON

National Division: Three
Final League Position at end 1992/93 Season: 3rd
League Playing Record:
P 11, W 8, D 1, L 2, Pts F 247, Pts A 169
Season Playing Record (including League matches/Pilkington cup etc):
P 37, W 30, D 1, L 6, Pts F 949, Pts A 507

PLAYING SQUAD 1992-93

15: I Steward, S Doyle
14: S Dovell, D Gillow
13: A Baker, A Cox
12: G Tutchings, A Turner
11: M Chatterton, M Hoskins
10: A Green, P Treseder
9: A Maunder, R James
8: R Baxter, J Batchelor
7: P Westgate, R Hutchinson, S Vincent
6: T Edbrooke, M Cathery, L Stratton
5: P Hodge, R Bess
4: H Langley
3: R Gibbins, S Byrne
2: G Meldon, R Puesley
1: P Sluman,. T Harris, J Sussex

MOST CAPPED PLAYERS

including British Lions Appearances
J Buchanan, 16
M Underwood, 5
R Madge, 4
D Manley, 4
P Nicholas, 3
A Brown 1

LEADING APPEARANCES FOR CLUB DURING SEASON 1992-93

A Green, 33
S Dovell, 31
R Gibbins, 31
R Baxter, 31
I Steward, 31
A Maunder, 30

LEADING SCORERS

A Green, Fly Half, 365
A Maunder, Scrum Half, 80
M Chattleton, Wing, 75
I Steward, Full Back, 72
s Dowell, Wing, 40
H Langley, 2nd Row, 40

EXETER FC

COURAGE LEAGUE RECORDS
HIGHEST SCORE : 48 V Askeans (48-13) 1O-1O-92 Home CL3
LARGEST WINNING MARGIN : 35 As above
HIGHEST SCORE AGAINST : 48 v Fylde (13-48) 3-1O-87 Away CL3
LARGEST LOSING MARGIN : 35 As above
DRAWN MATCHES : 3
CLEAN SHEETS : 2
FAILED TO SCORE : 2

INDIVIDUAL SCORING RECORDS
IN A MATCH
Most Points: 2O Andy Green v Met Pol 1O-11-9O Home CL3
Most Tries: 3 Mike Cathery v Birmingham 26-3-88 Home CL3 Andy Green v Met Pol
Most Conversions: 3 Andy Green v Nuneaton 29-2-92 Home, Roundhay 14-3-92 Away CL3,
v Askeans 1O-1O-92 Home CL3
Most Penalties: 5 Andy Green v W Hartlepool 28-1O-89 Home CL3, v Sheffield 28-3-92 Home CL3,
v Plymouth 14.11.92 Home CL3.
Most Drop Goals: 2 Andy Green v Sheffield 23-4-88 Home CL3.

IN A SEASON
Most Points: 122 Andy Green 1992-93 CL3
Most Tries: 5 Andy Maunder 1992-93 CL£
Most Conversions: 1O Andy Green 1992-93 CL3
Most Penalties: 31 Andy Green 1992-93 CL3
Most Drop Goals: 4 Andy Green 1987-88 CL3

IN A CAREER
Most Points: 438 Andy Green 1987-93
Most Tries: 16 Andy Maunder 1987-93
Most Conversions: 36 Andy Green 1992-93
Most Penalties: 98 Andy Green 1992-93
Most Drop Goals: 1O Andy Green 1992-93

SEASON BY SEASON LEADING SCORERS

	Most Points		Most Tries	
1987-88	42	Andy Green	3	Andy Green
1988-89	65	65 Malcolm Collins	4	Andy Maunder
1989-9O	99	Andy Green	2	Andy Green
199O-91	92	Andy Green	4	Jeff Tutchings
1991-92	77	Andy Green	4	Mark Chatterton Jon Davis
1992-93	122	Andy Green	5	Andy Maunder

*1O-11-9O Home CL3, M Chatterton v Headingley 23-11-91 Home CL3, Harry Langley 24-4-93 v Broughton Park Away CL3

FYLDE RUFC

Review of the Season

Following promotion in 1991-92, the loss of several players coupled with a crippling injury list gave Fylde's first full time coach, George Hook, a nigh on impossible task of keeping the club in league two. Those players who were fit played with plenty of spirit and achieved three draws and a one-point defeat against runners-up Waterloo. Things may have been different if the side had had a recognised goalkicker. For this season, England Colts coach, Graham Smith, will be in charge along with former Woodlands favourite Mike Dixon and, with Brendan Hanovan as new captain, the club is hopeful for a much improved campaign.

President: Malcolm Phillips
Chairman: Ray Woolley
Club Secretary: Peter Makin, 5 Ribblesdale Place, Preston, Lancashire, PR1 8BZ. Tel: (H) 0253 722713 (W) 0772 59625
Fixtures Secretary: David R Taylor, 18 St Georges Road, St Annes- on-Sea, Lancs, FY8 2AE. Tel: (H) 0253 781010 (W) 0995 61322.
Press Officer: Stewart Brown, 179 Hardhorn Road, Bulton-le-Fylde.
1993/94 1XV Captain: Brendan Hanavan
1993/94 1XV Coach: Graham Smith

CLUB PLAYING RECORD 1992-93 SEASON

National Division: Two
Final League Position at end 1992/93 Season: 11th
League Playing Record: P 12, W 0, D 3, L 9, Pts F 108, Pts A 290
Season Playing Record (including League matches/Pilkington cup etc): P 33, W 9, D 4, L 20, Pts F 420, Pts A 665

Jon Taylor releases the ball from a Fylde scrum v Moseley

183

FYLDE RUFC

PLAYING SQUAD 1992-93

Full Backs: M Jackson, J Roderick
Right Wing: D Collinge, B Hanavan
Centres: A Parker, S Connell, P Seed, J Atkins, A Russell, G Moffat
Left Wing: A Armitstead, S Taylor
Fly Half: I Barclay, S Gough
Scrum Half: P Rudd, S Barclay, C O'Toole
Props: C Burns, M Lloyd, R Akrill, M Heys
Hookers: A Yates, A Moffat
Locks: S Fletcher, D Howard, T Taylor, P O'Neill, D Young
Wing Forwards: G Russell, A Ireland, T Weighman, I Ashton, C Blackburn, J Nicholson, T Kalirai
No. 8: J Taylor, M Greatorex

MOST CAPPED PLAYERS

including British Lions Appearances
Bill Beaumont, 34
Malcolm Phillips, 25

LEADING SCORERS

Steve Gough, Fly Half
Ian Barclay, Fly Half

ADDITIONAL RESULTS 1992-93

No	Date	Opponents	Venue	Result
1	Sep 5	Middlesbrough	H	W21-13
2	Sep 12	Aspatria	H	W19-12
3	Oct 17	Orrell	A	L6-25
4	Nov 7	Leeds	H	W21-8
5	Nov 14	Liverpool St H	H	L8-22
6	Nov 28	Moseley	A	L6-19
7	Dec 5	Vale of Lune	A	D18-18
8	Dec 12	Rugby	H	W13-8
9	Dec 14	Nuneaton	H	W14-13
10	Dec 26	Preston Grasshoppers	H	W11-7
11	Dec 28	Blackburn	H	
12	Jan 1	Fylde Coast	H	
13	Jan 2	Waterloo	A	L5-53
14	Jan 17	Widnes	H	L7-11
15	Jan 23	Harrogate	H	L8-11
16	Jan 30	Durham U	H	W18-7
17	Feb 6	W Hartlepool	A	L13029
18	Feb 27	Sale	A	L18-40
19	Mar 6	Leeds	H	L19-25
20	Mar 20	St Mary's College Dublin	A	L8-15
21	Apr 10	Winnington Pk	H	W44-9
22	Apr 12	Gloucester	A	L8-25
23	Apr 17	Hartlepool Rovers	A	W33-5

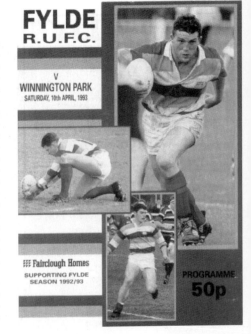

FYLDE R.U.F.C.
V
WINNINGTON PARK
SATURDAY, 10th APRIL, 1993

Fairclough Homes
SUPPORTING FYLDE
SEASON 1992/93

PROGRAMME
50p

FYLDE RUFC

COURAGE LEAGUE RECORDS

HIGHEST SCORE : 68 v Birmingham (68-7) 7-11-87 Home CL3
LARGEST WINNING MARGIN : 61 As above
HIGHEST SCORE AGAINST : 51 v Sale (3-51) 19-9-92 Away CL2
LARGEST LOSING MARGIN : 48 As above
DRAWN MATCHES : 6
CLEAN SHEETS : 1
FAILED TO SCORE : 1

INDIVIDUAL SCORING RECORDS
IN A MATCH

Most Points: 28 Steve Burnage v Birmingham 7-11-87 Home CL3
Most Tries: 4 Brendan Hanavan v Exeter 3-1O-87 Home CL3, v Birmingham 7-11-87 Home CL3
Most Conversions: 9 Steve Burnage v Birmingham 7-11-87 Home CL3
Most Penalties: 4 Steve Burnage v Rugby 14-1-98 Home CL3 v Lydney 1O-3 9O CL3,
Mike Jackson v Morley 13-1O-9O Home CL3, v Exeter 21-12-91 Away CL3,
v Richmond 11-1-92 Home CL3
Most Drop Goals: 1 On 8 occasions by 4 men

IN A SEASON

Most Points: 121 Steve Bunage 1987-88 CL3
Most Tries: 1O Brendan Hanavan 1987-88 CL3
Most Conversions: 3O Steve Burnage 1987-88 CL3
Most Penalties: 26 Mike Jackson 1991-92 CL3
Most Drop Goals: 2 Steve Burnage 1989-9O CL3

IN A CAREER

Most Points: 318 Steve Burnage 1987-91
Most Tries: 23 Brendan Hanavan 1987-93
Most Conversions: 45 Steve Burnage 1987-91
Most Penalties: 64 Steve Burnage 1987-91
Most Drop Goals: 4 Steve Burnage 1987-91

SEASON BY SEASON LEADING SCORERS

	Most Points			Most Tries	
1987-88	121	Steve Burnage	1O	Brendan Hanavan	
1988-89	88	Steve Burnage	4	Mark Hesketh	
1989-9O	91	Steve Burnage	7	Brendan Hanavan	
1990-91	62	Mike Jackson	5	Brendan Hanavan	
1991-92	1O6	Mike Jackson	4	Anthony Ireland	
1992-93	4O	Mike Jackson	2	John Nicholson Steve Gough	

FYLDE RUFC

Club Details
Colours: Claret, gold & white
Change of Colours: Maroon
Date Founded: 1919
Membership: Total 1,350, Full 1,150, Social 50, Junior/Youth/Minis 150.
Membership Fees: Full £55, Junior/Youth/Minis £10
Number of Teams: Senior 5, Junior 9
Programme Advertising Rates: On application

Ground Details
Ground Address: Woodlands Memorial Ground, Blackpool Road, Ansdell, Lytham St Annes.
Telephone: 0253 734733
Directions: Leave M5 at Exit 4 onto A583 (Preston, Kirkham) to traffic lights and turn right into Whitehill Road to next set of lights. Turn left onto Queensway. The ground is about 3 miles on left (after Blossoms Pub and RC Church on right).
Capacity: Total 7,450, Seated 450, Standing 7,000.
Ticket Prices: Adult £3.50, OAP/Child £2/£1
Clubhouse Facilities: Clubroom, tea bar, lounge bars, club shop.
Training Nights: Mondays & Thursdays

Fylde try scorer Alex Moffat on a typical burst v Morley

186

HAVANT RFC

President: Phil West
Chairman: Mick Chalk
Club Secretary: Colin Sewell, 6 Font Close, Titchfield Common, Fareham, Hants, PO14 4QH. Tel: (H) 0489 583417 (W) 0705 563904.
Fixtures Secretary: Mick Chalk, 16 Highclere Avenue, Havant, Hants, PO94 4RB. Tel: (H) 0705 472239 (W) 0705 822351 Ext 23155
Press Officer: Ray Quinn, Unit 6, Stratfield Park, Elettra Avenue, Waterlooville, Hants PO7 7NX. Tel: (W) 0705 241122 Fax: 0705 257596.
1993/94 1XV Captain: Will Knight
1993/94 1XV Coach: Rob Cunningham
Fund-Raising & Commercial: Colin Edwards Tel: (H) 0705 259336 (W) 0705 2551474.

Review of the Season

In our First Season of National Division we more than meet the challenge, only dropping 3 points but still finishing Top with Otley but losing out on promotion on points difference to Division Two.

In retrospect going from Diision.4 South to National Division Two would have been too big a step, and most members feel the New Division Three is a very attractive League.

14 Ex Colts were selected for 1st XV during the season including Captain Will Knight who started in Under 8 minis.

11 Members represented Hampshire in the A.D.T. County Championship in one fixture, which is Club Record.

The 2nd XV Dolphins represented Havant in the Hampshire Cup losing to Basingstoke in Semi Final.

3rd XV lost only one fixture but scored over 1000 points.

Mini, Juniors and Colts are still an essential part of the Club and thriving.

Ladies Team was seen for the first time at Hooks Lane and proved a great success.

Home spectator attendances have risen significantly and support to Away League Fixtures almost matched Home Support at some venues.

A Excellent Season.

Havant's forwards set up another attack in their efforts to win their last game of the season and a place in Division 2.

Havant RFC Squad and Officials 1992-93

188

HAVANT RFC

CLUB PLAYING RECORD 1992-93 SEASON

National Division: Three
Final League Position at end 1992/93 Season: 2nd
League Playing Record: P 11, W 8, D 1, L 2, Pts F 185, Pts A 93
Season Playing Record (including League matches/Pilkington cup etc): P 32, W 26, D 1, L 5, Pts F 810, Pts A 322

ADDITIONAL RESULTS 1992-93

No	Date	Opponents	Venue	Result
1	Sep 1	Newbury	H	W35-12
2	Sep 5	Sutton & Epsom	A	W8-6
3	Sep 12	High Wycombe	H	W14-13
4	Sep 19	London Welsh	A	L8-31
5	Oct 17	US Portsmouth	A	W26-0
6	Nov 7	Basingstoke	H	W26-25
7	Dec 5	Guildford	H	W27-12
8	Dec 12	St Marys Hosp	A	W46-3
9	Dec 19	Abbey	H	W37-5
10	Dec 26	Bournemouth	A	W22-3
11	Jan 2	Lewes	H	W51-
12	Jan 16	Jersey	A	W17-
13	Jan 23	Sidcup	H	W30-
14	Jan 30	L Scottish	H	W25-
15	Feb 6	Petersfield	H	W17-
16	Feb 20	Liverpool St Hel	H	W9-
17	Feb 20	Basingstoke	H	L9-
18	Feb 27	Rosslyn Park	A	L15-
19	Mar 6	Thurrock	H	W71-
20	Apr 3	Maidstone	A	W36-
21	Apr 10	Southend	H	W45-
22	Apr 17	Streatham/Croydon	H	W60-

COMPETITIONS WON DURING SEASON 1992-93

7 Counties Merit Winners
Bass Hants Cup Runners Up

PLAYING SQUAD 1992-93

Full Backs: R Ashworth, R Davey
Wings: J Bates, A Wilson, T Holmes
Centres: P Jenkins, S Boydell, S Parry, B Powell
S Off: P Russell, J Kaye
Scrum Half: I Tordey, B Gray
Props: D Rees, J Garrett, P Whittle, S Burns
Hookers: R Whitehead, M Vickers
Second Row: M Baldwin, G Curtis, B Rouse, S Morgan
Flankers: N Roach, N Berry, M Sheldon, B Smith
No. 8: W Knight, G Mullen

LEADING APPEARANCES 1992/93

R Ashworth, 29
R Whitehead, 26
D REes, 22
I Torpey, 22
M Baldwin, 22
R Davey, 21
J Garrett, 21
A Wilson, 20
J Bates, 20
W Knight, 18 (Capt)

LEADING SCORERS

R Ashworth, 147, (3T 28P 24C)
P Russell, 143 (5T 29C 18P 2DG)
J Buters, 100 (20T)
W Knight, 65 (13T)
N Roach, 45 (9T)
A Wilson, 40 (8T)
N Berry, 40 (8T)
P Jenkins, 35 (7T)
J Garrett, 35 (7T)
I Tompey, 25 (5T)
M Sheldon, 20, (4T)

HAVANT RFC

Club Details

Colours: Navy blue & white 4" hoops.
Change of Colours: Red.
Nickname: Hav
Date Founded: 1951.
Membership: Total 350, Full 150, Social 100, Junior/Youth/Minis 100.
Membership Fees: Full £30, Junior/Youth/Minis £20.
Number of Teams: Senior 6 + VETS, U21, U19, U17, Ladies, Junior.

Ground Details

Ground Address: Hooks Lane, Fraser Road, Bedhampton, Havant, Hants, PO9 3EJ.
Telephone: 0705 477843.
Directions: Fropm the A3(M) take B2177 to roundabout. Follow road signs to Bedhampton; straight over mini-roundabout. Straight across traffic lights then bear left at level crossing. Take second left (James Road) then left into Fraser Road at T- junction. Clubhouse is 200 yards on the right hand side.
Capacity: Total 3,000, Seated 200, Standing 2,800.
Ticket Prices: Adults £3.50 League £2.00 other.
Clubhouse Facilities: Two squash courts, large bar/function room, sunique "snug" bar.
Training Nights: Monday to Thursday.

MORLEY RFC

President: Jim Woodhead
Chairman: Trevor Richmond
Club Secretary: Bob Lloyd, 5 Shepley Bidge, Mirfield, West Yorkshire, WF14 9HR. Tel: (H) 0924 494612 (W) (Club Office) 0532 527598 Fax: (W) 0532 534144.
Fixtures Secretary: Brian Falshaw, 17 Rein Road, Morley, Leeds, LS27 0HZ. Tel: (H) 0532 539507 (C) 0836 610830.
Press Officer: G Fred Pickstone, Westbourne, St Andrews Avenue, Morley, Leeds, LS27 0JT. Tel: 0532 533508.
1993/94 1XV Captain: TBA
1993/94 1XV Coach: Robin Kay
Chairman of Rugby: H Chris L Leathley

Review of the Season

After the narrow escape from relegation in 1991-92, and drastic league reorganisation to come, we realised last September that to stay in Division 2 was going to be difficult, but not even the most pessimistic member foresaw such a disastrous league record. Our best result from the greatest commitment was at Wakefield where a decisive penalty went wide. We showed resilience, but faded in the final quarter, against Blackheath, the week after the club's heaviest defeat (at Nottingham). Against Fylde we were in front until the last five minutes and then thankful to gain a last gasp draw for our only point of the season.

Fifteen of twenty non-league games ended in our favour including one against Rugby from Division 1. From lower divisions only Bradford and Bingley beat us and we gained revenge later. In the Pilkington Cup we defeated Tynedale, giant killers of previous seasons, to reach round 4 for the first time.

Our re-formed U21 side had a remarkably good season, our colts retained the Yorkshire Cup and the Club's Junior Section continued to flourish at all ages. Many young players gained representative honours, notably flanker Ben Wade (Eng. Schools 18 gp) and threequarters Jonathan Shepherd (England Colts).

Some young players were given 1st XV experience and in the coming season a policy of youth development looks to be an important factor, if Morley are to survive in Division 3, which includes so many clubs that have accompanied them in dropping down from Division 2.

Morley v Blackheath — Tony Clark scoreing, Scott Benton looking on

Photo: Les Pratt

MORLEY RFC

CLUB PLAYING RECORD 1992-93 SEASON

National Division: Two
Final League Position at end 1992/93 Season: 13th
League Playing Record: P 12, W 0, D 1, L 11, Pts F 107, Pts A 374
Season Playing Record (including League matches/Pilkington cup etc): P 33, W 15, D 1, L 17, Pts F 597, Pts A 765

PLAYING SQUAD 1992-93

15: A Sales, J Hall, I Samuel
14: M Collins, M Lang, J Georgiou, S Wray
13: P White, J Georgiou, M Collins, A Crossley
12: C Emmerson, A Crossley, A Sales, J Georgious, M Collings, J Fieldhouse
11: T Clark, S Wray, J Georgiou, A Crossley
10: J Grayshon, G Jenkins, P White, J Georgiou
9: R Booth, S Cayzer, S Benton, J Tiffen
1: G Demaine, M Oxley, D McSwiney
2: A Bemrose, G Throup, D Irish
3: R Szabo, D McSwiney, M Faulkner
4: J Orwin, S Enright, C Holdsworth, G Parker, I Hill
5: N Kenyon, G Parker, C Holdsworth, D Falkingham, I Hill, J Stow
6: M Faulkner, J Moore, D Clarke, A Yule, A McGowan, B Wade
7: A Yule, J Moore, A McGowan, M Faulkner, D Topping, B Wade
8: D Clarke, G Parker, M Thomas, M Faulkner, I Hill

LEADING APPEARANCES FOR CLUB DURING SEASON 1992-93

P White, 31
G Demaine, 29
M Faulkner, 28
T Clark, 27
R Szabo, 27
J Orwin, 26

LEADING SCORERS

J Grayshon, Stand Off, 194
T Clark, Wing, 90
M Faulkner, Flanker, 45
P White, Centre, 25
M Thomas, No 8, 25
R Booth, Scrum Half, 22

MORLEY RFC

COURAGE LEAGUE RECORDS

HIGHEST SCORE : 49 v Liverpool St H (49-6) 14-3-92 Away CL2
LARGEST WINNING MARGIN : 43 As above
HIGHEST SCORE AGAINST : 78 v Nottingham (O-78) 24-1O-92 Away CL2
LARGEST LOSING MARGIN : 78 As above
DRAWN MATCHES : 3
CLEAN SHEETS : 2
FAILED TO SCORE : 4

INDIVIDUAL SCORING RECORDS
IN A MATCH

Most Points: 17 Jamie Grayshon v Birmingham 24-9-88 Away ALN
Most Tries: 3 Paul White v Winnington Park 28-4-9O Home ALN
Most Conversions: 5 Jamie Grayshon v Liverpool SH 14-3-92 Away CL2
Most Penalties: 4 Jamie Grayshon v Waterloo 1O-1O-92 Away CL2
Most Drop Goals: 2 Jamie Grayshon v Wakefield 13-2-93 Away CL2

IN A SEASON

Most Points: 91 Jamie Grayshon 1988-89 ALN
Most Tries: 6 Tony Clark 1988-89 ALN
Most Conversions: 9 Jamie Grayshon 1991-92 CL2
Most Penalties: 23 Jamie Grayshon 1988-89 ALN
Most Drop Goals: 3 Jamie Grayshon 1992-93 CL2

IN A CAREER

Most Points: 373 Jamie Grayshon 1987-93
Most Tries: 2O Tony Clark 1987-93
Most Conversions: 39 Jamie Grayshon 1987-93
Most Penalties: 83 Jamie Grayshon 1987-93
Most Drop Goals: 1O Jamie Grayshon 1987-93

SEASON BY SEASON LEADING SCORERS

	Most Points			Most Tries
1987-88	31	Jamie Grayshon	3	Tony Clark
1988-89	91	Jamie Grayshon	6	Tony Clark
1989-9O	78	Jamie Grayshon	5	Paul White
199O-91	5O	Jamie Grayshon	5	Mark Faulkner
1991-92	57	Jamie Grayshon	4	Tony Clark Martin Collins
1992-93	66	Jamie Grayshon	2	Tony Clark

MORLEY RFC

Club Details

Colours: Maroon, white & sky blue.
Change of Colours: Black.
Nickname: Maroons.
Date Founded: 1878.
Membership: Total 947, Full 585, Social 192, Junior/Youth/Minis 170.
Membership Fees: Full £40, Junior/Youth/Minis £7, Social £12.
Number of Teams: Senior 5, Junior & Colts 11.
Programme Advertising Rates: Full £280, Half £150, Qtr £80.

Ground Details

Ground Address: Scatchered Lane, Moreley, Leeds, LS27 0JJ.
Telephone: 0532 533487.
Fax: 0532 534144.
Directions: From West leave M62 Jcn 27, A650 to Wakefield 1.2 miles, turn left into St Andrews Avenue 0.3 miles to club. From East leave M62 Jcn 28, A650 to Bradford 1.7 miles, turn right into St Andrews Avenue 0.3 miles to club.
Capacity: Total 5,826, Seated 826, Standing 5,000.
Ticket Prices: Adult £3, OAP/Child/Student/Junior £1.50
Clubhouse Facilities: Three bars, function suite, president's lounge, physio room, office, club shop.
Training Nights: Monday & Thursday.

Morley v Middlesbrough — Stewart Cayzer passing the ball, Alistair Yule obscured by the referee!   Photo: Les Pratt

REDRUTH RFC

President: W J Bishop OBE JP
Chairman: W R Peters
Club Secretary: Ivor Horscroft, Silver Fields, Chapel Street, Redruth, Cornwall, TR15 2DT. Tel: (W) 0209 215941 Fax: (W) 0209 214019.
Fixtures Secretary: Jerry Penna, Chy Avalon, North Country, Redruth, Cornwall. Tel: (H) 0209 211520 (W) 0872 74282 Ext 2236.
Press Officer: N J Serpell, 68 Falmouth Road, Redruth, Cornwall, TR15 2QP.
1993/94 1XV Captain: Kevin Thomas
1993/94 1XV Coach: Terry Prior.

Review of the Season

Hopes were high that the Cornish club could survive a tough season and remain in the restructured Third Division. In the event they improved their standing by the necessary one place although the fact that the top four clubs were separated by one point at the end showed just how hard the battle had been.

The first half of the season promised much with all the home league games being won. Wins away against Plymouth and Leeds and a fiercely fought draw at Havant put the club within striking distance of the top of the division. Unfortunately the Christmas period saw a falling off in form.

Sheffield, on their first visit to Hell Fire Corner took advantage of this low point and the Reds went down 11-20. However the team picked themselves up and a superb performance at Otley saw the game shared. The two remaining home wins saw Third Division status secured.

In the Pilkington cup the club reached the fourth round for the first time in its history going down at home to Exeter. The club won the Bass Cornwall Knock Out Cup by beating St.Ives in the final.

Redruth in action against Sheffield

Photo: Packet Newspapers

Camborne visit Redruth

196

REDRUTH RFC

CLUB PLAYING RECORD 1992-93 SEASON

National Division: Three
Final League Position at end 1992/93 Season: 4th
League Playing Record: P 11, W 7, D 2, L 2, Pts F 175, Pts A 125
Season Playing Record (including League matches/Pilkington cup etc): P 38, W30, D 5, L 3, Pts F 815, Pts A 390

ADDITIONAL RESULTS 1992-93

No	Date	Opponents	Venue	Result
1	Sep 5	Taunton	H	W27-13
2	Sep 6	Richard Brighton XV	H	W38-26
3	Sep 8	Devonport Services	A	W54-3
4	Sep 12	Brixham	H	D20-20
5	Sep 19	Camborne	A	W24-11
6	Oct 17	Launceston	A	L11-18
7	Nov 7	Bridgewater & Albion	A	W7-3
8	Nov 28	L Welsh	H	W16-7
9	Dec 6	Launceston	H	W14-8
10	Dec 12	Penryn	A	W16-14
11	Dec 19	Penzance Newlyn	H	W27-0
12	Dec 26	Camborne	H	L9-40
13	Dec 28	Newquay	A	W12-3
14	Jan 2	Liskeard Looe	A	W17-3
15	Jan 16	Launceston	A	W10-3
16	Jan 23	Exeter	H	L3-8
17	Jan 30	Truro	H	W29-5
18	Feb 16	Stroud	H	W10-3
19	Feb 27	Camborne	A	W12-3
20	Mar 6	Penzance Newlyn	A	W27-12
21	Mar 20	Penryn	H	W26-8
22	Mar 27	Weston-Super-Mare	A	W29-25
23	Apr 9	St Marys Hosp	H	W50-7
24	Apr 10	Camborne	A	W25-16
25	Apr 12	Rugby	H	W40-0
26	Apr 17	Truro	A	W59-0
27	Apr 27	St Ives	A	W28-6

COMPETITIONS WON DURING SEASON 1992-93

Bass Cornwall K O Cup

PLAYING SQUAD 1992-93

Full Backs: K Thomas, S Blake
Wings: M Gomez, T Mead, A Knowles, S Wilkins, J Bownden
Centres: G Champion, A Bowden
Outside Halves: S Whitworth, M Handlye, S Moyle
Scrum Half: C Whitworth, C Read
Props: A Ellery, E Cowie, R Keast, R Tonkin, K Huxtable, J May
Hookers: B Andrew, M Phillips
Second Row: T Cook, D Roberts, P Elliott, I Eslick, S O'Sullivan
Flankers: S Roberts, G Williams, A Curtis, M Stearn
Locks: J Wedlake, A Hawken, D Penberthy

MOST CAPPED PLAYERS

including British Lions Appearances

R Sharp, 17
E Scott, 5
J Davey, 2
D Prout, 1
W Grylls, 1
B Solomon, 1

LEADING APPEARANCES FOR CLUB DURING SEASON 1992-93

A Ellery, 31
A Knowles, 30
K Thomas, 29
A Bowden, 28
T Cook, 27
C Whitworth, 27
G Williams, 27

LEADING SCORERS

K Thomas, Full Back, 198 (T4 C26 P42)
G Champion, Centre, 69 (T5 C10 P47 D1)
S Blake, Full Back 67 (T1 C13 P12)
A Knowles, Wing, 65 (T13)
C Whitworth, Scrum Half, 48 (T9 D1)
M Gomez, Wing, 35 (T7)

REDRUTH RFC

Club Details

Colours: Red.
Change of Colours: Black.
Nickname: The Reds.
Date Founded: 1875.
Membership: Total 1,057, Full 775, Social 100, Junior/Youth/Minis 177.
Membership Fees: Full £20, Junior/Youth/Minis £10, Social £5.
Number of Teams: Senior 4, Junior 12.

Ground Details

Ground Address: The Recreation Ground, North Street, Redruth, Cornwall.
Telephone: 0209 215520.
Directions: A30 West through Cornwall, leave at Redruth exit, over twin roundabouts then down hill past Avers Garage. Ground signposted on left at bottom junction.
Capacity: Total 15,000, Seated 670, Standing 14,330.
Ticket Prices: Adult £3 Ground £4 Stand, OAP/Child £1.50/£2
Clubhouse Facilities: Sponsors Bar, Lounge Bar, General Bar, Car parking.
Training Nights: Tuesday & Thursday.
Special Occassions in 1993-94
Hosting S.W. Division v All Blacks (30 October 1993).

RICHMOND FC

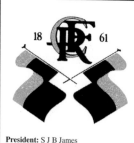

President: S J B James
Chairman: A P Hallett
Club Secretary: A V H Skeats, The Athletic Ground, Kew Foot Road, Richmond, Surrey, TW9 2SS. Tel: (H) 0932 567 573
Fixtures Secretary: V R Balchin, 11 Troutbeck Close, Twyford, Berks, RG10 9DA. Tel: (H) 0734 345765.
Press Officer: V J Cordington, The Athletic Ground, Kew Foot Road, Richmond, Surrey, TW9 2SS.
1993/94 1XV Coach: John Kingston
Director of Rugby: V J Cordington

Review of the Season

Highlights of the season were a fine away win at Northampton, a victory over Saracens and two drubbings of London Scottish. Two Argentinian XV's Banco Nationale and Lince were comprehensively beaten but form in the league was disappointing and at times inept and ill-disciplined.

Games expected to be won were thrown away although there were comprehensive wins ever Fylde and Morley and a victory snatched from the jaws of defeat at Coventry.

Selection policy opted for continuity but only in the friendly non-pressure games did the players at times live up to expectations.

There was no real success either in the Pilkington Cup, the club going out in the 3rd Round at home to Wakefield after an earlier win over Sudbury.

Martin Livesey established another record points tally and gradually through the season a number of U21 players emerged at top levels. They had come from the XV which won every game but one — that was drawn — amassing 930 points for and only 136 against.

Late success was gained in winning the Middlesex Sevens Plate Competition and the club is encouraged by the loyalty of the vast majority of players remaining at Richmond.

Gavin Thompson with the ball for Harlequin as Richmond defend   Photo: Joe McCabe

Richmond FC 1992-93. Standing: Amanda Watts (Physio), David Hilliard (Head Coach), Doug Goodwin, Jamie Allen, Daryl Sinclair, Phil Della-Sarina, Adrian McKay, Rob Rydon, Paul Carr, Jonathan Lewis, Eban Rollit, Tony Clucker, James Cook, Mart Venner, Peter Halsall (Asst. Coach), Mel Jones (1st XV Manager). Sitting: Dean Jeffrey, Jim Foster, Howard Lamb: Martin Livesey, Paul Greenwood, Tony Hallet (Chairman), Kevin Borocvich (Captain), Alan Skeats (Secretary), Doug Elliott, Chris Hornung, Jason Head, Jonathan Clark.

RICHMOND FC

Club Details

Colours: Old gold, red & black hoops.
Change of Colours: Black.
Date Founded: 1871.
Membership: Total 1,100, Full 600, Social 250, Junior/Youth/Minis 250.
Membership Fees: Full £45, Junior/Youth/Minis £20, Family £250.
Number of Teams: Senior 4, Junior 5.
Programme Advertising Rates: Full £1,000.

Ground Details

Ground Address: The Athletic Ground, Kew Foot Road, Richmond, Surrey TW9 2SS.
Telephone: 081 332 7112. **Fax:** 081 332 6775.
Directions: From M3 head East to London on A316. Three minutes from Richmond station.
Capacity: Total 4,840, Seated 840, Standing 4,000.
Ticket Prices: Adult £5.
Clubhouse Facilities: Members' bar/dining area, public bar, refreshments, club shop.
Training Nights: Monday & Wednesday.

ADDITIONAL RESULTS 1992-93

No	Date	Opponents	Venue	Result
1		London Welsh	H	W21-12
2		Northampton	A	W30-14
3		Basingstoke	A	W32-17
4		Nottingham	A	L12-17
5		Fylde	H	W29-6
6		Bedford	A	L16-22
7		Moseley	H	W28-21
8		L Scottish	A	W48-13
9		Sale	A	L10-21
10		Waterloo	H	L12-16
11		Sudbury	H	W37-5
12		L Irish	A	L12-16
13		Blackheath	H	L13-23
14		Wakefield	H	L22-25
15		Sheffield	A	W15-7
16		Bath	H	L22-38
17		L Scottish	A	W30-16
18		Harlequins	A	L30-34
19		Saracens	H	W14-5
20		Coventry	A	W18-13
21		Askeans	H	W5-21
22		Middlesbrough	H	W21-20
23		Nottingham	H	L13-20
24		N Gosforth	A	L9-20
25		L Irish	A	L18-19
26		Royal Navy	A	D23-23
27		Gloucester	A	L15-24
28		Banco de National	H	W57-29
29		Morley	A	W28-6
30		Los Linces	H	W57-29
31		Wakefield	H	W11-6
32		Leicester	H	L17-29
33		Met Police	A	W29-12
34		Rosslyn Park	A	L18-24

CLUB PLAYING RECORD 1992-93 SEASON

National Division: Two
Playing Record: P 34, W 18, L 15, D 1, Pts F 818, Pts A 650

PLAYING SQUAD 1992-93

Full Backs: J Clark, M Fairn
Wings: P Greenwood, A McKay, C Lloyd, M Hutton
Centres: D Elliott, P McAllister, R Rydon, J Cook
Fly Half: M Livesey, J Hoady, D Morris
Scrum Half: C Luxton, C Hornung
Props: K Borocvich, J Foster, D Sinclair
Hookers: J Allan, D Jeffrey
Second Row: P Carr, J Lewis, D Cooper
Flankers: H Lamb, P Della-Sarina, G Taylor, J Bower
No. 8: D Sole, E Rollitt

MOST CAPPED PLAYERS

including British Lions Appearances
A S Gould, 27
T P Reynolds, 25
P W Kininmouth, 21
C W Ralson, 21
N M Hall, 17
E T Gurdon, 16

TOP SCORERS

Martin Livesey 3T 43C 49P 4DG, Pts 650
Jonathan Clark 4T 15C 22P, Pts 116
Paul Greenwood 13T, Pts 65

RICHMOND FC

COURAGE LEAGUE RECORDS

HIGHEST SCORE : 86 v Headingley (86-8) 28-4-9O Home CL2
LARGEST WINNING MARGIN : 78 As above
HIGHEST SCORE AGAINST : 5O v Sale (9-5O) 1O-9-88 Away CL2
LARGEST LOSING MARGIN : 41 As above
DRAWN MATCHES : 4
CLEAN SHEETS : O
FAILED TO SCORE : 1

INDIVIDUAL SCORING RECORDS
IN A MATCH

Most Points: 2O Nick Preston v Bedford 27-3-88 Home CL2
Most Tries: 3 Phil Della-Savina v Nuneaton 28-3-92 Home CL3
Most Conversions: 7 Martin Livesey v Sheffield 25-4-92 Home CL3
Most Penalties: 6 Nick Preston v Bedford 27-3-88 Home CL2,
Martin Livesey v London Irish 8-4-89 Home CL2, Jon Clark v Lydney 14-3- 92 Home CL3
Most Drop Goals: 3 Martin Livesey v Northampton 19-11-88 CL2

IN A SEASON

Most Points: 12O Martin Livesey 1989-9O CL2
Most Tries: 7 Jim Fallon 1989-9O CL2
Most Conversions: 24 Martin Livesey 1989-9O CL2
Most Penalties: 2O Martin Livesey 1989-9O CL2 & 1992-93 CL2
Most Drop Goals: 6 Martin Livesey 1991-92 CL3

IN A CAREER

Most Points: 422 Martin Livesey 1988-93
Most Tries: 1O Mike Hutton 1988-93
Most Conversions: 6O Martin Livesey 1988-93
Most Penalties: 83 Martin Livesey 1988-93
Most Drop Goals: 12 Martin Livesey 1988-93

SEASON BY SEASON LEADING SCORERS

	Most Points			Most Tries
1987-88	6O	Simon Smith	5	Simon Pennock
1988-89	74	Martin Livesey	3	Paul Seccombe
1989-9O	12O	Martin Livesey	7	Jim Fallonon
199O-91	38	Martin Livesey	6	Mike Hutton
1991-92	95	Martin Livesey	6	Phil Della-Savina
1992-93	95	Martin Livesey	3	David Sole

ROSSLYN PARK FC

President: Dick Malthouse
Chairman: Roy Renolds
Club Secretary: David E Whittam FRCS, 37 Queens Road, Kingston upon Thames, Surrey, KT2 7SL. Tel: (H) 081 549 4209 (W) 081 672 1225 Ext 5205 Fax: (W) 081 944 8059.
Fixtures Secretary: Colin Horgan, Tylery, Parke Road, Sunbury on Thames,Middlesex, TW16 8BS. Tel: (H) 0932 785012.
Press Officer: Bernard Wiggins, 2 Beardsfolly Cottages, New Way Lane, Hurstpierpoint, West Sussex, BN6 9BD. Tel: (H) 0273 844028 (W) 0273 723434.
1993/94 1XV Captain: Andrew Holder
1993/94 1XV Coach: Roger Allison
Director of Rugby: Peter Berryman
Club Administrator: Rose Tanner.

Review of the Season

Sadly the high hopes that Park would manage to return to Division 1 were very soon dashed with an early season crop of injuries from which the Team never really recovered. A last minute penalty in the first League match was going to herald another season of near misses as far as League football was concerned. In two or three of the League matches which were of vital importance for survival Park went down by a single score and it thus became evident that with the seven teams being relegated Park were going to be one of them.

Albeit a fairly bleak season there were one or two promising young players emerging from the Under 21 Squad and that Team as a whole on a short post season to Spain showed that there is every reason to be optimistic about the future, that is of course providing the players stay at the Club, and as is becoming all too evident now players are beginning to polarise into one of three or four Clubs which is not a healthy thing as many people believe for the game.

The coming season is going to be a difficult one for many clubs and some believe it will be too much for some of them. The heavy League programme with Cup games involved will test the determination and physical ability of many players albeit in what is basically an amateur game. Hopefully with a new band of young enthusiastic players coupled with a new Director of Rugby, Park will be able to return once more to the higher echelons of the game.

Rosslyn Park 1st XV 1992-93

ROSSLYN PARK FC

CLUB PLAYING RECORD 1992-93 SEASON

National Division: Two
Final League Position at end 1992/93 Season: 8th
League Playing Record: P 12, W 5, D 0, L 7, Pts F 209, Pts A 199
Season Playing Record (including League matches/Pilkington cup etc): P 35, W 16, D 0, L 19, Pts F 726, Pts A 592

ADDITIONAL RESULTS 1992-93

No	Date	Opponents	Venue	Result
1	Sep 5	Coventry	H	L15-20
2	Sep 9	Maidenhead	H	W65-13
3	Sep 12	L Irish	A	W17-0
4	Sep 23	Ealing	A	W20-13
5	Sep 26	Walsall	H	W45-0
6	Oct 17	Cambridge U	A	W21-17
7	Nov 7	Plymouth	H	W49-3
8	Nov 14	L Scottish	H	L15-20
9	Nov 28	Wasps	H	L10-37
10	Dec 5	Moseley	H	L13-34
11	Dec 12	Saracens	A	L3-20
12	Dec 19	L Irish	H	W16-5
13	Jan 2	Bedford	H	L9-20
14	Jan 16	L Welsh	A	W16-8
15	Jan 23	Gloucester	A	L3-10
16	Jan 28	Eastwood (Australia)	H	L3-16
17	Jan 30	Wasps	A	L11032
18	Feb 6	Leicester	A	L10-52
19	Feb 20	Notingham	A	L15-17
20	Feb 27	Havant	H	W26-15
21	Mar 5	Streatham & Croydon		W82-0
22	Mar 20	Blackheath	H	W31-18
23	Apr 10	Bath	A	Cancelled
24	Apr 17	Harlequins	H	L22-23

MOST CAPPED PLAYERS

including British Lions Appearances

J Scott, 34
M Conclough, 25
A Ripley, 24
C Winn, 8
P Warfield, 8
C Kent, 5

LEADING APPEARANCES FOR CLUB DURING SEASON 1992-93

I Pickup, 30
R Moon, 24
A Holder, 22
S Roiser, 22
M Horrocks-Taylor, 21
J Graves, 20

LEADING SCORERS

J Graves, Full Back, 179
G Abraham, Fly Half, 115
Griffiths, Wing, 40
P Essenhigh, Prop, 40
P Roslin, Fly Half, 40
A Holder, Centre, 32

ROSSLYN PARK FC

COURAGE LEAGUE RECORDS

HIGHEST SCORE : 48 v Northampton (48-O) 27-4-91 Home CL1
LARGEST WINNING MARGIN : 48 As above
HIGHEST SCORE AGAINST : 64 v Orrell (14-64) 28-4-9O Away CL1
LARGEST LOSING MARGIN : 5O As above
DRAWN MATCHES : 3
CLEAN SHEETS : 2
FAILED TO SCORE : O

INDIVIDUAL SCORING RECORDS
IN A MATCH

Most Points: 22 John Graves v Coventry 13-2-93 Home CL2
Most Tries: 2 On 1O Occasions by 7 players, most times Mark Jermyn 3
Most Conversions: 4 John Graves v Bedford 31-3-9O Home CL1, v Liverpool SH 23-3-91 Home CL2
Most Penalties: 6 Gary Abraham v Morley 27-3-93 Home CL2
Most Drop Goals: 2 Paul Roblin v Goucester 4-1-92 CL1

IN A SEASON

Most Points: 92 John Graves 199O-91 CL1
Most Tries: 6 Tony Brooks 1987-88 CL2
Most Conversions: 12 John Graves 1988-89 CL1 & 199O-91 CL1
Most Penalties: 21 John Graves 1989-9O CL1
Most Drop Goals: 2 Paul Roblin 1991-92 CL1

IN A CAREER

Most Points: 444 John Graves 1987-93
Most Tries: 1O Tony Brooks 1987-93
Most Conversions: 43 John Graves 1987-93
Most Penalties: 111 John Graves 1987-93
Most Drop Goals: 4 Mark Jermyn 1987-93

SEASON BY SEASON LEADING SCORERS

		Most Points		Most Tries
1987-88	73	John Graves	6	Tony Brooks
1988-89	78	John Graves	3	Simon Hunter Richard Crawford Rob Nelson-Williams
1989-9O	87	John Graves	4	Mark Jermyn
199O-91	92	John Graves	3	Peter Taylor Guy Leleu Kelvin Wyles
1991-92	53	John Graves	2	Mark Thomas
1992-93	61	John Graves Gary Abraham	3	Paul Essenhigh

ROSSLYN PARK FC

Club Details
Colours: Red & white hoops.
Change of Colours: Dark Blue.
Nickname: The Park.
Date Founded: 1879.
Membership: Total 900, Full 700, Junior/Youth/Minis 150.
Membership Fees: Full £58, Junior/Youth/Minis £10, Other £50.
Number of Teams: Senior 4, Junior 5.
Programme Advertising Rates: Full £280.

Ground Details
Ground Address: Priory Lane, Roehampton, London, SW15 5JH.
Telephone: 081 876 1879.
Fax: 081 878 7527.
Directions: Ground situated at the junction of Upper Richmond Road (South Circular) and Roehampton Lane.
Capacity: Total 4,630, Seated 630, Standing 4,000.
Ticket Prices: Adults £5, OAP/Child £2.50.
Clubhouse Facilities: Large public bar, members bar, Presidents room, Kit & souvenir shop, cafteria, sponsors room.
Training Nights: Tuesday & Thursday.

Rosslyn Park's Gareth Allison about to clear his lines against Wakefield

LEAGUE THREE PROGRAMMES

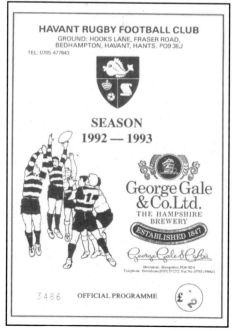

LEAGUE THREE PROGRAMMES

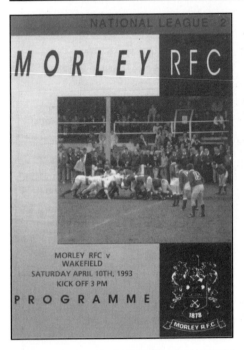

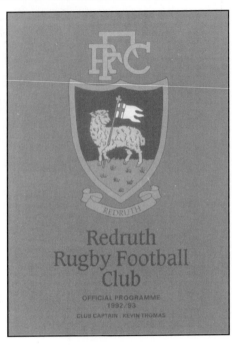

IN NEXT YEAR'S DIRECTORY

We will be publishing a full Match Day Programme survey giving prices, number of pages, pages of editorial, photos etc.

NATIONAL
LEAGUE
FOUR

MEMBER CLUBS
1993-94

THE BEST PACK IN THE CHAMPIONSHIP.

ASKEANS RFC

President: D S Wickerson
Chairman: W J Ruston
Club Secretary: Graham Terry, End Waye, Brookhurst Gardens, Southborough, Tunbridge Wells, Kent, TN4 0UA. Tel: (H) 0892 528996 (W) 071 387 9366
Fixtures Secretary: Mike Sidewick, 83 Borkwood Way, Orpington, Kent, BR6 9PB. Tel: 0689 857436.
Press Officer: John Ratcliffe, Boughtons, Leafy Grove, Keston, Kent. Tel: 0689 851846
1993/94 1XV Captain: Pete Rauh
1993/94 1XV Coach: Steve Hill

Review of the Season

The season 1992-93 was a tough and difficult one. Failure to retain a place in the third division was obviously a disappointment. However the loss of a number of talented players through injury and work commitments depleted our squad so that relegation to league 4 was hardly surprising. In fact the last five league games were all lost, partly due to the small size of the 1st XV squad.

However, all was not doom and gloom as our speedy bucks ran in 75 of the 99 scored during the season, Jamie Graham, Rob Subbians, Dave Osbourne and Chris Johns leading the way.

Most of the side will hopefully return next season and under coach Steve Hill and new skipper Peter Rauh 1993-94 should be better.

CLUB PLAYING RECORD 1992-93 SEASON

National Division: Three
League Playing Record: P 11, W 3, D 0, L 8, Pts F 132, Pts A 300
Season Playing Record (including League matches/Pilkington cup etc):
P 34, W 21, D 0, L 13, Pts F 720, Pts A 658

Askeans RFC 1992-93

ASKEANS RFC

PLAYING SQUAD 1992-93

Full Backs: D Russell, R Subbiani, M Crisp
Wings: D Osbourne, C Johns, R Graham
Centres: J Graham, S Montgomery, P Fletcher
Fly Half: C Taylor
Scrum Half: N Beytell, H Evans
Props: F Croxford, D Davies, R Hudson, S McManus, J Green
Hookers: A Gill, P Miles
Second Row: G Hill, T Crowe, C Trembath, M Fisher
Flankers: S Children, W Walker, T Keepax, S Francis, J Ohanlon, D Holroyd
No. 8: D Holder, S Hill

ADDITIONAL RESULTS 1992-93

No	Date	Opponents	Venue	Result
1	Sep 1	Old Colfeians	H	W11-6
2	Sep 5	Streatham & Croydon	H	W31-13
3	Sep 9	Harlequins	A	L12-85
4	Sep 12	Nuneaton	H	W45-11
5	Sep 19	Ruislip	H	W24-0
6	Sep 26	Ealing	H	W32-16
7	Oct 3	Loughborough Students	H	W44-0
8	Nov 7	Bedford	A	L12-21
9	Nov 29	Charlton Park	A	W48-3
10	Dec 5	Southend	A	W20-13
11	Dec 12	Sidcup	H	W34-3
12	Dec 19	Westcombe Park	H	W19-8
13	Jan 2	Sutton & Epsom	A	W34-30
14	Jan 16	Richmond	A	L21-51
15	Jan 24	Blackheath	H	W17-15
16	Jan 30	Bedford	H	L12-20
17	Feb 6	Cambridge University	A	W32-9
18	Feb 20	Blackheeath	A	W20-13
19	Feb 28	Thanet Wanderers	H	W28-3
20	Mar 6	Metropolitan Police	A	W27-11
21	Apr 10	Basingstoke	H	W27-9

MOST CAPPED PLAYERS

including British Lions Appearances
J A Gallagher, 18, 1987-89

LEADING APPEARANCES FOR CLUB

G Wickens, 546, 1953-79
P Dessent, 465, 1968-86
S Homewood, 427, 1972-88
D Kirby, 376, 1952-81
G Smith, 373, 1954-73
N Lockyer, 362, 1972-91

LEADING SCORERS (1992/93 Season)

C Taylor, Fly Half, 167
J Graham, Centre, 124
C Johns, Wing, 77
D Osbourne, Wing, 70
R Subbiani, Wing/Full Back, 60

ASKEANS RFC

COURAGE LEAGUE RECORDS
Highest score: 36 v Lydney (36-0) 11-1-92 Home CL3
Largest winning margin: 36 as above
Highest score against: 61 v Otley (6-61) 27-3-93 Away CL3
Largest losing margin: 55 as above
Drawn Matches: 5
Clean Sheets: 3
Failed to score: 0

INDIVIDUAL SCORING RECORDS
IN A MATCH
Most points: Colin Taylor v Plymouth 31-10-92 Away CL3
Most tries: 2 Jon Satterley v London Welsh 14-10-89 Home CL3, Chris Johns v Lydney 30-3-90 Away CL3, Steve Francis v Lydney 11- 1-92 Home CL3, David Osbourne v lydney 11-1-92 Home CL3
Most conversions: 4 Gareth Hughes v Lydney 11-1-92 Home CL3
Most penalities: 4 Aled Hughes v Vale of Lune 18-11-89 Home CLE, v Nuneaton 10-3-90 Home CL3
Most drop goals: Rob Gilden v Roundhay 28-4-90 Home CL3

IN A SEASON
Most points: 78 John Field 1988-89 CL3
Most tries: 6 Jon Satterley 1989-90 CL3
Most conversions: 10 John Field 1988-89 CL3
Most penalties: 18 John Field 1988-89 CL3
Most drop goals: 5 Rob Gilden 1989-90 CL3

IN A CAREER
Most points: 143 John Field 1988-92
Most tries: 13 Jaime Grahame 1989-93
Most conversions: 17 John Field 1988-92
Most penalties: 34 John Field 1988-92
Most drop goals: 6 Rob Gilden 1989-91

SEASON BY SEASON LEADING SCORERS

	Most Points			Most Tries
1988-89	78	John Field	2	G Jaques H Coirliss G Francis
1989-90	36	Aled Hughes	6	Jon Satterley
1990-91	65	John Field	3	Jaime Graham
1991-92	62	Gareth Hughes	4	Jaime Grahame
1992-93	68	Colin Taylor	3	Jamie Grahame

ASKEANS RFC

Club Details

Colours: Blue, black & white
Change of Colours: White with blue & black hoops
Date Founded: 1929
Membership: Total 625, Full 325, Social 150, Junior/Youth/Minis 150
Membership Fees: Full TBA, Junior/Youth/Minis £5.
Number of Teams: Senior 5, Junior 6
Programme Advertising Rates: TBA

ASKEAN

FOUNDED 1929

RUGBY FOOTBALL CLUB

Clubhouse & Ground: 60A BROAD WALK, KIDBROOKE, LONDON SE3 8NB.

Official Programme

Season 1992/93

Ground Details

Ground Address: 60A Broad Walk, Kidbrooke, London, SE3 8NB
Telephone: 081 856 1025
Directions: By train. Network South-East from Charing Cross, Waterloo East or London Bridge to Kidbrooke (25 min). Turn right out of station approach, join Kidbrooke Park Road, signposted "Local Traffic", then first right into Kidbrooke Way leading into Rochester Way. Broad Walk is the second turning on the left (10 mins). Llok for RAC sign marked "Askean RFC".
From South & West. Leave M25 at Jcn 2 (A2 London). Follow signs for London and after 10 miles take Kidbrooke Station turn off. At traffic lights (100 yards) turn right, marked "Local Traffic" into Kidbrook Park Road, then right again at next turning into Kidbrook Way, leading into Rochester Way. Broad Walk is the second turning on the left.
From Midlands and North. Leave M25 at Jcn with M11. At end of M11 follow signs A406 (Barking). Join A13 (London). Follow road to Blackwall Tunnel. Go through tunnel and continue to traffic lights, keep left and follow "Local traffic" signs. Bear left into Rochester Way and Broad Walk is the first turning on the left.
Capacity: Total 1,500, Seated 300, Standing 1,200
Ticket Prices: Adult £3
Clubhouse Facilities: Hall, 3 bars, squash courts, weights room.
Training Nights: Tuesday & Thursday

COURAGE
CLUBS CHAMPIONSHIP

214

ASPATRIA RUFC

President: N Lazonby
Chairman: D Miller
Club Secretary: M Hanley, 7 King Street, Aspatria, Cumbria, CA5 3AD. Tel: (H) 06973 20328 (W) 0946 815111 Fax: (W) 0946 815082
Fixtures Secretary: P Gray, Ingledene, 4 Queen Street, Aspatria, Cumbria, CA5 3AP. Tel: (H) 06973 21760
Press Officer: M Hanley (address as above)
1993/94 1XV Captain: Mark Richardson
1993/94 1XV Coach: David Robinson
Director of Coaching: Tom Borthwick

Review of the Season

The 1st XV had a poor start to the season and found National League Rugby a higher standard and faster pace than anticipated. It wasn't until the latter half of the season did the team get a consistent run together. We picked up 5 late league points the, finale coming against Havant on the last Saturday of the season.

Prior to this we won the Cumbria Cup for the 14th time in 16 years, with good derby wins over neighbours Wigton and Kendal. During 1992-93 we supplied eight players for the Cumbria County side.

In October 1992 we started a new changing room development which was completed in March 1993. We can now boast some of the finest facilities in the North of England. Our 2nd XV won the Cumbria Shield title and our 3rd XV had a record season scoring over 1000 points, so even though our league position could have been better it was far from a poor year.

CLUB PLAYING RECORD 1992-93 SEASON

National Division: Three
Final League Position at end 1992/93 Season: 9th
League Playing Record: P 11, W 3, D 1, L 7, Pts F 170, Pts A 308
Season Playing Record (including League matches/Pilkington cup etc): P 30, W 15, D 1, L 14, Pts F 533, Pts A 604

Aspatria RUFC 1992-93

ASPATRIA RUFC

Club Details

Colours: Black with red hoops
Change of Colours: Red shirts
Nickname: The Black/Reds
Date Founded: 1875
Membership: Total 970, Full 300, Social 600, Junior/Youth/Minis 70.
Membership Fees: Full £5, Junior/Minis £1
Number of Teams: Senior 3, Junior 2
Programme Advertising Rates: £100 per page

Ground Details

Ground Address: Bower Park, Station Road, Aspatria, Cumbria, CA5 2AJ.
Telephone: 06973 20420
Capacity: Unlimited with 250 seated.
Ticket Prices: Adult £3, OAP/Child £1.50
Clubhouse Facilities: Lounge, floodlights, meeting room, function room
Training Nights: Tuesday & Thursday

Special Occasions during 1993/94:

Opening of new changing room complex.

COMPETITIONS WON DURING SEASON 1992-93

Cumbria Cup Winners

ADDITIONAL RESULTS 1992-93

No	Date	Opponents	Venue	Result
1	Sep 5	Glasgow HK	H	W28-17
2	Sep 12	Fylde	A	L12-19
3	Sep 19	Bradford & Bingley	A	L9-23
4	Sep 26	Rugby	A	L19-60
5	Oct 17	Tynedale	A	L10-37
6	Nov 7	Northern	H	W20-0
7	Nov 28	Selkirk	A	L9-14
8	Dec 12	Kirkby Lonsdale	H	L6-11
9	Dec 19	Hartlepool Rovers	H	L8-21
10	Dec 26	Wigton	A	W16-10
11	Jan 16	Middlesbrough	H	W8-5
12	Jan 19	Carlisle	A	W12-9
13	Jan 30	Kelso	H	L12-14
14	Feb 6	Morley	A	L17-19
15	Feb 27	Durham City	H	W50-12

PLAYING SQUAD 1992-93

Full Backs: P Cusack, K Bethwaite
Wings: J Miller, C Marriott, D Murray, K McCartney
Centres: M Southward, N Winterton, B Stephenson, K Hetherington
Fly Half: A Harrison, A Guthrie
Scrum Half: S Doggart, D Petch
Props: S Irving, A Day, R Gypp, J McCune
Hookers: R Crichton, N Brown
Lock: T Clemenston, F Story, M Richardson, L Dent
Flankers: S Urquhart, N Wedgewood, M Maughan, M Brown, D Benson
No. 8: P Hancock

LEADING SCORERS (1992/93 Season)

A Harrison, Fly Half/Scrum Half, 169

BROUGHTON PARK FC

President: Laurie Rimmer
Chairman: Billy Seddon
Club Secretary: Ron Greenall, 260 Barlow Moor Road, Chorlton, Manchester, M21 2HA. Tel: 061 861 0457
Fixtures Secretary: David Ramsbottom, 9 Yewtree Grove, Heald Green, Cheadle, Cheshire, SK8 3TJ.
Press Officer: Don Evans, 71 Claude Road, Chorltonville, Manchester, M21 1DE. Tel: 061 881 6705
1993/94 1XV Captain: Chris Allen
1993/94 1XV Coach: B Jackson, P Stenhouse, M Mousdale

Review of the Season

The first XV playing record — certainly the worst for more than 35 years — was largely due to a depressing series of injuries which resulted in 47 players appearing for the 1st team. The pack was particularly affected and no less than seventeen different pairs played in the second row. Good possession, particularly from line-outs, was restricted which blunted the potential of some talented backs. When at full strength some exciting football was played and more than half the tries were scored by wing three quarters. Player of the year, right wing Martin Kelly, got 22 touchdowns and Steve Brown on the left came back from injury with 11 touchdowns in 17 games. With a strengthened squad the club look forward to a better season in 1993-94.

The second team, skippered by Kevin O'Brien, played enterprising rugby to win the Northern Merit table for second teams and the strength of the thriving junior section was rewarded when one of the mini teams won a "warm-up" game at Twickenham before the Pilkington Cup Final. Finally John Russell helped Lancashire retain the County Championship.

CLUB PLAYING RECORD 1992-93 SEASON

National Division: Three
Final League Position at end 1992/93 Season: 11th
League Playing Record: P 11, W 2, D 0, L 9, Pts F 136, Pts A 217
Season Playing Record (including League matches/Pilkington cup etc): P 33, W 12, D 0, L 21, Pts F 571, Pts A 581

Broughton Park FC   *Photo: John Fryer*

Broughton Park v Lichfield, Feb '93. Graham Higginbotham makes the tackle, Craig Tatton in support

Photo: John Fryer

BROUGHTON PARK FC

Club Details

Colours: Black & White
Change of Colours: Pale blue
Nickname: Park
Date Founded: 1882
Club Membership: Total 420, Full 160, Social 100, Junior/Youth/Minis 160
Membership fees: Full £40, Junior/Youth £15, Mini £10
Number of Teams: Senior 4, Junior 11
Programme Advertising Rates: TBA

Ground Details

Ground Address: Chelsfield Grove, Mauldeth Road, West Chorlton, Manchester, M21 5SU
Telephone: 061 881 2481
Directions: From end of M56 follow signs to city centre Manchester. At the fifth set of traffic lights turn left into Mauldeth Road West and follow road for 3/4 mile.
Capacity: Total 2,000, Seated, 400, Standing 1,600
Ticket Prices: Adults £2, Student/Junior/U16/OAP £1
Clubhouse Facilities: Clubroom/bar, lounge, kitchen
Training Nights: Tuesday & Thursday

ADDITIONAL RESULTS 1992-93

No	Date	Opponents	Venue	Result
1	Sep 2	Wigan	A	L6-14
2	Sep 5	Widnes	H	W14-3
3	Sep 12	Waterloo	H	L6-18
4	Sep 19	Vipers	A	W15-5
5	Oct 17	Vale of Lune	H	W51-18
6	Nov 7	Morley	A	L7-39
7	Dec 5	Morley	H	L10-17
8	Dec 12	Stourbridge	A	W19-9
9	Dec 19	Orrell	A	L0-11
10	Dec 30	Preston Grasshoppers	A	L12-20
11	Jan 16	Bradford & Bingley	A	L3-18
14	Jan 23	Northern	H	W44-7
15	Jan 30	Loughborough College	H	W51-22
16	Feb 6	Furness	H	W32-3
17	Feb 20	Lichfield	H	W20-17
18	Feb 27	Davenport	A	W25-11
19	Mar 6	Gosforth	H	L9-40
20	Mar 20	Harrogate	A	L20-28
21	Apr 10	Kendal	H	L18-20
22	Apr 12	Davenport	A	W36-6

PLAYING SQUAD 1992-93

15: K Knowles, S Evans, K O'Brien
14: M Kelly, A Speakman
13: G Higginsbotham, S Verbickas
12: M Fleet, M Watkinson
11: S Brown, A Pierce
10: A Rimmer, C Elliott
9: R Goodwin, N Mellor
1: J Russell (Capt), A O'Grady
2: O Babbins, P Wright
3: J Bennett, B Crawford
4: P Kirk, M Sever, A Whittle
5: L McIsaac, J Idenhen, P Moore
6: J Pimlott, R Glover
7: C Tatton, S Parson
8: C Allen, C Sever, I McClure

MOST CAPPED PLAYERS

including British Lions Appearances
A Neary, England 43 British Lions 1
K O'Brien, Ireland 3
B Jackson, England 2
M Leadbetter, England 2

LEADING APPEARANCES FOR CLUB

K O'Brien, 536, 20 seasons

LEADING SCORERS (1992/93 Season)

A Rimmer, Stand Off, 172
M Kelly, Right Wing, 110
S Brown, Left Wing, 55
A Pierce, Left Wing, 30

Photo: John Fryer

Broughton Park v Kendal, April '93. Jack Pimloctt evades a tackle with Craig Tatton in support

CLIFTON RFC

President: Grant Watson
Chairman: Norman Golding
Club Secretary: Peter Cumberlidge, 46 Worrall Road, Clifton, Bristol, BS8 2UE. Tel: (H) 0272 735048 (W) 0272 737993 Fax: (W) 0272 733167.
Fixtures Secretary: Brian "Ben" Jordan, 17 Royal Close, Henbury, Bristol, BS10 7XF. Tel: (H) 0272 504723
Press Officer: Brian "Ben" Jordan, 17 Royal Close, Henbury, Bristol, BS10 7XF. Tel: (H) 0272 504723
1993/94 1XV Captain: Wayne Hone
1993/94 1XV Coach: Peter Polledri

Review of the Season

Clifton were tipped by many pundits prior to the season to either retain 3rd Division status or gain the one promotion place. Sadly the tipsters would have lost their bets as the side failed to rediscover the form and consistency which saw them narrowly miss out on promotion in the previous season.

Lapses in concentration proved costly in early league defeats at Otley and Redruth which damaged their promotion hopes whilst their inability to win away from home eventually condemned them to relegation.

There were plus points with the move of prop Paul Cox to loose head to replace the departed Alan Sharp being a success, and Peter Naivalurua after missing 2 seasons with injury proving still to be a thrustful centre. In youngster Andy Heywood they have discovered a young back five forward with tremendous potential whilst products of the clubs highly successful junior section backs Charles Hemming and Aftab Hamib and forward Matt Dodd broke into the senior squad towards the end of the season.

Despite a mediocre season the future looks bright with the clubs junior section having its best ever season. Peter Polledri takes over from Alan Morley as coach and besides recruiting several promising young players he is determined not to lose the talent this section produces.

Clifton RFC 1992-93. Back row: Roger Jordan (Vice President), Mike Anderton (Vice President), Steve Hucker, Alan Kendall (Membership Secretary), Derek Farley (Vice President), Mike Skinner (Team Manager), Sally Cooper (Physio), Richard John, Nick Collins, Dave Mason, Chris Blake, Mark Wyatt, Paul Cox, Alan Morley (Coach), Pete Smith, Matt Brain, Bob Miller (Assistant Coach), Brian Jordan (Fixture Secretary), Sheridan Smith (Team Secretary). Middle row: Aftab Hamid, Kerry Lock, Paul Jeffrey, Peter Polledri (Captain), Wayne Hone, Lee Ashford, Mark Beresford, Nornam Golding (Chairman). Front row: Simon Hogg

CLIFTON RFC

CLUB PLAYING RECORD 1992-93 SEASON

National Division: Three
Final League Position at end 1992/93 Season: 8th
League Playing Record: P 11, W 4, D 2, L 5, Pts F 206, Pts A 175
Season Playing Record (including League matches/Pilkington cup etc): P 36, W 17, D 2, L 17, Pts F 753, Pts A 720

COMPETITIONS WON DURING SEASON 1992-93
Gloucester Under 15s & Under 17s Cup

ADDITIONAL RESULTS 1992-93

No	Date	Opponents	Venue	Result
1	Sep 5	Exeter	A	L27-30
2	Sep 12	Stroud	A	W60-10
3	Sep 19	Horsham	H	W431-10
4	Oct 13	Newbury	H	L6-18
5	Oct 17	Stourbridge	H	W27-12
6	Oct 31	Harlequins Wands	H	L10-30
7	Nov 7	Lydney	A	W9-6
8	Nov 28	Exeter	H	L3-19
9	Dec 5	Bristol	H	L15-28
10	Dec 12	Gloucester OB	H	W18-17
11	Dec 19	Weston Super Mare	H	W27-21
12	Dec 26	A Bath XV	H	L0-28
13	Jan 2	Brixham	H	W29-14
14	Jan 15	Bath	A	L3-43
15	Jan 23	Stroud	A	L3-18
16	Jan 26	Combination	H	W55-12
17	Jan 30	Torquay	A	W41-23
18	Feb 6	London Irish	A	L14-39
19	Feb 17	Royal Air Force	H	W33-25
20	Feb 23	Gloucester	A	L3-49
21	Feb 27	Walsall	A	W28-8
22	Mar 5	Portadown	H	W50-29
23	Mar 20	Berry Hill	A	W21-16
24	Apr 6	Lydney	A	L10-25
25	Apr 17	Blackheath	H	L12-15

PLAYING SQUAD 1992-93

Full Backs: M Beresford, A Freeman, M Lenthall
Wings: D Woodman, J Phillips, A Hamib, M Speakman, E Hardy, I Niven, S Hodges, A Hodges, P Crocker
Centres: M Brain, P Naivalurua, K Lock, R John, T Hall, C Hemming
Fly Half: S Hogg, J Lamb
Scrum Half: P Jeffery, M Newall, J Morris
Props: P Smith, P Cox, C Newth, S Whittingham, S Hucker
Hookers: L Ashford, M Cotton, P Allen
Locks: C Blake, S Mills, D Mason, A Heywood, D Parrot, R Ellerby, S Thomas
Flankers: P Polledri, W Hone, G Davis, D Hone, S Bedford, R Wood
No. 8: M Wyatt, N Collins

MOST CAPPED PLAYERS
including British Lions Appearances
R J K MacEver, 15, 1953-58
P D Young, 9, 1953-55
J A Bust, 5, 1872-76
A Budd, 5, 1878-1886

LEADING SCORERS (1992/93 Season)
S Hogg, Fly Half, 305 (Club Record)
D Woodman, Wing, 110
M Brave, Centre, 45
M Wyatt, No 8, 40
K Lock, Centre, 35
J Phillips, Wing, 35

CLIFTON RFC

COURAGE LEAGUE RECORDS

Highest score: 64 v Bournemouth (64-7) 19-9-87 Home SW1
Largest winning margin: 57 as above
Highest score against: 43 v Leeds (32-43) 24-4-93 Away CL3
Largest losing margin: 27 v Roundhay (7-34) 27-4-91 Away CL3
Drawn Matches: 3
Clean Sheets: 2
Failed to score: 2

INDIVIDUAL SCORING RECORDS
IN A MATCH

Most points: 24 Roger Gilbert v Bournemouth 19-9-87 Home SW1
Most tries: 4 Dave Cottrell v Askeans 4-1-92 Home CL3
Most conversions: 9 Roger Gilbert v Bournemouth 19-9-87 SW1
Most penalities: 5 Simon harvey v Metropolitan Police 23-9-89 Home D4S, Mark Beresford v Sheffield 22-9-90 Home CL3
Most drop goals: 2 Simon Harvey v Sudbury 14-10-89 Home D4S, Phil Cue v Lydney 23-3-90 Away CL3

IN A SEASON

Most points: 100 Simon Hogg 1991-92 CL3
Most tries: 8 Matt Brain 1991-92 CL3
Most conversions: 16 Roger Gilbert 1987-88 SW1, Simon Hogg 1991- 92 CL3
Most penalties: 19 Simon Hogg 1991-92 CL3
Most drop goals: 6 Simon Harvey 1989-90 SW1

IN A CAREER

Most points: 171 Simon Hogg 1991-93
Most tries: 25 Mark Wyatt 1988-93
Most conversions: 25 Simon hogg 1991-93
Most penalties: 34 Simon Hogg 1991-93
Most drop goals: 11 Simon Harvey 1987-91

SEASON BY SEASON LEADING SCORERS

	Most Points			**Most Tries**
1987-88	60	Roger Gilbert	7	Mike Speakman
1988-89	49	Roger Gilbert	4	Mark Trott
1989-90	83	Simon Harvey	6	Mark Trott Mark Wyatt
1990-91	32	Phil Cue	6	Dave Cottrell Mark Wyatt
1991-92	100	Simon Hogg	8	M Brain
1992-93	71	Simon Hogg	5	Mark Wyatt Doug Woodman

CLIFTON RFC

Club Details

Colours: White with thin lavender and black hoops
Change of Colours: Yellow
Nickname: The Club
Date Founded: 1872
Membership: Total 900, Full 350, Social 250, Junior/Youth/Minis 300.
Membership Fees: Full £30, Junior/Youth/Minis £15, Patron £30, Non Playing £7.50.
Number of Teams: Senior 7, Junior 11, Ladies 2
Programme Advertising Rates: TBA

Ground Details

Ground Address: Station Road, Cribbs Causeway, Henbury, Bristol, BS10 7TT.
Telephone: 0272 500445
Directions: Exit 17 off M5. Take A4018 (signposted Bristol West) down dual carriageway past ground on right over roundabout to next roundabout, return back down dual carriageway and turn left (signposted to Clifton RFC).
Capacity: Total 2,250, Seated 250, Standing 2,00.
Ticket Prices: Adult £3, OAP/Child £2/free
Clubhouse Facilities: Four bars, skittle alley, function room, conference facilities and squash courts.
Training Nights: Monday & Wednesday.

Pete Smith supported by hooker Lee Ashford feeds the ball back from a scrum   Photo: Bristol United Press

HARROGATE RUFC

President: John Englefield
Chairman: D Brown
Club Secretary: Allen Tattersfield, 23 St Helens Road, Harrogate, North Yorks. Tel: (H) 0423 885710 (W) 0532 832000 Fax: (W) 0532 832060.
Fixtures Secretary: Graham Siswick, 22a Hillway, Tranmere Park, Guiseley, Nr Leeds. Tel: (H) 0943 875620 (W) 0709 893046 Fax: (W) 0709 881150
Press Officer: B Rodney Spragg, Pear Treet Cottage, Town Street, Nidd, Harrogate, HG3 3DQ.
1993/94 1XV Captain: Jeremy Hopkinson
1993/94 1XV Coach: Peter Clegg
Chairman of Rugby Committee: B Rodney Spragg
Commercial Manager: Glyn Smith

Review of the Season

The stated aim of club coach Peter Clegg and captain Simon Croft was to win promotion. Harrogate were ultimately successful at the expense of Rotherham who had matched them game by game throughout the season.

The league season got off to a good start with wins over Stoke 19-13, Kendal 34-6, Nuneaton 25-16 and then a purple patch against Lichfield in which No.8 Steve Baker scored 5 tries in a 53-6 win. The decisive game against Rotherham in atrocious conditions resulted in a 6-6 draw which left honours even but Harrogate still had a substantial points differential advantage.

After the Christmas break the winning sequence continued including a 71-7 win against Towcestrians during which cornerstone of the pack John Woodthorpe sustained a serious knee injury which put him out of the rest of the season.

We were rapidly brought to earth in the next outing at Winnington Park where a 15-20 defeat resulted in despair which turned to joy when news came through that Rotherham had lost at Preston Grasshoppers thus earning a reprieve and the knowledge that two more victories would ensure promotion. A 20-5 home victory over Stourbridge and then a 29-12 win at Hereford completed a momentous season for the club.

In the Pilkington Cup a 25-15 home victory over Leamington lead to a second round tie at Moseley where the home club prevailed 16-12 in a hard fought and close contest.

Club captain Simon Croft together with Guy Easterby and John Woodthorpe represented Yorkshire whilst Mark Dodd was capped for England at U/16 level.

The second team retained the York Floodlit Competition Trophy. The Junior section went from strength to strength with membership increasing to 175 players and the annual Mini-Tournament attracted teams with a total of 400 players.

Harrogate RUFC 1992-93. Standing: Wendy Carswell (Physio), S Cameron, S Baker, J Hopkinson, S Croft (Captain), R Zoing, M Heap, R Bell, E Atkins. Front row: R Whyley, D Wheat, G Easterby, S Towse, P Taylor, I Hassall, C Reed   Photo: Harrogate Advertiser

HARROGATE RUFC

CLUB PLAYING RECORD 1992-93 SEASON

National Division: Four North
Final League Position at end 1992/93 Season: 1st
League Playing Record: P 12, W 10, D 1, L 1, Pts F 363, Pts A 115
Season Playing Record (including League matches/Pilkington cup etc): P 32, W 18, D 2, L 12, Pts F 787, Pts A 495

COMPETITIONS WON DURING SEASON 1992-93

Promotion to National Division Four

ADDITIONAL RESULTS 1992-93

No	Date	Opponents	Venue	Result
1	Sep 2	Sandal	H	W39-6
2	Sep 8	Bedford	H	L11-35
3	Sep 12	Edinburgh Accies	A	L17-48
4	Sep 19	Leamington PC	H	W25-15
5	Oct 17	Hartlepool Rovers	H	W62-12
6	Oct 24	Coventry	A	L7-20
7	Nov 7	Moseley PC	A	L12-16
8	Nov 28	Stockton	H	W50-12
9	Dec 5	Hull Ionians	A	L3-16
10	Dec 12	Orrell	H	L10-26
11	Dec 19	Vale of Lune	H	W60-3
12	Dec 28	Leeds	A	L14-24
13	Jan 15	Northampton	A	L14-36
14	Jan 23	Fylde	A	W11-8
15	Jan 30	Mel;rose	H	D8-8
16	Feb 6	Northern	A	L10-25
17	Feb 27	Cambridge University	A	L7-16
18	Mar 6	Waterloo	A	W30-18
19	Mar 20	Broughton Park	H	W28-20
20	Apr 10	Sheffield	A	L17-20

PLAYING SQUAD 1992-93

Full Backs: I Hassall, M Yates, S Ledger
Wings: R Bell, E Atkins, P Woolley, J-P Wong, G Kubu, J Riley
Centres: R Zoing, P Flavell, C Reed, E Cooke, T Hutchings, A Pearson
Stand Off: S Towse, R Shackleton
Scrum Half: G Easterby, G Cassidy, W Freeman, S Brown, R Eaden, G Irvine, K Miller
Props: A Simpson, J Woodthòrpe, S Cameron, A Brown, T Willis
Hookers: R Whyley, J Wade, B Sharkey
Lock: S Croft, P Taylor, D Croft, M Green, S Brown, M Ruthen
Flankers: D Wheat, M Heap, S Fawcett, A Pride, D Batchelor, P Buckland, M Farrar
No. 8: J Hopkinson, S Baker, S McCulloch

MOST CAPPED PLAYERS

including British Lions Appearances
P J Squires, 30, 1973-79
J Young, 24, 1968-73
T Grant, 6, 1960-64
I Shackleton, 4, 1970
I King, 3, 1954
A Pickering, 1, 1907

LEADING APPEARANCES FOR CLUB

Steve Fawcett, 561, 1978-93

LEADING SCORERS (1992/93 Season)

R Zoing, Centre, 231
S Baker, No 8/Blind Side, 70
G Easterby, Scrum Half, 70
M Yates, Standoff/Full Back, 60
R Bell, Wing, 40
P Woolley, Wing/Full Back, 40

HARROGATE RUFC

COURAGE LEAGUE RECORDS

Highest score: 71 v Towcestrians (71-7) 13-3-93 D4N
Largest winning margin: 64 as above
Highest score against: 50 v Otley (21-50) 22-9-90 D4N
Largest losing margin: 29 as above
Drawn Matches: 3
Clean Sheets: 2
Failed to score: 2

INDIVIDUAL SCORING RECORDS
IN A MATCH

Most points: 25 Steve Baker v Lichfield 14-11-92 Home D4N
Most tries: 5 Steve Baker v Lichfield 14-11-92 Home D4n
Most conversions: 9 Ralph Zoing v Towcestrians 13-3-93 Home D4N
Most penalities: 7 Ralph Zoing v Halifax 18-11-89 Home N1
Most drop goals: 1 Ralph Zoing v Otley 11-11-89 Away N1, v Lichfield 4-1-92 Away D4n, v, preston 8-2-92 Away D4N, Steve Towse v Towcestrians 14-3-92 Away D4N, v Kendall 3-10-92 Away D4N, Chris Reed v Towcestrians 13-3-93 Home D4N

IN A SEASON

Most points: 130 Ralph Zoing 1992-93 D4N
Most tries: 9 Jeremy Hopkinson 1990-91 D4N, Steve Baker 1992-93 D4N, Guy Easterby 1992-93 D4N
Most conversions: 29 Ralph Zoing 1992-93D4N
Most penalties: 22 Ralph Zoing 1989-90 N1
Most drop goals: 2 Ralph Zoing 1991-92 D4N

IN A CAREER

Most points: 405 Ralph Zoing 1987-93
Most tries: 16 Steve Baker 1988-93
Most conversions: 75 Ralph Zoing 1987-93
Most penalties: Ralph Zoing 1987-93
Most drop goals: 3 Ralph Zoing 1987-93

SEASON BY SEASON LEADING SCORERS

	Most Points			Most Tries
1987-88	28	Ralph Zoing	2	Andy Caldwell Dave Bowe
1988-89	64	Ralph Zoing	8	Clive Ware
1989-90	91	Ralph Zoing	4	Clive Ware
1990-91	47	Ralph Zoing	9	Jeremy Hopkinson
1991-92	45	Ralph Zoing	3	Steve Baker
1992-93	130	Ralph Zoing	9	Steve baker Guy Easterby

HARROGATE RUFC

Club Details

Colours: Red, amber & black, white shorts, red socks
Change of Colours: Red
Date Founded: 1871
Membership: Total 800
Membership Fees: Full £50, Junior/Youth/Minis £17
Number of Teams: Senior 6, Junior & mini 9, Colts 1
Programme Advertising Rates: Apply to
Communications Manager

Ground Details

Ground Address: The County Ground, Claro Road,
Harrogate, North Yorkshire.
Telephone: 0423 566966
Directions: Claro Road runs directly from the A59
between the County and Cranby Hotels
Capacity: Total 5,000, Seated 499
Ticket Prices: Adults £3.00
Clubhouse Facilities: Full catering facilities, two
bars, two hospitality rooms.
Training Nights: Seniors: Mon & Thurs, Colts: Wed,
Junior & Mini: Sun am

Harrogate's Craig Reed tackles Hereford's Dave Rogers.
Photo: Harrogate Advertiser

Harrogate skipper Simon Croft gets his boot to the ball with support from Richard Whyley, Steve Baker and Stuart Cameron
against Hereford, April 1993
Photo: Harrogate Advertiser

LEEDS RUFC

President: Ronnie Bigood
Chairman: Mike Palmer-Jones
Club Secretary: Mike Bigood, 4 West Hill Avenue, Leeds, LS7 3QH. Tel: (H) 0532 682784 (W) 0532 625382 Fax: (W) 0532 621251
Fixtures Secretary: Les Jackson, 4 Gledhow Wood Avnue, Leeds, LS8 1NY. Tel: (H) 0532 665544 (W) 0532 665544 Fax: 0532 665544.
Press Officers: Charles Hainsworth and Chris Thompson, 4, West Hill Avenue, Leeds, LS7 3QH.
Club Captain: Jon Eagle
Chairman of Promotions: Sue Jennings

Review of the Season

This was a very special season in many ways as the new club took the field after the merger of Headingley FC and Roundhay RUFC. Whilst sound finances and professional administration are necessities in a successful club these are purely requirements for a successful rugby operation, which is mainly judged on League results and in this regard Leeds just missed out. A closer examination of the rugby played throughout the club showed a high degree of success and enjoyment. Several new players joined the Club both before and during the season. In mid-August we went to Wensleydale for an intensive training weekend. The persistent rain was a portent to the season ahead as we failed on the wet league matches in October and November, but then recovered to remain unbeaten to the end of the season. The games against away at Exeter (33-28) and finally at home to Clifton (43-32) were simply breathtaking. All teams played entertaining rugby and an overall club record of 114 wins from 184 matches with 4289 points scored gave an average of 23 points per match for Under 16 upwards.

At the start of the year John Eaglerepresented the North against Wales 'B' and Paul Johnson, Jon Eagle, Alex Munro, David Breakwell and Neil Lineham were all involved with the Yorkshire effort at some stage of the season.

The Kirkstall ground has been sold subject to planning permission but will be used for the 9 Courage League matches in 1993-94 and Chandos for the friendlies and Cup games. We eagerly await developments for a new ground in 1994-95.

Leeds RUFC 1992-93. Back row: David Jennings (Team Manager), Bryan Green (1st XV Coach), Paul Johnson (1st XV Captain), Matt Hoskin, Nick Green, Neil Hargraves, Glynn Thompson, Neil Lineham, Paul Burkenshaw, Andrew Park, Craig Busby (Assistant Coach), Jim Murgatroyd (Fitness Trainer). Front row: Andy Turton, Adam Machell, Gary Walker, David Breakwell, Jon Eagle, Wayne Hartley, Kevin Bowling, Dan Eddie, Phil Griffin, Alex Munro.

LEEDS RUFC

ADDITIONAL RESULTS 1992-93

No	Date	Opponents	Venue	Result
1	Sep 1	Hull Ionians	H	W31-10
2	Sep 5	Preston Grasshoppers	H	W30-3
3	Sep 12	Northern	H	W24-6
4	Sep 19	Sedgley Park	A	W20-6
5	Oct 10	Liverpool St Helens	A	L14-21
6	Oct 17	Newcastle Gosforth	H	L26-37
7	Nov 7	Fylde	A	L6-21
8	Nov 28	Huddersfield	H	W30-23
9	Dec 5	Bradford & Bingley	H	L9-25
10	Dec 12	Kendal	H	W39-10
11	Dec 19	Waterloo	H	W23-3
12	Dec 28	Harrogate	H	W24-14
13	Jan 2	Leicester	A	Cancelled
14	Jan 9	Morley	A	L15-22
15	Jan 16	Rotherham	H	W33-12
16	Jan 23	Sale	H	L5-24
17	Jan 30	Vale of Lune	H	W100-8
18	Feb 6	Durham	H	W24-8
19	Feb 17	Halifax	H	Cancelled
20	Feb 20	Harlequins	A	W23-10
21	Feb 27	Rippon	A	W23-10
22	Mar 6	Fylde	A	W25-19
23	Mar 27	Roundhegians	H	W49-13
24	Mar 20	Morley	H	L15-28
25	Apr 7	Sheffield	A	L8-9
26	Apr 10	W. Hartlepool	H	L9-28
27	Apr 17	Middlesbrough	H	W31-27

CLUB PLAYING RECORD 1992-93 SEASON

National Division: Three
Final League Position at end 1992/93 Season: 6th
League Playing Record:
P 11, W 7, D 0, L 4, Pts F 228, Pts A 220
Season Playing Record (including League matches/Pilkington cup etc):
P 36, W 22, D 0, L 14, Pts F 853, Pts A 690

PLAYING SQUAD 1992-93

Full Backs: D Breakwell, G Walker, D Lowther, D Riley
Wings: J Eagle, M Hoskin, C Thornton, M Joyce, J Auckland
Centres: K Bowling, W Hartley, P Johnson, L douglas, R Blackburn
Fly Half: B Lloyd, D Eddie
Scrum Half: J Singleton, J Swarbrigg, D Andrew, A Turton
Props: A Park, M Cutter, C Head, A Machell, D Hayle, P Hardy
Hookers: N Lineham, A Munro, R Wollaston
Second Row: G Thompson, N Wilde, P Burkenshaw, M Atherton, P Owens
Flankers: N Green, P Griffin, N Hargreaves, S Lancaster, M Cooper, G Vernon-James, B Willis, A Gibb
No. 8: J Wilby, I Moule

MOST CAPPED PLAYERS

including British Lions Appearances
M Slemen (Lions), 31, 1976
M Regan, 1953-54
R Higgins (Lions), 1953-54
K Bearne (Scotland), 1960-61
R French, 1960-61
T Brophy, 1964-65
T Rudd, 1964-65
F Cotton (Lions), 1971
M Besse, 1992-78
D Roughley, 1972-78
J Horton, 1972-78
K Simms, 1985
D Morris, 1990

LEADING APPEARANCES FOR CLUB DURING SEASON 1992-93

D Breakwell, 34
N Green, 32
C Thornton, 30
J Singleton, 30
W Hartley, 29
N Hargreaves, 26

LEADING SCORERS

B Lloyd, Fly Half, 202
D Breakwell, Full Back, 91
J Eagle, Wing, 80
M Hoskin, Wing, 75
C Thornton, Wing, 70
D Eddie, Fly Half, 36

LEEDS RUFC

COURAGE LEAGUE RECORDS
Highest score: 43 v Clifton (43-32) 24-4-93 Home CL3
Largest winning margin: 20 v Broughton Park (30-10) 14-11-92 Away CL3
Highest score against: 35 v Havant (11-35) 26-9-92 Away CL3
Largest losing margin: 24 as above
Drawn Matches: 0
Clean Sheets: 0
Failed to score: 2

INDIVIDUAL SCORING RECORDS
IN A MATCH
Most points: 15 Chris Thornton v Exeter 13-3-93 Away CL3
Most tries: 3 Chris Thornton v Exeter 13-3-93 Away CL3
Most conversions: 4 Dan Eddie v Clifton 24-4-93 Home CL3
Most penalities: 4 Bob Lloyd v Askeans 13-2-93 Home CL3
Most drop goals: 1 Dan Eddie v Broughton park 14-11-92 Away CL3,
Bob Lloyd v Liverpool St Helens 27-3-93 Home CL3

IN A SEASON
Most points: 45 Bob Lloyd 1992-93 CL3
Most tries: 7 Chris Thornton 1992-93 CL3
Most conversions: 7 David Breakwell 1992-93 CL3
Most penalties: 10 Bob Lloyd 1992-93 CL3
Most drop goals: 1 Dan Eddie & Bob Lloyd 1992-93 CL3

IN A CAREER
Most points: 45 Bob Lloyd 1992-93
Most tries: 7 Chris Thornton1992-93
Most conversions: 7 David Breakewell 1992-93
Most penalties: 10 Bob Lloyd 1992-93
Most drop goals: Dan Eddie 7 bob Lloyd 1992-93

SEASON BY SEASON LEADING SCORERS

	Most Points			Most Tries	
1992-93	45	Bob Lloyd	7	Chris Thornton	

LEEDS RUFC

Club Details

Colours: Blue & gold
Change of Colours: Red
Date Founded: June 1991
Membership: Total 1,206, Full 660, Social 389, Junior/Youth/Minis 157.
Membership Fees: Full £30, Junior/Youth/Minis £5/£5/£3, Social £10
Number of Teams: Senior 6, Junior 6
Programme Advertising Rates: Full £175, Half £95, Qtr £45

Ground Details

Ground Address: Clarence Field, Bridge Road, Kirkstall, Leeds, LS5 3BN.
Telephone: 0532 755029
Capacity: Total 7,850, Seated 850, Standing 7,000.
Ticket Prices: Adult £3 OAP/Child £1.50
Clubhouse Facilities: Two bars, six changing rooms, three squash cours, weights room, medical room.
Training Nights: Monday & Thursday

David Breakwell, Leeds full back

Photo: Joe McCabe

LIVERPOOL ST HELENS FC

President: Dr J Ratchford
Chairman: W Magowan
Club Secretary: E Hyland, 22 Salisbury Road, Cressington Park, Liverpool, L19 0PJ. Tel: (H) 051 427 8831
Fixtures Secretary: J Robertson, 36 Beryl Road, Noctorum, Wirral, Merseyside. Tel: (H) 051 677 5611 (W) 051 427 7535
Press Officer: J Hetherington, 162 Broadway, Eccleston, St Helens, Merseyside. Tel: (H) 0744 54812.
1993/94 1XV Captain: K Simms
1993/94 Panel: G Jopnes, D Buttery, K Taberner, G Hitchen
Chairman of Rugby: A Walker
Treasurer: I Jackson
Club Steward: K Toole
Groundsman: M Greenall
Physiotherapist: Miss J Ross
Sponsorship Secretary: M Spaven

Review of the Season

In 1986 St. Helens RUFC merged with Liverpool FC (Liverpool being formed in December 1857 and is the oldest Rugby Football Club in the world whose membership is open to all) to form Liverpool St. Helens FC. For most of its short history LSH has played its rugby in the first and second divisions; last season however the club found itself in Division Three.

A recently organised committee set upon its considerable task of consolidation with vigour and determination and appointed Kevin Simms (England 1985) as its Club Captain. They expected his loyalty and enthusiasm to be highly infectious and the players responded. At the end of a much travelled season LSH found itself in the top half of Division Three. The highlight of the season was quite clearly the Lancashire Cup Final when, in a game dominated by LSH, Waterloo squeezed victory with a penalty in the dying seconds of the match.

Many players gained representative honours. Kevin Simms played for the Barbarians and captained the North of England. Gary French and Clive Cooper have also represented the North of England; Gary French played for Lancashire; Steve Gill, David Dahinton, Mark Elliott and Dean Crompton all played for Cheshire; Elliott Foster played for Durham and Ian Williams for Cumbria. Steve Cook played for Lancs. U21.

The Junior sections of the club continue to prosper with teams in all age groups from Under 7's to Under 19's. The U15 side was the most successful winning all of their seventeen matches, winning their Lancashire Cup, having five players representing Merseyside and completing the season with a successful tour to the Dordogne. The U19 played Scottish, Welsh and French sides with the minis entering tournaments at Waterloo, Preston and Windermere.

Next season the club hopes to support a Ladies Rugby Team.

The Senior Squad has been strengthened for season 1993-94 with the arrival of some new and some familiar faces.

Mark Sephton scoring his 26th try of the season in the Lancashire Cup Final against Waterloo

233

LIVERPOOL ST HELENS FC

CLUB PLAYING RECORD 1992-93 SEASON

National Division: Three
Final League Position at end 1992/93 Season: 7th
League Playing Record: P 11, W 5, D 0, L 6, Pts F 203, Pts A 130
Season Playing Record (including League matches/Pilkington cup etc): P 37, W 17, D 0, L 20, Pts F 630, Pts A 612

COMPETITIONS WON DURING SEASON 1992-93
Finalists Lancashire Cup

ADDITIONAL RESULTS 1992-93

No	Date	Opponents	Venue	Result
1	Sep 2	New Brighton	A	L10-14
2	Sep 5	Northern	H	W27-3
3	Sep 12	W Hartlepool	A	L0-56
4	Sep 19	Sheffield	A	L14-17
5	Oct 10	Leeds	H	W21-14
6	Nov 7	Nuneaton	H	W22-0
7	Nov 14	Fylde	A	W24-8
8	Nov 28	Halifax	H	W22-10
9	Dec 5	Orrell	H	L5-22
10	Dec 12	Wakefield	A	L17-50
11	Dec 19	Tynedale	A	L18-19
12	Jan 16	Waterloo	A	L10-34
13	Jan 17	Orrell	A	W10-0
14	Jan 23	Stourbridge	H	W27-14
15	Jan 30	Preston Grasshoppers	A	L0-10
16	Feb 6	Newcastle Gosforth	H	L6-47
17	Feb 7	Fleetwood	H	W22-12
18	Feb 27	Macclesfield	H	W44-22
19	Mar 6	Morley	A	L12-28
20	Mar 7	Sedgley Park	A	W47-6
21	Mar 20	Vale of Lune	A	L5-27
22	Mar 21	Waterloo	A	L11-13
23	Apr 10	Sale	A	L0-35
24	Apr 17	Birkenhead Park	H	W53-21

PLAYING SQUAD 1992-93

Full Backs: A Higgin, P Ramsden, R Saverimutto
Wings: M Sephton, D Crompton, N Walker, M Ellirt, N James
Centres: K Simms, J Lloyd, K Davies, S Bennison
Fly Half: A Higgin, P Ramsden, A Simpson
Scrum Half: G Eldoy, C Hughes, S Anders
Props: C King, S Gill, T Allen, I Harrison, R Hudson
Hookers: G French, R Whittle
Locks: C Cooper, P Dahinton, S Gughes, A Magowan, K Potter
Flankers: I Williams, N Hughes, R Spraton, E Foster, K Toole
No. 8: D Hendry
Utility Player & Super-sub: K Toole

MOST CAPPED PLAYERS
including British Lions Appearances
M Slemen (Lions), 31, 1976
M Regan, 1953-54
R Higgins (Lions), 1953-54
K Bearne (Scotland), 1960-61
R French, 1960-61
T Brophy, 1964-65
T Rudd, 1964-65
F Cotton (Lions), 1971
M Besse, 1972-78
D Roughley, 1982-78
J Horton, 1972-78
K Simms, 1985
D Morris, 1990

LEADING APPEARANCES FOR CLUB
T Morris, 334, 1970-82
W Murphy, 339
N Coleclough, 337
D Boult, 309
J Crellin, 305
J Hennigan, 300

LEADING SCORERS (1992-93 Season)
A Higgin, Full Back/Fly Half, 223 (1T 39P 5DG 43C)
M Sephton, Wing 3Qtr, 140 (28 T)
K Davies, Centre, 35 (7T)
K Simms, Centre, 15 (3T)

PLAYER OF THE YEAR:
Andy Higgin & Clive Cooper

234

LIVERPOOL ST HELENS FC

COURAGE LEAGUE RECORDS

Highest score: 77 v Aspatria (77-5) 13-3-93 Home CL3
Largest winning margin: 72 as above
Highest score against: 76 v Newcastle Gosforth (4-76) 29-2-92 Away CL2
Largest losing margin: 72 as above
Drawn Matches: 3
Clean Sheets: 2
Failed to score: 3

INDIVIDUAL SCORING RECORDS
IN A MATCH

Most points: 20 Mark Sephton v Aspatria 13-3-93 Home CL3, Dean Crompton v Aspatrai 13-3-93 Home CL3
Most tries: 4 Mark Sephton v Aspatria 13-3-93 Home CL3, Dean Crompton v Aspatria 13-3-93 Home CL3
Most conversions: Andy Higgin v Aspatria 13-3-93 Home CL3
Most penalities: 5 Tosh Askew v Bedford 30-4-88 Away, v Moseley 26-11-88 Away CL1
Most drop goals: 2 Nick Simms v Blackheath 9-1-88 Home CL2, Tosh Askew v Headingley 14-10-89 Home CL2

IN A SEASON

Most points: 96 Andy Higgin 1992-93 CL3
Most tries: 8 Mark Sephton 1992-93 CL3
Most conversions: 11 Andy Higgin 1992-93 CL3
Most penalties: 19 Andy Higgin 1992-93 CL3
Most drop goals: 4 Andy Higgin 1992-93 CL3

IN A CAREER

Most points: 155 Tosh Askew 1987-90
Most tries: 19 Mark Sephton 1989-93
Most conversions: 13 Andy Higgin 1990-93
Most penalties: 43 Tosh Askew 1987-90
Most drop goals: 4 Andy Higgin 1990-93

SEASON BY SEASON LEADING SCORERS

	Most Points			Most Tries
1987-88	34	Tosh Askew	3	Ian Gibbons John Shinwell
1988-89	55	Tosh Askew	3	Brendan Hanavan
1989-90	66	Tosh Askew	6	Mark Sephton
1990-91	31	Andy Higgin	2	Mark Sephton Paul Buckton
1991-92	26	Paul Ramsden	4	Mark Elliott
1992-93	96	Andy Higgin	8	Mark Sephton

LIVERPOOL ST HELENS FC

Club Details

Colours: Red, blue, black, white hoops, black shorts
Change of Colours: white jerseys
Nickname: LSH
Date Founded: 1857
Membership: Total 450
Membership Fees: Full £40
Number of Teams: Senior 5 + Vets, Junior 3 + Colts & Minis

Ground Details

Ground Address: Moss Lane, Windle, St Helens, Merseyside, WA11 7PL
Telephone: 0744 25708
Directions: M6 Junction 23, A580 (Liverpool) approx 5 miles A570 (Southport). Little opening immediately on left and left again.
Ticket Prices: £3.50 inc programme
Clubhouse Facilities: General bar, First XV area, sponsors lounge, presidents room, catering/dining room, physio/medical room.
Training Nights: Tuesday & Thursday

West Hartlepool in possession against Liverpool St Helens

PLYMOUTH ALBION RFC

President: Robert Hicks MP
Chairman: Vernon Pinches
Club Secretary: Roger Bowden, 7 Winnow Close, Staddiscombe, Plymouth, PL9 9RZ Tel: 0752 491642 Fax: 0752 777454
Fixtures Secretary: Andy Hoyston, 6 Beauly Close, Plympton, Plymouth
1993/94 1XV Captain: Mark Slade
1993/94 1XV Coach: Ray Westlake
Rugby Manager: Robert Evans

Review of the Season

Heavy defeats by Bristol and Harlequins set the scene for another relegation season for Albion. Eleven straight league defeats did not paint a true picture of a season that promised so much but delivered so little.

Albion's best period came around Christmas time with a win over arch rivals Exeter and another over second Division Coventry. These were followed by a closely contested match against Wasps and did much to bolster the expectations of both players and supporters. This optimism, however, was short lived as a league defeat at Clifton and county cup exit at Brixham doomed Albion to a fruitless season.

All is not lost, as Albion now field a young and experienced squad on which they hope to build a bright future and attempt a quick return to their former higher league status.

Not one of Plymouth Albion's players ceased to give their all throughout a disappointing and frustrating season and every credit must be given to them for the commitment and durability they have shown.

Will Carling is blocked but Harlequins inflicted a heavy defeat on 'Albion'   *Photo: Plymouth Evening Herald*

237

PLYMOUTH ALBION RFC

CLUB PLAYING RECORD 1992-93 SEASON

National Division: Three
Final League Position at end 1992/93 Season: 12th
League Playing Record: P 11, W 0, D 0, L 11, Pts F 130, Pts A 305
Season Playing Record (including League matches/Pilkington cup etc): P 37, W 12, D 0, L 25, Pts F 805, Pts A 1027

LEADING SCORERS

Martin Thompson, Fly Half, 92, Mark Slade, Centre, 71

Club Details

Colours: Cherry, green & white
Change of Colours: Red
Nickname: Albion
Date Founded: 1876
Membership: Total 440
Membership Fees: Full £10, Junior/Youth/Minis £8
Number of Teams: Senior 3
Programme Advertising Rates: Full £200, Half £120, Qtr 60

Ground Details

Ground Address: Beacon Park, Beacon Park Road, Peverell, Plymouth
Telephone: 0752 777454/772924
Fax: 0752 777454
Directions: A38 into Plymouth and follow signs to Home park. Turn right at second set of lights.
Capacity: total 3,000
Ticket Prices: Adult £3.50 & £4.50
Clubhouse Facilities: 2 Lounge bars, main bar, function room, sponsors bar
Training Nights: Mons & weds

Plymouth Albion on the attack

Photo: Plymouth Evening Herald

238

PLYMOUTH ALBION RFC

COURAGE LEAGUE RECORDS

Highest score: 57 v Metropolitan Police (57-3) 26-11-88 Home CL3
Largest winning margin: 54 as above
Highest score against: 54 v Newcastle Gosforth (54) 28-3-92 Away CL2
Largest losing margin: 37 v Sheffield (11-48) 24-4-93 Away CL3
Drawn Matches: 0
Clean Sheets: 1
Failed to score: 1

INDIVIDUAL SCORING RECORDS
IN A MATCH

Most points: 25 Dominic Cundy v Metropolitan Police 26-11-88 Home CL3
Most tries: 4 Steve Walkin v Birmingham 17-10-87 Away CL3, Ian Russell v Fyl;de 31-10-87 Away CL3
Most conversions: 8 Dominic Cundy v Metropolitan Police 26-11-88 Home CL3
Most penalities: 6 Mark Slade v Bedford 14-12-91 Home CL2
Most drop goals: 2 Dominic Cundy v Wakefield 10-9-88 Home CL2

IN A SEASON

Most points: 111 Martin Livesey 1987-88 CL3
Most tries: 8 Kevin Norris 1987-88 CL3 & Steve Walklin 1988-89 CL3
Most conversions: 23 Martin Livesey 1987-88 CL3
Most penalties: M18 Martin Livesey 1987-88 CL3
Most drop goals: 3 Dominic Cundy 1988-89 CL3

IN A CAREER

Most points: 115 Mark Slade 1990-93
Most tries: 17 Steve Walklin 1987-90
Most conversions: 23 Martin Livesey 1987-88
Most penalties: 22 Mark Slade 1990-93
Most drop goals: 3 Dominic Cundy 1988-89

SEASON BY SEASON LEADING SCORERS

	Most Points			Most Tries
1987-88	111	Martin Livesey	8	Kevin Norris
1988-89	101	Dominic Cundy	8	Steve Walkin
1989-90	36	Charlie Gibbitas	4	Ian Russel Steve Walklin
1990-91	44	Kevin Thomas	2	Charlie Gabbitas
1991-92	62	Mark Slade	2	By 5 players
1992-93	26	Martin Thompson	3	Mark Haimes

Albion's defence converges to stop a Harlequins break

SHEFFIELD RUFC

President: Andrew Reichwald
Chairman: Bryan O'Connor
Club Secretary: Jim Goulding, 34
Whinfell Court, Whirlow, Sheffield, S11
9QA Tel: (H) 0742 620543 (W) 0742
751776 Fax: (W) 0742 759242
Fixtures Secretary: Robert Dean, 94
Riverdale Road, Sheffield, S10 3FC. Tel:
(H) 0742 301021 (W) 0742 377036 Fax:
(W) 0742 839947
Press Officer: Martin Fay, 16
Devonshire Road, Sheffield S17.
1993/94 1XV Captain: David Kaye
1993/94 1XV Coach: Ged Glynn
**1st XV Manager & Chairman of
Selectors:** Bill Reichwald

Review of the Season

The 1992-93 season began on a high note with a special celebration game against Leicester to mark the opening of the new standard and the return to the newly-levelled pitch. A good game and a great performance by our players was watched by a large and responsive crowd who saw Leicester win 27-7 but Stuart Juds had the satisfaction of being the first ever 5 point try-scorer in English rugby.

Leicester went on to win the Pilkington Cup but we were the victims of the re-structuring of the National League, finishing just one place away from retaining Third Division status despite scoring more tries and points than in any other league season and registering our two biggest ever league wins.

Having lost six regular members from the previous year, the team took some time to settle and the final position was due largely to the poor start in losing the first two games to Clifton and Havant. Wins against Aspatria, Leeds and Broughton Park offset by a defeat at Otley meant that a victory away at Redruth in January was imperative and a memorable team performance achieved it.

By now the team had found rhythm and confidence and in March demolished Askeans 45-8 and then beat fellow-contenders Exeter in the best game of the season at Abbeydale. Wins in the final two games would have been sufficient but a bad half-hour at Liverpool proved disastrous and another huge win in the last home game against Plymouth was small consolation for having got so close without reward.

Overall more games were won than lost for the 18th consecutive year. Player of the year was prop Shaun McMain who forced his way into both Yorkshire and The North squads in his first season in senior rugby. Rob Parr was a courageous and hard-working captain and wing Mark Rogers broke the club record of points in a season with 297. Bill Reichwald retired after masterminding the win at Redruth in his 496th game for the club but there was excellent form throughout from youngsters Andy Morris, Stuart Juds, Dave Hill, Jos Baxendell and Jamie Morley.

Sheffield RUFC 1992-93. Standing: A Harrison, I Wright, J Baxendell, D Kaye, T Meadley, J Morley, M Kirk, N Crapper, W Reichwald (Manager). Sitting: A Morris, S Slater, S Juds, D Hill, R Parr (Captain), M Rodgers, S McMain, A Challenor, D Bosworth, D Watson

SHEFFIELD RUFC

CLUB PLAYING RECORD 1992-93 SEASON

National Division: Three
Final League Position at end 1992/93 Season: 5th
League Playing Record: P 11, W 7, D 0 L 4, Pts F 208, Pts A 134
Season Playing Record (including League matches/Pilkington cup etc): P 35, W 19, D 0, L 16, Pts F 627, Pts A 592

COMPETITIONS WON DURING SEASON 1992-93

18th Consecutive winning season

PLAYING SQUAD 1992-93

Full Backs: S Juds, M Allatt, A Dunkley
Wings: M Rodgers, J Morley
Centres: C Saul, J Baxendell, S Slater, M Kirk, M Old, G Glynn
Fly Half: D Hill, B Reichwald
Scrum Half: I Wright, C Fisher
Props: S McMain, D Bosworth, K Dawson, K Rawson
Hookers: A Challenor, A Harrison
Lock: D Kaye, T Meadley, G Davies, H Barrett
Flankers: R Parr, A Morris, M Rodgers, S Hodgson, M O'Connor
No. 8: D Watson, N Crapper

MOST CAPPED PLAYERS

including British Lions Appearances
A G B Old, 21

LEADING APPEARANCES FOR CLUB

W Reichwald, 496 1973-93
H Johnson, 340, 1956-73
G Goodliffe, 326, 1978-90
D Watson, 303, 1979-93
A Reichwald,. 302, 1975-89
M Pierce, 301, 1973-90

LEADING SCORERS (1992/93 Season)

M Rodgers, Wing, 297 (Club Record)
J Morley, Wing, 75

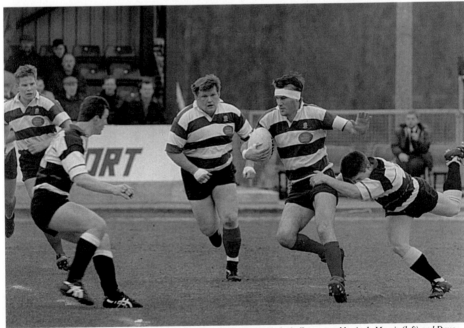

Sheffield v Exeter at Abbeydale Park, March 1993. No. 8 Dave Watson with the ball supported by Andy Morris (left) and Dave Bosworth (centre)
Photo: Sheffield Newspapers Ltd

SHEFFIELD RUFC

COURAGE LEAGUE RECORDS

Highest score: 48 v Plymouth (48-11) 24-4-93 Home CL3
Largest winning margin: 37 as above & v Askeans (45-8) 13-3-93 Away CL3
Highest score against: 57 v Richmond (3-57) 25-4-92 Away CL3
Largest losing margin: 54 as above
Drawn Matches: 3
Clean Sheets: 2
Failed to score: 2

INDIVIDUAL SCORING RECORDS
IN A MATCH

Most points: 25 Mark Rodgers v Askeans 13-3-93 Away CL3
Most tries: 2 on 15 occasions by 8 players - most times 4 Dave Fairclough
Most conversions: 4 Robin Goodliffe v Maidstone 8-4-88 Home CL3, Dave Hill v Plymouth 24-4-93 Home CL3
Most penalities: 6 Robin Goodliffe v Londonj Scottish 14-10-89 Home CL3, Mark Rodgersv Morley 23-2-91 Home CL3
Most drop goals: 1 Bill Reichwald v Nuneaton 7-12-91 Home CLe, Chris Thompson v Askeans 14-3-92 Home CL3, Mark Rodgers v Broughton Park 12-11-92 Home CL3

IN A SEASON

Most points: 108 Mark Rodgers 1990-91 CL3
Most tries: 8 David Fairclough 1988-89 CL3
Most conversions: 14 Robin Goodliffe 1988-89 CL3
Most penalties: 22 Mark Rodgers 1990-91 CL3
Most drop goals: 1 Bill Reichwald 1991-92 CL3, Chris Thompson 1991-92 CL3, Mark Rodgers 1992-93 CL3

IN A CAREER

Most points: 217 Mark Rodgers 1990-93
Most tries: 18 Kerry Morley 1987-92
Most conversions: 26 Robin Goodliffe 1987-90
Most penalties: 46 Mark Rodgers 1990-93
Most drop goals: 1 Bill Reichwald 1987-93, Chris Thompson 1990- 92, Mark Rodgers 1990-93

SEASON BY SEASON LEADING SCORERS

		Most Points			Most Tries
1987-88	56	Robin Goodliffe	3		Dave Fairclough David Watson
1988-89	71	Robin Goodliffe	8		Dave Fairclough
1989-90	61	Robin Goodliffe	5		Kerry Morley
1990-91	108	Mark Rodgers	7		Mark Rodgers
1991-92	71	Chris Thompson	2		Lan Wright J Morley K Morley
1992-93	62	Mark Rodgers	4		Stuart Juds

SHEFFIELD RUFC

Club Details

Colours: Blue & white hoops, navy blue shorts, red socks
Change of Colours: Red shirts
Nickname: Sheff
Date Founded: 1902
Membership: Total 650, Full 350, Social 150, Junior/Youth/Minis 150
Membership Fees: Full £35, Junior/Youth/Minis £2-£7.50, Other £20
Number of Teams: Senior 5, Junior 8
Programme Advertising Rates: £200 per page

Ground Details

Ground Address: Abbeydale Park, Totley rise, Sheffield, S17 3LJ
Telephone: 0742 367011
Fax: 0742 621054
Directions: Take A621 Abbeydale Road South from City Centre
Capacity: Total 1,000, Seated 250, Standing 750
Ticket Prices: Adult £2.00, OAP/Child Free
Clubhouse Facilities: Bars, restaurant, lounge, childrens room, snooker, squash etc.
Training Nights: Tuesday & Thursday

Sheffield v Plymouth Albion at Abbeydale Park, September 1992. Centre Simon Slater in possession with Chris Saul, Alistair Challenor and Dave Hill (left to right) also in the picture   *Photo: Sheffield Newspapers Ltd.*

SUDBURY RUFC

EST 1925

President: Tim McNeill
Chairman: Iain Hook
Club Secretary: Eric Benton, 45
Woodville Road, Ipswich, Suffolk, IP4
1PB. Tel: (H) 0473 212753 (W) 0473
232137
Fixtures Secretary: Gregory
Underwood, 11 Bures Road, Great
Curnard, Sudbury, Suffolk, CO10 0EJ.
Tel: 0787 73045
Press Officer: T McConnel, 7 Streetfield
Close, Shrimpling, Bury St Edmunds,
Suffolk
1993/94 1XV Captain: TBA
1993/94 1XV Coach: TBA
Commercial Manager: Iain Hook
Director of Coaching: Rob Lane

Review of the Season

Undoubtedly this has been the Club's greatest season, winning the Eastern Counties Spicers Cup for a record 7th time, winning League Division Four South and with it becoming a Senior Club. The success however has been the result of many years of hard work and can also be attributed to the forward thinking and endeavours of various Club players and officials during the last 1O years.

The advent of the Leagues saw Sudbury, on their current form at the time, placed in Division Four South where the Club has remained, slowly creeping up the League season by season.

Throughout this period the antipodean influence has been great. Initially through players such as All Blacks Albie Anderson and the following season Terry Wright and through the coaches John Phillips and this season Rob Lane from Manly. In addition to the coaching aspects the Club has learnt much in the way of application, attitude and fitness from the Southern Hemisphere. In addition, several Sudbury players have visited New Zealand on a exchange basis.

The Club's success had not been without its burdens, notably on the financial side where a loss has occurred in the previous two years. This year however, with the arrival of Bill Charity as Treasurer, financial control has once again been obtained. Ambitious plans are afoot to improve the existing facilities in a way of the sponsors lounge and grandstand.

The Club is obviously looking next season to consolidate its position and hopefully follow the example of Havant this season. To do this the Club will rely on the existing squad and new players which it is hoped will be attracted by the opportunity to play Senior Rugby locally.

As with most Clubs the League coupled with the recent success has increased the difficulty of finding suitable fixtures for the second and third teams, however Gregory Underwood, the Clubs Fixture Secretary for 26 years, is endeavouring to resolve the situation.

Whilst several players in the First Team Squad come from further afield a majority of players are local lads and many have risen right throughout the Club from the Colts. Obviously the appointment of Colin Pinnegar with some ten years first class experience was a major factor. Colin had been living locally for the past 5 years and therefore hardly counts as a import!

Following the Pilkington Cup first round win against local Division Four South rivals North Walsham the first League encounter was against Berry Hill and resulted in a very hard fought game which could have gone either way, the result being a 9-9 draw. The second fixture at home saw London Welsh humbled 18-6. This result was obviously significant. There followed an away match against Maidstone and hard fought home win against Southend before the comprehensive win 49-1O against Met Police away. The team then lost to Richmond in the second round of the Pilkington Cup away followed by a comprehensive 58-11 win against Thurrock. A minor hiccup against Walsall in a friendly occurred in December when with several key players missing, the side lost 5O-9 in atrocious weather conditions. The next league game was away in January with local rivals North Walsham resulting in a 2O-8 win. The end of the season saw home wins against Weston-Super-Mare, an away win against Basingstoke who came second in the League last year and a home win against Camborne where the two Pinnegar brothers came up against the third brother with the side winning 22-1O. A very close victory 22-2O against High Wycombe in the penultimate game ensured that the League Title was already won with the last game against Lydney still to play.

CLUB PLAYING RECORD 1992-93 SEASON

National Division: Four South
Final League Position at end 1992/93 Season: 1st
League Playing Record: P 12, W 11, D 1, L 0, Pts F 337, Pts A 130
Season Playing Record (including League matches/Pilkington cup etc): P 27, W 21, D 1, L 5, Pts F 711, Pts A 438

Sudbury RUFC 1992-93.

Photo: Ronald Bartlett

SUDBURY RUFC

Club Details

Colours: Navy with broad white hoop
Change of Colours: Claret with a broad blue hoop
Date Club Founded: 1925
Membership: Total 355, Full 150, Socail 205, Junior/Youth/Minis 92
Membership Fees: Full £40
Number of Teams: Senior 5, Junior 5
Programme Advertising Rates: Available on application

Ground Details

Ground Address: Moorsfield, Rugby Road, Great Curnard, Head Lane, Sudbury, Suffolk.
Telephone: 0787 77547
Fax: 0787 378462
Directions: Great Cornard - Head Lane into Rugby Road
Capacity: Plenty
Ticket Prices: Adult £3/£2
Clubhouse Facilities: Weights room, squash court, 12 changing rooms, showers, baths, bar catering, ladies and gents toilets
Training Nights: Seniors Tues & Thurs, Ladies Mon, Youth Wed

ADDITIONAL RESULTS 1992-93

No	Date	Opponents	Venue	Result
1	Sep 2	Presidents XV	H	W45-5
2	Sep 5	Wasps	H	L0-44
3	Sep 12	Cheshunt	H	W37-15
4	Sep 19	North Walsham	H	W19-12
5	Oct 17	Askeans	A	Cancelled
6	Nov 7	Richmond	A	L15-37
7	Nov 28	Barkers Butts	A	Cancelled
8	Nov 29	Bury St Edmunds	H	W61-3
9	Dec 5	Newbury	h	W25-24
10	Dec 12	Walsall	A	L9-50
11	Dec 19	Leighton Buzzard	H	W21-10
12	Jan 2	Norwich	A	Cancelled
13	Jan 16	Towcestrians	A	Cancelled
14	Jan 23	Reading	H	W16-9
15	Jan 24	Hadleigh	A	W56-3
16	Jan 30	Richmond	A	L14-27
17	Feb 7	Harwich	H	W48-8
18	Feb 20	Ipswich	H	W74-0
19	Feb 27	Eton Maor	H	W37-0
20	Mar 6	Stockwood Park	H	W66-11
21	Mar 20	Cambridge	H	W23-18
22	Apr 17	N Walsham	A	W9-8

COMPETITIONS WON DURING SEASON 1992-93

Courage League Title
Spicers Ecru Cup
Suffolk Cup

LEADING SCORERS

Steve Dyble, Full Back, 299
Steve Titcombe, Wing, 160
Marke Hett, Wing, 70
Steve Glen, Scrum Half, 45
G Atherton, Wing, 40
Tim Newcombe, Centre, 35
Nick Gregory, Fly Half, 23

SUDBURY RUGBY CLUB
RUGBY ROAD, GREAT CORNARD, SUDBURY, SUFFOLK.
TEL: (0787) 377547
COURAGE NATIONAL LEAGUE DIVISION 4

SUDBURY were the only club which already knew they were going to be promoted when they took the field for their final league game. They had already won the Southern section of Division Four and only needed a win, which was narrowly obtained, against Lydney to go through their league campaign unbeaten – a draw at Berry Hill last September being the only blemish. Four matches overall were lost – three friendlies and a Pilkington Cup second round match at Richmond (37-15). They have also regained both the Suffolk and Eastern Counties Cups and have won 25 of the 30 matches they played for a points situation of 912 scored and 414 conceded.

An accent on youth has paid dividends for the club, which was founded in 1925. England Colts have called on the services of Steve Glen and John Cowling from what is basically a young side with the experience coming from ex-Wasps lock Colin Pinnegar, the captain, and coaching administrator Rob Lane. In Steve Titcombe they have the top try-scorer in the British Isles, but it is teamwork which has been the main ingredient for success which they look to continue in next season's newly formed Fourth Division.

Register now to join Eastern Counties Premier Club

If you have ambitions to play at the highest level in the region, we would like to hear from you.
- 1993 National Division 4 South winners
- 1993 Eastern Counties Cup winners
- 5 Senior XVs • Ladies XV • Colts, Juniors and Minis.

New players, including students, coming to East Anglia are invited to join in our success.

Contact Tony Atherton (Membership Secretary) Tel: (0787) 379026

FIXTURES 1993-4

4th Sept	Barkers Butts	(H)	13th Nov	Aspatria*	(H)	12th Feb	Leeds*	(H)
11th Sept	Wasps Vandals	(A)	20th Nov	Clifton*	(A)	26th Feb	Aspatria*	(A)
18th Sept	Richmond 2	(A)	4th Dec	Broughton Park*	(H)	5th Mar	Spicers EC Cup	(H)
25th Sept	Ealing	(H)	11th Dec	Sheffield*	(H)	12th Mar	Clifton*	(H)
2nd Oct	Southend	(A)	18th Dec	Liverpool*	(A)	26th Mar	Broughton Park*	(A)
9th Oct	North Walsham	(A)	8th Jan	Askeans*	(H)	9th Apr	Sheffield*	(A)
23rd Oct	Plymouth*	(A)	15th Jan	High Wycombe	(H)	23rd Apr	Liverpool*	(H)
30th Oct	Harrogate*	(H)	22nd Jan	Plymouth*	(H)	30th Apr	Askeans*	(A)
6th Nov	Leeds*	(A)	29th Jan	Harrogate*	(A)	*Courage National League Div. 4		

What an excellent public relations exercise it was to distribute attractive coloured posters with information about the club as shown above.

Sudbury certainly don't miss any tricks in the publicity field as they also compiled a superb lavishly illustrated book (colour and black and white photos) showing press reports of all last season's matches. A superb effort!

LEAGUE FOUR PROGRAMMES

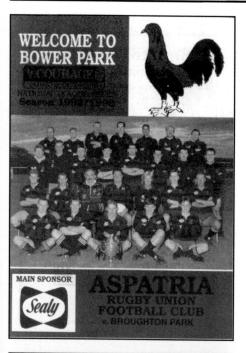

LEAGUE FOUR PROGRAMMES

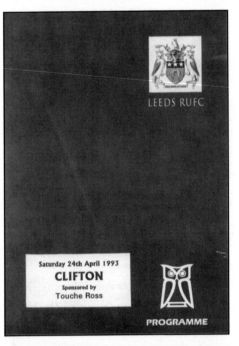

LEEDS RUFC

Saturday 24th April 1993

CLIFTON

Sponsored by
Touche Ross

PROGRAMME

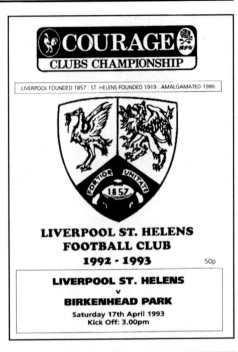

COURAGE
CLUBS CHAMPIONSHIP

LIVERPOOL FOUNDED 1857 : ST. HELENS FOUNDED 1919 : AMALGAMATED 1986

**LIVERPOOL ST. HELENS
FOOTBALL CLUB
1992 - 1993**   50p

LIVERPOOL ST. HELENS
v
BIRKENHEAD PARK

Saturday 17th April 1993
Kick Off: 3.00pm

**SHEFFIELD RUGBY UNION
FOOTBALL CLUB**

Founded 1902, Abbeydale Park, Sheffield

SEASON 1992 - 93

SHEFFIELD R.U.F.C.

ESTO FIDELIS

SUPPORTED
BY **TAYLOR
& EMMET**
SOLICITORS

COURAGE
CLUBS CHAMPIONSHIP

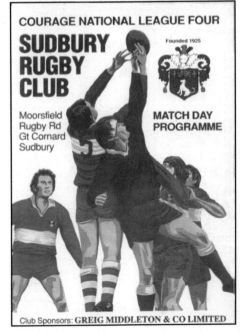

COURAGE NATIONAL LEAGUE FOUR

**SUDBURY
RUGBY
CLUB**   Founded 1925

Moorsfield
Rugby Rd
Gt Cornard
Sudbury

**MATCH DAY
PROGRAMME**

Club Sponsors: **GREIG MIDDLETON & CO LIMITED**

LEAGUE 5 NORTH

LEAGUE 5 SOUTH

RESULTS AND LEAGUE TABLES
1987-1993
LEAGUE 4 NORTH — Pages 252-255
LEAGUE 4 SOUTH — Pages 256-259

MEMBER CLUBS
1993-94

League 5 North & 5 South Official:
L C K Angel
1 Rochford Road
Basingstoke
Hampshire RG21 1TQ
Tel: (H) 0256 27935
(B) 0256 844844 x 4584

League 5 North & 5 South Registrar:
Julian Yeomans
Michael Humphreys & Partners Ltd
68 South Lambeth Road
Vauxhall
London SW8 1RL
Tel: (B) 071-820 9911

NATIONAL LEAGUE FOUR NORTH RESULTS

1987-88

		1	2	3	4	5	6	7	8	9	10	11
1	Birkenhead Park		7-6		9-26		10-21		16-28		28-3	
2	Broughton Park			19-6		34-9		24-12		16-20		20- 6
3	Derby	11-16			33-13		9-14		6-12		34-8	
4	Durham City		4-0			23-18		12-10		9-12		30-12
5	Lichfield	27-0		11-7			27-9		10-27		13-13	
6	Northern		15-13		3-12			6-22		17-27		14-14
7	Preston Grasshoppers	24-17		22-10		19-15			6-5		31-9	
8	Roundhay		20-6		6-12		0-0			4-8		16-3
9	Rugby	20-0		28-16		24-12		21-3				
10	Solihull		7-14		0-24		7-16		0-12			9-21
11	Stourbridge	13-14		21-4		9-6		86-15		11-0		

1988-89

		1	2	3	4	5	6	7	8	9	10	11
1	Birmingham				12-33	0-29		7-20		0-10	0-31	
2	Broughton Park			45-9			14-9		10-0			23-9
3	Durham City	34-0			9-16	20-13		16-24				22-10
4	Lichfield		12-3	15-9			6-15		17-6	6-10		
5	Morley		10-34		13-3		12-10		15-13	6-15		
6	Northern	52-7			19-10	21-9		6-10				16-9
7	Preston Grasshoppers		13-30	31-12			15-25		25-7	11-4		
8	Rounday	79-0			10-10	13-9		22-9				48-12
9	Stoke		12-17	3-9			9-6		9-19		13-3	.
10	Stourbridge		18-3	0-12			28-15		0-10			9-3
11	Winnington Park	63-3			16-0	23-16		16-12		27-6		

1989-90

		1	2	3	4	5	6	7	8	9	10	11
1	Broughton Park				16-10	13-17		9-7	67-3			
2	Durham City	24-22			13-3			22-13		21-22		
3	Kendall	6-33	22-21				18-6				18-13	18-10
4	Lichfield			0-10		12-7	9-3					15-9
5	Morley		12-6	19-13			16-12					25-19
6	Northern	17-4	18-21					22-16	9-15			
7	Preston Grasshoppers			16-3	10-7	3-10					9-12	12-9
8	Stoke			7-15	6-12	0-25		6-15				18-25
9	Stourbridge			10-6	22-15	13-15		17-7	20-6			
10	Walsall	9-20	14-20				9-18		10-3	12-15		
11	Winnington Park	9-15	19-6				15-19			13-4	27-20	

1990-91

		1	2	3	4	5	6	7	8	9	10	11	12	13
1	Birmingham		3-16		9-9	6-42		15-9				13-17	15-22	
2	Durham			23-2	6-3	15-15		6-12				3-16	10-11	
3	Harrogate	30-12					14-14		21-50	25-15	48-12	6-16		
4	Hereford			29-6		10-34	3-12			13-9	21-9	15-24		
5	Kendal			7-13			6-13		3-16	12-6	19-0	7-4		
6	Lichfield	18-13	25-8						7-37	11-16	27-17	24-7		
7	Northern			4-18	18-3	16-16	6-9						17-10	18-12
8	Otley	51-15	29-3		50-0			43-6					36-0	36-0
9	Preston Grasshoppers	21-12	13-0					14-19	16-4		36-3	23-0		
10	Stoke	12-3	25-3					13-13	11-40			6-10	9-23	
11	Stourbridge	18-0	12-16					10-10	7-32				20-13	6-9
12	Walsall			0-12	22-7	12-13	12-13			9-20				15-13
13	Winnington			22-6	9-9	21-17	13-4			0-3	35-9			

1991-92

		1	2	3	4	5	6	7	8	9	10	. 11	12	13
1	Aspatria			21-12			2-15		16-0	3-0	23-0	24-9		
2	Durham City	15-26					13-9		24-15	3-22	12-18	9-21		
3	Harrogate		9-6		12-19	13-22	18-0						26-14	13-7
4	Hereford	21-18	31-0				33-4				33-10		9-6	4-3
5	Kendal	3-13	18-6		9-9		14-4						10-4	18-10
6	Litchfield			25-24	13-23	6-38	9-16						21-14	19-12
7	Northern	13-41	10-11						10-24	6-26	13-6	7-9		
8	Preston G'hoppers			16-13	42-14	13-14	0-10						13-6	28-3
9	Stourbridge			32-8	10-12	21-3	9-17		3-24		10-23			
10	Towcestrians			3-7	6-15	18-6	0-21		4-9					22-10
11	Vale of Lune			10-15		6-12	9-9		6-11	8-15	15-13			
12	Walsall	9-26	6-16					19-15		10-14	12-10	18-6		
13	Winnington Park	3-13	29-18					22-7		20-0		19-10	21-21	

1992-93

		1	2	3	4	5	6	7	8	9	10	11	12	13
1	Durham		7-33	31-10	19-6				10-28				6-7	35-17
2	Harrrogate					54-6	25-16	36-3		19-13	20-5	71-7		
3	Hereford		12-29	11-7		14-15		0-8			19-19	38-10		
4	Kendal		6-34			6-20		19-12		36-17	6-9	25-13		
5	Lichfield	54-11					42-6	15-12		12-16	14-12	13-13		
6	Nuneaton	18-17		22-13	13-36				10-28				16-9	5-36
7	Preston Grasshoppers	8-10					13-3		10-6	9-7	17-16	28-7		
8	Rotherham		6-6	20-7	30-16	34-12							36-11	16-5
9	Stoke	20-11		14-5		15-14		13-15					32-6	20-9
10	Stourbridge	10-12					17-16	12-14		14-6			27-0	9-11
11	Towcestrians	27-17					11-6		11-26	19-32	9-12		10-12	
12	Walsall		14-21	29-6	3-10	2-10		12-14						26-8
13	Winnington Park		20-15	12-12	8-9		17-8	9-10			15-0			

COURAGE LEAGUE FIXTURES

1993-94 NATIONAL LEAGUE FIVE NORTH

December 18 (Week 15)
Kendal v Walsall
Nuneaton v Preston Grasshoppers
Birmingham Solihull v Rotherham
Durham City v Lichfield
Hereford v Winnington Park
Stoke-on-Trent v Bradford & Bingley

October 23 (Week 8)
Kendal v Nuneaton
Bradford & Bingley v Preston Grasshoppers
Winnington Park v Rotherham
Stourbridge v Lichfield
Hereford v Durham City
Stoke-on-Trent v Birmingham Solihull

January 8 (Week 18)
Rotherham v Durham City
Preston Grasshoppers v Birmingham Solihull
Walsall v Nuneaton
Bradford & Bingley v Kendal
Winnington Park v Stoke-on-Trent
Stourbridge v Hereford

October 30 (Week X2)
Birmingham Solihull v Kendal
Durham City v Stoke-on-Trent
Lichfield v Hereford
Rotherham v Stourbridge
Preston Grasshoppers v Winnington Park
Walsall v Bradford & Bingley

January 29 (Week X5)
Kendal v Winnington Park
Nuneaton v Bradford & Bingley
Birmingham Solihull v Walsall
Durham City v Preston Grasshoppers
Lichfield v Rotherham
Stoke-on-Trent v Stourbridge

November 13 (Week 10)
Kendal v Durham City
Nuneaton v Birmingham Solihull
Winnington Park v Walsall
Stourbridge v Preston Grasshoppers
Hereford v Rotherham
Stoke-on-Trent v Lichfield

February 12 (Week 22)
Preston Grasshoppers v Lichfield
Walsall v Durham City
Bradford & Bingley v Birmingham Solihull
Winnington Park v Nuneaton
Stourbridge v Kendal
Hereford v Stoke-on-Trent

November 20 (Week 11)
Durham City v Nuneaton
Lichfield v Kendal
Rotherham v Stoke-on-Trent
Preston Grasshoppers v Hereford
Walsall v Stourbridge
Bradford & Bingley v Winnington Park

March 12 (Week 26)
Kendal v Hereford
Nuneaton v Stourbridge
Birmingham Solihull v Winnington Park
Durham City v Bradford & Bingley
Lichfield v Walsall
Rotherham v Preston Grasshoppers

December 4 (Week 13)
Kendal v Rotherham
Nuneaton v Lichfield
Birmingham Solihull v Durham City
Stourbridge v Bradford & Bingley
Hereford v Walsall
Stoke-on-Trent v Preston Grasshoppers

March 26 (Week 28)
Walsall v Rotherham
Bradford & Bingley v Lichfield
Winnington Park v Durham City
Stourbridge v Birmingham Solihull
Hereford v Nuneaton
Stoke-on-Trent v Kendal

December 11 (Week 14)
Lichfield v Birmingham Solihull
Rotherham v Nuneaton
Preston Grasshoppers v Kendal
Walsall v Stoke-on-Trent
Bradford & Bingley v Hereford
Winnington Park v Stourbridge

April 9 (Week 30)
Nuneaton v Stoke-on-Trent
Birmingham Solihull v Hereford
Durham City v Stourbridge
. Lichfield v Winnington Park
Rotherham v Bradford & Bingley
Preston Grasshoppers v Walsall

NATIONAL LEAGUE 4 NORTH TABLES

1987-88

	P	W	D	L	F	A	Pts
Rugby	10	9	0	1	184	100	18
Durham	10	8	0	2	165	100	16
Roundhay	10	6	2	2	131	67	14
Preston G'hprs	10	5	1	4	178	149	11
Northern	10	5	1	4	121	137	11
Broughton Park	10	5	0	5	152	106	10
Stourbridge	10	5	0	9	132	134	10
Lichfield	10	4	0	6	150	165	8
Birkenhead Park	10	4	0	6	117	179	8
Derby	10	2	0	8	136	197	4
Solihull	10	0	0	10	59	219	0

1990-91

	P	W	D	L	F	A	Pts
Otley	12	11	0	1	424	89	22
Lichfield	12	8	1	3	177	152	17
Preston G'hprs	12	8	0	4	192	109	16
Winnington Park	12	7	1	4	167	148	15
Kendal	12	6	2	4	191	132	14
Harrogate	12	6	1	5	220	204	13
Northern	12	5	3	4	148	169	13
Stourbridge	12	5	1	6	134	161	11
Walsall	12	5	0	7	149	176	10
Durham City	12	4	1	7	109	185	9
Hereford	12	3	2	7	122	208	8
Stoke	12	2	1	9	126	278	5
Birm. Solihull	12	1	1	10	116	265	3

1988-89

	P	W	D	L	F	A	Pts
Roundhay	10	8	1	1	235	81	17
Broughton Park	10	8	0	2	179	92	16
Stourbridge	10	6	0	4	118	79	12
Northern	10	5	0	5	188	155	10
Winnington Park	10	5	0	5	188	155	10
Preston G'hprs	10	5	0	5	161	141	10
Durham City	10	5	0	5	172	157	10
Morley	10	5	0	5	135	141	10
Lichfield	10	4	1	5	112	113	9
Stoke on Trent	10	3	0	7	88	138	9
Birmingham	10	0	0	10	29	171	0

1991-92

	P	W	D	L	F	A	PD	Pts
Aspatria	12	11	0	1	253	100	153	22
Hereford	12	10	1	1	223	133	90	21
Kendal	12	8	1	3	157	123	34	17
Preston G'Hprs	12	8	0	4	195	123	72	16
Lichfield	12	6	1	5	174	177	-3	13
Stourbridge	12	6	0	6	163	137	26	12
Harrogate	12	6	0	6	170	175	-5	12
Winnington Park	12	4	1	7	159	173	-14	9
Towcestrians	12	4	0	8	123	153	-30	8
Durham City	12	4	0	8	133	215	-82	8
Walsall	12	3	1	8	139	187	-48	7
Vale of Lune	12	3	1	8	119	185	-66	7
Northern	12	2	0	10	105	232	-127	4

1989-90

	P	W	D	L	F	A	Pts
Broughton Park	10	8	0	2	246	111	16
Morley	10	8	0	2	169	115	16
Stourbridge	10	7	0	3	146	133	14
Durham City	10	6	0	4	195	169	12
Kendal	10	6	0	4	130	136	12
Preston G'hprs	10	5	0	5	122	109	10
Lichfield	10	5	0	5	110	121	10
Northern	10	4	0	6	139	144	8
Winnington Park	10	4	0	6	142	152	8
Walsall	10	2	0	8	143	183	4
Stoke	10	0	0	10	88	257	0

1992-93

	P	W	D	L	F	A	PD	Pts
Harrogate	12	10	1	1	363	115	248	21
Rotherham	12	10	1	1	259	123	136	21
Preston G'hprs	12	8	0	4	144	140	4	16
Stoke on Trent	12	7	0	5	193	168	25	14
Lichfield	12	6	1	5	221	224	-3	13
Kendal	12	6	0	6	182	189	-7	12
Walsall	12	6	0	6	165	179	-14	12
Durham City	12	6	0	6	179	219	-40	12
Stourbridge	12	5	1	6	161	144	17	11
Winnington Park	12	5	1	6	167	165	2	11
Hereford	12	2	2	8	147	216	-69	6
Nuneaton	12	2	0	10	138	269	-131	4
Towcestrians	12	1	1	10	118	286	-168	3

1987-88

	1	2	3	4	5	6	7	8	9	10	11
1 Askeans		14-0		14-3		17-12		13-4		23-9	
2 Camborne			17-6		23-13		9-7		10-8		10-10
3 Cheltenham	3-20			11-15		16-12		15-0		4-16	
4 Havant		6-7			19-11		6-10		25-15		14-10
5 Lydney	25-3		26-12			10-0		21-0		24-3	
6 Salisbury		6-6		3-17			9-15		28-4		10-0
7 Sidcup	3-3		17-9		6-9			20-3		12-8	
8 Southend		6-18		12-4		9-4			3-0		10-3
9 Streatham Croydon	9-18		6-19		10-20		6-16			9-13	
10 Stroud		31-9		9-7		19-10		10-16			11-10
11 Sudbury	15-16		23-6		23-14		12-12		19-3		

1988-89

	1	2	3	4	5	6	7	8	9	10	11
1 Camborne			45-12	21-18			18-0		6-19	33-13	
2 Cheltenham	10-34				3-35	16-6		20-4			15-15
3 Ealing		12-6			17-21	3-15		53-12			13-10
4 HAvant		23-4	29-4				6-3		15-6	29-7	
5 Lydney	27-12			16-16		14-9		47-0			17-7
6 Redruth	9-9			15-6			11-0		14-4		15-0
7 Salisbury			9-9	13-10		9-32			22-15	13-6	
8 Sidcup	9-20			16-19		4-26	9-37				4-11
9 Southend		13-19	18-17		16-15			15-10		3-25	
10 Stroud		0-20	18-3		9-16	15-16		20-6			
11 Sudbury	9-0			0-6			23-7		25-6	41-6	

1989-90

	1	2	3	4	5	6	7	8	9	10	11
1 Basingstoke		12-12			3-13		6-12		28-7	34-10	
2 Camborne			24-21	13-11		29-3		10-16			
3 Cheltenham	24-13				12-17				10-15	0-10	
4 Clipton	24-3		19-10				33-24		44-7		
5 Havant		3-13		18-26		22-6					21-7
6 Maidstone	6-20		22-7	6-22			3-36		6-24		
7 Metropolitan Police		20-11			25-0				46-0	15-9	14-9
8 Redruth	14-9		14-10	3-12		35-0	3-6				
9 Salisbury		8-26			9-16			6-39			6-17
10 Southend		13-7			13-13			0-3	12-10		12-16
11 Sudbury	22-10		10-13	17-28		36-3		22-12			

1990-91

		1	2	3	4	5	6	7	8	9	10	11	12	13
1	Basingstoke			10-0	32-10				15-6		0-4		10- 12	27-19
2	Camborne	12-5				17-12	18-25	30-12		26-6		19-6		
3	Cheltenham		25-18		12-25				6-15		3-7		25-10	18-35
4	Ealing	12-6		29-9		9-17	22-6		13-14		12-16			
5	London Welsh	12-13		31-7	18-26		6-16		32-10		26-12			
6	Maidenhead		6-20			22-6	6-28			9-18			9-8	10-9
7	North Walsham	8-12		23-17	39-11				16-16		6-16		13-7	
8	Redruth		24-6			26-7	18-16					20-6	25-0	23-4
9	Southend	3-27		19-12	0-7			27-12	16-12	9-17				
10	Sudburm		11-6			20-9	12-17	16-19				24-20		22-9
11	Weston-S-Mare		24-10			7-12	18-7	21-8		21-18		6- 18		

1991-92

		1	2	3	4	5	6	7	8	9	10	11	12	13
1	Basingstoke		22-13		16-7		9-7			18-6	38-6	11-3		
2	Camborne			18-15		10-8		19-9	21-14				3-17	14-11
3	Ealing	8-28				12-8	12-15			10-28	10-13	10-12		
4	Havant		34-9	42-3				42-12	19-6				16-9	25-10
5	High Wycombe	13-7			7-10		23-14			25-12	33-9	25-22		
6	London Welsh		35-15		6-9			18-15	29-18				34-12	36-19
7	Maidstone	0-7		21-18		9-12				12-10	20-10	31- 17		
8	Met. Police	0-15		40-7		3-14		7-3		3-13	10-15			
9	North Walsham		6-17		7-9	3-21					30-3	6-0		23-9
10	Sidcup		9-17		3-32	6-49						10-3	4-27	15-21
11	Southend		12-10		3-56		13-26		19-15				7- 21	15-20
12	Sudbury	6-22		25-0		25-12		13-15	30-13	25-9				
13	Weston-S-Mare	19-25		28-7		6-16		7-0	10-17				15-22	

1992-93

		1	2	3	4	5	6	7	8	9	10	11	12	13
1	Basingstoke		25-16		12-5			19-8	10-6			9-16		37-6
2	Berry Hill			16-16			14-22	18-6	18-7			9-9		18-18
3	Camborne	12-8				6-32	13-8			17-12	11-5		34- 11	
4	High Wycombe		7-10	8-10				22-5	29-17			20-22		27-5
5	London Welsh	36-16	44-3		13-8					42-12	46-21	45-14		
6	Lydney	20-18			19-18	6-5				11-3	20-26	15-14		
7	Maidstone			11-10		23-35	8-28		5-38	,5-36		16-13		
8	Metropolitan Police			19-3		27-32		7-13		16- 16	10-49			14-16
9	North Walsham	3-16	8-29		10-8			14-11	10-13			8-20		
10	Southend	11-6	31-25		12-6			37-10		15-16		11-6		
11	Sudbury			22-10		18-6	20-17				24-11		58- 11	41-14
12	Thurock	6-16	23-6		25-28			34-14	6-27	11-18				
13	Weston-S-Mare			16-38		10-17	24-8			6-10	3-0		23-0	

COURAGE LEAGUE FIXTURES

December 18 (Week 15)
Basingstoke v Southend
Camborne v Maidstone
High Wycombe v London Welsh
Lydney v Berry Hill
North Walsham v Tabard
Weston-super-Mare v Metropolitan Police

October 23 (Week 8)
Basingstoke v Camborne
Metropolitan Police v Maidstone
Tabard v London Welsh
Reading v Berry Hill
North Walsham v Lydney
Weston-super-Mare v High Wycombe

January 8 (Week 18)
London Welsh v Lydney
Maidstone v High Wycombe
Southend v Camborne
Metropolitan Police v Basingstoke
Tabard v Weston-super-Mare
Reading v North Walsham

October 30 (Week X2)
High Wycombe v Basingstoke
Lydney v Weston-super-Mare
Berry Hill v North Walsham
London Welsh v Reading
Maidstone v Tabard
Southend v Metropolitan Police

January 29 (Week X5)
Basingstoke v Tabard
Camborne v Metropolitan Police
High Wycombe v Southend
Lydney v Maidstone
Berry Hill v London Welsh
Weston-super-Mare v Reading

November 13 (Week 10)
Basingstoke v Lydney
Camborne v High Wycombe
Tabard v Southend
Reading v Maidstone
North Walsham v London Welsh
Weston-super-Mare v Berry Hill

February 12 (Week 22)
Maidstone v Berry Hill
Southend v Lydney
Metropolitan Police v High Wycombe
Tabard v Camborne
Reading v Basingstoke
North Walsham v Weston-super-Mare

November 20 (Week 11)
Lydney v Camborne
Berry Hill v Basingstoke
London Welsh v Weston-super-Mare
Maidstone v North Walsham
Southend v Reading
Metropolitan Police v Tabard

March 12 (Week 26)
Basingstoke v North Walsham
Camborne v Reading
High Wycombe v Tabard
Lydney v Metropolitan Police
Berry Hill v Southend
London Welsh v Maidstone

December 4 (Week 13)
Basingstoke v London Welsh
Camborne v Berry Hill
High Wycombe v Lydney
Reading v Metropolitan Police
North Walsham v Southend
Weston-super-Mare v Maidstone

March 26 (Week 28)
Southend v London Welsh
Metropolitan Police v Berry Hill
Tabard v Lydney
Reading v High Wycombe
North Walsham v Camborne
Weston-super-Mare v Basingstoke

December 11 (Week 14)
Berry Hill v High Wycombe
London Welsh v Camborne
Maidstone v Basingstoke
Southend v Weston-super-Mare
Metropolitan Police v North Walsham
Tabard v Reading

April 9 (Week 30)
Camborne v Weston-super-Mare
High Wycombe v North Walsham
Lydney v Reading
Berry Hill v Tabard
London Welsh v Metropolitan Police
Maidstone v Southend

NATIONAL LEAGUE 4 SOUTH TABLES

1987-88

	P	W	D	L	F	A	Pts
Askeans	10	8	1	1	141	83	17
Sidcup	10	7	2	1	130	72	16
Lydney	10	7	0	3	173	99	14
Camborne	10	5	2	3	113	119	12
Havant	10	5	0	5	116	102	10
Stroud	10	5	0	5	112	114	10
Southend	10	5	0	5	63	108	10
Sudbury	10	3	2	5	125	106	8
Salisbury	10	3	1	6	84	94	7
Cheltenham	10	3	0	7	95	152	6
Streatham/Croydon	10	0	0	10	70	173	0

1988-89

	P	W	D	L	F	A	Pts
Lydney	10	8	1	1	240	98	17
Havant	10	8	1	1	177	92	17
Camborn	10	6	1	3	198	126	13
Redruth	10	6	1	3	136	81	13
Sudbury	10	5	1	4	141	89	11
Cheltenham	10	4	2	4	122	151	10
Salisbury	10	4	1	5	113	139	9
Southend	10	4	0	6	116	168	8
Ealing	10	3	0	7	144	188	6
Stroud	10	3	0	7	119	180	6
Sidcup	10	0	0	10	74	168	0

1989-90

	P	W	D	L	F	A	Pts
Met. Police	10	9	0	1	255	74	18
Clifton	10	8	1	1	240	122	17
Redruth	10	7	0	3	151	84	14
Camborne	10	6	1	3	164	113	13
Havant	10	5	1	4	132	126	11
Sudbury	10	5	0	5	162	138	10
Southend	10	4	2	4	124	125	10
Basingstoke	10	3	1	6	138	144	7
Cheltenham	10	2	0	8	107	201	4
Maidstone	10	2	0	8	64	237	4
Salisbury	10	1	0	9	74	247	2

1990-91

	P	W	D	L	F	A	Pts
Redruth	12	12	0	0	225	79	24
Basingstoke	12	9	0	3	187	104	18
Lon. Welsh	12	7	0	5	235	165	14
Camborne	12	6	0	6	204	179	12
Weston S-Mare	12	6	0	6	192	182	12
North Walsham	12	5	2	5	170	180	12
Sudbury	12	6	0	6	160	172	12
Havant	12	5	0	7	157	173	10
Southend	12	5	0	7	152	194	10
Ealing	12	5	0	7	174	218	10
Maidstone	12	4	1	7	122	164	9
Maidenhead	12	4	1	7	130	208	9
Cheltenham	12	2	0	10	150	240	4

1991-92

	P	W	D	L	F	A	PD	Pts
Havant	12	11	0	1	301	91	210	22
Basingstoke	12	11	0	1	218	88	130	22
Lon. Welsh	12	9	0	3	292	160	132	18
Sudbury	12	8	0	4	235	150	85	16
High Wycombe	12	8	0	4	196	139	57	16
Camborne	12	7	0	5	166	195	-29	14
North Walsham	12	5	0	7	153	152	1	10
Maidstone	12	5	0	7	147	180	-33	10
Weston S-Mare	12	4	0	8	175	215	-40	8
Met. Police	12	3	0	9	149	195	-46	6
Southend	12	3	0	9	134	240	-106	6
Sidcup	12	3	0	9	103	290	-187	6
Ealing	12	0	1	11	112	286	-174	2

1992-93

	P	W	D	L	F	A	PD	Pts
Sudbury	12	11	1	0	337	130	207	23
London Welsh	10	10	0	2	353	170	183	20
Lydney	12	8	0	4	187	170	17	16
Cambourne	12	7	1	4	180	168	12	15
Basingstoke	12	7	0	5	192	145	47	14
Southend	12	6	1	5	196	189	7	13
Berry Hill	12	4	3	5	187	216	-29	11
High Wycombe	12	5	0	7	196	160	36	10
Met Police	12	4	1	7	201	207	-6	9
Weston S-Mare	12	4	1	7	154	226	-72	9
North Walsham	12	4	0	8	125	209	-84	8
Maidstone	12	2	0	10	122	306	-184	4
Thurrock	12	2	0	10	147	295	-148	2

LEAGUE 5 NORTH PROGRAMMES

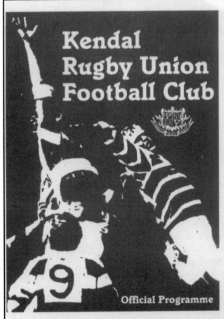

BIRMINGHAM & SOLIHULL RFC

Club President: J P Gallagher
Club Chairman: R Sutton
Club Secretary: A Henderson, 9 Grey Mill Close, Monkspath, B90 4TE. Tel (H) 021 745 7198
Fixture Secretary: A Morden, Station Farm, 40 Station Road, Solihull. Tel (H): 0675 442462 (W) 021 643 2736
Press Officer: B Montegue, 9 Coppice Drive, Acocks Green, Birmingham.
1993/94 IXV Captain: Max Reeve
1993/94 IXV Coach: Malcolm Swain
Chairman of Mini Rugby: C Thompson

Review of the Season

The 1991-92 season had, on the whole, been disappointing. Hwever, the last seven games were won and the club looked forward to the start of the 1992-93 season with confidence.

Confidence which, as it turned out, was not misplaced. By Christmas only three games had been lost and comprehensive wins in the seven league games saw Birmingham and Solihull sitting on top of Midlands Division One. Having already beaten their nearest rivals, (at that time) Barkers Butts, the club was also progressing well in th elocal North Midlands Cup Competition.

Consequently the 1992-93 season was already being regarded by some as the best since the merger of Birmingham RFC and Solihull RUFC in 1989. But in 1993 it got even better. Only one defeat was recorded in the second half of the season. That a league fixture, away to Leamington. However, this was more than compensated for, one week later, with an impressive defeat of old rivals Stourbridge in the semi-final of the North Midlands Cup. This was bettered one month later in the final against Hereford; Birmingham Solihull turned in the best performance of the season, scoring five tries in their 35-3 victory. One trophy in the cabinet and one to go: The Midlands Division One Championship. This was finally secured by beating Mansfield, at home, on April 3rd 1993.

CLUB PLAYING RECORD 1992-93 SEASON

National Division: Midlands Division One
Final League Position at end 1992/93 season: 1st
Season Playing Record: P 30, W 25, D 1, L 4

ACHIEVEMENTS/COMPETITIONS WON DURING SEASON:

Champions, Midlands Division One
North Midlands M&B Sales Cup

Club Details

Colours: Black, red, white and yellow quarters, black shorts
Nickname: Bees
Membership Total 160
Membership Fees: Full £40, Juniors/Youths/Minis £5, Other £20
Number of Teams: Senior 5 + colts

Ground Details:

Ground Address: Sharmant Cross Road, Solihull, B91 1RQ
Telephone No: 021 705 7995
Directions: M42 junction with A34. Follow signs to Birmingham. Turn right at 3rd traffic lighs - 1.5 miles on right.
Ticket Prices Adults £1.00
Clubhouse Facilities: Bar & lounge
Training Nights: Tuesday & Thursday

PLAYING SQUAD 1992-93

15: M Gallagher, M Shelton
14: A Smallwood, T Smedley
13: D Read, J Burrell
12: G Smith, K Jervis
11: N Perry, D Mason
10: P Wheeler, J Russell
9: T Colbourne, I Cummings
1: R Hetherington, R Lee
2: C Barbor, L Cummings
3: M Reeve, A Verlander
4: M Crees, H Rose
5: A Crees, R McCrainor
6: R Richardson, C Hazard
7: J Brennan, J Dight
8: J Bentley, S Wharton

LEAGUE 5 NORTH PROGRAMMES

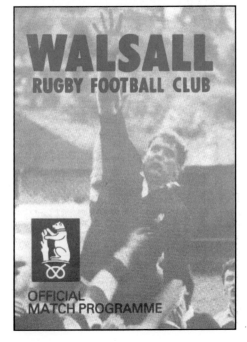

BRADFORD & BINGLEY RFC

Club Details

Colours: Red, amber and black hoops
Change of Colours: Black shirts
Nickname: The Bees
Date Club Founded: 1982 - Former Clubs Bradford 1866, Bingley 1876.
Advertising Rates: £110 per page.
Membership Total 1100, Full 190, Social 553, Juniors/Youths/Minis 200
Membership Fees: Full £27.50, Juniors/Youths/Minis £6, Other £6.
Number of Teams: Senior 7, Junior 8.

Club President: W P Dennis
Club Chairman: I Kelt
Club Secretary: J S Oddy, The Coach House, Warren Farm, Slate Quarry Lane, Eldwick, Bingley, Yorkshire BD16 3NP. Tel (H) 0274 563254 (W) 0274 729792 Fax 0274 390768.
Fixture Secretary: W K Wilkinson, Green Acres, 42 Station Lane, Birkenshaw, Bradford, BD11 2JE. Tel (H)0274 681231 (W) 0274 681231 Fax 0274 681231
Press Officer: C Dennis, Bradford & Bingley RFC, Wagon Lane, Bingley, BD16.
1993/94 IXV Captain: Shaun Bainbridge
1993/94 IXV Coach: Robert Hood
Commercial Manager: Cliff Dennis
Director of Coaching: Roger Pickering
First XV Manager: Richard Greaves
Second XV Coach: Keith Jones
Second XV Manager: James Driver

Ground Details:

Ground Address: Wagon Lane, Bingley, Yorkshire.
Telephone No: 0274 560468
Fax No: 0274 551895
Directions: Follow A650 (Signposted Keighley) out of Bradford for 5 miles to Beckfoot Grammar School. Turn right just before school on Wagon Lane, Ground 150 yards ahead.
Capacity: Total 3,500, Seated 200.
Ticket Prices Adults £3, OAP/Child £1.
Clubhouse Facilities: 2 bars, function room, ample car parking.
Training Nights: Tuesday & Thursday

CLUB PLAYING RECORD 1992-93 SEASON

National Division: North Division One
Final League Position at end 1992/93 season: 1st.
League Playing Record: P 12, W 11, D 1, L 0, Pts F 333, Pts A 106
Season Playing Record: P 36, W 29, D 1, L 6, Pts F 805, Pts A 431

ACHIEVEMENTS/COMPETITIONS WON DURING SEASON
North Division One Winners
Semi-finalists Yorkshire.

MOST CAPPED PLAYERS
(including British Lions appearances)
C Radacanu, 6, 1986-89

LEADING SCORERS:
J Hewitt, Wing, 410

DURHAM CITY RFC

President: Richard Wilkinson
Club Secretary: Bob Elston, 18 Mayorswell Field, Claypath, Durham, DH1 1JW (or Clubhouse if urgent). Tel: (H) 091 386 3245 (W) 0207 507001.
Fixtures Secretary: Jim Thompson, Cherry Tree House, West End, Wolsingham, Co. Durham. Tel: 0388 528071 (W) 091 378 0201.
Press Officer: Geoff Pennington, 45 Broomside Lane, Belmont, Durham, DH1 2QT.
1993/94 1XV Captain: Jon Bland
1993/94 1XV Coach: Steve Rutland
Chair of Rugby Development: Geoff Moore
Chair of House & Social Development: Ralph Blacklock
Chair of Corporate Development & Sponsorship: Chris Roberts
Treasurer: Ian Smith
Executive Development Officer: Ted Wood.

Review of the Season

A disappointing season even though we achieved our most comfortable position in the league for a few seasons. However a very young squad of players did very well in the second half of the season when the league performances of the season were produced in the 1O-8 win at Preston and the 35-17 victory over Warrington Park at Hollow Drift. In the friendly matches a superb game of attacking rugby against West Hartlepool saw our opponents score late points to win 36-29 and an all-round team display saw off North One champions Bradford and Bingley 24-11.

Outstanding contributions were made by the young centre combination of Mark Stevenson and Mark Veide whilst full back Devin McCallium was always a threat at full-back. Up front back row forwards Rob Milton, Andy Bolam and Ian Cornelius supplied pace and aggression with the front five providing emerging players in Mark Knight, Mark Binors and Graham Wanless. Popular captain Paul Rogers hands over to Jon Bland for season 1993-94 and he will be supported by an impressive vice-captain, back row forward Steve Carss.

With the club structure being radically altered during the summer better support for the team is expected to produce the basis from which we will achieve our objectives — first class rugby for all and promotion.

CLUB PLAYING RECORD 1992-93 SEASON

National Division: Four North
Final League Position at end 1992/93 Season: 8th
League Playing Record: P 12, W 6, D 0, L 6, Pts F 179, Pts A 219
Season Playing Record (including League matches/Pilkington cup etc):
P 34, W 15, D 0, L 19, Pts F 596, Pts A 742

DURHAM CITY RFC

Club Details

Colours: Dark blue and gold
Change of Colours: White
Nickname: City
Date Founded: 1872
Membership: Total 700, Full 200, Social 250, Junior 50, Youth 100, Mini 100.
Membership Fees: Full £28, Junior/Youth/Mini £6, Associate £11.
Number of Teams: Senior 5, U21, U17, U19, Colts, Juniors, Minis aged 8-16.
Programme Advertising Rates: Full £150, Half £85, Qtr £60.

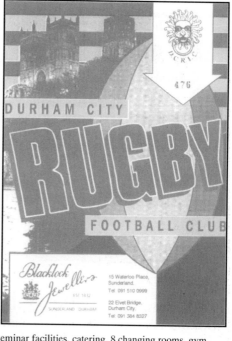

Ground Details

Ground Address: Hollow Drift, Green Land, Durham DH1 3JU
Telephone: 091 386 1172
Directions: Leave A1(M) at A690 junction. Follow city centre sign at roundabout at end of dual carriageway. At next roundabout turn left over river. At traffic lights by County Hotel turn left into Old Elvet. 400 yds fork left into Green Lane. Club 200 yds on right.
Capacity: 5,000 (seated 300, standing 4,700).
Ticket Prices: Adult £2. OAP/Child £1.
Clubhouse Facilities: Club bar, lounge bar, dining room, seminar facilities, catering, 8 changing rooms, gym, physio room.
Training Nights: Senior Tues & Thurs 7.30pm. Colts Wed 7pm.

Durham City RFC 1992-93
Back Row: M Howard, M Stevenson, P Heslop
Middle Row: J Dadidson (Physio), S Eddie (Rugby Chairman), A Bolam, G Wanless, S Carss, K Lycett, J Warwick, S Rutland (Coach), R Wilkinson (Team Secretary)
Front Row: M Knight, M Horn, R Milton, M Veide, I Smith (President), P Rogers (Captain), C Mattison, J Bland, S Kirkup

HEREFORD RFC

President: Rory Davis
Chairman: Derek Miles
Club Secretary: Gareth Lewis, 11 Geoffrey Avenue, Hereford, HR1 1BZ. Tel: (H) 0432 267080 (W) 0432 761611
Fixtures Secretary: Robert Mason, Merrivale Farm, Little Birch, Herefoprd, HR2 8BA. Tel: (H) 0981 540 032 (W) 0981 540 032.
Press Officer: Humphrey Davies, 104 Cotterell Street, Hereford
1993/94 1XV Captain: Mark Osborne
1993/94 1XV Coach: Steven Bradley

CLUB PLAYING RECORD 1992-93 SEASON

National Division: Four North
Final League Position at end 1992/93 Season: 11th
League Playing Record: P 12, W 2, D 2, L 8
Season Playing Record (including League matches/Pilkington cup etc): P 31, W 14, D 2, L 15

COMPETITIONS WON DURING SEASON 1992-93
Pilkington Cup 2nd Round
Stafforshire Colts Cup Winners & 7s

COMPETITIONS WON DURING SEASON 1992-93
RU North Midlands Cup

LEADING APPEARANCES FOR CLUB DURING SEASON 1992-93
Simon Williams, 30

LEADING SCORERS
John Watkins, Lock, 96 — 17 games

Mark Osborne, Prop.
1993-94 1st XV Captain

HEREFORD RFC

Club Details

Colours: Red shirts/Black shorts
Change of Colours: Black shirts/Black shorts
Date Founded: 1870
Membership: Total 200 + minis & youth, Full 150, Social 50, Junior/Youth/Minis 100, Colts 30
Membership Fees: Full £40, Junior/Youth/Minis £5
Number of Teams: Senior 4
Programme Advertising Rates: Negotiable

Ground Details

Ground Address: Wyeside, Hereford, NR4 9UT.
Telephone: 0432 273410
Directions: Follow inner relief road to Greyfriars Bridge, turn right into Barton Road, 300 yards over hump back bridge.
Capacity: Total 2,000, Seated 200, Standing 1,800.
Ticket Prices: Adults £2.00, OAP/Child Half price.
Clubhouse Facilities: Bar, stand, Changing, Small but adequate.
Training Nights: Seniors: Tues & Thurs, Youth: Wed, Minis: Sunday am, Colts: Thurs.

ADDITIONAL RESULTS 1992-93

No	Date	Opponents	Venue	Result
1	Sep 19	Amber Valley	A	W6-3
2	Oct 17	Lydney	H	L8-10
3	Nov 7	Coventry	A	L34-16
4	Dec 5	Brum & Solihull	A	W10-9
5	Dec 13	Whitchurch	H	W29-5
6	Dec 19	Cinderford	H	W37-10
7	Jan 2	Berry Hill	H	W17-3
8	Jan 17	Aston Old Eds	A	W16-0
9	Jan 30	Winnington Park	H	L13-23
10	Feb 13	Broughton Park	H	W17-10
11	Feb 21	Camp Hill	A	W7-6
12	Feb 27	Wolverhampton	H	W17-10
13	Mar 6	Plymouth Albion	H	W34-14
14	Mar 21	Brum & Solihull	N	L35-0
15	Apr 10	Lydney	A	20-14
16	Apr 17	Syston	H	W15-0

Spencer Goodall, No 8. 1992-93 1st XV Captain.

KENDAL RUFC

Chairman: Ian W Hutton
Club Secretary: Paul A Ruiz, 29 Mint Street, Kendal, LA9 6DS. Tel: 0539 720686 (W) 0539 721741
Fixtures Secretary: TBA
Press Officer: John Hutton, 168 Vicarage Drive, Kendal, LA9 5BX. Tel: 0539 733152
1993/94 1XV Captain: Howard Nicholson
1993/94 1XV Coach: Peter Kremer/Neil Rollings
Assistant Secretary & Vice Chairman: Peter Davy
Treasurer: Mike Carradus
Team Manager: Ray Lee
Team Secretary: Roger Wilson

Review of the Season

This has been an important year for the Club in a number of ways. On the playing side the 1st XV completed a demanding fixture list, comfortably placed in National Division 4 North; the 2nd XV rounded off a good season by winning the Westmoreland and Furness Cup: the 3rd XV were happily able to field stronger sides than has sometimes been the case in recent years; the U21 XV played in a manner which promises well for the future of the Club; and the Junior XVs, although occasionally having difficulty in fielding full sides, played keen and attractive Rugby. The Minis continue to thrive under enthusiastic leadership.

Although, as has been said, the 1st XV finished in a good League position, there must be a element of disappointment after the very high hopes which were held last September, especially when the season opened with a splendid performance against Orrell and an emphatic win in the first league game against Nuneaton. This was followed by a series of below par and inexplicable performances in the league, which killed off any promotion hopes well before Christmas. It is greatly to the credit of the players, the captain and the coaches that they did not allow the season to disintegrate completely from that low point, as it could so easily have done, but rallied themselves to end the season in credit. Ian Downham is to be congratulated and thanked for his dedication to the demanding job of Club Captain, as are Peter Kremer and Neil Rollings for their work as team coaching organisers. For the forthcoming season the top three Courage Leagues have been divided into four smaller leagues. The league in which Kendal will be playing has been re-named National League 5, North, though the level at which we are placed remains the same.

Kendal 1st Xv 1992-93

KENDAL RUFC

Club Details

Colours: Black & amber.
Change of Colours: White, black & amber.
Date Founded: 1905.
Membership: Total 471, Full 219, Social 150, Junior/Youth/Minis 100.
Membership Fees: Full £25, Junior/Youth/Minis free.
Number of Teams: Senior 3.
Programme Advertising Rates: Qtr £50.

Ground Details

Ground Address: Mint Bridge, Shap Road, Kendal, Cumbria.
Telephone: 0539 724239.
Directions: Follow A6 for Penrith. Keep left at Duke of Cumberland. Club 500m on the left.
Capacity: Total 1,000, Seated 450.
Ticket Prices: Adults £2.50, OAP £1.
Clubhouse Facilities: Bar, lounge, dining room, gym & changing rooms.
Training Nights: Tuesday & Thursday.

ADDITIONAL RESULTS 1992-93

No	Date	Opponents	Venue	Result
1	Sep 1	Orrell	H	L16-45
2	Sep 12	Middls/Brgh	A	L12-41
3	Sep 19	Newcastle Gosforth	A	L3-27
4	Oct 17	Waterloo	A	L5-38
5	Nov 7	Penrith	H	W 22-15
6	Nov 28	Cockermouth	H	W65-8
7	Dec 5	Sale	A	L6-37
8	Dec 12	Leeds	A	L10-39
9	Dec 26	Furness	A	W41-3
10	Jan 23	Sheffield	H	W8-6
11	Jan 30	Birkenhead Park	h	W19-9
12	Feb 6	Carlisle	H	W32-11
13	Feb 27	Northern	A	W18-8
14	Mar 6	Kirkby LS/DL	H	W47-3
15	Mar 20	Aspatria	A	L7-26
16	Mar 28	Dudley	H	W49-20
17	Apr 9	Vickers	H	W15-0
18	Apr 10	Broughton Park	A	W23-20
19	Apr 12	Wharfedale	H	W29-13
20	Apr 17	Bradford & Bingley	A	L24-32
21	Apr 24	Huddersfield	H	D15-15

CLUB PLAYING RECORD 1992-93 SEASON

National Division: 4 North
Final League Position at end 1992/93 season: 6th
League Playing Record:
P 12, W 6, D 0, L 6, Pts F 182, Pts A 189
Season Playing Record:
P 33, W 18, D 1, L 14, Pts F 652, Pts A 598

PLAYING SQUAD 1992-93

Full Back: J Hudson, D Airey
Wing: J Bill, P Dodds, M Fell, J Hoggarth, M Plummer, P Hubbard
Centre: M Healey, M Mace, S Healey, P Dalzell, J Slater, K Sanderson
Stand Off: A Dolan, D Bell
Scrum Half: D Sharpe, M Airey, R Morris
Prop: J Bracken, S Pratt, B Coxon, P Hutton, N Pearson, S Hulme, G Rigg
Hooker: L Woof, M Nicholson, I Thompson
Lock: R Stewart, H Nicholson, P Hancock, M Capstick, P Wright
Back Row: I Downham, R Stowe, M Thomas, S Whitehead
No 8: P Kremer, H Batey

LEADING APPEARANCES FOR CLUB

1 Downham (Capt), 30, 1992/93
S Hulme, 30, 1992/93
M Mace, 28, 1992/93
D Sharpe, 28, 1992/93

LEADING SCORERS 1992-93

J Hudson, Full Back, 140 (17 games)
P Dodds, Full back or wing, 78 (20 games)
J Bill, Wing, 65 (13 Tries)
D Bell, Stand Off, 62
P Hubbard, Wing, 60 (12 Tries).

TOP TRY SCORERS (1992/93)

J Bill, 13, P Hubbard, 12
P Dodds, M Healey, 6
J Hudson, 5, D Bell, 4
A Dolan, D Sharpe, H Nicholson, M Thomas, 3
M Mace, S Hulme, M Fell, P Kremer, 3

LICHFIELD RUFC

FOUNDED
1874

President: W M Lineey
Chairman: D Beck
Club Secretary: S Godfrey, 1 Old College House, Dam Street, Lichfield, Staffs, WS13 6AA. Tel: (H) 0543 268539 (W) 021 454 7033 Fax: (H) 0543 419958 (W) 021 456 1079.
Fixtures Secretary: A G Young, 5 Covey Close, Lichfield, Staffs. Tel: (H) 0543 262832.
Press Officer: David Lewis, 52 Stafford Road, Lichfield, Staffs, WS13 7BZ. Tel: (H) 0543 254985 (W) 0602 580313.
1993/94 1XV Captain: Paul Tinsley
1993/94 1XV Coach: Barry Broad
Director of Playing: Dave Lewis
1st Team Manager: John Parker
Assistant Coach: Chris O'Callaghan
Commercial Manager: Jim Ashpole

Review of the Season

By recent standards, the 1992/93 season has to be viewed as a disappointment. It was, however, a season of consolidation with the side having to accommodate a number of new and/or young players.

Despite a definite shortage of bulk and size up front, a season long problem, the opening three months were relatively successful with some creditable league performances and a commendable defeat against Waterloo in the Pilkington Cup.

The second half lacked success through having to field far too many sides with numerous changes, which led to a lack of self confidence which simple compounded the original deficiencies. Nevertheless, Lichfield finished fifth in the Courage League Division 4 North which was an acceptable return on the season.

Dave Richards, captain, was the leading points scorer with 254 points but the side lacked a proven try scorer and Jason Powell, from the back row, ended the season with eight tries.

CLUB PLAYING RECORD 1992-93 SEASON

National Division: Four North
Final League Position at end 1992/93 Season: 5th
League Playing Record: P 12, W 6, D 1, L 5, Pts F 221, Pts A 224
Season Playing Record (including League matches/Pilkington cup etc): P 31, W 14, D 1, L 16, Pts F 613, Pts A 556

Lichfieeld RUFC 1992-93

LICHFIELD RUFC

Club Details

Colours: Myrtle Green.
Change of Colours: Yellow.
Date Founded: 1874.
Membership: Total 350, Full 200, Social 50, Junior/Youth/Minis 200.
Membership Fees: Full £27.50, Junior/Youth/Minis £5, Non-playing £20.
Number of Teams: Senior 6 + U21 + Colts + Ladies.
Programme Advertising Rates: Contact Jim Ashpole.

Ground Details

Ground Address: Cooke Fields, Tamworth Road, Lichfield, Staffs.
Telephone: 0543 263020.
Fax: 0543 419958.
Directions: A51 Tamworth Road from Lichfield, rear of Horse & Jockey.
Capacity: Total 4,000, Seated 400, Standing 3,600.
Ticket Prices: Adults £2.50, OAP/Child £1.
Clubhouse Facilities: Two large changing rooms, 2 first team weights rooms, large club room, lounge, first aid, sponsors lounge.
Training Nights: Tues & Thurs. Selection Mon eve.

COOKE FIELDS
TAMWORTH ROAD
LICHFIELD

SEASON
1992/93

FOUNDED 1874

NATIONAL LEAGUE
DIVISION 4
NORTH

Lichfield
RUGBY CLUB

OFFICIAL
PROGRAMME

ADDITIONAL RESULTS 1992-93

No	Date	Opponents	Venue	Result
1		Burton		W6-0
2		Derby		W13-0
3		Penrith		W52-3
4		Wolverhampton		L19-21
5		Waterloo		L8-39
6		Derby		L8-12
7		Leamington		L7-21
8		Newcastle		L8-12
9		Worcester		W32-13
10		Wasps II		L26-47
11		Walsall		L9-18
12		Weston-S-Mare		L6-20
13		Northern		W13-10
14		Broad Street		L0-12
15		Broughton Park		L17-20
16		Nottingham Uni		W67-0
17		Berry Hill		W23-12
18		Stoke		L10-16
19		Cheltenham		L5-55

COMPETITIONS WON DURING SEASON 1992-93

Pilkington Cup 2nd Round
Stafforshire Colts Cup Winners & 7s

LEADING APPEARANCES FOR CLUB DURING SEASON 1992-93

D Richards, 27
T Burden, 24
C Ward, 22
S Hemstock, 22
K Borthwick, 21
G Smith, 21
J Powell, 21
S Ptolomy, 20
T Bartlett, 19
T Butler, 16
T Cartwright, 16

LEADING SCORERS

D Richards, Scrum Half, 254
J Powell, Flank Forward, 32 (8T)

NUNEATON RFC

President: K J Howells
Chairman: D N Cake
Club Secretary: E W Ballard, 20 Grove Road, Stockingford, Nuneaton, CV10 8JR. Tel: (H) 0203 328094 (W) 0203 383925 Fax: (W) 0203 383925
Fixtures Secretary: John Davies, 3 Saints Way, Nuneaton, CV10 0UU.
Press Officer: E W Ballard, 20 Grove Road, Stockingford, Nuneaton, CV10 8JR. Tel: (H) 020328094 (W) 0203 383925 Fax: (W) 0203 383925.
1993/94 1XV Captain: Paul Flowers
1993/94 1XV Coach: TBA
Marketing Manager: Brian Haven.

Club Details

Colours: Red, white & black hoops.
Change of Colours: Black or red.
Nickname: Nuns.
Date Founded: 1879.
Membership: Total 500, Full 400, Social 50, Junior/Youth/Minis 250.
Membership Fees: Full £30, Junior/Youth/Minis £16, Family £42.
Number of Teams: Senior 5, Junior/Youth/Minis 14.
Programme Advertising Rates: Full £225, Half £115, Qtr £55.

Ground Details

Ground Address: Harry Cleaver Ground, Attleborough Road, Nuneaton, Warks, CV11 4JQ.**Telephone:** 0203 383925/383206 (office).
Fax: 0203 383925.
Directions: From M1:M1- M6 Jcn 3, A444 Nuneaton, follow signs to town centre. Last island before twon adjacent to railway arches take Rugby/Lutterworth sign. Pass school and Pingles Leisure Centre on left. urn left opposite the Bull into Attleborough Road, At Y junction bear left passing Shell garage and Rugger Tavern on left. Turn left into lane, Pingles Overflow Car Park next to some grey and red gates.
Training Nights: Mon & Thurs.
Special Occasions during 1993/94:
Semi Final Provincial Cup. Final Warwickshire Cup (Hosted).

NUNEATON RFC

ADDITIONAL RESULTS 1992-93

No	Date	Opponents	Venue	Result
1	Sep 2	Burton	H	W18-9
2	Sep 5	Halifax	H	W41-10
3	Sep 8	Nottingham	A	W41-10
4	Sep 12	Askeans	A	L15-47
5	Oct 3	Exeter	H	L6-33
6	Oct 14	Northampton		Cancelled
7	Oct 17	Cheltenham	A	L23-16
8	Nov 7	Leeds	A	L20-0
9	Nov 28	Bradford & Bingley	H	L9-19
10	Dec 5	Rugby		Cancelled
11	Dec 19	Fylde	A	L13-14
12	Jan 2	Lydney	H	Cancelled
13	Jan 16	Loughborouh	A	L22-17
14	Jan 23	High Wycombe	H	L8-24
15	Jan 30	Blackheath	H	L9-37
16	Feb 3	Rugby	H	L123-6
17	Feb 20	Leicester	H	
18	Feb 27	Plymouth	A	L35-10
19	Mar 3	Moseley	A	Cancelled
20	Mar 6	Stroud	H	L26-27
21	Mar 17	Coventry	A	L20-60
22	Apr 7	Rugby	A	A0-48
23	Apr 12	Pontypool	A	Cancelled
24	Apr 17	Bridgewater	H	L21-23

CLUB PLAYING RECORD 1992-93 SEASON

National Division: 4 North
Final League Position at end 1992/93 season: 10th
League Playing Record:
P 12, W 2, D 0, L 10, Pts F 143, Pts A 268
Season Playing Record:
P 30, W 4, D 0, L 26, Pts F 388, Pts A 889

LEADING SCORERS:

Simon Reid, Full Back, 138
Vasile Ion, Centre, 40

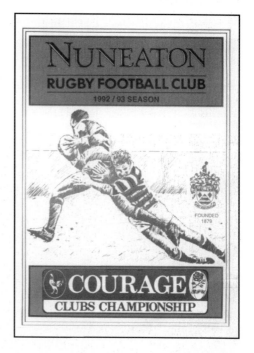

Nuneaton RFC 1992-93

Back Row: Paul Stone (Coach), J Parker (Committee), Tony Howley (Chairman), John Davies (President), John Phillips (Match Secretary), Mark Mitchell (Flanker), Paul Sharp (Lock), Ian Croft (No 8), John Cannon (Prop), Eric Ballard (Secretary), Gary Wainwright (Team Manager), Phil Carter (Assistant Coach)

Centre: J Brain (Lock), Andy Moore (Prop), Simon Reid (Full-back), Vasile Ion (Centre), Gary Sharp (Hooker, Captain), Paul Mitchell (Scrum half), Phil Moreton (Prop), Allan Taylor (Flanker), Chris Southall (Fly half)

Front Row: Danny Masser (Centre), Steve Newman (Wing), Mick Vowles (Wing), Tom Temple (Scrum half)

Photo: J Jarvis, Nuneaton Heartland Evening News

PRESTON GRASSHOPPERS RFC

President: Richard C H Eastwood JP
Chairman: George E Thompson
Club Secretary: Leslie Anson, Oak Tree, 110 Whittingham Lane, Broughton, Preston, PR3 5DD. Tel: (H) 0772 862050
Fixtures Secretary: John M Powell, 121 Bare Lane, Bare, Morecambe, LA4 4RD. Tel: (H) 0524 424514
Press Officer: Leslier Anson, Oak Tree, 110 Whittingham Lane, Broughton, Preston, PR3 5DD. Tel: (H) 0772 862050
1993/94 1XV Captain: Philip J Crayston
1993/94 1XV Coach: John Morgan
Administration Officer: Ken Moore
Chairman of Rugby: Bob Bailey
Programme Editor & Sponsorship Co-Ordinator: John Hetherington
Hon Treasurer: Jim Powdrell
Finance Chairman: Johnm Muirhead
Bar Chairman: Robbie Jarvis

Review of the Season

Finishing third in Division 4 North may be regarded as satisfactory in view of the fact that it is Hoppers highest league placing to date but in truth it could and should have been much better. Three of the four defeats were from below par performances.

Progress was not helped by a number of injuries particularly those of long term to Paul Shipley who looked as though he was heading for a high points aggregate when he was injured way back in October and missed the rest of the season, to Jim Moore against Fylde on Boxing Day and to lock Neil Battersby who was playing his best rugby since his Colts days. Indeed over 60 players were on 1st XV duty during the season but the value of a settled side was illustrated in the final two months of the season when we won 8 of the last 9 matches in a period when few changes were necessary.

Wade Dooley's appearances were restricted by his continued England career but a real bonus came when coach John Morgan, formerly of Bridend, decided to start playing again. A young side predominantly made up of ex Colts (there were 12 in the team at Walsall for the final league game of the season) gained considerably from his experience and the leadership of Phil Crayston, the first ex mini to captain the 1st XV, and who won the Player of the Year Trophy and is deservedly reappointed Captain for 1993/94.

CLUB PLAYING RECORD 1992-93 SEASON

National Division: 4 North
Final League Position at end 1992/93 season: 3rd
League Playing Record: P 12, W 8, D 0, L 4, Pts F 144, Pts A 146
Season Playing Record: P 36, W 21, D 0, L 15, Pts F 537, Pts A 626

Preston Grasshoppers RFC 1992-93. Back Row: John Morgan (Coach), Bill Johnson (Coach), Neil Ashton, Dave Percy, Jim Moore: Steve Holden, Mike Sword, Wade Dooley, Joe Hindle, John Chesworth, Richard Crayston, Gez Swarbrick, Mick Parker, Helen Thompson (Physio), John Crayston (Team Manager). Front Row: Peter Carter, Eric Dean, Andy Taylorson, Phil Crayston (Captain), Lloyd Bell, Paul Shipley, John Bleasdale, John Black.   Photo: Lancashire Evening Post

PRESTON GRASSHOPPERS RFC

Club Details

Colours: Navy blue & white.
Change of Colours: Emerald green.
Nickname: Hoppers.
Date Founded: 19869.
Membership: Total 1,315, Full 788, Social 242, Junior/Youth/Minis 285.
Membership Fees: Playing £30, Full £20, Vice Presidents £36, Junior/Youth/Minis £8, Social £10.
Number of Teams: Senior 7, Youth 2, Junior/Minis 9
Programme Advertising Rates: Full £80, Half £45, Qtr £25.

Ground Details

Ground Address: Lightfoot Green, Fulwood, Preston, PR4 0AP.
Telephone: 0772 863546/863027 (press box)
Directions: M6 Jcn 32. Follow Garstands sign, turn left towards Preston, left again, in 50 yds, follow INWOL signs, ground 1 mile from motorway.
Capacity: Total 2,700, seated 250.
Ticket Prices: Adults £3, members £2, OAP/Child £1
Clubhouse Facilities: Large function & clubroom, lounge bar, hospitality suite, committee room, 8 clubhouse rooms, shower area, 4 squash courts, shooting range.
Training Nights: Monday, Wednesday & Thursday.

ADDITIONAL RESULTS 1992-93

No	Date	Opponents	Venue	Result
1	Sep 5	Leeds	A	L3-30
2	Sep 9	West Park	H	W17-3
3	Sep 12	Widnes	H	W14-8
4	Sep 19	Middlesbrough	A	L15-32
5	Oct 17	Hull Ionians	A	L13-21
6	Nov 7	Rugby	A	L6-94
7	Nov 28	Sheffield	H	W6-0
8	Dec 5	West Hartlepool	A	L0-25
9	Dec 12	Morley	A	L10-37
10	Dec 19	Wharfedale	A	L7-44
11	Dec 26	Fylde	A	L7-11
12	Dec 28	Broughton Park	H	W20-12
13	Jan 2	Bradford & Bingley	H	L8-22
14	Jan 17	Waterloo (Lancs Cup)	A	L0-48
15	Jan 23	Vale of Lune	A	W25-5
16	Jan 30	Liverpool St Helens	H	W10-0
17	Feb 6	Wigton	A	W26-12
18	Feb 20	Waterloo	A	L5-13
19	Feb 27	Tynedale	H	W22-14
20	Mar 6	Wigan	H	W21-9
21	Mar 20	Blackburn	A	W53-3
22	Apr 3	Sandal	H	W12-6
23	Apr 9	Vale of Lune	H	W58-9
24	Apr 17	Northern	H	W36-28

COMPETITIONS WON DURING SEASON

Lancashire Colts Cup Finalists
National Colts Sevens Semi-finalists

SPECIAL OCCASSIONS IN 1993-94

Lancashire v Yorkshire (18 September 1993), Canadian Tour July 1994.

PLAYING SQUAD 1992-93

Full backs: E Dean, M Walker
Wings: J Hindle, A Taylorson, P Shipley, B Greenwood, B Whyte, R Stanier, S Mulholland, I Bruce, J Kilner
Centres: J Chesworth, J Moore, D Whittingham, B Thompson, A Christopherson, N McDiarmid, J Llewellyn, C Worth
Stand Off: G Swarbrick, M Kirby, J Musson, D Scott, I Jackson, R Grayson
Scrum Half: D Percy, J Bleasdale, Aitchison
Props: R Crayston, J Holden, L Bell, S Evans, J Nixon, M Clay, S Parisi
Hookers: P Carter, J Black, J Davy, N Quirk, M Maddox
Locks: W Dooley, P Crayston, N Battersby, J Laker, R McWilliam, M Bailey
Flankers: S Holden, J Kay, T Edwards, M Parker, D Grant, M Salmon, R Dransfield, N Leeming
No 8: J Morgan, M Sword.

MOST CAPPED PLAYERS

(including British Lions appearances):
Wade A Dooley, 58 (3), 1985-93
A N Hornby, 9, 1877-82, R Hunt, 4, 1881-82,
W H Hunt, 4, 1876-78, J T Hunt, 3, 1882-84

LEADING APPEARANCES FOR CLUB

Roy Dransfield, 479, 1975-93
Dave Percy, 421, 1978-93
Graham Cox, 421, 1973-88
Stan Sherlock, 326, 1974-86
Alan Wyllie, 285, 1978-91
Mick Parker, 273, 1978-93

LEADING SCORERS

Lex Swarbrick, Fly Half/Wing, 103
Joe Hindle, Wing, 72
Andy Taylorson, Wing/Full Back, 72
Jim Musson, Fly Half, 36
Paul Shipley, Wing, 31 (only 4 matches (injured))
Barry Greenwood, Wing, 30

ROTHERHAM RUFC

President: Peter Moran
Chairman: Allan Williams
Club Secretary: Keith Oxley, 119 Broom Lane, Rotherham, S60 3NN Tel: (H) 0709 542887 (W) 0742 523389.
Fixtures Secretary: Andy Fraser, 10 Birch Close, Killamarsh, Sheffield. Tel: 0742 482051 (W) 0742 760245.
Press Officer: Allan Williams, 116 Grange Road, Rotherham, S60 3LL. Tel: (H) 0709 364190 (W) 0742 461156
1993/94 1XV Captain: Kevin Plant
1993/94 1XV Coach: Barry Forster

Review of the Season

Following their three promotions in 5 seasons, Rotherham made a determined bid for the National 4 North title, in the end losing out on points difference to Harrowgate, the two clubs had shared a 6-6 draw on a dreadful day, weather-wise, in November and Rotherham were always chasing after that. The one league defeat in March at Preston probably sealed matters but it all went to the last game of the season when both clubs won.

In a season marred by a succession of injuries the overall form was quite good and a number of young players forced their way into the side. For the first time in the club's history Rotherham reached the County Cup Final and despite going down 22-5 to the National Division 3 winners Otley they contributed to an entertaining final and dominated the first half.

The 2nd XV won the local S.Yorkshire Trophy and with an U.21 side likely next season the future is looking bright.

Richard Selkirk gives up the captaincy after 5 seasons, but intends to carry on playing. Kevin Plant takes over the captains role, with Craig West as Vice-Captain.

CLUB PLAYING RECORD 1992-93 SEASON

National Division: 4 North
Final League Position at end 1992/93 season: 2nd
League Playing Record: P 12, W 10, D 1, L 1, Pts F 259, Pts A 123
Season Playing Record: P 33, W 26, D 1, L 6, Pts F 871, Pts A 458

Rotherham RUFC 1992-93 Yorkshire Cup Final team   Photo: Garnett Dickinson

ROTHERHAM RUFC

Club Details

Colours: Maroon & sky blue hoops.
Change of Colours: Maroon.
Date Founded: 1923.
Membership: Total 400, Full 180, Social 120, Junior/Youth/Minis 100.
Membership Fees: £8, Junior/Youth/Minis £5/£10/£5
Number of Teams: Senior 4 + U21, Junior 8.
Programme Advertising Rates: Full £100.

Ground Details

Ground Address: Clifton Lane, Rotherham.
Telephone: 0709 370763.
Directions: (a) Leave M1 at Jcn 33. Follow Rotherway for half a mile to roundabout. Take second exit signposted Bawtry 3/4 mile. Traffic lights, straigh on up hill to roundabout. Exit first left. Follow road into centre of town. Ground approx. I mile on right. (b) Leave M18 at Jcn 1. Follow signs to Rotherham. After 2 miles approx at second roundabout (Breeks Hotel), fork right. At next roundabout (Stag Inn) second exit. Follow road into centre of town. Ground approx 1 mile on right.
Capacity: Full 1,500, 250 seated, 1,250 standing.
Ticket Prices: Adults £2 League, £1.50 other, OAP/Child 50p.
Clubhouse Facilities: Full time steward, 3 bars, function room.
Training Nights: Monday & Thursday.

Andy Challinor charging forward against Otley
Photo: Garnett Dickinson

ADDITIONAL RESULTS 1992-93

No	Date	Opponents	Venue	Result
1	Sep 5	Birkenhead Park	H	W41-12
2	Sep 19	Wigan	A	W63-20
3	Oct 17	Northern	H	W44-13
4	Nov 28	Hartlepool Rovers	H	W35-0
5	Dec 5	Sandal	A	W18-8
6	Dec 12	Hul Ionians	H	W17-15
7	Dec 19	Halifax	H	59-17
8	Dec 28	Old Crossleyans	A	20-12
9	Jan 16	Leeds	A	L12-33
10	Jan 23	Widnes	A	W23-5
11	Jan 30	West Hartlepool	H	L28-42
12	Feb 6	Sheffield	A	L13-21
13	Feb 20	Tynedale	A	L15-35
14	Feb 27	Hudersfield	H	W31-15
15	Mar 6	Stockton	A	W22-15
16	Mar 13	Otley	A	W32-15
17	Mar 16	Thornensians	H	W48-3
18	Mar 20	West Park	H	W5-16
19	Apr 7	Wharfedale	H	W8-3
20	Apr 14	Bradford & Bingley	H	W26-13
21	Apr 27	Otley	A	L5-22

ACHIEVEMENTS DURING SEASON

Runners up Yorkshire Cup

LEADING APPEARANCES FOR CLUB

P Scott, 222, 1983-93
K Plant, 198, 1986-93
R Selkirk, 194, 1986-93
J Dudley, 193, 1984-93
L Rick, 164, 1987-93
G Treece, 153, 1986-93

LEADING SCORERS

K Plant, Stand Off, 139
S Worrall, Scrum Half, 107
T Turner, Centre, 80
P Scott, Wing, 80
A Challinor, Back Row, 75

STOKE-ON-TRENT RUFC

President: Fhil Tarakaniec
Chairman: Les Hart
Club Secretary: Stephen Beck, 10 Hillside Close, Fulford, Stoke- on-Trent, ST11 9RU. Tel: (H) 0782 398090 (W) 0952 291471 Fax: (W) 0952 291437.
Fixtures Secretary: Ron Groves, 18 Inglewood Grove, Porthill, Stoke-on-Trent, ST5 0DZ. Tel: (H) 0782 637622.
Press Officer: Tom Maskrey, 225 Weston Road, Meir, Stoke- on- Trent, ST3 6EF.
1993/94 1XV Captain: Simon Robson
1993/94 1XV Coach: Tosh Askew
1st XV Team Manager: Keith Roberts
Chairman of Selectors: Tony Brindley

Review of the Season

1992/93 season proved to be one of the best on record for the club, certainly the most successful since the introduction of leagues. Finishing 4th in Division 4 (North) and winning the Staffordshire Cup for the first time, having been runners-up on four previous occasions during the last 8 years.

The excellent results over the season were achieved despite some crippling injuries to key players, winger Ken Bates and centre Andy Burrows were unavailable through injury from early October (Ken Bates unfortunately has had to finish playing), Steve Teasdale, Ian Gittens and Steve Maskrey were other influential figures who missed a significant number of games. In all 48 players were used in the 1st XV. However on the positive side a number of young emerging players were able to make their mark, in particular centres Simon Ashcroft (21), Mark Smith (19), winger Adrian Buckley (2O), full back Matthew Lamplugh (2O), prop Mick Hill (2O) and stand off Jason Britton (19).

The results this season have not been achieved without a great deal of hard work from many people, both on and off the field, but particularly from coach 'Tosh' Askew and captain England 'B' scrum half Simon Robson.

CLUB PLAYING RECORD 1992-93 SEASON

National Division: 4 North
Final League Position at end 1992/93 season: 4th
League Playing Record: P 12, W 7, D 0, L 5, Pts F 193, Pts A 168
Season Playing Record: P 29, W 19, D 1, L 9, Pts F 750, Pts A 349

Stoke-on-Trent RUFC 1992-93 with the Staffordshire Cup   *Photo: Staffordshire Sentinel Newspapers*

STOKE-ON-TRENT RUFC

Club Details

Colours: Dark blue/light blue stripes.
Change of Colours: Red.
Date Founded: 1884.
Membership: Total 400, Full 280, Social 20, Junior/Youth/Minis 120.
Membership Fees: Full £26, Playing £26, Vice President £20, Youth £2, Junior 50p, Social £5, Ladies £5.
Number of Teams: Senior 4, Colts 1, Junior 6.
Programme Advertising Rates: Full £50, Half £30.

Ground Details

Ground Address: Hartwell Lane, Nr Barlaston, Stoke-on- Trent Staffordshire, ST3 7NG.
Telephone: 0782 372807.

PLAYING SQUAD 1992-93

15: S Teasdale, M Lamplugh
14: A buckley, K Bates
13: S Ashcrof, M Smith
12: N Simms, A Burrows
11: D Potts, F Forster
10: A Askew, J Brittan, K Stetcher
9: S Robson, M Harding, C Hobbs
8: S Maskrey, S Russell
7: I Gittens, R Brown
6: N Binns, Titchenor
5: T Bainbridge, M Cockrell
4: N Phillips
3: M Hill, G Barker
2: J Cheadle, J Furnival
1: S Groves, R Bradley

Directions: From the north use either M6 or M1. From M1 follow A38 then A50. Turn left at first set of traffic lights on outskirts of city (A520). After approx 3 miles take road to Barlaston. Club 1 mile on left. From M6 leave at Jcn 15, follow A34 north, then follow sign for Barlaston. Club through village, 1 mile right. From south leave M6 at Jcn 14, follow A34 north, directions then as above.
Capacity: Total 3,000, 2,750 standing, 250 seated.
Ticket Prices: Adults £2 league matches, £1.50 other matches. Chidren free at all matches.
Clubhouse Facilities: Large clubhouse & lounge bar.
Training Nights: Monday & Thursday.

COMPETITIONS WON DURING SEASON

Staffordshire Cup

LEADING APPEARANCES FOR CLUB1992/93

J Cheadle, Hooker, 28
S Robson, Scrum Half, 25
N Simms, Centre, 25
N Phillips, 2nd Row, 24
D Potts, Winger, 24
N Binns, Flanker, 24

LEADING SCORERS

S Ascroft, Centre/Stand Off, 112 (3T 21P 17C)
S Teasdale, Full Back, 100 (7T 11P 16C)
N Simms, Centre, 73 (11T 2P 6C)
S Robson, Scrum Half, 70 (14T)
D Potts, Winger, 60 (12T)
S Maskrey, No 8, 50 (10T)

Full back Matthew Lamplugh making a break in the final League game against Nuneaton Photo: Staffordshire Sentinel Newspapers

279

STOURBRIDGE RFC

President: Nigel Price
Club Secretary: Bob Browne, 41 Western Road, W Hagley, Stourbridge, W Midlands, DY9 0JY. Tel: (H) 0562 882020 (W) 021 423 2345 Fax: (W) 021 423 1907.
Fixtures Secretary: Alan McReadie, 24 Leavale Road, Norton, Stourbridge, West Midlands. Tel: (H) 0384 373904 (W) 0384 373904.
Press Officer: Ceri Davies, 3 Eggington Road, Woolaston, Stourbridge, West Midlands. Tel: (H) 0384 376201 (W) 0905 748404.
1993/94 1XV Captain: Tom Jeavons-Fellows
1993/94 1XV Coach: Kevin Astley

Review of the Season

Stour's promotion hopes were effectively ended by the second week in October as successive narrow defeats by Lichfield (12-14), Rotherham (12-14) and Preston (16-17) left them pointless after their opening three league fixtures. They recovered to secure National league rugby for 1993-4 with victories over Midland rivals Walsall, Towcestrians, Stoke and Nuneaton, and a draw against Hereford. Worryingly for next season's campaign their sole success against northern opposition was a 9-6 victory at Kendal.

Fly half Simon Pennington, a newcomer from Moseley, dominated the points scoring with almost half Stour's points; the only try scorer in double figures was winger Richard Trigg with 13.

Second Row Nick Perry's last remaining hopes of collecting silverware were dashed when Birmingham-Solihull won at Stourton in the semi-final of the North Midlands Cup. Nick — a one club man who made his First XV debut aged just 16 in 1977— hands over the captaincy to hooker Tom Jeavons-Fellows who should know a thing or two about trophies. His father John is Chairman of the RFU Competitions Sub-Committee!

There is increased optimism for next season with Stour's 2nd XV having scored a club record 1300 points in 1992-3. They were led by Tim Grenfell who scored an incredible 53 tries from fly half, giving him a season's points total of 265 without a single kick at goal, believed to be a UK record.

CLUB PLAYING RECORD 1992-93 SEASON

National Division: 4 North
Final League Position at end 1992/93 season: 9th
Achievements/Competitions won during season:
North Midlands Cup Semi-finalists. 2nd Winners of Kidderminster ITC Cup

Stourbridge 1st XV 1992-93

Photo: Ceri Davies

STOURBRIDGE RFC

Club Details

Colours: Navy blue shirts with narrow white hoops, navy blue shorts.
Change of Colours: Green & blue hoops, blue shorts.
Date Founded: 1876.
Membership: Total 700, Full 500, Junior/Youth/Minis 200.
Number of Teams: Senior 6, Junior 10.

Ground Details

Ground Address: Bridgnorth Road, Stourton, Stourbridge, West Midlands, DY7 6QZ.
Telephone: 0384 393889.
Capacity: 3,000 (all standing).
Ticket Prices: Adults £1.50, OAP/Child Nil.
Clubhouse Facilities: Two tier clubhouse, 2 lounges, club bar, 8 changing rooms, weights & gym rooms.
Training Nights: Tuesday & Thursday 7.00pm.

PLAYING SQUAD 1992-93

Full Back: A Taft
Wing: S Baker, M Harris, J Thompson, D Timmington, R Trigg
Centre: P Bate, M Crowfoot, A Tapper, M Wilson
Fly Half: T Grenfell, S Pennington
Scrum Half: C Parsons
Prop: P Farrar, H Jeavons-Fellows, R Merritt
Second Row: C Bishop, N Perry, P Ralph, M Ramsbottom, J Taylor
Flanker: S Barnes, G Howgate, P Ralph, D Smallman, M Stacey, N Tibbetts
No 8: M Ramsbottom, M Stacey, J Wainwright

MOST CAPPED PLAYERS

(including British Lions appearances):
Huw Davies, 21, 1981-87

LEADING APPEARANCES FOR CLUB

J Wainwright, 356, 1977-93, N Perry, 344, 1977-93
N Price, 329, 1980-92, C Davies, 327, 1977-92
R Edwards, 292, 1977-93, J Shaw, 268, 1982-93
A Dickens, 264, 1978-89, P Dodge, 260, 1977-88

LEADING SCORERS 1992-93

S Pennington, 266 (5T 63P 26C), R Trigg, 65 (13T)
J Thompson, 25 (5T), M Harris, 20 (4T)
C Parsons, 20 (4T), M Wilson, 20 (4T)

Stour scrum half Chris Parsons gets the ball away in the North Midlands Cup Semi-Final versus Birmingham Solihull

Photo: Ceri Davies

281

WALSALL RFC

President: D H Peacock
Chairman: R M Harding
Club Secretary: D E Horton, 53 Stonnall Road, Aldridge, Walsall, West Mids, WS9 8JZ. Tel: (H) 0922 55320 (W) 0922 722622 Fax: (W) 0922 239894.
Fixtures Secretary: M IFriar, 8A Beacon Street, Walsall, West Midlands, WS1 2DL. Tel: (H) 0922 36243.
Press Officer: K H W Clews, 20 Fallowfield Road, Walsall, West Midlands, WS5 3DL. Tel: (H) 0922 37528.
1993/94 1XV Captain: Gary Taylor
1993/94 1XV Coach: Colin Jarvis

Review of Season

A year after avoiding relegation by a last day whisker, Walsall completed their best season since promotion in 1989 with their highest finish in the National Leagues, the produce of lots of spirit, guts and exciting adventure that capitalised on the Law changes and compensated for the handicap of a small, lightweight pack.

Of key elements the first was the arrival of the Till brothers, stepping up from the lowest rung of the Courage ladder — their only previous experience was with Rugeley — and playing to the manner born with skill and panache. Peter, in the engine-room, was Walsall's only ever-present while the younger Gary scored 17 superb tries from flank, not one a snip!

Then in the Autumn two players of immerse influence made remarkably successful comebacks, former vice-captain Mike Friar at full-back after three years of major knee trouble and operations, and ex-captain Rob Harding a mere six months after a near-fatal car accident when he was impaled for two hours to his driving seat by a 3" thick wooden fence post through his abdomen.

No.8 Richard Coleman was in outstanding all-round form all season, Richard Mills achieved his highest aggregate yet, high in the Unisys point-scoring charts for the third year running, and once Mike Friar returned Jim Flynn could return to partner Steve Allen at centre, producing rock-solid midfield defence.

In the League, Walsall were outplayed by Rotherham, Stoke and Stourbridge (hitherto winless and as shocked as Walsall at a victory fashioned from two early scores), but their other defeats were the result of their own errors: ultimate champions Harrogate, dominated and visibly rattled, Kendal and Preston were all beneficiaries of gift scores.

But Walsall completed a very comfortable double in League and Staffordshire Cup over local rivals Lichfield before losing the Final to Stoke by a long, late penalty goal after dictating the match, and they claimed a 4-O scalp success rate over League 4 South counterparts Sudbury (5O-9)!, Lydney, High Wycombe and Weston-super-Mare. Only four non-league fixtures were lost.

WALSALL RFC

Club Details

Colours: Scarlet jerseys, black shorts, scarlet stockings.
Change of Colours: Black shirts (red collar & cuffs), black shorts.
Date Founded: 1922.
Membership: Total 500, Full 250, Social 100, Junior/Youth/Minis 150.
Membership Fees: Full £35, Junior/Youth/Minis £7.50.
Number of Teams: Senior 5, Junior 1.
Programme Advertising Rates: £75 full page.

CLUB PLAYING RECORD 1992-93 SEASON

National Division: 4 North
Final League Position at end 1992/93 season: 7th
League Playing Record:
P 12, W 6, D 0, L 6, Pts F 165, Pts A
Season Playing Record:
P 34, W 24, D 0, L 10, Pts F 688, Pts A 459

ACHIEVEMENTS/COMPETITIONS WON DURING SEASON:

Staffordshire Cup runners up
Burton Floodlights 7s winners

PLAYING SQUAD 1992-93

15: M Friar, T Stansfield, J Flynn
14: R Bateman, D Wild, J Rowe
13: S Allen, J Flynn
12: J Flynn, S Allen, R Bateman
11: K Ellis, R Bateman, D Wild
10: R Mills, R Edmonds
9: A Stewart, N Millward, J Dowdeswell
1: G Taylor
2: D Haley, G Green
3: M Johnson, M Pittaway, S Lea
4: R Harding, M Ellis, P Till
5: P Till
6: G Till
7: G Tillott, G Till
8: R Coleman, S Till

Ground Details

Ground Address: Delves Road, Walsall, West Midlands, WS1 3JY.
Telephone: 0922 26818.
Directions: (From the North) Exit M6 Jcn 9, turn left to Walsall, fork right on ring road, across 4 sets of traffic lights, club 2nd road on left.
Capacity: Total 800.
Ticket Prices: Adults £2, OAP/Child Nil.
Clubhouse Facilities: Excellent bar, dining room and kitchen facilities.
Training Nights: Tuesday & Thursday.

MOST CAPPED PLAYERS

(including British Lions appearances):
T J Cobner (Wales & Lions), 22, 1974-78
J G Webster (England), 12, 1972-75
P Ringer (Wales), 8, 1978-80
R H St J B Moon (Wales), 3, 1993

LEADING APPEARANCES FOR CLUB:

A O Evans, 336, 1970-88
N J Archer, 335, 1973-90
R M Hardin, 301, 1981-93

LEADING SCORERS:

R Mills, Fly Half, 275 (2T 35C 62P 3D)
G Till, Wing Forward, 85 (17T)
J Rowe, Wing, 45 (9T)
M Friar, Full Back, 40 (8T)
R Bateman, Wing, 30 (5T)
S Allen, Centre, 25 (5T)
R Coleman, No 8, 25 (5T)

Walsall RFC 1st XV 1992-93
Back Row: Gary Till, Peter Till, Mark Ellis, Jim Flynn, Rob Harding, Richard Coleman, Steve Allen, Dave Wild, Jonathon Rowe, Andy Stewart, Darren Haley
Front Row: Richard Bateman, Mike Friar, Graham McDonald (Asst Coach), Colin Jarvis (Club Coach), Don Peacock (President), Geraint Tillott (Captain), Martin McCluney (Chairman), Gary Taylor, Richard Mills, Jeff Tromans (Chairman of Selectors), Jim Deare (Team Manager)

WINNINGTON PARK

FOUNDED 1907

President: Roy Palin
Chairman: Rupe Cragg
Club Secretary: Alex Simpson, 14 Applefield, Northwich, Cheshire, CW8 4TE. Tel: (H) 0606 782943 (W) 0270 759759 Fax: (W) 0270 759166
Fixtures Secretary: Chris Cleave, Westerley, West Toad, Weaverham, Northwich, Cheshire, CW8 1HQ. Tel: (H) 0606 853999 (W) 0925 752016
Press Officer: Chris Hardy, 36 Park Street, Northwich, Cheshire, CW8 1HQ. Tel: (H) 0606 79115 (W) 0606 41511
1993/94 1XV Captain: David Nicholls
1993/94 1XV Coach: Graham Lievesley
Chairman Playing Grounds: Doug Hill
Club Coach: Vince Murphy
Chairman Mini & Juniors: Brandon Parkey

Review of the Season

The disappointment of finishing 8th in National Division 4 North was countered by winning the Cheshire Cup, beating New Brighton 38-12. The performances in the league improved as the season continued with a more settled team starting to perform to expectations. The best performance being the only league defeat of champions Harrogate.

The club was well represented at county level with Matthew Farr, David Alcock, John Farr and Adrian Bird are playing in the Cheshire squad. The undoubted final of the season was U21 Paul Rees who progressed from the colts straight into the 1st XV a capped 25 excellent performances by making the North U21 squad. The mini and junior set up continues to prosper with U11 & U16 winning their respective Cheshire cups and the U14 losing in the final.

Mike Hall was again the points scorerwith123 points from 7 tries, 14 conversions and 2O penalties with Steve Foster again second with 97 points. John Farr with 17 was the top try scorer.

Matthew Farr captained the side as well as producing some fine performances on the field. He leaves to join Orrell to be replaced as captain by lock, David Nicholls.

CLUB PLAYING RECORD 1992-93 SEASON

National Division: Five North
Final League Position at end 1992/93 Season: 8th
League Playing Record: P 12, W 5, D 1, L 6, Pts F 159, Pts A 174
Season Playing Record (including League matches/Pilkington cup etc):
P 32, W 20, D 2, L 10, Pts F 705, pts A 463

COURAGE CLUBS CHAMPIONSHIP

WINNINGTON PARK RFC

Club Details

Colours: White with sky & royal blue circlet
Change of Colours: Alternate light & dark blue hoops
Nickname: Park
Date Founded: 1907
Membership: Total 500, Full 250, Social 50, Junior/Youth/Minis 200
Membership Fees: Full £25, Junior/Youth/Minis £6, Other £15
Number of Teams: Senior 6, Junior/Minis 9, Youth 2
Programme Advertising Rates: Full £120, Half £65

Ground Details

Ground Address: Burrows Hill, Hartford, Northwich, Cheshire, CW8 3AA
Telephone: 0606 74242
Directions: One mile from Hartford turn off A556, turn left by traffic lights at Hartford Church into Bradburns Lane, then right into Beach Road B5152. Burrows Hill is first left and ground is on right.
Capacity: 5,000
Ticket Prices: Adult £1 (Cup matches £2)
Clubhouse Facilities: Excellent two storey clubhouse with fine lounge bar, 6 changing rooms downstairs
Training Nights: Mondays & Thursdays

COMPETITIONS WON DURING SEASON 1992-93
Cheshire Cup winners

MOST CAPPED PLAYERS including British Lions Appearances
D Morris, England 14, Lions 3
D Wrench, 3

LEADING APPEARANCES FOR CLUB DURING SEASON 1992-93
J Cundick, 30
J Farr, 29
A McGarrigle, 28
M Farr, 27
D Nichol, 27
D Allcock, 27
M Hall, 27

LEADING SCORERS
M Hall, Full Back, 123
S Foster, Fly Half, 97
J Farr, Scrum Half, 85
A McGarrigle, No 8, 65
J Owens, Wing, 50
P Broughton, Wing, 50

BASINGSTOKE R.F.C.

CLUB PLAYING RECORD 1992-93 SEASON

National Division: 4 South
Final League Position at end 1992/93 season: 5th
League Playing Record: P 12, W 7, D 0, L 5, Pts F 192, Pts A 145
Season Playing Record: P 31, W 16, D 1, L 14, Pts F 552, Pts A 444

ACHIEVEMENTS/COMPETITIONS
WON DURING SEASON
Winners Bass Hampshire Cup
Runners Up Middlesex 7's Plate

President: JG Evans CBE TD
Chairman: DA Williams
Secretary: A Paynter, 152 Pack Lane, Kempshott, Basingstoke RG22 5HR. Tel: (0256) 27857 (H) (0256) 843191 (W)
Treasurer: RD Cummins

Basingstoke RFC 1992-93. Back row: M Humberstone (Coach), R Rowledge, J Ford, A Pittaway, P Polson, S Kearns, G Hurst, A Ralph, M John, N Proctor, D McKay, A Paynter (Hon Sec), L Johnson (Coach) Front Row: J Hilliard, M Culley, P Hawkins, DA Williams (Chairman), I Lillington (Captain), P Goodall, J Palmer, P Wilkinson
Photo: Mark Heath

BASINGSTOKE R.F.C.

Club Details

Colours: Amber shirts, navy shorts
Change of Colours: Navy shirts
Nickname: Stoke
Founded: 1948
Number of Teams: Senior 5 Junior 8
Training Nights: Monday & Wednesday
Membership: Total Membership: 584, Full Members: 386, Social Members: 101, Junior/Youth/Minis:37
Membership Fees: Full: £10, Junior/Youth/Minis: £5, Other: £5

Ground Details

Address: Down Grange, Pack Lane, Basingstoke, Hants
Telephone: 0256 23308
Clubhouse Facilities: Lounge Bar, Main Bar, Committee Bar,Dining Room, Weights Room, 8 Changing Rooms
Spectator Capacity: Seated 250 Standing 4,000
Ticket Prices: Adults £1

ADDITIONAL RESULTS 1992-93

No	Date	Opponents	Venue	Result
1	Sep 5	Bracknell	H	W17-7
2	Sep 9	Reading	A	L16-25
3	Sep 12	Richmond	H	L17-32
4	Sep 19	Lydney	A	L6-13
5	Oct 17	Guildford/Godalming	H	L17-21
6	Nov 7	Havant	A	L25-26
7	Nov 28	Maidenhead	A	D15-15
8	Dec 5	Camberley	H	W35-10
9	Dec 19	Sutton & Epsom	A	W23-9
10	Jan 2	Wimborne	H	W26-0
11	Jan 23	Harlequins W	A	L0-8
12	Jan 30	Exeter	H	L7-22
13	Feb 7	US Portsmouth	H	W40-0
14	Feb 20	Havant	A	W18-9
15	Feb 27	Westcombe Park	A	W13-12
16	Mar 5	Salisbury	A	Cancelled
17	Mar 20	Alton	H	W37-3
18	Apr 10	Askeans	A	L9-27
19	Apr 17	Henley	A	W21-13
20	Apr 24	Nottingham	A	L18-47

PLAYING SQUAD 1992-93

Backs & Half Backs: R Rowledge, S Kearns, N Procter, P Wilkinson, A Perry, D McKay, J Hilliard, P Simon, G Power, A Lowe, N Connor, M John, B Mercer, P Goodall, J Palmer
Forwards: I Lillington, J Ford, A Pittaway, J Angill, A Ralph, R Whitney, P Knight, P Polson, P Hawkins, M Culley, A Hotchkiss, M Bushnell, M Rushworth, A Hill.

LEADING APPEARANCES FOR CLUB: (1992/93)

I Lillington, 28
R Rowledge, 27
J Ford, 27
S Kearns, 26
A Ralph, 26
Q Hawkins, 18

LEADING SCORERS:

R Rowledge, Full Back, 208
B Mercer, Wing, 60

BERRY HILL RFC

President: R W Jenkins JP
Chairman: John Evans
Club Secretary: T J Baldwin, Hill Brink, Joyford Hill, Coleford, Glos, GL16 7HA.
Tel: (H) 0594 832539 (W) 0594 562631
Fixtures Secretary: Geoff Goddard, 71A Cheltenham Road, Gloucester, GL2 0JG.
Tel: 0452 306749.
Press Officer: John Belcher, Spion Kop, Joyford Hill, Berry Hill, Coleford, Glos.
Tel: 0594 823349.
1993/94 1XV Captain: Nick Haris
1st XV Manager: John Kear
2nd XV Manager: John Cole
3rd & 4th XV Manager: Brian Harris
Colts Manager: Roy Morgan
Hon. Treasurer: Ivan Baldwin
Club Doctor: Dr J Camp
Club Physio: Dave Powell
Club Steward: Mrs Jo Elsmore

Review of the Season

Last season was Berry Hill's Centenary Season and first year in National Division rugby. It was a very difficult season with a difficult league. Pilkington Cup and Centenary Programme to fulfil but the Club's membership and support began with morale very high.

Unfortunately the playing strength weakened by a series of injuries in unusual positions. For example a star winger John Bick suffered a horrific ankle injury on the first Saturday fixture of the season and will never play again. Others are kept out of the game for long periods which interrupted continuity and made the Selectors life very difficult.

On the positive side all the teams were involved in excellent centenary games, the 1S5XV retained their place in National Division rugby, and the United XV triumphed in the South West 2nd XV merit table with a 100% record.

Two new memorial trophies were initiated in honour of deceased ex-players, both of which were one, and the Serons squad won the Hereford Serons Tournament with a good display.

All the players continue to be "home grown" with new talent continuing to develop through the mini, junior and colts teams and several gained country honours, both at senior and colts levels.

Berry Hill 1st XV 1992-93

BERRY HILL RFC

Club Details

Colours: Black & Amber
Date Founded: 1893
Membership: Full/Playing Members 80+, Vice Presidents 101, Life Members 15, Social Members 150, Junior/Youth/Minis 120.
Membership Fees: Full £5, Junior/Youth/Minis Free, Social £2.
Number of Teams: Senior, 4, Colts 1, Junior & minis 6.

Ground Details

Ground Address: Lakers Road, Berry Hill, Coleford, Glos GL16 7LY.
Telephone: 0594 833295.
Directions: From Birmingham & North: M6 and M5. Come off at Tewkesbury (Jcn 8) on M50 to Ross-on-Wye. Dual carriageway A40 to Monmouth. At Monmouth turn left at traffic lights over Wye Bridge taking A1436 through Staunton Village. At Berry Hill pass petrol station on left and opposite is Dean Forest Caravan Sales. At next crossroads turn left into Park Road and then first right into Lakers road. (Monmouth to Berry Hill approx 5 miles). **From East Midlands:** Make for Gloucester. Out of Gloucester over bridge on A40 as far as Huntley. Left at Huntley on A1436 through Mitcheldean. Continue on this road until reaching Dean Forest College and Lakers Comprehensive School on right. Just after school at crossroads turn right into Park Road and then first right into Lakers Road (Gloucester to Berry Hill approx 20 miles).**From London, South & South East:** Use M4 to Seven Bridge. On crossing bridge immediately off for Chepstow using A466 through Wye Valley, Tintern, Llandogo towards Monmouth. On approaching Monmouth on the A466, turn right on A1436 up the hill through Staunton Village. At Berry Hill you will pass petrol station on left and at next crossroads turn left into Park Road, and first right into Lakers Road. (Monmouth to Berry Hill approx 5 miles).
From South West: Make for Severn Bridge and then as per instructions.
Capacity: 2,000+. No permanent seating, temporary for special occassion matches.
Ticket Prices: Adults £2, Student/Junior/U16/OAP £1, programme free with entry price.
Clubhouse Facilities: Players bar, lounge bar, 6 changing rooms, showers, kitchen, 4 toilets.
Training Nights: Seniors Mon & Wed, Colts Tues, Juniors/Minis Sunday mornings.

CLUB PLAYING RECORD 1992-93 SEASON

National Division: Four South
Final League Position at end 1992/93 Season: 7th
League Playing Record: P 12, W 4, D 3, L 5, Pts F 182, Pts A 217
Season Playing Record (including League matches/Pilkington cup etc):
P 41, W 16, D 3, L 22, Pts F 805, Pts A 798

COMPETITIONS WON DURING SEASON 1992-93

1st XV
Hereford 7s Tournament
Dave Harris Memorial Cup
Bert James Memorial cup

2nd XV
Champions - South West Merit Table

PLAYING SQUAD 1992-93

Full Backs: W Tippins, M Wells
Wings: M Fennell, R Smith, J Elsmore, G Baglin, L Baker (& P Tingle)
Centres: P Tingle, G Jones, R Morgan, P Greenway, J Price
Fly Half: J Powell, A Howells (L Osborne)
Scrum Half: L Osborne, B Richards, P Hunt
Props: A Powles, B K Harris, A Jones, J Hoare, C Revill, J Ruck
Hookers: P Baldwin, M Gunter (C Revill)
Flankers: R Powles, I Bell, T Ruck, S Hall, N Devine, P Aston
No. 8: J Horrobin, M Smith, G Alexander
Locks: W Harris, I Symour, J Evans, D Kear

LEADING APPEARANCES FOR CLUB

M Smith, 700, 1972-1993

LEADING SCORERS

L Osborne, Scrum Half/Cenre, 205
J Powell, Outside Half, 176

CAMBORNE RFC

Club President: David Roberts
Club Chairman: Merrill Clymo
Club Secretary: W J C Dunstan, "The
Retreat", 11 Station Hill,
Prale-An-Beeble, Camborne, Cornwall,
TR14 0JT. Tel (H) 0209 831373 (W)
0736 795456 Fax: 0736 797075
Fixture Secretary: E T Pascoe, 51 St
Meriadoc Road, Camborne, Cornwall.
Tel 0209 718158
Press Officer: Malcolm Roach, 23
Dolcoath Road, Camborne, Cornwall.
1993/94 IXV Captain: Tommy Adams
Team Secretary: Edwart White
Sponsorship Secretary: Dennis Gorfin
Assistant General Secretary: Alan
Thomas

Club Details
Colours: Cherry & white
Change of Colours: Blue
Date Founded: 1878
Nickname: The Cherry & Whites
Membership Total 450, Full 350, Social 100, Juniors/Youths/Minis 200
Membership Fees: Full £25, Juniors/Youths/Minis £10, Playing £20,
OAPs £10.
Number of Teams: Senior 3, Junior 10

Ground Details:
Ground Address: The Recreation Ground, Camborne, Cornwall
Telephone No: 0209 713227
Directions: Leave A30 Camborne/Redruth bypass at Junction "Camborne
West". Follow signs for "Recreation Ground".
Capacity: Total 9,200, Seated 777
Ticket Prices Adults £1.50, Student/Junior/OAP 80p
Clubhouse Facilities: Large function room, lounge bar, presidents bar,
committee rooms, full kitchen, meals available for spectators. Accessibility
and facility for disabled.
Training Nights: Mondays & Wednesdays

Camborne RFC 1992-93

CAMBORNE RFC

CLUB PLAYING RECORD 1992-93 SEASON

National Division: 4 South
Final League Position at end 1992/93 season: 4th
League Playing Record: P 12, W 7, L 4, Pts F 180, Pts A 168
Season Playing Record: P 36, W 22, D 2, L 12, Pts F 796, Pts A 439
Achievements/Competitions won during season:
Winners West Briton County Sevens

LEADING APPEARANCES FOR CLUB

Nigel Pellowe, 1003, 1969-93
Bobby Tonkin, 710, 1967-85
Frank Butler, 530, 1968-88
David Kingston, 520, 1967-82
Ivor Moyle, 508, 1955-70
John Rockett, 507, 1956-74

LEADING SCORERS:

Darren Chapman, Stand Off, 193
Ian Pollard, Wing, 124
Kelvin Smitham, Win, 80
David Weeks, Full Back, 55
Tommy Adams (Capt), Lock, 40
andrew Kitching, Centre, 38

Flanker Kevin Penrose setting up possession in the Camborne v Redruth Pilkington Cup match.

291

HIGH WYCOMBE RUFC

President: John Brine
Chairman: Rodney hills
Club Secretary: Don Dickerson, 3 Talbot Avenue, High Wycombe, Bucks, HP13 5HZ. Tel: (H) 0494 532024 (W) 0494 441211 Fax: (W) 0494 440345
Fixtures Secretary: Terry Baker, 5 Orchard Way, Holmer Green, High Wycombe, Bucks. Tel: (H) 0494 713047 (W) 0494 456430.
Press Officer: Dudley Scott, 84 Kings Ride, Penn, Bucks.
1993/94 1XV Captain: Mike Hinch
1993/94 1XV Coach: Simon Edwards
Treasurer: John Read (34th Season)
Team Secretary: Mike Baud (32nd Season)
Vice Chairman: Eric Wilsher

Review of the Season

This season saw our slowest start for a number of years, losing 7 out of the first 13 games played including the Pilkington Cup second round game away at Tabard where our running game was not allowed to develop against a good pack on a narrow pitch.

At the end of the first half of our league campaign we looked in distinct danger of relegation with games being lost often by narrow margins, again, the edge was missing from our running game, the run of the ball deserted us and we could not get the ball between the posts at critical points in games. But, after half term our game started to come together and we finished in a more comfortable position with 5 games won and 7 lost. The most enjoyable and closest games were against London Welsh and Sudbury, both of which we should have won but didn't.

In the Bucks Cup Campaign, we overcame Pennanians and Bletchley fairly comfortably before running into old rivals Harlow where after the usual hard game we pulled away in the last 1O minutes to win 31-16. In the final a spirited game from Chiltern gave our supporters some heart stopping moments but we finally crept home 21-18.

Bush Office Equipment Merit Tables Games were used as opportunities to blood up and coming players and give support players from the first XV squad first XV match experience and we finished a respectable third. We look forward to the 93/94 season and renewing old acquaintances both on and off the field of play.

High Wycombe RUFC 1992-93

Photo: Bucks Free Press

HIGH WYCOMBE RUFC

Club Details

Colours: Black, green & white hoops.
Change of Colours: Black.
Nickname: WYCS
Date Founded: In present form 1929 (original Club in 1891).
Membership: Total 769, Senior playing 212, Juniors 91, Vice Presidents 297, Minis 135, Colts 34.
Number of Teams: Senior 8, Juniors 5.
Programme Advertising Rates: £120 full page, pro rata for part page.

Ground Details

Ground Address: Kingsmead Road, High Wycombe, Bucks HP11 1JB.
Telephone: 0494 524407.
Capacity: Unlimited
Ticket Prices: Adults League only £2, OAP/Child Nil.
Clubhouse Facilities: Two bars, kitchen, main club room, club shop, toilets, baths & showers, changing rooms, physio room, floodlights.
Training Nights: Tuesdays & Thursdays.

CLUB PLAYING RECORD 1992-93 SEASON

National Division: Four South
Final League Position at end 1992/93 Season: 8th
League Playing Record: P 12, W 5, D 0, L 7, Pts F 196, Pts A 160
Season Playing Record (including League matches/Pilkington cup etc): P 33, W 23, D 0, L 10, Pts F 832, Pts A 365

ACHIEVEMENTS/COMPETITIONS WON DURING SEASON 1992-93

Buckinghamshire County Cup
Reached Second Round of the Pilkington Cup
Terry Baker played his thousandth game for the Club during the 92/93 season & is still going strong!

LEADING APPEARANCES FOR CLUB DURING SEASON 1992-93

P Smith, 33
M Saltmarsh, 31
M Cussell, M Hinch, 28
F Walton, 27
J Hewes, 26
J Bartlett, 25
N Dinstdale, 24
C Roddick, 23
C Hayward, 22
M Cartwright, 21
P Ayton, Kevin Titlcombe, 20
C Preston, 19
R Cuvter, 18
R Hawking, A Russell, 16
B Jeans, 12
L Tebb 11

LEADING SCORERS (1992/93 SEASON)

P Smith, Full Back, 271 (16T 31P 44C)
J Hewes, Wing, 110 (22T) + 40 (8T) for 2nd XV
C Roddick, Centre, 90 (14T)

LONDON WELSH RFC

President: V T Watkins
Chairman: Brig. R James C.B.E.
Club Secretary: Pete Taylor, 16 Monks Road, Virginia Water, Surrey, GU25 4RR. Tel: (H) 0344 842070 (W) 0932 857433 Fax: (W) 0932 852377.
Fixtures Secretary: Colin Bosley, 21 Ellesmere Avenue, London, NW7 3EX. Tel: (H) 081 906 0799.
Press Officer: TBA
1993/94 1XV Captain: TBA
1993/94 1XV Coach: Bill Calcraft
Playing Manager/Director of Coaching: S J Dawes O.B.E.

Review of the Season

Although promotion was narrowly missed for the third consecutive season, the Welsh played their finest rugby for years. In the aftermath of Mark Douglas's departure for Northampton, the side lost a critical game at Sudbury. Apart from this, and a surprising lapse at Lydney, the record was without blemish. And in reaching the third round of the Pilkington Cup, the Welsh trenched Havant by 31-8.

The Welsh were dazzling entertainers, scoring 131 tries and 970 points in their 40-game campaign. The side passed 40 points on nine occasions, trouncing Cambridge University, who fielded ten of their Blues, by 55-17 in an extraordinary display of running rugby. The Welsh still have one of the formidable fixture lists in Britain, and won notable victories over London Scottish (25-24) and Rugby (15-14). There was also a transformation in Wales, where they almost shocked Llanelli, at Stradey Park, and Cardiff, at the Arms Park.

Mike Hamlin and Nigel Scrivens were key acquisitions from Gloucester. Hamlin scored 295 points, to break the club's all-time individual scoring record, while Bicky Bell (15), Owen Robins (11), GuyLeleu (11) and Colin Chaarvis (10) led the try- scoring. The squad was led by hooker, Andy Tucker.

London Welsh 1992-93 Back Row: Bill Calcraft (Coach), Ginny Marcell (Physio), Guy Leleu, Lee Thomas, Graeme Peacock, Owen Davies, Nigel Scrivens, Mark Herbert, Colin Charvis, Steve Thomas, Alan Andrews, Dafydd Jones (Match Secretary), John Dawes (Playing Controller), Seated: Rhodri Phillips, Richard Nicholas, Michael Dawes, Julian Davies, Andy Tucker (Captain), Martin Pritchard, Tim Pike, Mike Hamlin, Owen Roberts

LONDON WELSH RFC

CLUB PLAYING RECORD 1992-93 SEASON

National Division: Four South
Final League Position at end 1992/93 Season: 2nd
League Playing Record: P 12, W 10, D 0, L 2, Pts F 353, Pts A 170
Season Playing Record (including League matches/Pilkington cup etc): P 40, W 24, D 1, L 15, Pts F 970, Pts A 723

Club Details

Colours: Scarlet
Change of Colours: Green
Nickname: Exiles
Date Founded: 1885
Membership: Total 1,800, Full 1,600, Social 1,500, Junior/Youth/Minis 200.
Membership Fees: Full £40, Junior/Youth/Minis £7.
Number of Teams: Senior 6, Junior 11.
Programme Advertising Rates: £400 per page.

Ground Details

Ground Address: Old Deer Park, Kew Road, Richmond, Surrey, TW9 2AZ.
Telephone: 081 940 1604
Fax: 081 940 2368
Directions: Half mile north of Richmond Station, adjacent Kew Gardens.
Capacity: Total 7,200, Seated 1,200.
Ticket Prices: Adults £3.50, OAP/Child £1.50.
Clubhouse Facilities: 3 bars, 2 function rooms, shop.
Training Nights: Tuesdays & Thursdays.

ADDITIONAL RESULTS 1992-93

No	Date	Opponents	Venue	Result
1	Sep 5	Richmond	A	L18-21
2	Sep 12	Bedford	A	L3-39
3	Sep 19	Havant (PC1)	H	W31-8
4	Sep 30	W. London Ins.	H	W13-8
5	Oct 17	Rugby	H	W15-14
6	Nov 7	Henley (PC2)	A	W40-18
7	Nov 28	Redruth	A	L7-16
8	Nov 29	Civil Service (MC2)	H	W40-0
9	Dec 5	Wasps	H	D16-16
10	Dec 12	Northampton	H	L3-37
11	Dec 19	Bath	A	L7-37
12	Dec 26	Llanelli	A	L13-15
13	Jan 2	L. Scottish	H	W25-24
14	Jan 16	Rosslyn Park	H	L8-16
15	Jan 17	Barclays Bank (MC3)	H	W18-8
16	Jan 23	Glamorgan W.	H	L12-15
17	Jan 30	Saracens	A	L22-36
18	Feb 5	Cardiff	A	L16-22
19	Feb 7	Feltham (MC4)	A	W44-0
20	Feb 20	Abertillery		W 34-12
21	Feb 27	Glamorgan W.	H	W30-26
22	Feb 28	Ruislip (MCQF)	A	L12-13
23	Mar 6	Esher	H	W52-17
24	Mar 13	Cam. Uni	H	W55-17
25	Mar 20	Llanharan	H	W20-18
26	Apr 10	Coventry	H	W14-3
27	Apr 12	Newport	A	L15-40
28	Apr 17	Nottingham	A	L34-57

PLAYING SQUAD 1992-93

Full Backs: R Phillips, D Lubliner, R Walters
Wings: O Robins, M Bell, D Prendeville, A Sandilands, G Gittins, I Stooksbury, P Walters
Centres: T Pike, G Leleu, M Dawes, P Futter, S J Thomas, T Tolcher, J Williams
Fly Half: M Hamlin, L Evans
Scrum Half: G Phillips, R Nicholas, M Douglas, A Morgan
Props: M Pritchard, M Herbert, R Thomas, J P Davies, J Harrison, A Andrews
Hookers: A Tucker, M Humphreys-Evans, R Jones
Flankers: C Charvis, L Thomas, R Westlake, G Thomas, K Edwards, E Wilkes, C Beg, R Sweeney, M Russell, C Haines, M Shirburne- Davies
No. 8: G Peacock
Lock: O Davies, N Scrivens, J Fletcher, R Ford, D Harries, J H Davies

LEADING APPEARANCES FOR CLUB DURING SEASON 1992-93

M Hamlin, 32, 1, G Peacock, 31, 4
O Robins, 31, 3, O Davies, 30, 1
T Pike, 29, 3, G Leleu, 28, 12, M Pritchard, 28, 2

LEADING SCORERS

M Hamlin, Stand Off Half, 295 (6T 65C 43P 2D)
M Bell, Wing, 75 (15T)
O Robins, Wing/Full Back, 55 (11T)
G Leleu, Centre, 55 (11T)
L Evans, Stand Off Half, 53 (1T 6C 10P 2D)
C Charvis, Flanker, 50 (10T)

LEAGUE 5 SOUTH PROGRAMMES

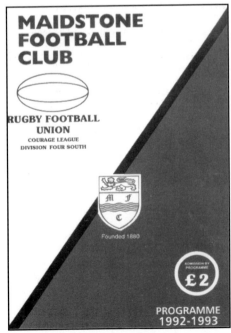

LYDNEY RFC

Club President: T C Bailey
Club Chairman: Dr P Catlin
Club Secretary: A John Jones, 5 Kimberley Close, Lydney, Glos, GL15 5AE. Tel (H) 0594 842709 (W) 0594 841470 Fax (W) 0594 844604
Fixture Secretary: Richard Powell, Skaint Mesto, Park Hill, Whitecroft, Lydney, Glos.
Press Officer: Gordon Sargent, Woodfalls, Forest Road, Bream, Lydney, Glos.
1993/94 IXV Captain: N Nelmes
1993/94 IXV Coach: TBA

Review of the Season

Following relegation from National Division three after Season 1991-92 and the resulting large number of player defections it was natural that Lydney RFC embarked upon last season with a certain degree of trepidation. However, the feared struggle for survival in Division Four South did not materialise as the rebuilt side pressed for promotion, ending the season in third place.

The choice of Hooker Nick Nelmes as captain proved an inspired move, leading by example he brought the best out of the squad of local players including many who had progressed through the club's Colts and United teams.

The team's success was built on powerful display by the forwards who dominated the opposition packs and created the opportunities for Outside Halford to seal victory. Halford ended the campaign with 260 points, which included a number of last minute efforts to win vital league games. Top try scorer was Scrum-Half and club Player of the Year, Johnny Edwards.

CLUB PLAYING RECORD 1992-93 SEASON

National Division: 4 South
Final League Position at end 1992/93 season: 3rd
League Playing Record: P 12, W 8, D 0, L 4, Pts F 187, Pts A 170
Season Playing Record: P 38, W 24, D 3, L 11, Pts F 565, Pts A 447

Club Details

Colours: Black & white hoops
Change of Colours: Red
Date Founded: 1887
Nickname: Severnsiders
Membership Total 600, Social 150
Membership Fees: Full £25, Juniors/Youths/Minis £10
Number of Teams: Senior 3, Junior 3

Ground Details:

Ground Address: Regentsholm, Regent Street, Lydney, Glos, GL15 5RS
Telephone No: 0594 842479
Directions: Turn into Swan Lane off A48. Take 1st left and 2nd right.
Capacity: Total 2,000 +, Seated 500
Ticket Prices Adults £2, OAP/Child £1
Clubhouse Facilities: Bary - Players Bar/Dining Room, Sponsors Bar
Training Nights: Tuesday & Thursday

PLAYING SQUAD 1992-93

Full Backs: M Donser, T Stone
Wings: A Saint, S Wakcham
Centres: R Mills, A James
Outside Halves: A Halford, R Peglar
Scrum Halves: J Edwards, M Powell
Props: G Williams, G Townsend, N Bartlett, R Smith
Hookers: N Nelmes, J Nicholls
Locks: R Williams, S Hale
Blindsiders: D Wailing, R Rees
Outsiders: R Lewis, S Wakeham

LEADING SCORERS

Andy Halford, Outside Half, 260
Johnny Edwards, Scrum Half, 55

MAIDSTONE FC

Club President: CCL Hitchcock
Club Chairman: DG Catt
Club Secretary: David Pares, inster Lodge, Otham Lane, Bearsted, Maidston, Kent, ME15 8SL. Twl (H) 0622 861246 (W) 0622 692206 Fax: 0622 690243
Fixture Secretary: Tony Kelleher, 5 conway Road, Maidstone, Kent, ME16 0HD. Tel (H) 0622 754872
Press Officer: Ray Vale, 18 Upper Mill, Waterinbury, Maidstone, Kent, ME18 5PD. Tel & Fax 0622 812700.
1993/94 IXV Captain: Steve Millward
1993/94 IXV Coach: To be announced
Chairman of Selectors: Roger Bentley
Coaching Co-ordinator: John Legge

Review of the Season

It was only Thurrock's unfortunate deduction of two points that saved Maidstone from relegation from Courage National Division Four South. Injuries to key players, notably their captain Douglas Craig for the first half of the season did not help but their light pack found it difficult to contain some of the other sides in the league.

Their league wins against Weston-Super-Mare and Camborne proved vital to give the club the points to stay up.

However it was three of their forwards, Martin Downey (pro), Peter Catt (lock) and Joe Challie (Flank) who were selected for all three of Kent's county championship matches.

Leading appearances for the club were sorum half Sean Charlton (31) along with fly half/centre John Hogarth (31) with Simon Kew (wing) and Zane Hedge (prop) both with 29 appearance each, Simon Kew again topped the points scoring with 11O.

CLUB PLAYING RECORD 1992-93 SEASON

National Division: 4 South
Final League Position at end 1992/93 season: 12th
League Playing Record: P 12, W 2, D 0, L 10, Pts F 122, Pts A 306
Season Playing Record: P 32, W 13, D 0, L 19, Pts F 495, Pts A 751

Maidstone FC 1992-93 Back row: Karen Costello (Physio), Peter Danckert (Coach), Zane Hedge, Clive Cashell, Ian Wilkinson, George Broughton, Jim Hall, Peter CAtt, Simon Wright, Alan Osenton, Sean Carlton, David Elliott, Alan Wood, Ian Barnes, Martin Cooper (Team Manager). Front row: Peter Mattinson, David Charlton, John Hogarth, Peter Yorke, David Catt Senior (Chairman), Douglas Craig (Captain), Simon Kew, Dominic Baxter, Keith Crump, Steve Millward, Steve Tunnicliffe.

MAIDSTONE FC

Club Details

Colours: Red, white & black hoops
Change of Colours: Green
Date Founded: 1880
Membership Total 650, Playing 150, Vice Presidents 290, Juniors/Youths/Minis 210.
Programme Advertising Rates: £100 per page
Number of Teams: Senior 5

Ground Details:

Ground Address: William Day Memorial Ground, The Mote, WIllow Way, Maidstone, Kent
Telephone No: 0622 754159

Directions: From London or the west on M20, turn off at the A249 Sittingbourne/Maidstone junction. Turn right towards town, the eastwards towards Ashford on new roundabout. Right at next traffic lights in Square Hill, 2nd left into Mote Avenue, turn right into Willow Way. Ground 100 yards on the left.
Capacity: 1,500-2,00, Seated 100
Ticket Prices Adults £2
Clubhouse Facilities: Full shower and chaning room facilities, referees room, 2 lounge bars, full kitchen facilities.
Training Nights: Tuesday & Thursday

ADDITIONAL RESULTS 1992-93

No	Date	Opponents	Venue	Result
1	Sep 5	Gravesend	A	W20-19
2	Sep 12	Westcombe Park	A	L25-29
3	Sep 19	Lewes	A	W17-11
4	Oct 17	Old Mid Whitiftians	H	W19-11
5	Nov 1	Sheppey (Kent Cup)	H	W39-9
6	Nov 28	Reading	A	L10-34
7	Dec 5	Streatham/Croydon	H	W25-5
8	Dec 12	London Welsh SV	A	W20-18
9	Dec 19	Barking	A	L3-15
10	Jan 16	Old Colfeians	H	W25-14
11	Jan 23	Beckenham (Kent Cup)	A	W13-10
12	Jan 30	Leighton Buzzard	H	W18-3
13	Feb 6	Cheshunt	H	W37-17
14	Feb 20	Sutton/Epsom	A	L15-19
15	Feb 27	Harlequins XV	H	L10-41
16	Mar 6	Sidcup	W	W25-16
17	Mar 20	Ealin	A	L28-52
18	Apr 3	Havant	H	L15-36
19	Apr 10	Blackheath	A	L7-76
20	Apr 17	Newbury	H	L7-36

PLAYING SQUAD 1992-93

15: D Craig, S Knight
14: P Mattinson, D Charlton
13: A Sanger
12: D Baxter, D Elliott
11: S Kew, S Tunnicliffe
10: J Hogarth
9: S Charlton
1: Z Hedge
2: S Millward, K Crump
3: M Downey, P york
4: P Catt, M Scott, S Wright
5: T Challis, G Brouhton
6: I Wilkinson, J Osenton
7: J Challis
8: C Cashell

LEADING APPEARANCES FOR CLUB: (1992/93 SEASON)

Sean Charlton, 31
John Hogarth, 31
Simon Kew, 29
Zane Hedge, 29
Peter Mattison, 28
Clive Cashell, 27

LEADING SCORERS: (1992/93 SEASON)

Simon Kew, Wing, 110
John Hogarth, Fly Half/Centre, 75
Peter Mattison, Wing, 40

METROLITAN POLICE RFC

President: Paul Condon QPM
Chairman: David Veness
Club Secretary: David Barham, MPAA Office, Room G11, Wellington House, Buckingham Gate, London SW1E 6BE. Tel: (H) 081 422 4966 (W) 071 230 7108/9
Fixtures Secretary: Simon Gill, 10 Prestbury Crescent, Woodmansterne, Surrey. Tel: 0737 353184 (W) 071 230 2175
Press Officer: Ron Bellis, 29 Greencourt Road, Petts Wood, Kent.
1993/94 1XV Captain: Kevin Walsh

Review of the Season

What promised to be a very good season quickly slipped into mediocrity and the high ratio of injuries to key players cannot be used as the sole reason for this rapid decline.

Statistically — since the introduction of leagues — it was still one of our better seasons — second only to 1989/9O the year we were promoted. Also, in each of the previous three seasons, not only has the number of wins increased progressively but so too has the method of scoring points i.e. more tries scored and more penalties, conversions and dropped goals converted.

However, our league results are still disappointing, we must all realise that the statistics of last season should and could have been vastly improved; too often we allowed a winning game to slip from our grasp. With more determination, better organisation and a greater level of fitness the majority would have resulted in a win. We have a number of very good, young players within the club and they must be encouraged to do everything possible to train together and work for each other. (The MPRFC must be unique in the Courage Leagues to have such a problem!!). Only in this way will we develop into a CLUB with promotion being a realistic aim.

ADDITIONAL RESULTS 1992-93

No	Date	Opponents	Venue	Result
1	Sep 2	Ruislip	H	W38-0
2	Sep 5	Maidenhead	A	L8-21
3	Sep 9	Esher	A	W30-6
4	Sep 12	Vale of Lune		W31-6
5	Sep 19	Stourbridge	A	L5-22
6	Oct 10	Towcestrians	A	L13-20
7	Oct 17	Reading	A	L8-19
8	Nov 7	Hammersmith/Fulham	H	W34-3
9	Nov 29	Hackney (Cup)	A	W10-3
10	Dec 2	RAF	H	L15-21
11	Dec 5	L. Irish	A	L15-72
12	Dec 12	Newbury	H	W39-14
13	Dec 19	Blackheath	A	L3-26
14	Dec 30	Rosslyn Park	A	Postponed
15	Jan 2	Stroud	H	L8-29
16	Jan 16	Taunton	H	L21-22
17	Jan 17	St. Nicholas OB	A	W32-5
18	Jan 23	Streatham/Croydon	H	W20-14
19	Jan 30	US Portsmouth	A	W17-8
20	Jan 1	Ruislip (Cup 4)	A	L0-6
21	Feb 7	Saracens	J	L0-42
22	Feb 20	Cheltenham	H	W13-6
23	Feb 24 ,	Royal Navy	H	W25-8
24	Feb 27	Nottingham	A	L0-65
25	Mar 3	Army	H	L14-25
26	Mar 6	Askeans	H	L11-27
27	Mar 20	Sidcup	A	W11-7
28	Apr 6	Northampton	A	L10-35
29	Apr 16	Richmond	H	L12-29

PLAYING SQUAD 1992-93

15 — J Lunn, K Walsh, A Summons, G Chesterton, S Gill

14 — A Cater, P Breeds, S Stockton, B Sweeney

13 — R Plant, P Daly, F Armstrong, I Dobson

12 — R Ferry, R Williams, N Sinclair, S Welch, S Jones

11 — R williams, P Wakeford, E Weatherley, P Softly

10 — K Noble, M Broom, I Burrell, M Ratana

9 — M Wood, G Fryer, R Jenkins, G Davies, E Jones

8 — N Johnson, M Gammage, A Cooke, I Russell

7 — C Welsh, R Galvin, P Schmidt, N Evans, S Williams

6 — G Tavey, P Turner, P Galvin, R Foreman, R Dowling

5 — P Thompson, P Rogers, D Nesling, J Tunn

4 — M Skuse, G Raybould, D Rinzivillo

3 — A Stewart, M Booth, I Warlow, J Bolwell

2 — D Bennett, P Tappin, D Heckels, J Nicholl, A Kearns

1 — D Barham, M Kerslake, P Spittles, N May

LEADING SCORERS 1992-93

M Wood, Scrum Half, 95
A Carter, Wing 3Qtr, 84
J Lunn, Full Back, 66
M Broom, Outside Half, 47
R Williams, Wing 3Qtr, 43
R Ferry, Centre, 30

METROPOLITAN POLICE RFC

CLUB PLAYING RECORD 1992-93 SEASON

National Division: 4 South
Final League Position at end 1992/93 Season: 9th
League Playing Record: P 12, W 4, D 1, L 7, Pts F 201, Pts A 207
Season Playing Record (including League matches/Pilkington cup etc): P 40, W 16, D 1, L 23, Pts F 644, Pts A 768

Club Details

Colours: Blue & white hoops
Change of Colours: Blue
Date Founded: 1923
Membership: Total 350, Full 225, Social 125.
Membership Fees: £10, Junior/Youth/Minis £5, Other £10

Ground Details

Ground Address: Metropolitan Police (Imber Court) Sports Club, Ember Lane, East Molsey, Surrey, KT8 0BT.

Telephone: 081 398 1267.
Directions: From West, Junction 12 M25 onto M3 to Sunbury, then A308 to Hampton. From East, Junction 10 M25, turn left onto A3 for Kingston, first roundabout turn right for Cobham, use A307 from Cobham to Esher.
Capacity: Total 3,750, seated 750, standing 3,000.
Ticket Prices: £3, Student/Junior/U16/OAP 50p.
Clubhouse Facilities: General sports club.
Training Nights: Tuesday & Thursday evenings.

A Police break against Saracens. Photo: Joe McCabe

NORTH WALSHAM RFC

CLUB PLAYING RECORD 1992-93 SEASON
National Division: Four South

COMPETITIONS WON DURING SEASON 1992-93
Norfolk Cup, EC cup finalists, Pilkington Cup Qualifiers

SPECIAL OCCASIONS IN 1993-94
Erection of full floodlights and ground extension

President: Patrick Dye
Chairman: Keith Jarvis
Club Secretary: B Egerton, 144 Cromer Road, Norwich, Norfolk, NR6 6NX. Tel: (H) 0603 789851
Fixtures Secretary: Louis Bough, Home Cittase, King Street, Neatishead, Norfolk. Tel: (H) 0692 630661 (W) 0692 630276
1993/94 1XV Captain: Ian Fox
1993/94 1XV Coach: Richard Flatters
Financial Officer: Alan Jackson
Players Manager: Ian Woodcock
Marketing Manager: Tony Marcantorio
Ground Manager: Billy Hammond

North Walsham RFC 1992-93

NORTH WALSHAM RFC

Club Details

Colours: Green & black
Change of Colours: All white
Date Founded: 1962
Membership: Total 450, Full 100, VP 230, Junior/Youth/Minis Very many
Number of Teams: Senior 5, Junior 6 + minis
Programme Advertising Rates: TBA

Ground Details

Ground Address: Norwich Road, Scottow, Nr North Walsham, Norfolk
Telephone: 0692 69461
Capacity: Unlimited
Ticket Prices: Adults £2
Clubhouse Facilities: Purpose built with bar, catering, physio, gym, shop & showering facilities
Training Nights: Tues & Thurs

ADDITIONAL RESULTS 1992-93

Date	Opponents		Result
Sep 2	Bedford	A	L0-43
Sep 5	London Irish	A	L6-20
Sep 12	Leighton Buzzard	A	L0-8
Sep 19	Sudbury	A	L12-19
Oct 17	Newark	A	W19-0
Nov 7	Beccles	A	W18-3
Nov 28	Fakenham	H	W30-3
Dec 12	Eton Manor	A	L0-5
Dec 19	Norwich	A	W8-0
Dec 26	President's XV	H	W43-12
Jan 17	West Norfolk	A	W20-13
Jan 23	Bishops Stortford	H	W10-3
Jan 30	Lowestoft & Yarmouth	A	W19-7
Feb 7	Norwich	A	W3-0
Feb 20	Cheshunt	H	W24-10
Feb 27	Chingford	H	W32-3
Mar 6	Ipswich	H	W18-7
Mar 20	Barking	A	W13-6
Apr 17	Sudbury	A	L8-9

PLAYING SQUAD 1992-93

C Poole, B Fitzgerald, M Scott, T Ridley, M Yaxley,
J Lockhart, G Furlong, D Lythgoe, R Hargrave,
J Hargrave, P Anthony, J van Poortuleit, B Yaxley,
L Cutting, S Matthews, I Baker, M Goodhall, R Scott,
C Lomax, S Lewis, D Hook, M Lovatt, S Wottell,
S Rossi, R Young, I Fox, N Greenhall, L Dane,
M Charman, N Sherman, A Smith, A Ford,
T Kingsmill

LEADING SCORERS

Tony Kingsmill, Centre/Outside Half, NK (Tries)
Mark Lovett, Outside Half, NK (points)

COURAGE CLUBS CHAMPIONSHIP

READING RFC

President: John Lucas
Chairman: Peter Walker
Club Secretary: Mike Wickson, 21 Lunds Farm Road, Woodley, Reading, Berks, RG5 4PZ. Tel: (H) 0734 695999 (W) 0734 475022.
Fixtures Secretary: Sefton Hewitt, 21 Purfield Drive, Wargrave, Reading, Berks RG10 8AP. Tel: (H) 0734402909 (W) 0734 722666.
Press Officer: Lorcan Mullally, 35 Western Elms Avenue, Reading, Berks RG3 2AL. Tel: (H) 0734 572357 (W) 0734 475022.
1993/94 1XV Captain: John Dixon
Director of Rugby: Mike Tewkesbury

Review of the Season

Reading Rugby Club, founded in 1898 as Berkshire Wanderers before changing its name to Reading in 1953, has recently completed an outstanding season.

The most important achievement has been winning the Courage South-West Division One League to gain promotion to the National Leagues. Despite losing the first league match, they won all the others in what was a very competitive section. Reading will now play in the new Division Five south.

Mike Tewkesbury, coach in the 1990/91 season, came back to the Reading club in July 1992 and with a dedicated team assisting was the catalyst in the club's triumph. Success did not end there because the Reading also captured their forth Bisley Southern Merit Table Championship, a seventh Berkshire Cup title, and regained the prestigious David Cairns Memorial Trophy. To add icing to the cake, the sevens squad won their way into the Middlesex Finals at Twickenham for the first time ever.

Then in June 1993 the club won the Rugby World/Whitbread "Junior Club of the Month" award, an honour they had achieved once before in September 1986.

Reading's 1992-93 playing record speaks for itself. Top points scorer was full-back Phil Belshaw with 284 points. Winger Rodney Hutson was top try scorer with 12.There have been some outstanding wins such as 46-10 v Gordon League (League, away), Newbury 46-26 (Berkshire Cup, away) and Windsor 35-10 (Berkshire Cup Final, home). Then there were their five victories over sides from higher divisions including Berry Hill (A), Basingstoke (H) and Metropolitan Police (H). One of Reading's outstanding games of the season was the away defeat 16-9 to Sudbury (Suffolk) in January. This was their only defeat between Christmas 1992 and the end of the season.

Reading's Berkshire Cup Winning Squad. Back row: Lee Slater, Curtis Hutson, Danny Pratt, Ian McGeever, Rodney Hutson, Phil Belshaw, John Dixon, Roger Clark, Ian Turrell, Greg Way. Rfont row: Kevin (Taff) Jones, Michael Lacey, Simon Millsop, Dave Wells (Captain), Ian Armstrong, Simon Rogers

READING RFC

Club Details

Colours: Mrytle & white hoops, blue shorts
Change of Colours: Blue shirts
Date Founded: 1898
Membership: Total 350, Full 350, Social 60, Junior/Youth/Minis 120.
Membership Fees: Full £144, Junior/Youth/Minis £9, Other £35/£12.
Number of Teams: Senior 5, Junior 4.
Programme Advertising Rates: £150

Ground Details

Ground Address: Holme Park, Sonning Lane, Sonning, Reading, Berks RG4 0SJ.
Telephone: 0734 696592/690030.
Directions: Signposted from A4 one mile east of Junction with A329(M).
Capacity: Total 2,000, seated 250, standing 1,750.
Ticket Prices: Adults £2, OAP/Child Nil.
Clubhouse Facilities: 3 bars, function room, weights room, 2 squash courts.
Training Nights: Tuesday & Thursday

ADDITIONAL RESULTS 1992-93

No	Date	Opponents	Venue	Result
1	Sep 6	Redingensians		W31-16
2	Sep 9	Basingstoke		W25-16
3	Sep 12	Berry Hill		W26-14
4	Sep 19	Abbey		W17-9
5	Sep 26	Newbury		L11-26
6	Oct 3	Maidenhead		W32-7
7	Oct 10	Torquay		W18-6
8	Oct 17	Met Police		W19-8
9	Oct 24	Penryn		W24-19
10	Oct 31	Sherborne		W18-14
11	Nov 7	Mountain Ash		L8-39
12	Nov 14	Henley		W11-6
13	Nov 21	Brixham		W18-3
14	Nov 28	Maidstone		W34-16
15	Dec 5	Ruislip		W17-8
16	Dec 12	Guildford & Godalming		W29-6
17	Dec 19	High Wycombe		L6-10
18	Jan 2	Bournemouth		W45-10
19	Jan 9	Cinderford		W11-0
20	Jan 23	Sudbury		L9-16
21	Jan 30	Thurrock		W17-8
22	Feb 7	Newbury		W46-26
23	Feb 13	Cheltenham		W35-5
24	Feb 20	Marlow		W42-7
25	Feb 27	Ealing		W31-18
26	Mar 7	Maidenhead		W18-12
27	Mar 13	Gordon League		W46-10
28	Mar 21	Windsor		W35-10
29	Mar 27	Salisbury		W27-3
30	Apr 9	Detscher RC Hamburg		W36-0
31	Apr 17	Esher		W29-20
32	Apr 24	St Ives		W16-0

CLUB PLAYING RECORD 1992-93 SEASON

National Division: Five South
Final League Position at end 1992/93 Season: Top of SW1
League Playing Record:
P 12, W 11, D 0, L 1, Pts F 267, Pts A 99
Season Playing Record (including League matches/Pilkington cup etc):
P 32, W 28, D 0, L 4, Pts F 782, Pts A 367

COMPETITIONS WON DURING SEASON 1992-93

SW1 Champions
Berkshire County Champions
Southern Merit Table Champions
Cairns Trophy Winners
Middlesex 7s Finals

PLAYING SQUAD 1992-93

15: P Belshaw
14: R Hutson, D Harper, J Cowen
13: M Lacey, S Millsop
12: J Dixon, T Bell
11: M Alexander, K Boatman
10: G Way, S Rogers
9: D Wells (Capt), J Dixon
1: A Farrant, L Slater, D Hartley, B Baker
2: K Jones, J Harris
3: I Turrell
4: D Pratt, S Smith
5: C Hutson, P Webster
6: R Clark
7: I Armstrong, T Bell
8: P Roberts
6/8: I McGeever
7/8: R Nicholson

SOUTHEND RFC

Review of the Season

The season has seen a successful rebuilding of the 1st XV squad under the active and dedicated captaincy of David Catchpole and the coaching of Phil Lane and Graham Hankey. The growth in strength is indicated by the improvement in results as the season progressed, with a draw and two very narrow defeats initially, being overlaid by a series of successes. We enjoyed close contests with our friends from Cornwall and Gloucestershire and our near neighbours.

Representative Honours were won by a number of our players at county level and our captain, with 28 tries, was third in that category in the Courage League listing.

The supporting sides and in particular, the Priors captained by Aubrey Webb, had an enjoyable and successful season, as did our juniors with our Under 16's winning the county championship. Our women's team, playing in Division III contributed to an excellent year for the club.

President: D P Creffield
Chairman: John Jarvis
Club Secretary: D P Creffield, 10 Clifftown Parade, Southend-on- Sea, Essex, SS1 1DP. Tel: (H) 0702 330696 (W) 0227 264466 Fax: (W) 0277 217916.
Fixtures Secretary: Tom Webb, 28 St James Gardens, Westcliff-on- Sea, Essex, SS0 0BU. Tel: 0702 342888.
Press Officer: Gerry lambe, 79 Liestan Way, Southend-on-Sea, Essex, SS1 2XQ. Tel: 0702 61058.
1993/94 1XV Captain: J King
1993/94 1XV Coach: P Lane
Rugby Co-Ordinator: A Dawson
Treasurer: B Meredith
Chief Coach: P Lane
Chairman Marketing: John Jarvis.

CLUB PLAYING RECORD 1992-93 SEASON

National Division: Four South
Final League Position at end 1992/93 Season: 6th
League Playing Record: P 12, W 6, D 1, L 5, Pts F 196, Pts A 189

Southend RFC 1992-93

SOUTHEND RFC

Club Details
Colours: Brown & white shirts, white shorts & brown socks
Date Founded: 1870
Membership: Total 446, Full 343, Social 71, Junior/Youth/Minis 32.
Membership Fees: TBA
Number of Teams: Senior 6, Junior 10.
Programme Advertising Rates: TBA

Ground Details
Ground Address: Warners Park, Sutton Road, Southend-on-Sea, Essex, SS2 5RR.
Telephone: 0702 546682.
Directions: A127 to Southend, last roundabout 2nd exit into Priory Crescent, follow road into Gastern Avenue. At 1st roundabout take 1st exit into Sutton Road, 1st roundabout into Chandlers Way. Club at end of industrial estate.
Capacity: Total 1,500, seated 150.
Ticket Prices: Adults Nil, OAP/Child Nil.
Clubhouse Facilities: Bar, catering, sponsors room, gym, medical, shop.
Training Nights: Mondays & Thursdays

PLAYING SQUAD 1992-93
Full Backs: D Taylor, K Harman
Wings: M Fix, R Sant, S Malcolm, N Schofield, P Davis, D Burrows
Centres: A Bexley, M Sexton, M Fix, R Schofield, C Baynes
Half Backs: P Brooks, J King, S Pitchford, M Jones
Front Row: P Daly, C Dyton, W Hallett, S Rogers, A Webb, D Pearce, A Matthews, S Warner, L Parker
Locks: S Easton, M Kent, A Dawson, G Farmer
Wing Forwards: J Bailey, S Canavan, I Dale, K Baynes, G Mee, S Haith
No. 8: D Catchpole, P Raker, C Hudson

TABARD RFC

President: D Burrows
Chairman: B Brennan
Club Secretary: P Wood, 90 The Campions, Borehamwood, Herts, WD6 5QF
Fixtures Secretary: C Carmichael, 10 Chandos Road, Borehamwood, Herts, Tel: (H) 081 953 9006
Press Officer: Peter Cook, 32 Pinewood Close, Borehamwood, Herts
1993/94 1XV Captain: R Malone
1993/94 1XV Coach: I Jones

Review of the Season

Tabard moved into the National Leagues with their final victory of the 1992-93 season, topping London 1, with only one defeat and one drawn game in their first season at that level. The promotion came at the end of a season which also saw them in the third round of the Pilkington cup, losing to Northampton at their Cobden Hill home, winning the Herts Presidents Cup for the fifth time with a 26 to 12 victory over local rivals Cheshunt and topping the Herts Merit table for the fifth consecutive year.

Tabards league performance last season saw exciting games although an injury time victory over Barking, 8 points to 7, was probably the closest. In the end they had to win against Sutton and Epsom to clinch the title and this they did with a fine 31 points to 21 victory.

Tabard start the new season with a new Captain, second row Dick Malone, who replaces back row player Martin Richards. Martin took the side into London 1 last year and the National Leagues this year and was the leading try scorer although fullback Simon Tansley and stand off Nick Churchman both scored more points. In their endeavours the team were ably assisted by the coaching team headed by Ivor Jones.

CLUB PLAYING RECORD 1992-93 SEASON

National Division: Division 5 South
Final League Position at end 1992/93 Season:
League Playing Record: P 12, W 10, D 1, L 1, Pts F 230, Pts A 127
Season Playing Record (including League matches/Pilkington cup etc):
P 32, W 26, D 2, L 4, Pts F 687, Pts A 347

Pilkington Cup 3rd Round v Northampton at Tabard

TABARD RFC

Club Details

Colours: Navy blue with yellow band edged with red
Change of Colours: Red, blue & yellow quarters
Nickname: Tabs
Date Founded: 1951
Membership: Total 300, Full 150, Social 150
Membership Fees: Full £30, Junior/Youth/Minis £10, VPs £25
Number of Teams: Senior 5, Junior 1
Programme Advertising Rates: £50

Ground Details

Ground Address: Cobden Hill, Radlett, Herts
Telephone: 0923 855561
Capacity: 2,000
Ticket Prices: Adults £2
Clubhouse Facilities: Sponsors bar, weights room, fitness centre
Training Nights: Tues & thurs

LEADING SCORERS

S Tansley, 173
M Richards, 120
N Churchman, 119

PLAYING SQUAD 1992-93

Full Backs: B Lloyd, S Tansley
Wings: P Wood, A gilbert, J Allen, M Evans
Centres: S Bibby, D Robjohns, D Niven, M Lemon, T Smithers, S Lloyd
Fly Half: N Churchman
Scrum Half: R Long, G West
Props: R Welsh, D warnoer, N Gough
Hookers: M Trippick, R Botterman
Second Row: D Malone, J Sjollema, J Woodhead
Flankers: G Pratt, S Reynolds, I Smith, J Johnson
No. 8: M Richards

Herts Presidents Cup Final v Cheshunt at OMT Croxley Green

WESTON-SUPER-MARE

President: Dr G W J Papworth
Chairman: J N Brentnall
Club Secretary: Clayton Hope, 24 Feniton, Clovelly Road, Worle, Weston-Super-Mare, Avon BS22 0LN. Tel: (H) 0934 511834.
Fixtures Secretary: Roy Main, 142 Quantock Road, Weston-Super- Mare, Avon, BS23 4DP. Tel: (H) 0934 417864 (W) 0934 625643.
Press Officer: Roy Main, 142 Quantock Road, Weston-Super-Mare, Avon, BS23 4DP. Tel: (H) 0934 417864 (W) 0934 625643.
1993/94 1XV Captain: Richard Fear
1993/94 1XV Coach: Chris Williams
General Manager: Roy Main
Chairman of Rugby: Bill Poole
Marketing Committee Manager: Bill Caddick
Ground Committee Chairman: Andy Ballard
Social Committee Chairman: John Fry

Review of the Season

After an indifferent start to the season the Club Coach John Ackerman parted company with the club mid-way through November.

Colin Reeves ex-Club Captain took over for the second time, the club's coaching duties. After a great deal of hard work the mid-season results were beginning to show promise with some good wins especially in the league against Lydrey and Met. Police. After this period the club was hit with the worst series of long term injuries to first team squad members, that even the oldest members could remember.

Club Captain Mike Morsdale was one of the first to go with a double fracture of his cheekbone. Paul Whatley and Paul Redman both current county players sustained fractured ankles and the injury list continued to grow. The coaches job became very difficult and consequently results suffered badly. The players who were drafted into the side tried very hard and hopefully gained valuable experience for the future.

During the end of May, the Club provided ten players for Somerset's Italian tour.

With new coach Chris Williams from Bristol taking up his duties in July there is a great deal of optimism both on and off the field for next season.

CLUB PLAYING RECORD 1992-93 SEASON

National Division: Four South
Final League Position at end 1992/93 Season: 10th
League Playing Record: P 12, W 4, D 1, L 7, Pts F 154, Pts A 226
Season Playing Record (including League matches/Pilkington cup etc): P 37, W 13, D 2, L 22, Pts F 623, Pts A 679

Weston Super Mare FC 1992-93

WESTON-SUPER-MARE RFC

Club Details

Colours: Royal Blue
Change of Colours: Red
Date Founded: 1875
Membership: Total 725, Full 440, Social 325
Number of Teams: Senior 3, Junior 7
Programme Advertising Rates: TBA

Ground Details

Ground Address: Recreation Ground, Drive Road, Weston-super-Mare, Avon.
Telephone: 0934 623118 (Managers Office) 0934 625643
Directions: M5 Jucn 21. Follow A320 into New Bristol Road, then Lockig road into Weston-super-Mare about 2.5 miles. 3rd set of traffic lights, left over railway bridge, 4th exit off roundabout into ground.
Capacity: 6,499 (seated 499, standing 6,000)
Ticket Prices: Adults £2 Student/Junior/U16/OAP £1
Clubhouse Facilities: Large clubhouse, committee room, lounge bar, skittle alley, caravan site, extensive hard standing car park, gymnasium.
Training Nights: Monday and Wednesday.

LEADING APPEARANCES FOR CLUB DURING SEASON 1992-93

P Thatcher, 33
A Croker, 33
A Fisher, 33
S Knight, 32
J Sampson, 31
J Cornish, 30

LEADING SCORERS

P Thatcher, Full back, 239
C Heath, Wing, 35
M Mousdale, Scrum Half, 30
P Whjatley, Right Wing, 30
D Steele, Wing, 25

PLAYING SQUAD 1992-93

Full Backs: P Thatcher, P Munden C Sheryn
Wings: C Larking, P Whatley, C Heath, D Steele, C Brown, D Murphy
Centres: M Bamsey, S Watts, P Denham, P Forde, D Hannam, J Robinson, G Russell
Fly Half: S Harvey, J Ritchie, p tincknell
Scrum Half: M Mousdale, N Coleman, A Gaulton, J Snelling
Props: A Croker, A Fisher, B Popham, A Marsh, C Roberts, S Turvey, J Board
Hookers: I Mitchell, G Hill, R Coles
Locks: J Sampson, J Cornish, P Sloman, R Main
Flankers: R Fear, S Knight, G Sparks, J Stanniland, N Beaver
No. 8: P Redman, L Walsh, M Philip

LEAGUE 5 SOUTH PROGRAMMES

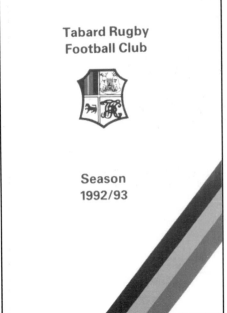

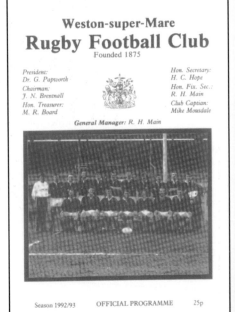

THE REGIONAL DIVISIONS

NORTHERN

MIDLAND

LONDON & SOUTH EAST

SOUTH WEST

NORTHERN DIVISION

OFFICIALS 1993-94

CHAIRMAN, League Sub-Committee
R. Archer, Brookfield House, Scotland Head, Winlaton, Tyne & Wear NE21 6PL (H) 091 414 3532

N.E. CO-ORDINATOR AND YORKSHIRE LEAGUES
L. Bentley, 32 Moorhead Terrace, Shipley, W. Yorkshire BD18 4LB (H) 0274 585460

N.W. CO-ORDINATOR AND LANCASHIRE LEAGUES
W. Chappell, Seawood House, Carter Road, Kents Bank, Grange-over- Sands, Cumbria LA11 7AS (H) 0539 533456

DURHAM
R.T. Thoburn, 70 Theresa Street, Blaydon, Tyne & Wear (H) 091 414 2669

NORTHUMBERLAND
I. Rae, 196 Broadway, Tynemouth, Tyne & Wear NE30 3RY (H) 091 259 2136

CHESHIRE
M.J. Lord, 68 Hoole Road, Chester, Cheshire CH2 3NL (H) 0244 312702 (B) 051 356 6241

CUMBRIA
J. Hamer, 55 Rush Green Road, Lymm, Cheshire WA13 9PS (H) 0925 755504 (W) 051 548 6756

LEAGUE SECRETARIES
North One R. Holmes, 7 Ashdene Crescent, Crofton, Wakefield, W. Yorks WF4 1PL (H) 0924 863151 (B) 0226 286484.

North Two G. Davies, Stansfield Cottage, West Todmorden, Lancs OL14 8DD (H) 070681 2891

N.E. One I. Clarke, 109 Dryden Road, Low Fell, Gateshead NE9 5TS (H) 091 487 5480 (B) 091 232 5091 x 4087

N.E. Two J. Scott, 8 Main Street, Cherry Burton, Beverley, East Yorks (H) 0532 495666

Durham/North One S. Harrison, 9 Gillside Grove, Roker, Sunderland, Tyne & Wear SR6 9PQ (H) 091 548 4272

Durham/North Two Mrs Joyce Baty, 5 Brooklands, Ponteland, Northumberland NE20 9LZ (H) 0661 23527

Durham/North Three Anthony Brown, 22 Mill Crescent, Hebburn, Tyne & Wear NE31 1UQ (H) 091 469 3716

Yorkshire One Jim Cooper, 8 Otterwood Bank, Foxwood Hill, Acomb, York YO2 3JS (H) 0904 797858 (B) 0904 628 982

Yorkshire Two Ron Lewis, 33 Swift Way, Sandal, Wakefield, W. Yorkshire WF2 6SQ (H) 0924 253049 (W) 0532 435301

Yorkshire Three Terry McCreedy, 42 Fearnville Place, Leeds, W. Yorks LS8 3OY. (H) 0532 655065 (B) 0274 727524

Yorkshire Four Mrs Carol Brown, 2 Lytham Gardens, Skipton, N. Yorkshire BD23 2TR (H) 0756 791475

Yorkshire Five P Hazeldine, 90 Fairburn Drive, Garforth, Leeds LS25 2JD (H) 0532 866035 (B) 0532 869091

N.W. One Alan Johnson, 6 Rugby Drive, Titherton, Macclesfield, Cheshire (H) 0625 614697

N.W. Two Ivon Hodgeson, 22 Capesthorne Close, Holmes Chapel, Cheshire CW4 7EN (H) 0477 33406

Cumbria/North Lancs Roger Bott, 123 Albert Road West, Heaton, Bolton, Lancs BL1 5ED (H) 0204 41376

Cumbria Bill Hopkinson, Far Hey Head Farm, Littleborough, Rochdale, Lancs OL15 9NS (H) 0706 379879 (B) 0706 347474 x 4531

North Lancs One Colin Barton, 4 Oulderhill Drive, Rochdale, Lancs OL11 5LB (H) 0706 350312

North Lancs Two Ian Scott Brown, Brunsholme, Pendleview, Grindleton, Nr. Clitheroe, Lancs BB7 4QU (H) 0200 40102 (B) 0254 582749 / 57846

Cheshire/South Lancs Mike Massey, Fieldside, Grange Road, Bowden, Cheshire (H) 061 928 2997

Cheshire Ken Pushon, 24 Newcombe Road, Holcombe Brook, Nr. Bury, Lancs (H) 0204 884886

South Lancs Vic Thomas, 5 Portree Close, Winton, Eccles, Manchester M30 8LX (H) 061 788 7274

NORTHERN DIVISION

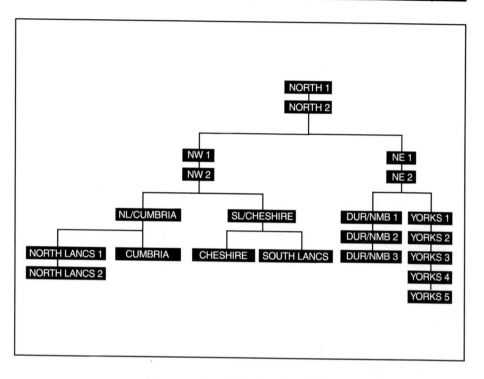

ADMINISTRATIVE RULES

On League Saturdays, both Clubs will telephone the match result through to their League Secretary. Both clubs will also confirm within 48 hours the result and score in writing together with the list of players and replacements featuring in the match to the League Secretary on a card signed by the referee.

a.   In the case of Northern Division Leagues 1 and 2, North West Leagues 1 and 2 and North East Leagues 1 and 2, such telephone calls shall be made not later than 5.30pm on the evening of the game and the League Secretary shall report the results to Snowdon Sports Editorial, PO Box 154, Sheffield S10 4BW. Tel: Sheffield 0742 303093/4 (24 hour answering copy line).

b.   The remaining League Secretaries will telephone the results as soon as possible, but in any case not later than 3.00pm on the Sunday following the games to Snowdon Sports Editorial at the above numbers.

c.   In Northern Division Leagues 1 and 2 the League Secretaries will remit to the Chairman the scores and

results in writing within 48 hours. The remaining League Secretaries will remit the results and the scores in writing to their North East or North West co-ordinator within 48 hours.

d.   In the case of an abandoned match the Secretary of the League must be supplied by the home Club with a certificate signed by the Referee indicating the point at which the match was abandoned, and the score.

e.   These arrangements do not prohibit local publicity and Clubs are advised to maintain and improve local publicity by informing their local press as usual.

f.   Any Club failing to notify the result in accordance with this Rule shall on the first occasion during a season be fined £10, on the second occasion be fined £25 and on the third occasion there will be a recommendation to the RFU that the Club be suspended or expelled from the League. Should payment of fines not be honoured within 28 days of the date of the invoice, the offending club will lose 2 league points.

NORTHERN DIVISION

December 18 (Week 15)
Stockton v Wharfedale
Hull Ionians v Sandal
Wigton v Hartlepool Rovers
Middlesbrough v Tynedale
Vale of Lune v Huddersfield
Manchester v Widnes

October 23 (Week 8)
Stockton v Hill Ionians
Widnes v Sandal
Huddersfield v Hartlepool Rovers
Northern v Tynedale
Vale of Lune v Middlesbrough
Manchester v Wigton

January 8 (Week 18)
Hartlepool Rovers v Middlesbrough
Sandal v Wigton
Wharfedale v Hull Ionians
Widnes v Stockton
Huddersfield v Manchester
Northern v Vale of Lune

October 30 (Week X2)
Wigton v Stockton
Middlesbrough v Manchester
Tynedale v Vale of Lune
Hartlepool Rovers v Northern
Sandal v Huddersfield
Wharfedale v Widnes

January 29 (Week X5)
Stockton v Huddersfield
Hull Ionians v Widnes
Wigton v Wharfedale
Middlesbrough v Sandal
Tynedale v Hartlepool Rovers
Manchester v Northern

November 13 (Week 10)
Stockton v Middlesbrough
Hull Ionians v Wigton
Huddersfield v Wharfedale
Northern v Sandal
Vale of Lune v Hartlepool Rovers
Manchester v Tynedale

February 12 (Week 22)
Sandal v Tynedale
Wharfedale v Middlesbrough
Widnes v Wigton
Huddersfield v Hull Ionians
Northern v Stockton
Vale of Lune v Manchester

November 20 (Week 11)
Middlesbrough v Hull Ionians
Tynedale v Stockton
Hartlepool Rovers v Manchester
Sandal v Vale of Lune
Wharfedale v Northern
Widnes v Huddersfield

March 12 (Week 26)
Stockton v Vale of Lune
Hull Ionians v Northern
Wigton v Huddersfield
Middlesbrough v Widnes
Tynedale v Wharfedale
Hartlepool Rovers v Sandal

December 4 (Week 13)
Stockton v Hartlepool Rovers
Hull Ionians v Tynedale
Wigton v Middlesbrough
Northern v Widnes
Vale of Lune v Wharfedale
Manchester v Sandal

March 26 (Week 28)
Wharfedale v Hartlepool Rovers
Widnes v Tynedale
Huddersfield v Middlesbrough
Northern v Wigton
Vale of Lune v Hull Ionians
Manchester v Stockton

December 11 (Week 14)
Tynedale v Wigton
Hartlepool Rovers v Hull Ionians
Sandal v Stockton
Wharfedale v Manchester
Widnes v Vale of Lune
Huddersfield v Northern

April 9 (Week 30)
Hull Ionians v Manchester
Wigton v Vale of Lune
Middlesbrough v Northern
Tynedale v Huddersfield
Hartlepool Rovers v Widnes
Sandal v Wharfedale

HARTLEPOOL ROVERS FC
Ground Address: The Friarage, West View Road, Hartlepool, Cleveland TS24 0BP. Tel: 0429 267741. **Club Secretary:** Mr David Close, 32 Greenside Avenue, Horden, Durham SR8 4QX. Tel: (H) 091 586 0850.
Press Officer: c/o Mr Philip Mitchell, 44 Victoria Road, Hartlepool, Cleveland. Tel: (H) 0429 272750 (W) 0429 866542.
Club Colours: White shirt, black shorts, red socks.

HUDDERSFIELD RUFC
Ground Address: Tandem Ground, Waterloo, Huddersfield HD5 0AN. Tel: 0484 423864, 0484 517569. **Club Secretary:** A R Field, 54 Quarry Lane, Lascelles Hall, Huddersfield HD5 0AR. Tel: (H) 0484 534318 (W) 0484 424055. **Press Officer:** Nigel J Lee, Inglewood House, Birkby Hall Road, Birkby, Huddersfield. Tel: (H) 0484 549733 (W) 0484 539922
Club Colours: White, claret and gold.

HULL IONIANS RUFC
Ground Address: Brantingham Road, Elloughton, Brough, N. Humberside. Tel: 0486 667342. **Club Secretary:** Peter Sharp, 38 Corby Park, North Ferriby, N. Humberside HU14 3AY. Tel: (H) 0482 631819 (W) 0482 803933. **Press Officer:** Brian Norman, 34 Manor Drive, Elloughton, Brough HU15 1JA. Tel: (H) 0482 666014 (W) 0482 663660. **Club Colours:** Red, white, blue, green quarters, blue shorts, red socks.

MANCHESTER FC
Ground Address: Grove Park, Grove Lane, Cheadle Hulme, Cheadle, Cheshire SK8 7NE. Tel: 061 485 1115. **Club Secretary:** Mike Morgan, 62 Moss Road, Billinge, Lancashire WN5 7BT. Tel: (H) 0695 623201 (W) 0422 375391. **Press Officer:** Alan Hanson, 1 Hazelbadge Road, Poynton, Cheshire SK12 1HE. Tel: (H) 0625 875636 (W) 061 236 4071. **Club Colours:** Red & white hooped jerseys, white shorts, red socks.

MIDDLESBROUGH RUFC
Ground Address: Acklam Park, Green Lane, Middlesbrough, Cleveland TS5 7SL. Tel: 0642 818567. **Club Secretary:** Don Brydon, 20 Westwood Avenue, Linthorpe, Middlesbrough, Cleveland TS5 5PY. Tel: (H) 0642 819954 (W) 0642 222279. **Press Officer:** Mike Read, April Cottage, Back Lane, Osmotherley, North Yorkshire. Tel: (H) 0609 883525 (W) 0642 242753.
Club Colours: Maroon jerseys, white shorts.

NORTHERN FC
Ground Address: McCracken Park, Great North Road, Gosforth, Newcastle upon Tyne NE3 2DG. Tel: 091 236 3369 (payphone 091 236 8341). **Club Secretary:** Mrs P M Spong, McCracken Park Great North Road, Gosforth, Newcastle upon Tyne NE3 2DG. Tel: (W) 091 236 3369. **Press Officer:** W D Ritchie, McCracken Park Great North Road, Gosforth, Newcastle upon Tyne NE3 2DG. Tel: (W) 091 236 3369.
Club Colours: White shirt, navy shorts, red socks.

SANDAL RUFC
Ground Address: Milnthorpe Green, Stanbridge Lane, Sandal, Wakefield, West Yorkshire WF2 7JD. Tel: 0924 250661. **Club Secretary:** Len Bedford, 14 Lindale Mount, Batley Road, Wakefield, West Yorkshire WF2 0BH. Tel: (H) 0924 379263 (W) 0532 778778.
Club Colours: Maroon, gold & white.

STOCKTON RFC
Ground Address: Norton Cricket Club, Station Road, Norton, Cleveland. Tel: 0642 554031. **Club Secretary:** Denis Chisman, 16 Dunettar Avenue, Eaglescliffe, Stockton, Cleveland. Tel: (H) 781339 (W) 615439.

FINAL TABLE

	P	W	D	L	F	A	PD	Pts
Bradfd & Bingley	12	11	1	0	324	106	218	23
Tynedale	12	9	0	3	323	111	212	18
Wharfdale	12	7	0	5	216	208	8	14
Sandal	12	6	1	5	205	129	76	13
Middlesbrough	12	6	1	5	185	160	25	13
Hull Ionians	12	6	0	6	206	208	-2	12
Widnes	12	6	0	6	164	175	-11	12
Stockton	12	6	0	6	138	160	-22	12
Hartlepool Rovers	12	5	0	7	161	182	-21	8
Wigton	12	3	1	8	121	220	-99	7
Vale of Lune	12	3	1	8	167	291	-124	7
Northern	12	3	1	8	124	276	-152	7
Lymm	12	4	0	8	133	244	-111	6

Press Officer: John Robinson, 17 Rook Lane, Norton, Stockton, Clevemand TS20 1SB. Tel: (H) 0642 557288 (W) 0642 433069.
Club Colours: Red shirts, white shorts.

TYNEDALE RFC
Ground Address: Tynedale Park, Corbridge, Northumberland NE45 5AY. Tel: 0434 632997. **Club Secretary:** A C Smith, West Fell, Ladycutter Lane, Corbridge, Northumberland NE45 5RZ. Tel: (H) 0434 632044 (W) 091 490 1111. **Press Officer:** J B Shotton, 3 Millfield Court, Hexham, Northumberland. Tel: (H) 0434 607546 (W) 0434 320598.
Club Colours: Blue & white hoops: white shorts, blue stockings with white tops.

VALE OF LUNE RUFC
Ground Address: Powderhouse Lane, Lancaster. Tel: 0524 64029. **Club Secretary:** Peter Fell, Vale of Lune RUFC, Powderhouse Lane, Lancaster, Lancashire. Tel: (H) 0524 416519. **Press Officer:** Mr S R Vernon, 16 Slyne Road, Bolton-le-Sands, Lancaster. Tel: (H) 0524 822092 (W) 0524 416830.
Club Colours: Cherry & white hooped shirts, navy blue shorts, cherry & white hooped stockings.

WHARFEDALE RUFC
Ground Address: Wharfeside Avenue, Threshfield, Skipton, North Yorks BD23 5BS. Tel: 0756 752547. **Club Secretary:** Gordon H Brown, Wharfemead, Wood Lane, Grassington, Skipton, North Yorks BD23 5ND. Tel: (H/W) 0756 752410 (FAX) 0756 752123. **Press Officer:** Keith Lewis, Willowbank Road, Cross Hills, Keighley, West Yorks BD20 8AA. Tel: (H) 0535 634318.
Club Colours: Emerald green (or dark blue).

WIDNES RUFC
Ground Address: Heath Road, Widnes, Cheshire WA8 7NU. Tel: 051 424 2575. **Club Secretary:** Ian Barker, 14 Amelia Lane, Widnes, Cheshire WA8 9FR. Tel: (H) 051 423 4128 (W) 061 721 2326.
Press Officer: R C Wasson, 27 Phythian Cres, Penwith. Tel: (H) 092 572 3483.
Club Colours: Black & red.

WIGTON RUFC
Ground Address: Lowmoor Road, Wigton. Tel: 06973 42206. **Club Secretary:** Abdrew D J Huntington, Bridge Mill, Woodrow, Wigton, Cumbria CA7 0AX. Tel: (H) 06973 44898 **Press Officer:** Dave Branthwaite, Arenal Yealsgate, Carlisle, Cumbria. Tel: (H) 09657 402 (W) 06973 43512.
Club Colours: Green shirts, white shorts.

NORTHERN DIVISION

NORTH TWO
1993-94
FIXTURES

October 23 (Week 8)
Macclesfield v Alnwick
Wigan v West Park
Northwich v Halifax
Carlisle v O.Crossleyans
York v Lymm
W.P.Bramhope v Bridlington

October 30 (Week X2)
Bridlington v Macclesfield
Lymm v W.P.Bramhope
O.Crossleyans v York
Halifax v Carlisle
West Park v Northwich
Birkenhead Park v Wigan

November 13 (Week 10)
Macclesfield v Lymm
Alnwick v Bridlington
Northwich v Birkenhead Park
Carlisle v West Park
York v Halifax
W.P.Bramhope v O.Crossleyans

November 20 (Week 11)
Lymm v Alnwick
O.Crossleyans v Macclesfield .
Halifax v W.P.Bramhope
West Park v York
Birkenhead Park v Carlisle
Wigan v Northwich

December 4 (Week 13)
Macclesfield v Halifax
Alnwick v O.Crossleyans
Bridlington v Lymm
Carlisle v Wigan
York v Birkenhead Park
W.P.Bramhope v West Park

December 11 (Week 14)
O.Crossleyans v Bridlington
Halifax v Alnwick
West Park v Macclesfield
Birkenhead Park v W.P.Bramhope
Wigan v York
Northwich v Carlisle

December 18 (Week 15)
Macclesfield v Birkenhead Park
Alnwick v West Park
Bridlington v Halifax
Lymm v O.Crossleyans
York v Northwich
W.P.Bramhope v Wigan

January 8 (Week 18)
Halifax v Lymm
West Park v Bridlington
Birkenhead Park v Alnwick
Wigan v Macclesfield
Northwich v W.P.Bramhope
Carlisle v York

January 29 (Week X5)
Macclesfield v Northwich
Alnwick v Wigan
Bridlington v Birkenhead Park
Lymm v West Park
O.Crossleyans v Halifax
W.P.Bramhope v Carlisle

February 12 (Week 22)
West Park v O.Crossleyans
Birkenhead Park v Lymm
Wigan v Bridlington
Northwich v Alnwick
Carlisle v Macclesfield
York v W.P.Bramhope

March 12 (Week 26)
Macclesfield v York
Alnwick v Carlisle
Bridlington v Northwich
Lymm v Wigan
O.Crossleyans v Birkenhead Park
Halifax v West Park

March 26 (Week 28)
Birkenhead Park v Halifax
Wigan v O.Crossleyans
Northwich v Lymm
Carlisle v Bridlington
York v Alnwick
W.P.Bramhope v Macclesfield

April 9 (Week 30)
Alnwick v W.P.Bramhope
Bridlington v York
Lymm v Carlisle
O.Crossleyans v Northwich
Halifax v Wigan
West Park v Birkenhead Park

ALNWICK RFC
Ground Address: Greensfield St James, Alnwick, Northumberland. Tel: 0665 602342.
Club Secretary: S A Brierley, East Cawledge Farm, Alnwick, Northumberland NE66 2HB.
Press Officer: R A Bingham, 4 St Genges, Alnick. Tel: (H) 0665 602041 (W) 0665 602234.
Club Colours Royal blue.

BIRKENHEAD PARK FC
Ground Address: Upper Park, Park Road North, Birkenhead, Merseyside L41 8AA. Tel: 051 652 4646 Fax: 051 670 1648.
Club Secretary: J G Smith, as above.
Club Colours: Red, white, navy blue hoops, white shorts, red socks.

BRIDLINGTON RUFC
Ground Address: Dukes Park, Queensgate, Bridlington, E Yorkshire. Tel: 0262 676405.
Club Secretary: Phil Preston, as above. Tel:(H) 0262 602851 (W) 0262 603979.
Press Officer: Stan Wright, as above. Tel:(H) 0262 675230 (W) 0262 671533
Club Colours: Blue with amber hoops.

CARLISLE RFC
Ground Address: Warwick Road, Carlisle. Tel: 0228 21300
Club Secretary N J Laycock, 90 Greystone Road, Carlisle, Cumbria CA1 2DD. Tel 0228 22895 (W) 0228 20277
Press Officer: R Singleton, 78 Holmbrook Road, Carlisle. Tel: (H) 0228 38815 (W) 0228 23456
Club Colours: Irregular navy blue, red and white hoops.

HALIFAX RUFC
Ground Address: Standlven Memorial Ground, Keighly Road, Ovendon, Halifax, W Yorkshire. Tel: 0422 365926.
Club Secretary: A V Edwards, 6 Heath Street, Savile Park, Halifax, W Yorkshire HX3 0DJ. Tel:(H) 0422 356314 (W) 0422 360272.
Press Officer: G Davies, Stansfield Cottage West, Todmorden, Lancashire. Tel: 0706 812891
Club Colours Dark blue, light blue & white hoops.

LYMM RFC
Ground Address: "Beeechwood", Crouchly Lane, Lymm, Cheshire. Tel: 0925 753212.
Club Secretary: J E Knowles, "The Limes". 151 Chester Road, Grappenhall, Warrington, Cheshire WA4 2SB. Tel: 0925 267385
Press Officer: M Pritchard, 3a West Hyde, Lymm, Cheshire WA13 0HA. Tel:(H) 0925 757364 (W) 061 236 7687.
Club Colours: Black, green, white hoops, black shorts.

MACCLESFIELD RUFC
Ground Address: Priory Park, Priory Lane, Macclesfield SK10 4AE. Tel: 0625 827899.
Club Secretary: T McCreery, 20 Carnoustie Drive, Macclesfield SK10 2TB. Tel: (H) 0625 615488 (W) 061 832 5085.
Press Officer: Geoff Allen, 69 Tytherington Drive, Macclesfield. Tel 0625 432345 (W) 0625 61000.
Club Colours: Blue & white hoops.

NORTHWICH RUFC
Ground Address: Moss Farm, Northwich, Cheshire. Tel: 0606 79987
Club Secretary: Ron McLavery, 7 Pear Tree Drive, Wincham, Northwich CW9 6EZ. Tel: (H) 0565 733997 (W) 0606 74481.
Press Officer: Phil Clarke, 18 Darwin Street, Castle, Northwich. Tel: (H) 0606 781441 (W) 0606 737044.
Club Colours: Black shirts and shorts.

FINAL TABLE

	P	W	D	L	F	A	PD	Pts
Manchester	12	10	0	2	302	103	199	20
Huddersfield	12	10	0	2	247	111	136	20
York	12	9	0	3	295	106	189	18
West Pk Bramhope	12	9	0	3	270	97	173	18
Old Crossleyans	12	9	0	3	222	144	78	18
Alnwick	12	8	0	4	196	152	44	14
West Pk St Helens	12	7	0	5	207	179	28	14
Northwich	12	4	0	8	145	235	-90	8
Wigan	12	4	0	8	124	229	-105	6
Birkenhead Park	12	3	0	9	120	246	-126	6
Carlisle	12	3	0	9	127	275	-148	6
Halifax	12	2	0	10	153	265	-112	4
Sandbach	12	0	0	12	64	363	-299	0

OLD CROSSLEYANS RUFC
Ground Address: Stand Even House, Broomfield Avenue, Halifax, W Yorkshire HX3 0JF. Tel: 0422 823662.
Club Secretary: Keith Davies, 23 School Close, Ripponden, Sowebby Bridge, W Yorkshire HX6 4HP. Tel: (H) 0422 823662 (W) 051 677 0171.
Press Officer: John Philburn, 57 Wakefield Road, Lightcliffe, Halifax HX3 8AQ. Tel: (H) 0422 201463 (W) 0274 575511.
Club Colours: Navy with white & amber hoops.

WEST PARK BRAMHOPE RUFC
Ground Address: The Sycamores, Bramhope, Leeds. Tel: 0532 671437.
Club Secretary: Bill Barrack, Lynholme, 15 Eastgate Close, Bramhope, Leeds LS16 9AA. Tel: 0532 242540.
Press Officer: Paul Hatfield, 25 Pool Road, Otley, Leeds. Tel: (H) 0943 467950 (W) 0532 464415.
Club Colours: Black & gold.

WEST PARK (ST HELENS) RFC
Ground Address: Eccleston Hill, Prescot Road, St Helens, Merseyside. Tel: 0744 26138.
Club Secretary: William Bold, as above.
Press Officer: J P Burbridge, 14 Carmelite Crescent, Eccleston, St Helens, Merseyside WA10 5LP. Tel: 0744 21320.
Club Colours: Green & gold.

WIGAN RUFC
Ground Address: Douglas Valley, Wingates Road, Leyland Mill Lane, Wigan. Tel:0942 42556.
Club Secretary: Graham Heeley, 30 Darley Road, Hawkley Hill, Wigan. Tel: (H) 0942 201360 (W) 061 486 6211.
Press Officer: Roy Knowles, 7 Langdale Avenue, Wigan WN1 2HW. Tel: 0942 38135.
Club Colours: Black, white irregular hoops.

YORK RUFC
Ground Address: Clifton Park, Shipton Road, York YO3 6RE. Tel: 0904 623602.
Club Secretary: Brian McClure, 15 Stubden Grove, York YO3 4UY. Tel: 0904 691026.
Press Officer: Peter Johnson, 44 The Paddock, York YO2 6AW. Tel: 0904 792012.
Club Colours: Green, black and white hoops.

NORTHERN DIVISION

NORTH WEST ONE
1993-94
FIXTURES

December 18 (Week 15)
Caldy v New Brighton
Oldershaw v Kirkby Lonsdale
Chester v Ashton on Mersey
Sandbach v Davenport
Blackburn v Cockermouth
Mersey Police v Sedgley Park

October 23 (Week 8)
Caldy v Oldershaw
Sedgley Park v Kirkby Lonsdale
Cockermouth v Ashton on Mersey
St Edwards O.B. v Davenport
Blackburn v Sandbach
Mersey Police v Chester

January 8 (Week 18)
Ashton on Mersey v Sandbach
Kirkby Lonsdale v Chester
New Brighton v Oldershaw
Sedgley Park v Caldy
Cockermouth v Mersey Police
St Edwards O.B. v Blackburn

October 30 (Week X2)
Chester v Caldy
Sandbach v Mersey Police
Davenport v Blackburn
Ashton on Mersey v St Edwards O.B.
Kirkby Lonsdale v Cockermouth
New Brighton v Sedgley Park

January 29 (Week X5)
Caldy v Cockermouth
Oldershaw v Sedgley Park
Chester v New Brighton
Sandbach v Kirkby Lonsdale
Davenport v Ashton on Mersey
Mersey Police v St Edwards O.B.

November 13 (Week 10)
Caldy v Sandbach
Oldershaw v Chester
Cockermouth v New Brighton
St Edwards O.B. v Kirkby Lonsdale
Blackburn v Ashton on Mersey
New Brighton v Davenport

February 12 (Week 22)
Kirkby Lonsdale v Davenport
New Brighton v Sandbach
Sedgley Park v Chester
Cockermouth v Oldershaw
St Edwards O.B. v Caldy
Blackburn v Mersey Police

November 20 (Week 11)
Sandbach v Oldershaw
Davenport v Caldy
Ashton on Mersey v Mersey Police
Kirkby Lonsdale v Blackburn
New Brighton v St Edwards O.B.
Sedgley Park v Cockermouth

March 12 (Week 26)
Caldy v Blackburn
Oldershaw v St Edwards O.B.
Chester v Cockermouth
Sandbach v Sedgley Park
Davenport v New Brighton
Ashton on Mersey v Kirkby Lonsdale

December 4 (Week 13)
Caldy v Ashton on Mersey
Oldershaw v Davenport
Chester v Sandbach
St Edwards O.B. v Sedgley Park
Blackburn v New Brighton
Mersey Police v Kirkby Lonsdale

March 26 (Week 28)
New Brighton v Ashton on Mersey
Sedgley Park v Davenport
Cockermouth v Sandbach
St Edwards O.B. v Chester
Blackburn v Oldershaw
Mersey Police v Caldy

December 11 (Week 14)
Davenport v Chester
Ashton on Mersey v Oldershaw
Kirkby Lonsdale v Caldy
New Brighton v Mersey Police
Sedgley Park v Blackburn
Cockermouth v St Edwards O.B.

April 9 (Week 30)
Oldershaw v Mersey Police
Chester v Blackburn
Sandbach v St Edwards O.B.
Davenport v Cockermouth
Ashton on Mersey v Sedgley Park
Kirkby Lonsdale v New Brighton

NORTH WEST ONE

ASHTON-ON-MERSEY RUFC
Ground Address: Bankey Lane off Carrington Lane, Ashton-on- Mersey, Sale, Cheshire M33 5NP. Tel: 061 973 6637
Club Secretary: Max Nobbs, 116 Mercer Street, Newton-le-Willows, Merseyside WA12 9TL. Tel: 0925 220350.
Press Officer: Steve Holland, 32 Bosdin Road, Flixton, Manchester M31 3PD. Tel: 061 747 1430.
Club Colours: Maroon shirts, navy shorts, maroon socks, white tops.

BLACKBURN RUFC
Ground Address: Ramsgreave Drive, Blackburn BB1 8NB. Tel: 0254 247669.
Club Secretary: M J Walker, 6 Westviews Place, Revidge, Blackburn BB2 6JG. Tel: (H) 0254 671474 (W) 0204 308431.
Club Colours: Blue.

CALDY RFC
Ground Address: Paton Field, Lower Caldy Crossroads, West Kirby, Wirral, Merseyside. Tel: 051 625 8043.
Club Secretary: Andrew Blackstock, The Willows, Manorial Road, Parkgate, South Wirral, Cheshire L64 6QW. Tel: (H) 051 336 2402 (W) 051 327 1381.
Press Officer: Kevin Doolan, 37 Appletree Grove, Great Sutton, Cheshire. Tel: 051 348 0119.
Club Colours: Sable, claret, gold & silver hoops, black shorts.

CHESTER RUFC
Ground Address: Hare Lane, Vicars Cross, Chester. Tel: 0244 336017.
Club Secretary: Stephen Maddox, 8 Fairfield Road, Hoole, Chester CH2 3RN. Tel:(H) 0244 345438 (W) 051 691 8498.
Press Officer: Brian Baister.
Club Colours: Red shirts, white shorts.

COCKERMOUTH RUFC
Ground Address: Laithwaite, Low Road, Cockermouth. Tel: 0900 824884.
Club Secretary: Bill McDowell, 10 The Green, Cockermouth, Cumbria CA13 9AS. Tel: (H) 0900 824274 (W) 06973 20234.
Club Colours: Black and amber.

DAVENPORT RUFC
Ground Address: Bridge Lane Memorial Grounds, Headlands Road, Bramhill, Stockport, Chesire. Tel: 061 439 2150.
Club Secretary: M Hargreaves, 80 Ladybridge Road, Cheadle Hume, Cheshire SK8 5NZ. Tel: 061 485 8450.
Press Officer: Colin Buckley, 30 Ramillies Avenue, Cheadle Hume, Cheshire SK8 7AL. Tel:061 485 6030.
Club Colours: Red, green & white.

KIRKBY LONSDALE RUFC
Ground Address: Raygarth, Underly Park, Kirkby, Lonsdale. Tel: 05242 71780.
Club Secretary: Richard Harkness, 7-9 Mitchelgate, Kirkby, Lonsdale. Tel: (H) 05242 71137 (W) 0524 943160.
Press Officer: James Thompson, Kearstwick Cottage, Kearstwick, Nr Kirkby Lonsdale, Via Carnforth. Tel: (H) 05242 71330 (W) 05242 71555.
Club Colours: Red, black, amber hoop, black shorts.

MERSEYSIDE POLICE RUFC
Ground Address: Club House, Riversdale Road. Aigburth, Liverpool, Merseyside. Tel: 051 427 2208.
Club Secretary: D/Sgt Andy Ward, 229 Pensby Road, Hiswall, Wirral L61 5VA. Tel: (H) 051 342 8825 (W) 051 777 3682.
Club Colours: Blue, white, black quarters.

FINAL TABLE

	P	W	D	L	F	A	PD	Pts
Macclesfield	12	12	0	0	310	68	242	24
New Brighton	12	9	1	2	243	103	140	19
Merseyside Police	12	9	0	3	180	84	96	18
St Edwards OB	12	7	1	4	165	148	17	15
Ashton on Mersey	12	6	1	5	106	111	-5	13
Caldy	12	7	0	5	184	217	-33	12
Chester	12	5	0	7	215	159	56	10
Cockermouth	12	5	0	7	112	186	-74	10
Blackburn	12	4	0	8	165	183	-18	8
Davenport	12	5	0	7	131	197	-66	8
Sedgley Park	12	4	0	8	149	188	-39	6
Wirral	12	2	0	10	85	243	-158	4
Egremont	12	1	1	10	111	292	-181	2

NEW BRIGHTON RUFC
Ground Address: Reeds Lane, Moreton, Wirral. Tel: 051 677 1873.
Club Secretary: Mrs B M Bowers, 4 Murrayfield Drive, Moreton, Wirral L46 3RS. Tel: 051 678 2654.
Press Officer: Mr V Gibson, 16 Clwyd Street, Wallasey, Wirral L45 5EX. Tel: 051 691 2089.
Club Colours: Light blue, dark blue, white.

OLDERSHAW RUFC
Ground Address: Belvedere Playing Field, Belvedere Road, Liscard, Wallasey, Merseyside. Tel: 051 638 4379.
Club Secretary: Neil Johnson, 4 Marshlands Road, Wallasey Village, Merseyside L45 8JE. Tel: 051 638 4097.
Press Officer: Willy Gardner, 52 Greenwood Lane, Wallasey, Merseyside. Tel: (H) 051 637 1856 (W) 051 666 2222.
Club Colours: Navy with gold hoops.

ST EDWARDS OLD BOYS RUFC
Ground Address: St Edwards College, Sandfield Park, West Derby, Liverpool, Merseyside. Tel: 051 228 1414.
Club Secretary: David Pheonix, 11 Linden Drive, Huyton, Merseyside L36 5TT. Tel: 051 489 1221.
Press Officer: Mark Seddon, 50 Acacia Avenue, Huyton, Merseyside L36 5 TP. Tel: 051 489 7932.
Club Colours: Royal blue; broad horizontal blue band.

SANDBACH RUFC
Ground Address: Bradwall Road, Sandbach, CW11 9AP. Tel: 0270 762457.
Club Secretary: John Gater, 7 Colley Lane, Sandbach, Cheshire CW11 0HE. Tel: (H) 0270 764035 (W) 0260 283815.
Press Officer: George Salthouse, Tyhalen, 20 Barrow Way, Oakley Grange, Sandbach, Cheshire CW11 9PB. Tel: (H) 0270 766260 (W) 021 233 4976.
Club Colours: Green with red band.

SEDGLEY PARK RUFC
Ground Address: The Clubhouse, Park Lane, Whitefield, Manchester. Tel: 061 766 5050.
Club Secretary: Mark G Mold, 32 Vicarage Avenue, Cheadle Hume, Cheshire SK8 7JW. Tel: (H) 061 486 0496 (W) 061 794 4755.
Club Colours: Claret & old gold hoops, white shorts, maroon socks.

NORTHERN DIVISION

NORTH WEST TWO
1993-94
FIXTURES

October 23 (Week 8)
Wirral v Netherhall
Old Salians v Wilmslow
Old Aldwinians v Penrith
Warrington v Ruskin Park
Vagabonds v Rochdale
Rossendale v Ormskirk

October 30 (Week X2)
Ormskirk v Wirral
Rochdale v Rossendale
Ruskin Park v Vagabonds
Penrith v Warrington
Wilmslow v Old Aldwinians
Egremont v Old Salians

November 13 (Week 10)
Wirral v Rochdale
Netherhall v Ormskirk
Old Aldwinians v Egremont
Warrington v Wilmslow
Vagabonds v Penrith
Rossendale v Ruskin Park

November 20 (Week 11)
Rochdale v Netherhall
Ruskin Park v Wirral
Penrith v Rossendale
Wilmslow v Vagabonds
Egremont v Warrington
Old Salians v Old Aldwinians

December 4 (Week 13)
Wirral v Penrith
Netherhall v Ruskin Park
Ormskirk v Rochdale
Warrington v Old Salians
Vagabonds v Egremont
Rossendale v Wilmslow

December 11 (Week 14)
Ruskin Park v Ormskirk
Penrith v Netherhall
Wilmslow v Wirral
Egremont v Rossendale
Old Salians v Vagabonds
Old Aldwinians v Warrington

December 18 (Week 15)
Wirral v Egremont
Netherhall v Wilmslow
Ormskirk v Penrith
Rochdale v Ruskin Park
Vagabonds v Old Aldwinians
Rossendale v Old Salians

January 8 (Week 18)
Penrith v Rochdale
Wilmslow v Ormskirk
Egremont v Netherhall
Old Salians v Wirral
Old Aldwinians v Rossendale
Warrington v Vagabonds

January 29 (Week X5)
Wirral v Old Aldwinians
Netherhall v Old Salians
Ormskirk v Egremont
Rochdale v Wilmslow
Ruskin Park v Penrith
Rossendale v Warrington

February 12 (Week 22)
Wilmslow v Ruskin Park
Egremont v Rochdale
Old Salians v Ormskirk
Old Aldwinians v Netherhall
Warrington v Wirral
Vagabonds v Rossendale

March 12 (Week 26)
Wirral v Vagabonds
Netherhall v Warrington
Ormskirk v Old Aldwinians
Rochdale v Old Salians
Ruskin Park v Egremont
Penrith v Wilmslow

March 26 (Week 28)
Egremont v Penrith
Old Salians v Ruskin Park
Old Aldwinians v Rochdale
Warrington v Ormskirk
Vagabonds v Netherhall
Rossendale v Wirral

April 9 (Week 30)
Netherhall v Rossendale
Ormskirk v Vagabonds
Rochdale v Warrington
Ruskin Park v Old Aldwinians
Penrith v Old Salians
Wilmslow v Egremont

NORTH WEST TWO

EGREMONT RUFC
Ground Address: Bleach Green, Egremont, Cumbria. Tel: 0946 820645.
Club Secretary: W H F Moran, 58 Dent View, Egremont, Cumbria, CA22 2ET. Tel: (H) 0946 822119 (W) 09467 72443.
Press Officer: W H F Moran, 58 Dent View, Egremont, Cumbria, CA22 2ET. Tel: (H) 0946 822119 (W) 09467 72443.
Club Colours: Black & yellow.

NETHERHALL RUFC
Ground Address: Netherhall Park, Netherhall Road, Maryport, West Cumbria. Tel: 0900 815833.
Club Secretary: Paul Bartlett, 66 Garborough Close, Crosby, Near Maryport, West Cumbria. Tel: (H) 0900 818420.
Press Officer: B Davidson, 12 Sycamore Road, Netherton, Maryport, Cumbria. Tel: (H) 0900 814961.
Club Colours: Claret & gold.

OLD ALDWINIANS RUFC
Ground Address: Audenshaw Park, Droylsden Road, Audenshaw, Manchester. Tel: 061 301 1001.
Club Secretary: Graham Hatton J.P., Oak Drive SPO, 655 Manchester Road, Denton, Manchester, M34 2NA. Tel: (H) 061 336 2528 (W) 061 336 2528.
Press Officer: Stan Wood, Oak Drive SPO, 655 Manchester Road, Denton, Manchester, M34 2NA. Tel: (W) 061 339 9669.
Club Colours: Red & white hoops, navy blue shorts.

OLD SALIANS RUFC
Ground Address: Rookwood, Clarendon Crescent, Sale, Cheshire, M33. Tel: 061 973 7250.
Club Secretary: K F Sheldon, 4 Oban Drive, Sale Moor, Sale, Cheshire, M33 2SY. Tel: (H) 061 962 2878 (W) 061 839 5050.
Club Colours: Navy blue with white band, blue shorts.

ORMSKIRK RUFC
Ground Address: Green Lane, Ormskirk. Tel: 0695 572523.
Club Secretary/Press Officer: Les Bumford, 55 Wicks Lane, Formby, Merseyside, L37 2YD. Tel: (H) 07048 78702 (W) 051 934 4428.
Club Colours: Dark blue, light blue & green hoops.

PENRITH RUFC
Ground Address: Vintors Park, Penrith, Cumbria, CA11 8RG. Tel: 0768 6315Ɫ.
Club Secretary: T R Coulden, 8 Oearson Court, Penrith, Cumbria, CA11 8QA. Tel: (H) 0768 62815 (W) 0768 66786.
Press Officer: G Bevan, 9A Bridge House, Mainway, Lancaster, LA1 2AZ. Tel: (H) 0524 35339.
Club Colours: Myrtle green with white hoops.

ROCHDALE RUFC
Ground Address: Moorgate Avenue, Bamford, Rochdale, OL11 5LU. Tel: 0706 46863.
Club Secretary: Tim M S Taylor, 61 Augusta Close, Rochdale, OL12 6HT. Tel: (H) 0706 345971 (W) 061 872 2411.
Press Officer: D Leslie Clarke, 25 Berkley Drive, Rochdale, OL16 7HL. Tel: (H) 0706 50685.
Club Colours: Maroon & white hoops.

ROSSENDALE RUFC
Ground Address: Sports Centre, Newchurch Road, Rawtenstall, Rossendale, BB4 7SW. Tel: 0706 229152.
Club Secretary: P Brotherton, 47 Poulton Avenue, Accrington, Lancs, BB5 5EP. Tel: (H) 0254 234310 (W) 0282 772511.
Club Colours: Maroon.

FINAL TABLE

	P	W	D	L	F	A	PD	Pts
Oldershaw	12	10	0	2	244	105	139	20
Kirkby Lonsdale	12	9	0	3	196	162	34	18
Old Salians	11	8	0	3	169	81	88	16
Old Aldwinians	12	7	1	4	174	105	69	15
Netherhall	12	7	0	5	160	136	24	14
Ormskirk	11	6	1	4	236	144	92	13
Wilmslow	11	6	0	5	135	149	-14	12
Vagabonds	9	5	0	4	119	95	24	10
Warrington	12	5	0	7	117	203	-86	10
Rochdale	12	4	0	8	81	177	-96	8
Rossendale	12	4	0	8	102	162	-60	4
Workington	12	2	0	10	102	216	-114	4
South Liverpool	12	1	0	11	101	241	-140	0

RUSKIN PARK RFC
Ground Address: Ruskin Drive, St Helens, Merseyside, WA10 6RD. Tel: 0744 22893.
Club Secretary: S Smith, 23 Stuart Road, Windle, St Helens, Merseyside, WA10 6HU. Tel: (H) 0744 27394 (W) 0744 696804.
Press Officer: W Griffiths, 32 Markfield Crescent, Islands Brow, St Helens, Merseyside. Tel: (H) 0744 56091.
Club Colours: Royal blue, black & white.

VAGABONDS (IOM) RUFC
Ground Address: Glencrutchery Road, Douglas, Isle of Man. Tel: 0624 661996.
Club Secretary: Ian Forrest, Arkadia, Alexander Drive, Douglas, Isle of Mane. Tel: (H) 0624 676106 (W) 0624 623991.
Press Officer: Mike Hewison, 46 Meadow Crescent, Ashbourne Parke, Braddan, Isle of Man. Tel: (H) 0624 670602 (W) 0624 673241.
Club Colours: White with irregular yellow & black bands, black shorts.

WARRINGTON RUFC
Ground Address: Bridge Lane, Addleton, Warrington. Tel: 0925 264591.
Club Secretary: G P Robinson, 8 Bellhouse Lane, Grappenhall, Warrington, WA4 2SD. Tel: (H) 0925 261644.
Press Officer: Neil Pearson, 103 Marina Avenue, Great Sankey, Warrington. Tel: (H) 0925 417243.
Club Colours: Red, white & green.

WILMSLOW RUFC
Ground Address: Memorial Ground, Pownall Park, Kings Road, Wilmslow. Tel: 0625 522274.
Club Secretary: W J M Williams, 19 The Circuit, Wilmslow, SK9 6DA. Tel: (H) 0625 530909.
Press Officer: P Ord, 52 Badger Road, Macclesfield, SK10 2EP. Tel: (H) 0625 429230.
Club Colours: Sky blue, maroon & white hoops.

WIRRAL RFC
Ground Address: Memorial Ground, Thornton Common Road, Clatterbridge, Wirral, Merseyside. Tel: 051 334 1309.
Club Secretary: Peter Darch, 19 Tanar Close, Spital, Bebington, Wirral, Merseyside, L63 9AN. Tel: (H) 051 346 1299 (W) 051 639 8181.
Press Officer: Barry Evans, 19 Osmaston road, Prenton, Wirral, Birkenhead, L42 8PY. Tel: (H) 051 609 0051 (W) 051 709 1543.
Club Colours: Maroon & white.

NORTHERN DIVISION

CUMBRIA & LANCASHIRE NORTH 1993-94 FIXTURES

October 23 (Week 8)
Oldham v Vickers
Moresby v Fleetwood
Upper Eden v Tyldsley
Calder Vale v Windermere
Metrovick v Smith Bros
St Benedicts v Workington

October 30 (Week X2)
Workington v Oldham
Smith Bros v St Benedicts
Windermere v Metrovick
Tyldsley v Calder Vale
Fleetwood v Upper Eden
Furness v Moresby

November 13 (Week 10)
Oldham v Smith Bros
Vickers v Workington
Upper Eden v Furness
Calder Vale v Fleetwood
Metrovick v Tyldsley
St Benedicts v Windermere

November 20 (Week 11)
Smith Bros v Vickers
Windermere v Oldham
Tyldsley v St Benedicts
Fleetwood v Metrovick
Furness v Calder Vale
Moresby v Upper Eden

December 4 (Week 13)
Oldham v Tyldsley
Vickers v Windermere
Workington v Smith Bros
Calder Vale v Moresby
Metrovick v Furness
St Benedicts v Fleetwood

December 11 (Week 14)
Windermere v Workington
Tyldsley v Vickers
Fleetwood v Oldham
Furness v St Benedicts
Moresby v Metrovick
Upper Eden v Calder Vale

December 18 (Week 15)
Oldham v Furness
Vickers v Fleetwood
Workington v Tyldsley
Smith Bros v Windermere
Metrovick v Upper Eden
St Benedicts v Moresby

January 8 (Week 18)
Tyldsley v Smith Bros
Fleetwood v Workington
Furness v Vickers
Moresby v Oldham
Upper Eden v St Benedicts
Calder Vale v Metrovick

January 29 (Week X5)
Oldham v Upper Eden
Vickers v Moresby
Workington v Furness
Smith Bros v Fleetwood
Windermere v Tyldsley
St Benedicts v Calder Vale

February 12 (Week 22)
Fleetwood v Windermere
Furness v Smith Bros
Moresby v Workington
Upper Eden v Vickers
Calder Vale v Oldham
Metrovick v St Benedicts

March 12 (Week 26)
Oldham v Metrovick
Vickers v Calder Vale
Workington v Upper Eden
Smith Bros v Moresby
Windermere v Furness
Tyldsley v Fleetwood

March 26 (Week 28)
Furness v Tyldsley
Moresby v Windermere
Upper Eden v Smith Bros
Calder Vale v Workington
Metrovick v Vickers
St Benedicts v Oldham

April 9 (Week 30)
Vickers v St Benedicts
Workington v Metrovick
Smith Bros v Calder Vale
Windermere v Upper Eden
Tyldsley v Moresby
Fleetwood v Furness

CUMBRIA/LANCASHIRE NORTH

CALDER VALE RUFC
Ground Address: Holden Road, Reedley, Burnley, Lancashire. Tel:0282 424337.
Club Secretary: A J Ennis, 28 Applecross Drive, Burnley BB10 4JP. Tel: (H) 0282 459079 (W00204 390712.
Press Officer: J Sinclair, 7 Pitt Street, Padiham. Tel:(H) 0282 779428 (W) 0282 450204.
Club Colours: Old gold, royal blue ringed shirts, blue shorts & stockings.

FLEETWOOD RUFC
Ground Address: Melbourne Avenue, Fleetwood. Tel:0253 874774.
Club Secretary: Trevor Jones, The Cottage, Derby Road, Poulton- le-Fylde. FY7 7AF. Tel: (H) 0253 899352 (W) 0253 772128.
Press Officer: John Muir, 61 Lovons Drive, Poulton-le-Fylde FY6 8EZ. Tel: (H) 0253 884610 (W) 0253 873481.
Club Colours: Green/gold shirts, blue shorts.

FURNESS RUFC
Ground Address: Stawberry Grounds, Abbey Road, Barrow-in-Furness, Cumbria. Tel:0229 825226.
Club Secretary: J H Malkinson, 64 Hawcoat Lane, Barrow-in- Furness, Cumbria LA14 4HQ. Tel: (H) 0229 824938 (W) 0229 63064.
Club Colours: Blue & white.

METROVICK RFC
Ground Address: MacPherson Park, Finny Bank Road, Sale, Manchester M33 1LR. Tel:061 976 7061.
Club Secretary: Peter Coppock, 65 Central Road, West Didsbury, Manchester M20 9YD.Tel: (H) 061 445 2335 (W) 061 834 3224.
Club Colours: Black & white hoops.

MORESBY RUFC
Ground Address: Walk Mill, Moresby Parks, Whitehaven, Cumbria.
Club Secretary: Jeffrey Peet, Middle Croft, Tallentire, Nr Cockermouth, Cumbria. Tel:(W) 09467 73141.
Club Colours: Red shirt, white shorts.

OLDHAM RUFC
Ground Address: Manor Park, Bryth Road, Bardsley, Oldham. Tel: 061 624 6383.
Club Secretary: T J Brown, 12 Tilton Street, Oldham OL1 4JA, Tel: (H) 061 620 1878 (W) 0254 57149.
Press Officer: 19 Thornley Lane, Oldham OL4 5RP. Tel: (H) 061 624 4526 (W) 061 665 2721.
Club Colours: Red & white hoops, blue shirts, red socks.

ST BENEDICTS RUFC
Ground Address: Newlands Avenue, Mirehouse, Whitehaven. Tel: A Relph 0946 62490.
Club Secretary: 264 Meadow Road, Mirehouse, Whitehaven, Cumbria. Tel: 0946 64076.
Club Colours: Amber & black/Emerald green & black.

SMITH BROS RUFC
Ground Address: Seven Fields, Brantley, Whitehaven. Tel:0946 65905.
Club Secretary: G Ryan, 17 Mirehouse Road, Whitehaven, Cumbria CA28 9RW. Tel: (H) 0946 693754 (W) 0946 68176.
Press Officer: George Irvin, 116 Victoria Road, Whitehaven, Cumbria. Tel: 0946 695164.
Club Colours: Blue & white.

FINAL TABLE

	P	W	D	L	F	A	PD	Pts
Penrith	12	9	0	3	226	103	123	18
Windermere	12	8	1	3	287	128	159	17
Calder Vale	12	8	1	3	201	115	86	17
Oldham	12	7	2	3	172	158	14	16
St Benedicts	12	7	0	5	175	137	38	14
Moresby	12	7	0	5	190	156	34	14
Metrovick	12	6	2	4	160	144	16	14
Furness	12	6	1	5	140	134	6	13
Vickers	12	5	1	6	147	214	-67	11
Tyldesley	12	3	1	8	148	169	-21	7
Upper Eden	12	3	0	9	153	223	-70	6
De la Salle (Salf'd)	12	2	0	10	109	260	-151	4
Keswick	12	2	1	9	116	293	-177	3

TYLDESLEY RUFC
Ground Address: Well Street. Tydesley M29 8HW. Tel: 0942 882967.
Club Secretary: Fred Eckersley, 48 Hough Lane, Tydesley M29 8NW. Tel: (H) 0942 876074 (W) 061 794 6215.
Press Officer: Alf Yates, 6 Parkfield Close, Astley M29 7BE. Tel: 0942 874651.
Club Colours: Royal blue shirts, white shorts.

UPPER EDEN RUFC
Ground Address: Pennine Park, Westgarth Road, Kirkby Stephen, Cumbria CA17 4TD. Tel: 07683 71585.
Club Secretary: S H Moffat, 1 The Arcade, Market Street, Kirkby Stephen, Cumbria. Tel: 07683 71794.
Press Officer: R Harper, Hilltop Farm, Crosby Garrett, Kirkby Stephen, Cumbria. Tel: 07683 71452.
Club Colours: Black & white hoops.

VICKERS RUFC
Ground Address: Hawcoat Lane, Barrow-in-Furness, Cumbria. Tel: 0229 825296.
Club Secreatry: A T Mason, 48 Crosland Park, Barrow-in-Furness, Cumbria LA13 9NH. Tel: (H) 0229 821624 (W) 0229 820628.
Club Colours: Maroon & white.

WINDERMERE RUFC
Ground Address: Dawes Meadow, Longlands, Bowness-on-Windermere, Cumbria LA23 3AS. Tel: 05394 43066.
Club Secretary: R Nigel Rimmer, Langrigge Close, Langirgge Drive, Bowness-on-Windermere, Cumbria LA23 3AF. Tel: (H) 05394 45540 (W) 0539 720028.
Club Colours: Amber shirts, black shorts.

WORKINGTON RUFC
Ground Address: Ellis Sports Ground, Mossbay Road, Workington CA14 3XZ. Tel:0900 602625.
Club Secretary: M J Heaslip, 32 Elizabeth Street, Workington CA14 4DB. Tel: (H) 0900 66339 (W) 0900 65656.
Press Officer: John Murray, 35 Clifton Road, Workington. Tel: (H) 0900 62496.
Club Colours: Black & white hoops.

NORTHERN DIVISION

NORTH LANCS ONE
1993-94
FIXTURES

October 23 (Week 8)
Blackpool v Colne & Nelson
Bolton v Old Bedians
Th'Cleveleys v Dukinfield
Broughton v Clitheroe
Eccles v Chorley
Burnage v De La Salle
Ashton-u-Lyme v Bury

October 30 (Week X2)
De La Salle v Blackpool
Chorley v Burnage
Clitheroe v Eccles
Dukinfield v Broughton
Old Bedians v Th'Cleveleys
Bury v Bolton
Ashton-u-Lyme v Colne & Nelson

November 13 (Week 10)
Blackpool v Chorley
Colne & Nelson v De La Salle
Th'Cleveleys v Bury
Broughton v Old Bedians
Eccles v Dukinfield
Burnage v Clitheroe
Bolton v Ashton-u-Lyme

November 20 (Week 11)
Chorley v Colne & Nelson
Clitheroe v Blackpool
Dukinfield v Burnage
Old Bedians v Eccles
Bury v Broughton
Bolton v Th'Cleveleys
De La Salle v Ashton-u-Lyme

December 4 (Week 13)
Blackpool v Dukinfield
Colne & Nelson v Clitheroe
De La Salle v Chorley
Broughton v Bolton
Eccles v Bury
Burnage v Old Bedians
Ashton-u-Lyme v Th'Cleveleys

December 11 (Week 14)
Clitheroe v De La Salle
Dukinfield v Colne & Nelson
Old Bedians v Blackpool
Bury v Burnage
Bolton v Eccles
Th'Cleveleys v Broughton
Ashton-u-Lyme v Chorley

December 18 (Week 15)
Blackpool v Bury
Colne & Nelson v Old Bedians
De La Salle v Dukinfield
Chorley v Clitheroe
Eccles v Th'Cleveleys
Burnage v Bolton
Broughton v Ashton-u-Lyme

January 8 (Week 18)
Dukinfield v chorley
Old Bedians v De La Salle
Bury v Colne & Nelson
Bolton v Blackpool
Th'Cleveleys v Burnage
Broughton v Eccles
Clitheroe v Ashton-u-Lyme

January 29 (Week X5)
Blackpool v Th'Cleveleys
Colne & Nelson v Bolton
De La Salle v Bury
Chorley v Old Bedians
Clitheroe v Dukinfield
Burnage v Broughton
Ashton-u-Lyme v Eccles

February 12 (Week 22)
Old Bedians v Clitheroe
Bury v Chorley
Bolton v De La Salle
Th'Cleveleys v Colne & Nelson
Broughton v Blackpool
Eccles v Burnage
Ashton-u-Lyme v Dukinfield

March 12 (Week 26)
Blackpool v Eccles
Colne & Nelson v Broughton
De La Salle v Th'Cleveleys
Chorley v Bolton
Clitheroe v Bury
Dukinfield v Old Bedians
Burnage v Ashton-u-Lyme

March 26 (Week 28)
Bury v Dukinfield
Bolton v Clitheroe
Th'Cleveleys v Chorley
Broughton v De La Salle
Eccles v Colne & Nelson
Burnage v Blackpool
Old Bedians v Ashton-u-Lyme

April 9 (Week 30)
Colne & Nelson v Burnage
De La Salle v Eccles
Chorley v Broughton
Clitheroe v Th'Cleveleys
Dukinfield v Bolton
Old Bedians v Bury
Blackpool v Ashton-u-Lyme

NORTH LANCS ONE

ASHTON-UNDER-LYNE RFC
Ground Address: St Albans Avenue, Ashton-under-Lyne. Tel: 061 330 1361.
Club Secretary: Dennis Gee, 26 Burnedge Lane, Grasscroft, Oldham OL4 4EA. Tel: (H) 0457 872823 (W) 061 303 9482.
Press Officer: David Bruce, 11a Thornlea Avenue, Hollinwood, Oldham. Tel:061 681 3463.
Club Colours: Red, black & amber hoops, black shorts.

BLACKPOOL RUFC
Ground Address: Fleetwood Road, Norbreck, Blackpool, Lancashire. Tel: 0253 853308.
Club Secretary: Cliff Wainscott, 15 Stafford Avenue, Poulton-le- Fylde, Lancashire FY6 8BJ. Tel: 0253 885151.
Press Officer: Howell Williams, "Nelson Hotel", 38 Palatine Road, Blackpool, Lancashire. Tel: (H) 0253 20629.
Club Colours: Red & blue hoops, black shorts.

BOLTON RUFC
Ground Address: Northfield Pavilion, Avenue Street, Bolton BL1 3AW. Tel: 0942 363710.
Club Secretary: R D Pemberton, Grasmere House, 23 Wilkinson Street, Leigh, Lancashire WN7 4DQ. Tel: 0942 678257.
Club Colours: Red & white hoops.

BROUGHTON RUFC
Ground Address: Yew Street, Broughton, Salford M7 9HL. Tel: 061 792 2920.
Club Secretary: John Wileman, as above. Tel: (H) 061 792 9441 (W) 061 238 2567.
Press Officer: Alan Smith, as above. Tel: (H) 061 792 2920. And J Wileman.
Club Colours: Blue, amber and maroon.

BURNAGE FC
Ground Address: Varley Park, Battersea Road, Heaston, Mersey, Stockport. Tel: 061 432 2150.
Club Secretary: P Higgins, 434 Didsbury Road, Heaton, Mersey Stockport, Cheshire SK4 3BY. Tel: (H) 061 431 4090 (W) 0565 653015.
Press Officer: Stuart Hogg, 12 Marmington Road, Theadle, Cheshire SK8 1NJ. Tel: (H) 061 428 4507 (W) 061 833 8111.
Club Colours: Black & white.

BURY RUFC
Ground Address: Radcliffe Road, Bury, Lancashire. Tel: 061 764 1528.
Club Secretary: G J Hilton, 66 Twiss Green Lane, Culcheth, Warrington, Cheshire. Tel: (H) 0925 762119 (W) 0925 762975.
Press Officer: L S Smith, 196 Dundee Lane, Ramsbottom, Bury, Lancashire. Tel: 0706 824599.
Club Colours: Red, gold, blue hoops, navy blue shorts.

CHORLEY RUFC
Ground Address: "Brookfields", Chancery Road, Astley Village, Chorley, Lancashire PR7 1XP. Tel: 0257 268806.
Club Secretary: P Godwin, 20 Gaythorne Avenue, Preston, Lancashire PR1 5TA. Tel: (H) 0772 791544 (W) 0257 244335.
Club Colours: Black & white hoops.

CLITHEROE RUFC
Ground Address: Littlemoor Park, Littlemoor Road, Clitheroe. Tel: 0200 22261.
Club Secretary: John Hyde, Moorhey Cottage, Knowle Green, Longridge, Preston PR3 2KE.
Press Officer: Ian Scott Brown, Brunsholme, Pendle View, Grindleton, Clitheroe BB7 4QU. Tel: (H) 0200 440102 (W) 0254 582749.
Club Colours: Maroon & gold hoops.

FINAL TABLE

	P	W	D	L	F	A	PD	Pts
Fleetwood	13	12	0	1	438	108	33	24
Burnage	13	11	0	2	261	111	150	22
Bolton	13	10	0	3	227	183	44	20
Chorley	13	8	0	5	158	161	-3	16
Bury	13	7	1	5	199	170	29	15
Thornton Clevelys	13	8	0	5	215	158	57	14
Blackpool	13	6	0	7	198	199	-1	12
Broughton	13	5	1	7	137	216	-79	11
Colne & Nelson	13	5	1	7	162	252	-90	11
Old Bedians	13	4	1	8	115	199	-84	9
Ashton-under-Lyne	13	5	0	8	92	187	-95	6
Marple	13	3	0	10	116	246	-130	6
Littleborough	13	4	0	9	128	215	-87	4
Heaton Moor	13	0	2	11	91	206	-115	2

COLNE & NELSON RUFC
Ground Address: Holt House, Harrison Drive, Colne, Lancashire. Tel:0282 863339.
Club Secretry: K Thornton, 12 Camden Street, Nelson, Lancashire BB9 0BL. Tel: 0282 613612.
Press Secretary: R Tindall. 80 Ruskin Avenue, Colne, Lancashire. Tel: 0282 869685.
Club Colours: All black.

DE LA SALLE (SALFORD) RUFC
Ground Address: College Playing Fields, Lancaster Road, Salford. Tel: 061 789 2261.
Club Secretary: R Rogerson, 113 Moorfield Road, Salford, M6 7GD. Tel: (H) 061 737 5259 (W) 061 205 2213.
Press Officer: J Collins, 8 Oakwood Drive, Salford M6 7NQ. Tel: (H) 061 736 1317 (W) 061 775 7928.
Club Colours: Claret & gold hoops.

DUKINFIELD RUFC
Ground Address: Blocksages Playing Fields, Birch Lane, Dukinfield, Cheshire. Tel:061 343 2592.
Club Secretary: Ernie Taylor, 52 Gower Road, Hyde, Cheshire SK14 5AD. Tel: (H) 061 366 9541 (W) 0706 47422.
Club Colours: Blue & gold hoops.

ECCLES RFC
Ground Address: Gorton Street, Peel Green, Eccles, Manchester M30 8LX. Tel: 061 789 2613.
Club Secretary: M Dutton, 10 Ashley Drive, Swinton, Manchester M27 3AX. Tel: 061 794 2904.
Press Officer: Vic Thomas, 5 Portree Close, Off Cambell Road, Winton, Eccles, Manchester M30 8LX. Tel: (H) 061 788 7274.
Club Colours: Navy blue & white hoop shirts and stockings; white shorts.

OLD BEDIANS RFC
Ground Address: Underbank Farm, Millgate Lane, Didsbury, Manchester.
Club Secretary: Ms Lynn Connor, 17 Brixton Avenue, Manchester M20 3JF. Tel: 061 434 0519.
Press Officer: Dave Price, as above. Tel (W) 061 832 7211.
Club Colours: Blue shirts & socks; white shorts.

THORNTON CLEVELEYS RUFC
Ground Address: Fleetwood Road North, Thornton Cleveleys, Lancashire. Tel: 0253 854104.
Club Secretary: Michael Boardman, 41 Roylen Avenue, Carleton, Poulton-le-Fylde, Lancashire FY6 7PH. Tel: (H) 0253 890099 (W) 0253 332487.
Club Colours: Red, black & amber hoops; black shorts.

NORTHERN DIVISION

NORTH LANCS TWO
1993-94
FIXTURES

October 23 (Week 8)
Lostock v British Aerospace
Shell Carrington v Marple

October 30 (Week X2)
Littleborough v Lostock

November 13 (Week 10)
Lostock v Heaton Moor
British Aerospace v Littleborough

November 20 (Week 11)
Heaton Moor v British Aerospace
Agecroft v Lostock

December 4 (Week 13)
Lostock v North Manchester
British Aerospace v Agecroft
Littleborough v Heaton Moor

December 11 (Week 14)
Agecroft v Littleborough
North Manchester v British Aerospace
Marple v Lostock

December 18 (Week 15)
British Aerospace v Marple
Littleborough v North Manchester
Heaton Moor v Agecroft

January 8 (Week 18)
North Manchester v Heaton Moor
Marple v Littleborough
Shell Carrington v Lostock

January 29 (Week X5)
British Aerospace v Shell Carrington
Heaton Moor v Marple
Agecroft v North Manchester

February 12 (Week 22)
Marple v Agecroft
Shell Carrington v Littleborough

March 12 (Week 26)
Heaton Moor v Shell Carrington
North Manchester v Marple

March 26 (Week 28)
Shell Carrington v Agecroft

April 9 (Week 30)
North Manchester v Shell Carrington

NORTH LANCS TWO

AGECROFT RUFC
Ground Address: Ordsall Sports Centre, Craven Drive, Salford, Lancashire, M6 6QW. Tel: 061 848 0646.
Club Secretary: M Whitby, 28 Grange Street, Salford, Lancashire, M6 5PR. Tel: (H) 061 743 1060 (W) 061 228 4824.
Press Officer: M Whitby, 28 Grange Street, Salford, Lancashire, M6 5PR. Tel: (H) 061 743 1060 (W) 061 228 4824.
Club Colours: Black & red hoops.

FINAL TABLE

	P	W	D	L	F	A	PD	Pts
Clitheroe	8	7	0	1	197	57	140	14
Dukinfield	8	7	0	1	212	74	138	14
North Manchester	8	4	00	4	86	87	-1	6
Lostock	7	1	0	6	39	185	-146	2
Agecroft	7	0	0	7	40	193	-153	0

BAe WARTON RUFC
Ground Address: BAe Lostock, Lostock Lane, Lostock, Bolton. Tel: 0204 696551/68516.
Club Secretary: Gavin J Rowlandson, 32 Preston Road, Lytham St Annes, Lancs, FY8 5AA. Tel: (H) 0253 738912 (W) 0772 852972.
Press Officer: Jason Mills, 30 Devona Avenue, Marton, Blackpool, Lancs, FY4 4NU. Tel: (H) 0253 692287 (W) 0772 852122.
Club Colours: Blue & white quarters, blue shorts.

HEATON MOOR RUFC
Ground Address: Green Lane, Heaton Moor, Stockport, SK4 2NF. Tel: 061 432 3407.
Club Secretary: P Jackson, 35 Stanley Road, Heaton moor, Stockport, SK4 4HW. Tel: (H) 061 442 9061 (W) 0928 717070 Ext 2224.
Press Officer: M P McDermott, 10 Curtis Road, Heaton Mersey, Stockport, SK4 3JX. Tel: (H) 061 442 0818 (W) 061 499 1322.
Club Colours: Red, black & amber.

LITTLEBOROUGH RUFC
Ground Address: Deep Lane, Rakewood, Littleborough, Lancs. Tel: 0706 370220.
Club Secretary: John Dawson, 11 Coleridge Drive, Smith Bridge, Littleborough, OL15 0RA. Tel: (H) 0706 373707.
Press Officer: John Dawson, 11 Coleridge Drive, Smith Bridge, Littleborough, OL15 0RA. Tel: (H) 0706 373707.
Club Colours: Green, black & amber hoops.

LOSTOCK RFC
Ground Address: Lostock Lane, Lostock, Bolton.
Club Secretary: R Fletcher, 19 Shaftesbury Avenue, Lostock, Bolton. Tel: (H) 0204 698362 (W) 0204 66551 Ext 3677.
Press Officer: R Fletcher, 19 Shaftesbury Avenue, Lostock, Bolton. Tel: (H) 0204 698362 (W) 0204 66551 Ext 3677.
Club Colours: All black.

MARPLE RUFC
Ground Address: Wood lane, Marple, Stockport, Cheshire.
Club Secretary: M J Cleverly, 16 Lyme Grove, Marple, Stockport, Cheshire, SK6 7nW. Tel: (H) 061 449 8393 w(W) 061 419 2520.
Club Colours: Red & black.

NORTH MANCHESTER & OLDHAM COLLEGES RUFC
Ground Address: Victoria Avenue East, Moston, Manchester, M10 9SH. Tel: 061 682 9234.
Club Secretary: B H Stott, 8 Barlea Avenue, New Moston, Manchester, M10 0WL. Tel: (H) 061 682 0541.
Press Officer: A Hudson, 9 Ivy Drive, Alkrington, Middleton, Manchester, M24 1WA.
Club Colours: Green & black hoops or purple.

SHELL CARRINGTON RUFC
Ground Address: Carrington Lane, Carrington, Manchester. Tel: 061 775 5737.
Club Secretary: J B Bush, 249 Woodsend Road, Urmston, Manchester, M31 2QB. Tel: (H) 061 748 9066 (W) 061 776 3103.
Press Officer: J B Bush, 249 Woodsend Road, Urmston, Manchester, M31 2QB. Tel: (H) 061 748 9066 (W) 061 776 3103.
Club Colours: Red & yellow.

NORTHERN DIVISION

CUMBRIA 1993-94 FIXTURES

October 23 (Week 8)
Ambleside v Creigton
British Steel v Whitehaven

October 30 (Week X2)
Keswick v Ambleside
Millom v British Steel

November 13 (Week 10)
Ambleside v Carnforth
Creigton v Keswick

November 20 (Week 11)
Carnforth v Creigton
Greengarth v Ambleside

December 4 (Week 13)
Ambleside v Silloth
Creigton v Greengarth
Keswick v Carnforth

December 11 (Week 14)
Greengarth v Keswick
Silloth v Creigton
Whitehaven v Ambleside

December 18 (Week 15)
Ambleside v Millom
Creigton v Whitehaven
Keswick v Silloth
Carnforth v Greengarth

January 8 (Week 18)
Silloth v Carnforth
Whitehaven v Keswick
Millom v Creigton
British Steel v Ambleside

January 29 (Week X5)
Creigton v British Steel
Keswick v Millom
Carnforth v Whitehaven
Greengarth v Silloth

February 12 (Week 22)
Whitehaven v Greengarth
Millom v Carnforth
British Steel v Whitehaven

March 12 (Week 26)
Carnforth v British Steel
Greengarth v Millom
Silloth v Whitehaven

March 26 (Week 28)
Millom v Silloth
British Steel v Greengarth

April 9 (Week 30)
Silloth v British Steel
Whitehaven v Millom

CUMBRIA

AMBLESIDE RUFC
Ground Address: Galava Park, Borrans Road, Ambleside, Cumbria. Tel: 05395 32536.
Club Secretary: A Stephenson, West Lea, Smithy Brow, Ambleside, Cumbria. Tel: (H) 05394 32173.
Press Officer: A Sallomons, Church Stile, Grasmere, Cumbria. Tel: (H) 05394 453.
Club Colours: Amber & black stripes.

BRITISH STEEL RUFC
Ground Address: Moss Bay Works, Moss Bay, Workington, Cumbria. Tel: 0900 603570.
Club Secretary: B Rumney, 70 Church Road, Harrington, Workington, Cumbria. Tel: (H) 0946 830413.
Press Officer: B Rumney, 70 Church Road, Harrington, Workington, Cumbria. Tel: (H) 0946 830413.
Club Colours: Red, white & blue hoops, black shorts.

CARNFORTH RFC
Ground Address: Carnforth High School, Kellet Road, Carnforth.
Club Secretary: John Marsden, "Whinfell", 9 Edenmount Way, Carnforth, LA5 9XN. Tel: (H) 0524 734832 (W) 0860 848151.
Press Officer: Alan Hardy, 4 Preston Street, Carnforth, LA5 9BY. Tel: (H) 0524 733799 (W) 0524 33066.
Club Colours: Black & green hoops, black shorts, green stockings.

CREIGHTON RUFC
Ground Address: Canns Field, Caxton road, Off Newtown Road, Carlisle. Tel: 0228 21169.
Club Secretary: David Thomlinson, 146 Moorhouse Road, Carlisle, CA2 7QR. Tel: (H) 0228 35111 (W) 0228 24379.
Press Officer: David Thomlinson, 146 Moorhouse Road, Carlisle, CA2 7QR. Tel: (H) 0228 35111 (W) 0228 24379.
Club Colours: Navy Blue, scarlet collars & cuffs, white shorts.

GREEN GARTH RUFC
Ground Address: Greengarth Hall, Holmrook, Cumbria. Tel: 09467 24202.
Club Secretary: Ian Sharp, 1 Pelham Drive, Calderbridge, Seascale, Cumbia. Tel: (H) 0946 841 744 (W) 0946 820 206.
Press Officer: Steven Edgar, 14 The Limes, Orgill, Egremont. Tel: (H) 0946 821 479.
Club Colours: Maroon & gold.

KESWICK RUFC
Ground Address: Davidson Park, Keswick, Cumbria. Tel: 07682 72823.
Club Secretary: M E Bowman, 3 Briar Rigg, Keswick. Tel: (H) 02682 74878.
Club Colours: Navy bue, green & yellow hoops, white shorts.

MILLOM RUFC
Ground Address: Wilson Park, The Dunes, Haverigg, Millom, Cumbria. Tel: 0229 770401.
Club Secretary: P Hartley, 50 Palmers Lane, Millom, Cumbria, LA18 5EE. Tel: (H) 0229 774407 (W) 0229 772300.
Press Officer: P Hartley, 50 Palmers Lane, Millom, Cumbria, LA18 5EE. Tel: (H) 0229 774407 (W) 0229 772300.
Club Colours: White & blue.

FINAL TABLE

	P	W	D	L	F	A	PD	Pts
Smith Bros	8	8	0	0	153	76	77	14
British Steel	8	7	0	1	131	41	90	12
Creighton	8	5	0	3	110	79	31	10
Carnforth	8	3	1	4	97	137	-40	7
Millom	8	4	0	4	86	101	-15	6
Whitehaven	8	3	0	5	73	121	-48	6
Ambleside	8	2	0	6	101	158	-57	4
Green Garth	8	1	1	6	56	130	-74	3
Silloth	8	2	0	6	33	88	-55	0

SILLOTH RUFC
Ground Address: Old Marshalling Yard, Eden Street, Silloth, Carlisle, Cumbria. Tel: 0697 331492.
Club Secretary: R Edwards, Mayfair, Beckfoot, Silloth, Cumbria. Tel: (H) 06973 31382.
Press Officer: D Wood, Esk St, Silloth Cumbria. Tel: (H) 06973 21318.
Club Colours: Green & black hoops.

WHITENHAVEN RUFC
Ground Address: The Playground, Richmond Terrace, Whitehaven, Cumbria. Tel: 0946 695253.
Club Secretary: Ernest McConnell, 38 Loop Road South, Whitehaven, Cumbria. Tel: (H) 0946 692225.
Press Officer: Ernest McConnell, 38 Loop Road South, Whitehaven, Cumbria. Tel: (H) 0946 692225.
Club Colours: Maroon & white hoops, white shorts.

NORTHERN DIVISION

CHESHIRE & LANCASHIRE SOUTH 1993-94 FIXTURES

October 23 (Week 8)
Liverpool College v Southport
St Marys O.B. v Sefton
Aspull v Leigh
Eagle v Old Anselmians
Crewe & Nantwich v Newton-le-Willows
Kersal v Old Parkonians

October 30 (Week X2)
Old Parkonians v Liverpool College
Newton-le-Willows v Kersal
Old Anselmians v Crewe & Nantwich
Leigh v Eagle
Sefton v Aspull
South Liverpool v St Marys O.B.

November 13 (Week 10)
Liverpool College v Newton-le-Willows
Southport v Old Parkonians
Aspull v South Liverpool
Eagle v Sefton
Crewe & Nantwich v Leigh
Kersal v Old Anselmians

November 20 (Week 11)
Newton-le-Willows v Southport
Old Anselmians v Liverpool College
Leigh v Kersal
Sefton v Crewe & Nantwich
South Liverpool v Eagle
St Marys O.B. v Aspull

December 4 (Week 13)
Liverpool College v Leigh
Southport v Old Anselmians
Old Parkonians v Newton-le-Willows
Eagle v St Marys O.B.
Crewe & Nantwich v South Liverpool
Kersal v Sefton

December 11 (Week 14)
Old Anselmians v Old Parkonians
Leigh v Southport
Sefton v Liverpool College
South Liverpool v Kersal
St Marys O.B. v Crewe & Nantwich
Aspull v Eagle

December 18 (Week 15)
Liverpool College v South Liverpool
Southport v Sefton
Old Parkonians v Leigh
Newton-le-Willows v Old Anselmians
Crewe & Nantwich v Aspull
Kersal v St Marys O.B.

January 8 (Week 18)
Leigh v Newton-le-Willows
Sefton v Old Parkonians
South Liverpool v Southport
St Marys O.B. v Liverpool College
Aspull v Kersal
Eagle v Crewe & Nantwich

January 29 (Week X5)
Liverpool College v Aspull
Southport v St Marys O.B.
Old Parkonians v South Liverpool
Newton-le-Willows v Sefton
Old Anselmians v Leigh
Kersal v St Marys O.B.

February 12 (Week 22)
Sefton v Old Anselmians
South Liverpool v Newton-le-Willows
St Marys O.B. v Old Parkonians
Aspull v Southport
Eagle v Liverpool College
Crewe & Nantwich v Kersal

March 12 (Week 26)
Liverpool College v Crewe & Nantwich
Southport v Eagle
Old Parkonians v Aspull
Newton-le-Willows v St Marys O.B.
Old Anselmians v South Liverpool
Leigh v Sefton

March 26 (Week 28)
South Liverpool v Leigh
St Marys O.B. v Old Anselmians
Aspull v Newton-le-Willows
Eagle v Old Parkonians
Crewe & Nantwich v Southport
Kersal v Liverpool College

April 9 (Week 30)
Southport v Kersal
Old Parkonians v Leigh
Newton-le-Willows v Eagle
Old Anselmians v Aspull
Leigh v St Marys O.B.
Sefton v South Liverpool

CHESHIRE & LANCASHIRE SOUTH

ALTRINCHAM (KERSAL) RFC
Ground Address: Kersal Drive, Seelfox Avenue, Timperley, Altringham, Cheshire. Tel: 061 973 9517.
Club Secretary: Dominic Leach, 19 Dawson Road, Altringham WA14 5JP. Tel (H) 061 941 3085 (W) 061 925 1851.
Club Colours: Red, white & black hoops.

ASPULL RFC
Ground Address: Woodshaw Park, Woods Road, Aspull, Wigan, Lancashire. Tel: 0942 831611.
ClubSecretary: Geoff Gregson, 26 Lyndon Avenue, Shevington, Wigan, Lancashire WN6 8BT. Tel: (H) 0257 421421 (W) 0942 492221.
Press Officer: Gary Owen, 476 Bolton Road, Aspull, Wigan. Tel: (H) 0942 833724 (W) 0204 696146.
Club Colours: Sky & navy blue hoops.

CREWE & NANTWICH RUFC
Ground Address: Whitehouse Lane, Nantwich, Cheshire CW5 6HH. Tel: 0270 626155.
Club Secretary: A G Jones, 9 Gingerbread Lane, Nantwich, Cheshire CW5 6NH. Tel: (H) 0270 625737 (W) 0270 213261.
Club Colours: White with black circlet.

EAGLE RUFC
Ground Address: Thornton Road, Crest Sankey, Warrington, Cheshire. Tel: 0925 32926.
Club Secretary: V Sandwell, 23 Waterworks Lane, Winnwick, Warrington WA2 8LH. Tel: (H) 0925 50367 (W) 0925 830007.
Club Colours: Black & white hoops.

LEIGH RUFC
Ground Address: Round Ash Park, Hand Lane, Leigh, Lancashire WN7 3NA. Tel: 0942 673526.
Club Secretary: Dave Eccles, 51 Turton Close, Locking Stumps, Chashire WA3 7LU. Tel: (H) 0925 825078 (W) 0925 822632.
Press Officer: Alban Westwell, 140 Chestnut Drive, South Leigh, Lancashire WN7 3JY. Tel: (H) 0942 671017
Club Colours: Black with amber hoop.

LIVERPOOL COLLEGIATE OLD BOYS RUFC
Ground Address: Millbank. Tel: 051 228 7132.
Club Secretary: Robert Smith, 4 Staveley Road, Garston, Liverpool L19 9AS. Tel: 051 427 6534 (W) 051 229 4556.
Press Officer: Peter Barnes, Beech Cottage, 98 Mill Lane, West Derby, Liverpool L12 7JD. Tel: 051 270 2146.
Club Colours: Light & dark blue hoops.

NEWTON-LE-WILLOWS RUFC
Ground Address: Crow Ln East, Newton-le-Willows, Merseyside. Tel: 0925 224591.
Club Secretary: Paul Baynes, 19 Bikley Street, Newton-le-Willows. Tel: (H) 0925 228851 (W) 061 832 7046.
Club Colours: Amber & royal blue.

OLD ANSELMIANS RUFC
Ground Address: Malone Field, Eastham Village Road, Eastham, South Wirral. Tel: 051 327 1613.
Club Secretary: Tony Neville, 33 Stapleton Avenue, Greasby, Wirral L49 2QT. Tel: (H) 051 678 4154 (W) 051 350 1696.
Press Officer: Steve Varey, 14 Seaview Avenue, Liscard, Wallabey, Wirral L45 4RA. Tel: (H) 051 637 0659 (W) 051 639 7531.
Club Colours: Navy, gold & white irregular hoops.

FINAL TABLE

	P	W	D	L	F	A	PD	Pts
Ruskin Park	11	10	1	0	233	85	148	21
Kersal	9	8	0	1	158	69	89	16
Old Parkonians	10	7	0	3	173	93	80	14
Aspull	10	6	1	3	181	129	52	13
Crewe & Nantwich	10	6	0	4	149	102	47	12
Leigh	10	5	0	5	159	121	38	10
Liverpool Collegiate	11	4	0	7	153	159	-6	8
Newton-le-Willows	9	3	0	6	73	166	-93	6
St Marys OB	10	2	1	7	78	144	-66	5
Eagle	10	1	1	8	74	148	-74	3
Southport	9	2	0	7	90	213	-123	2
Douglas (IOM)	7	1	0	6	70	216	-146	2

PARKONIANS RUFC
Ground Address: H M Curphey Memorial Ground, Holm Lane, Oxton, Birkenhead, Nerseyside L43 2HD. Tel: 051 652 3105.
Club Secretary: P L Mullen, 8 Deerwood Crescent, Little Sutton, South Wirral L66 1SE. Tel: (051) 051 339 1270 (W) 051 448 6280.
Press Officer: M J Evans, 109 Temple Road, Prenton, Birkenhead. Tel: 051 608 4708.
Club Colours: Maroon, blue & white shirts & socks; white shorts.

ST MARY'S OLD BOYS RUFC
Ground Address: St Mary's Old Boys Playing Fields, Gorsey Lane, Hightown, Merseyside. Tel: 051 924 1774.
Club Secretary: Mark Cunningham, 48 Cambridge Avenue, Crosby, Liverpool L23 7XW. Tel: 051 924 5201.
Press Officer: Desmond Lennon, 20 Queensway, Waterloo, Liverpool. Tel: 051 920 7660.
Club Colours: Maroon, blue & yellow hoops.

SEFTON RUFC
Ground Address: The Clubhouse, Thornhead Lane, off Leyfield Road, West Derby, Liverpool L12. Tel: 051 228 9092.
Club Secretary: Graham Price, 5 Avolon Road, West Derby, Liverpool L12 9ER. Tel: (H) 051 220 1043 (W) 051 922 3077.
Press Officer: R Langshaw, 3 Chatterton Road, Liverpool L14 1PA. Tel: 051 259 1847.
Club Colours: Red & white hoop shirt & socks; blue shorts.

SOUTH LIVERPOOL RUFC
Ground Address: Bridgefield, Forum Sports Centre, Halewood, Knowsleg. Tel: 051 443 2124.
Club Secretary: L Sherrington, 14 Brook Way, Great Sankey, Warrington, Cheshire. Tel: 0925 726768.
Press Officer: Dave Edge, 93 Millwood Road, Speke, Liverpool L24 2HR. Tel: 051 425 4018 (W) 051 486 2930.
Club Colours: Amber & black quarters.

SOUTHPORT RUFC
Ground Address: Waterloo Road, Hillside,Southport, Merseyside PR8 4QW. Tel: 0704 569906.
Club Secretary: A R Coakley, 26 Brocklebank Road, Hesketh Park, Southport PR9 9LP. Tel: 0704 538341.
Press Officer: G Jackson, 43 Kenilworth Road, Southport. Tel: 0704 578362.
Club Colours: Red, black & amber.

NORTHERN DIVISION

CHESHIRE
1993-94
FIXTURES

October 23 (Week 8)
Hoylake v Shell Stanlow
Wallasey v Port Sunlight
Congleton v Moore
Helsby v Prenton

October 30 (Week X2)
Moore v Helsby
Port Sunlight v Congleton
Bowden v Wallasey

November 13 (Week 10)
Shell Stanlow v Prenton
Wallasey v Holmes Chapel
Congleton v Bowden
Helsby v Port Sunlight

November 20 (Week 11)
Prenton v Hoylake
Moore v Shell Stanlow
Bowden v Helsby
Holmes Chapel v Congleton

December 4 (Week 13)
Shell Stanlow v Port Sunlight
Hoylake v Moore
Helsby v Holmes Chapel

December 11 (Week 14)
Port Sunlight v Hoylake
Bowden v Shell Stanlow
Wallasey v Congleton

December 18 (Week 15)
Shell Stanlow v Holmes Chapel
Hoylake v Bowden
Prenton v Moore
Helsby v Wallasey

January 8 (Week 18)
Port Sunlight v Prenton
Holmes Chapel v Hoylake
Congleton v Helsby

January 29 (Week X5)
Shell Stanlow v Wallasey
Prenton v Bowden
Moore v Port Sunlight

February 12 (Week 22)
Bowden v Moore
Holmes Chapel v Prenton
Wallasey v Hoylake
Congleton v Shell Stanlow

March 12 (Week 26)
Shell Stanlow v Helsby
Hoylake v Congleton
Moore v Holmes Chapel
Port Sunlight v Bowden

March 26 (Week 28)
Holmes Chapel v Port Sunlight
Wallasey v Prenton
Helsby v Hoylake

April 9 (Week 30)
Prenton v Congleton
Moore v Wallasey
Bowden v Holmes Chapel

CHESHIRE

BOWDON RUFC
Ground Address: Clay Lane, Timperley, Altrincham, Cheshire. Tel: 061 980 8321.
Club Secretary: J Piatkiewicz, 14 Queens Road, Hale, Altrincham, Cheshire WA15 9HF. Tel: (H) 061 941 5503 (W) 0925 51277 x3497.
Club Colours: Claret, white, black.

CONGLETON RUFC
Ground Address: Hankinson's Field. Clubhouse: Park Street, Congleton. Tel: 0260 273338.
Club Secretary: Dennis Thorley, 46 Bladon Crescent, Alsager ST7 2BG. Tel: (H) 0270 878293.
Club Colours: Red, white, red, black hoops.

HELSBY RUFC
Ground Address: Helsby Sports & Social Club, Chester Road, Helsby. Tel: 0928 722267.
Club Secretary: Eric Lamb, 5 Firbank Road, Elton, Nr Chester CH2 4LY. Tel: (H) 0928 724039.
Club Colours: Black & amber hoops.

HOLMES CHAPEL RUFC
Ground Address: c/o Holmes Chapel Leisure Centre, Holmes chapel, Cheshire. Tel: 0477 534401.
Club Secretary: Mark Finch, 54 Primrose Chase, Goostrey, Cheshire CW4 8LJ. Tel: (H) 0477 535368.
Club Colours: Shirts: Blue & gold hoops. Shorts: Black. Socks: Royal blue.

HOYLAKE RFC
Ground Address: Melrose Avenue, Hoylake, Wirral L47 3BU. Tel: 051 632 2538.
Club Secretary: Susan Kirton, 7 Meadowcroft Road, Meals, Wirral L47 6BG. Tel: (H) 051 632 5540 (W) 051 632 7456.
Club Colours: Green, red, white hoops.

MOORE RUFC
Ground Address: Moss Lane, Moore, Nr Warrington, Cheshire WA4 6UP. Tel: 0925 740473.
Club Secretary: Mr David Dean, 39 Pheasant Walk, High Legh, Knutsford, Cheshire WA16 6QA. Tel: (H) 0925 755498 (W) 061 927 7070.
Press Officer: Mr James Stockton, 10 Weybridge Close, Dudlows Green, Appleton, Warrington, Cheshire WA4 5LZ. Tel: (H) 0925 861058.
Club Colours: Black & gold hoops.

PORT SUNLIGHT RUFC
Ground Address: Green Lane, "The Clubhouse" Leverhulme Playing Fields, Port Sunlight, Wirral. Tel: 051 334 1063.
Club Secretary: Paul Cromby, 17 Donne Avenue, Bebington Spital. Tel: (H) 051 334 1063 (W) 051 207 4949.
Press Officer: Steve Cooke, 51 Chatham Road, Rock Ferry. Tel: (H) 051 644 8007 (W) 051 350 2878.
Club Colours: Black & white hoops.

PRENTON RUFC
Ground Address: The Club House, Prenton Dell Road, Prenton, Wirral L43 3BS. Tel: 051 608 1501.
Club Secretary: Paul Foster, 8 Rake Close, Upton, Wirral L49 0XD. Tel: (H) 051 678 6634 (W) 051 708 7100.
Club Colours: Gold & maroon.

FINAL TABLE

	P	W	D	L	F	A	PD	Pts
Old Anselmians	10	8	0	2	348	98	250	16
Wallasey	10	7	0	3	201	90	111	14
Congleton	10	7	0	3	193	147	46	14
Bowdon	10	7	0	3	154	146	8	14
Port Sunlight	10	6	0	4	222	107	115	12
Prenton	10	5	0	5	114	90	24	8
Hoylake	10	5	0	5	132	142	-10	8
Shell Stanlow	10	3	0	7	89	210	-121	4
Holmes Chapel	10	3	0	7	86	234	-148	4
Moore	10	2	0	8	61	217	-156	2
Helsby	10	2	0	8	84	260	-176	0

SHELL (STANLOW) RFC
Ground Address: The Shell Club, Chester Road, Whitby, Ellesmere Port. Tel: 051 355 2364.
Club Secretary: Mr A R J Dale, 12 Archers Way, Great Sutton, South Wirral, Cheshire L66 2RY. Tel: (H) 051 339 7823 (W) 051 355 2157 x231.
Club Colours: Amber shirts, white shorts, red socks.

WALLASEY
Ground Address: Cross Lane, Leasowe Road, Wallasey, Wirral. Tel: 051 638 1486.
Club Secretary: Mr J A Burton, 14 Seaview Lane, Irby, Wirral, Merseyside L61 3UL. Tel: (H) 051 648 4341 (W) 061 236 3707
Press Officer: Mr R Walker, 15 Ruthin Court, Ellesmere Port, S Wirral, Cheshire. Tel: (H) 051 355 3967.
Club Colours: Red/black/white hoops.

NORTHERN DIVISION

LANCASHIRE SOUTH
1993-94
FIXTURES

October 23 (Week 8)
Halton v Birchfield
Didsbury Toc H v Mossley Hill

October 30 (Week X2)
Manchester YMCA v Didsbury Toc H
Birchfield v Lucas

November 13 (Week 10)
Hightown v Mossley Hill
Lucas v Douglas
Vulcan v Birchfield

November 20 (Week 11)
Manchester YMCA v Hightown
Douglas v Vulcan
Halton v Lucas

December 4 (Week 13)
Mossley Hill v Manchester YMCA
Vulcan v Halton
Didsbury Toc H v Birchfield

December 11 (Week 14)
Douglas v Didsbury Toc H
Lucas v Vulcan

December 18 (Week 15)
Hightown v Birchfield
Didsbury Toc H v Halton

January 8 (Week 18)
Birchfield v Mossley Hill
Douglas v Hightown
Lucas v Didsbury Toc H

January 29 (Week X5)
Hightown v Halton
Mossley Hill v Douglas
Manchester YMCA v Birchfield
Didsbury Toc H v Vulcan

February 12 (Week 22)
Douglas v Manchester YMCA
Halton v Mossley Hill
Lucas v Hightown

March 12 (Week 26)
Hightown v Vulcan
Mossley Hill v Lucas
Manchester YMCA v Halton

March 26 (Week 28)
Lucas v Manchester YMCA
Vulcan v Birchfield

April 9 (Week 30)
Hightown v Didsbury Toc H
Manchester YMCA v Vulcan
Birchfield v Douglas

LANCASHIRE SOUTH

BIRCHFIELD RUFC
Ground Address: Albright & Wilson Recreation Club, Birchfield Road, Widnes, Cheshire, WA8. Tel: 051 424 3222.
Club Secretary: David Rowlands, 30 Kirkham Road, Widnes, Cheshire, WA8 6RG. Tel: (H) 051 420 6054.
Press Officer: Kevin McDonnal, 108 Hurst Street, Widnes, Cheshire. Tel: (H) 051 424 4259 (W) 051 424 6731.
Club Colours: Maroon jerseys.

DIDSBURY TOC H RFC
Ground Address: Ford Lane, Didsbury, Manchester. Tel: 061 446 2146.
Club Secretary: Peter Bradley, 8 Barnard Avenue, Heaton Moor, Stockport SK4 4EP. Tel: (H) 061 432 0496 (W) 061 788 9611.
Press Officer: John Scott, 15 Aveson Avenue, Chorlton-cum-Hardy, Manchester M21. Tel: 061 860 7908.
Club Colours: Black with broad amber band; black shorts & socks.

DOUGLAS (IOM) RUFC
Ground Address: Port-E-Chee, Poraddan, Isle of Man. Tel: 0624 676493.
Club Secretary: P E Garnett, 3 Ridgeway, St Douglas, Isle of Man. Tel: (H) 0624 629037 (W) 0624 624535.
Press Officer: PE Garnett, 3 Ridgeway, St Douglas, Isle of man. Tel: (H) 0624 629037 (W) 0624 624535.
Club Colours: Maroon & gold band.

HALTON RUFC
Ground Address: ICI Recreation Club, Liverpool Road, Widnes. Tel: 051 424 2355.
Club Secretary: S G Dennett, 267 Lunts Heath Road, Widnes, Cheshire, SA8 9BB. Tel: (H) 051 424 3978.
Press Officer: S G Dennett, 267 Lunts Heath Road, Widnes, Cheshire, SA8 9BB. Tel: (H) 051 424 3978.
Club Colours: Navy & white hoops, navy shorts.

HIGHTOWN RUFC
Ground Address: Sandy Lane, Hightown, Merseyside, L38. Tel: 051 929 2330.
Club Secretary: John Houghton, APT, 63 East Waterloo Dock, Liverpool, L3 7BE. Tel: (H) 051 258 1315 (W) 0860 827225.
Press Officer: Billy Humphray, 95 Hythe Avenue, Litherland, Liverpool, L3 7QB. Tel: (H) 051 920 6249 (W) 051 922 7260.
Club Colours: Navy, chocolate & white hoops.

LUCAS RUFC
Ground Address: Walton Sports Centre, Walton Hall Avenue, Liverpool, L4 9XP. Tel: 051 523 3472.
Club Secretary: I Whitehead, 14 Aylton Road, Liverpool, L36 2LU. Tel: (H) 051 449 2137 (W) 051 709 5951.
Press Officer: I Whitehead, 14 Aylton Road, Liverpool, L36 2LU. Tel: (H) 051 449 2137 (W) 051 709 5951.
Club Colours: Blue.

MANCHESTER YMCA RFC
Ground Address: The Hollies, Mersey Road, Didsbury, Manchester. M20.
Club Secretary: B D Coleman, 62 Peel Brow, Ramsbottom, Bury, BL6 0AG. Tel: (H) 0706 827452 (W) 061 643 4009.
Press Officer: G Triggs, 108 Pilsworth Road, Heywood, Lancashire, OL10 3BH.
Club Colours: Red, black & white hoops.

MOSSLEY HILL RUFC

FINAL TABLE

	P	W	D	L	F	A	PD	Pts
Sefton	9	8	0	1	214	71	143	16
Eccles	9	8	0	1	174	79	95	16
Manchester YMCA	9	6	1	2	160	92	68	13
Birchfield	9	5	0	4	134	95	39	10
Halton	9	3	1	5	96	186	-90	7
Vulcan	9	5	0	4	152	112	40	6
Didsbury TOC H	9	4	1	4	77	93	-16	5
Mossley Hill	9	2	1	6	104	180	-76	5
Hightown	9	1	1	7	85	165	-80	1
Lucas	9	0	1	8	69	276	-207	1

Ground Address: Mossley Hill Road, Liverpool, L18. Tel: 051 724 3411.
Club Secretary: A Pealing, 41 Shirley Road, Liverpool, L19 7NU. Tel: (H) 051 427 4954 (W) 051 228 3565.
Press Officer: A Pealing, 41 Shirley Road, Liverpool, L19 7NU. Tel: (H) 051 427 4954 (W) 051 228 3565.
Club Colours: Maroon & gold hoops.

VULCAN RUFC
Ground Address: The Sportsfield, OPff Wargrave Road, Newton-le- Willows, Merseyside. Tel: 0925 224180.
Club Secretary: D W Lodge, 19 Pipit Avenue, Newton-le-Willows, Merseyside, WA12 9RG. Tel: (H) 0925 225108 (W) 0925 225171.
Club Colours: All black with broad amber band.

NORTHERN DIVISION

NORTH EAST ONE 1993-94 FIXTURES

December 18 (Week 15)
Selby v Pontefract
Blaydon v Old Brodleians
Gateshead Fell v Morpeth
Driffield v Roundhegians
Thornensians v Doncaster
Redcar v Novocastrians

October 23 (Week 8)
Selby v Blaydon
Novocastrians v Old Brodleians
Doncaster v Morpeth
Keighley v Roundhegians
Thornensians v Driffield
Redcar v Gateshead Fell

January 8 (Week 18)
Morpeth v Driffield
Old Brodleians v Gateshead Fell
Pontefract v Blaydon
Novocastrians v Selby
Doncaster v Redcar
Keighley v Thornensians

October 30 (Week X2)
Gateshead Fell v Selby
Driffield v Redcar
Roundhegians v Thornensians
Morpeth v Keighley
Old Brodleians v Doncaster
Pontefract v Novocastrians

January 29 (Week X5)
Selby v Doncaster
Blaydon v Novocastrians
Gateshead Fell v Pontefract
Driffield v Old Brodleians
Roundhegians v Morpeth
Redcar v Keighley

November 13 (Week 10)
Selby v Driffield
Blaydon v Gateshead Fell
Doncaster v Pontefract
Keighley v Old Brodleians
Thornensians v Morpeth
Redcar v Roundhegians

February 12 (Week 22)
Old Brodleians v Roundhegians
Pontefract v Driffield
Novocastrians v Gateshead Fell
Doncaster v Blaydon
Keighley v Selby
Thornensians v Redcar

November 20 (Week 11)
Driffield v Blaydon
Roundhegians v Selby
Morpeth v Redcar
Old Brodleians v Thornensians
Pontefract v Keighley
Novocastrians v Doncaster

March 12 (Week 26)
Selby v Thornensians
Blaydon v Keighley
Gateshead Fell v Doncaster
Driffield v Novocastrians
Roundhegians v Pontefract
Morpeth v Old Brodleians

December 4 (Week 13)
Selby v Morpeth
Blaydon v Roundhegians
Gateshead Fell v Driffield
Keighley v Novocastrians
Thornensians v Pontefract
Redcar v Old Brodleians

March 26 (Week 28)
Pontefract v Morpeth
Novocastrians v Roundhegians
Doncaster v Driffield
Keighley v Gateshead Fell
Thornensians v Blaydon
Redcar v Selby

December 11 (Week 14)
Roundhegians v Gateshead Fell
Morpeth v Blaydon
Old Brodleians v Selby
Pontefract v Redcar
Novocastrians v Thornensians
Doncaster v Keighley

April 9 (Week 30)
Blaydon v Redcar
Gateshead Fell v Thornensians
Driffield v Keighley
Roundhegians v Doncaster
Morpeth v Novocastrians
Old Brodleians v Pontefract

NORTH EAST ONE

BLAYDON RFC
Ground Address: Crow Trees, Hexham Road, Swalwell, Newcastle Upon Tyne NE16 3BN. Tel No: O91 414 2528.
Club Secretary: T N Brown 5 The Avenue, Axwell Park, Blaydon-on- Tyne, Tyne & Wear, NE21 5ND. Tel No: O91 4142698.
Press Officer:J M Huxley, The Mount, 59 Sunniside Road, Sunniside, Newcastle Upon Tyne, NE16 5NF. Tel No: O91 488 728O.
Club Colours: Scarlet Jerseys, White shorts.

DONCASTER RUFC
Ground Address: Sandall Beat Lane, off Armthorpe Road, Doncaster
(No correspondence please). Tel No: O3O2 831388.
Club Secretary: John Lowe, 57 Wroot Road, Finningley, Doncaster, South Yorkshire, DN9 3DR. (H) O3O2 77O275.
Press Officer: John Lowe
Club Colours: Blue with 2 red and white hoops.

DRIFFIELD
Ground Address: Kelleythorpe, Driffield, East Yorkshire. Tel No: O377 256598.
Club Secretary:I.M.Douglas, 65 Lowndes Park, Driffield, YO25 7BE.
Tel No: (H) O377 253489
Press Officer: A R Wilson, Westwick, Beverley Road, Driffields YO25 7SA. Tel No: (H) O377 25243O.
Club Colours: Blue, black and white irregular hoops, blue shorts and socks.

GATESHEAD FELL RFC
Ground Address: Hedley Lawson Park, Eastwood Gdns, Low Fell, Gateshead, NE9 5UB. Tel No: O91 4875739.
Club Secretary: John McMillan, 95, Kells Lane, Low Fell, Gateshead, NE9 5XX. Tel No: (H) O91 48O7O355
Club Colours: Dark Blue/Light Blue (Narrow) rings.

KEIGHLEY RUFC
Ground Address: Skipton Road, Utley, Keighley, West Yorkshire, BD2O 6DT. Tel No: O535 6O2174.
Club Secretary: Michael T Greaves, Holmlea, Summerhill Lane, Steeton, Keighley, West Yorkshire, BD2O 6RX. Tel No: (H) O535 653192 (W) O535 6O5646.
Press Officer:W Alden Phillips, 7 Thornhill Road, Streeton, Keighley, W Yorkshire BD2O 6SU. Tel No: O535 654125.
Club Colours: Scarlet green and white hoops.

MORPETH RFC
Ground Address: Grange House Field, Mitford Road, Morpeth, NE61 3RJ. Tel No: O67O 512508
Club Secretary: Ken Fraser, Solway House, De Merley Road, Morpeth, Northumberland NE61 1HZ. Tel No: (H) O67O 511208 (W) O67O 822625 X 2O1 O67O 829378 Fax.
Press Officer: Ian Pringle, Manor Farm, Ulgham, Norpeth Northumberland, NE61 3AT. Tel No: O67O 790807.
Club Colours: Scarlet and white hoops.

NOVOCASTRIANS RUFC
Ground Address: Sunderland Park, The Drive, High Heaton, Newcastle upon Tyne, NE7 7SY. Tel No: O91 266 1247.
Club Secretary:R B Pollock, 1O1 Marine Avenue, Whitley Bay, Tyne
& Wear, NE26 3LN.Tel No: (H) O91 2511562 (W) O91 296O3O3
Press Officer: John Scott (Director of Marketing), Follifoot, Grenville Court, Ponteland, Newcastle Upon Tyne NE2O 9MT. Tel No:(H) O661825OO2.
Club Colours: Shirts/socks - red black and white hoops - white shorts.

FINAL TABLE

	P	W	D	L	F	A	PD	Pts
Bridlington	12	10	0	2	284	110	174	20
Blaydon	12	8	2	2	307	92	215	18
Selby	12	7	1	4	179	135	44	15
Old Brodleians	12	7	0	5	168	152	16	14
Morpeth	12	7	0	5	152	138	14	14
Novocastrians	12	5	3	4	148	129	19	13
Keighley	12	6	0	6	153	117	36	12
Redcar	12	5	1	6	121	199	-78	9
Pontefract	12	4	1	7	153	154	-1	7
Gateshead Fell	12	3	1	8	119	277	-158	7
Thornensians	12	2	1	9	95	242	-147	5

OLD BRODLEIANS RUFC
Ground Address: Woodhead, Denholme Gate Road, Hipperholme, Halifax WX3 8JU. Tel No: O422 2O27O8
Club Secretary:S D Heaton, Sutcliffe Wood Farm, Hove, Brighouse, West Yorkshire HD6 2QW. Tel No: O484 721628 (W) O274 687719.
Press Officer: S D Heaton,Sutcliffe Wood Farm, Hove, Brighouse, West Yorkshire Hd6 2QW.
Club Colours: Black with red and white hoops.

PONTEFRACT RFC
Ground Address: Moor Lane, Carleton, Pontefract, West Yorks, WF8 3RX. Tel No: O977 7O265O.
Club Secretary:R Peacock, 12 Fairview, Carleton, Pontefract, WF8 3NT. Tel No: O977 7O2284 (W) O977 677421.
Press Officer: N Bowmer, 16 Mill Hill Close, Darrington, Pontefract, WF8 3BE. Tel No: O977 795O64.
Club Colours: Blue, white shorts.

REDCAR RUGBY UNION FOOTBALL CLUB
Ground Address: Mackinlay Park, Green Lane, Redcar, Cleveland TS1O 3RW. Tel No: 482733.
Club Secretary: Dr Palmer,address as above.
Club Colours: Red white black.

ROUNDHEGIANS RFC
Ground Address: The Memorial Ground, Chelwood Drive, Leeds 8. Tel No: O532 667377.
Club Ssecretary: A J Rowell, 16, The Moorlands, Shadwell Lane, Leeds LS17 8AB. Tel No: (H) O532 669278 (W) O532 61OO22
Press Officer: P Armsstrong. 6 Woodhall Park Grove, Leeds 28, Tel No: O532 53O43.
Club Colours: Green, black and white hoops.

SELBY RUFC
Ground Address: Sandhill Lane, Leeds Road, Selby, North Yorkshire. Tel No: O757 7O36O8.
Club Secretary: M.W.M Blackwell, 6 Blackwell Grain Ltd, Market Weighton Road, Selby, YO8 7LD. Tel No: O757 289111.
Press Officer: W Wharram, C/O Selby RUFC Sandhill Lane, Leeds Road, Selby, North Yorkshire. Tel NO: O757 228863.
Club Colours: Red green gold hoops.

THORNENSIANS RUFC
Ground Address: The Clubhouse, Coulman St, Thorne, Doncaster, South Yorkshire, Tel No: O4O5 812746
Club Secretary: Ian Robson, Windyridge Cottage, Selby Road, Thorne, Doncaster, Yorks. Tel No:(H) O4O5 812360 (W) O4O5 81220O,
Press Officer: Ian Robson. Address as above.
Club Colours: Blue/black/white.

NORTHERN DIVISION

NORTH EAST TWO
1993-94
FIXTURES

October 23 (Week 8)
Westoe v Horden
Bramley v Hull
Ashington v Ripon
Blyth v Rockcliffe
Goole v Acklam
Cleckheaton v Beverley

October 30 (Week X2)
Beverley v Westoe
Acklam v Cleckheaton
Rockcliffe v Goole
Ripon v Blyth
Hull v Ashington
Whitby v Bramley

November 13 (Week 10)
Westoe v Acklam
Horden v Beverley
Ashington v Whitby
Blyth v Hull
Goole v Ripon
Cleckheaton v Rockcliffe

November 20 (Week 11)
Acklam v Horden
Rockcliffe v Westoe
Ripon v Cleckheaton
Hull v Goole
Whitby v Blyth
Bramley v Ashington

December 4 (Week 13)
Westoe v Ripon
Horden v Rockcliffe
Beverley v Acklam
Blyth v Bramley
Goole v Whitby
Cleckheaton v Hull

December 11 (Week 14)
Rockcliffe v Beverley
Ripon v Horden
Hull v Westoe
Whitby v Cleckheaton
Bramley v Goole
Ashington v Blyth

December 18 (Week 15)
Westoe v Whitby
Horden v Hull
Beverley v Ripon
Acklam v Rockcliffe
Goole v Ashington
Cleckheaton v Bramley

January 8 (Week 18)
Ripon v Acklam
Hull v Beverley
Whitby v Horden
Bramley v Westoe
Ashington v Cleckheaton
Blyth v Goole

January 29 (Week X5)
Westoe v Ashington
Horden v Bramley
Beverley v Whitby
Acklam v Hull
Rockcliffe v Ripon
Cleckheaton v Blyth

February 12 (Week 22)
Hull v Rockcliffe
Whitby v Acklam
Bramley v Beverley
Ashington v Horden
Blyth v Westoe
Goole v Cleckheaton

March 12 (Week 26)
Westoe v Goole
Horden v Blyth
Beverley v Ashington
Acklam v Bramley
Rockcliffe v Whitby
Ripon v Hull

March 26 (Week 28)
Whitby v Ripon
Bramley v Rockcliffe
Ashington v Acklam
Blyth v Beverley
Goole v Horden
Cleckheaton v Westoe

April 9 (Week 30)
Horden v Cleckheaton
Beverley v Goole
Acklam v Blyth
Rockcliffe v Ashington
Ripon v Bramley
Hull v Whitby

NORTH EAST TWO

ACKLAM RUFC
Ground Address: Talbot Park, Saltersgill Avenue, Middlesborough, Cleveland, TS4 3PR. Tel No: 0642 321397.
Club Secretary: Paul Pearson, Blackhall Sands, Acklam, Middlesborough. Tel No: (H) 0642 596433 (W) 0325 461231.
Pess Officer: Paul Pearson. Address as above.
Club Colours: Green/black.

ASHINGTON J.W. RFC
Ground Address: Recreation Ground, Ellington Road, Ashington, Northumberland, Tel No: 0670 814123.
Club Secretary: John Nicholson, 13 Avebury Avenue, Sherbourne Park, Stakeford, Northumberland, NE62 5HE. Tel No:(H) 0670 828458 (W) 091 2323451 Ex 62326.
Press Officer A F Bewick, 21 Till Grove, Ellington, Morpeth, Northumberland. Tel No: (H) 0670 860076.
Club Colours: Royal blue and amber hoops.

BEVERLEY RUFC
Ground Address: Beaver Park, Norwood Beverley. Tel No: 0482 870306.
Club Secretary: Andrew Winter, 4 The Vineyards, Leven, Beverely HV17 5LD. Tel No: (H) 0964 543981 (W) 0482 885027.
Press Offficer: John Scott, 8 Main Street, Cherry Burton, Beverley, Tel No: (H) 0964 551340.
ClubColours: Green brown and white.

BLYTH RFU
Ground Address: Plessey Road, Blyth, Northumberland, Tel No: 0670 352063.
Club Secretary:I R Stewart, 10 Coronation St, Blyth, Northumberland, Tel No: (H) 0670 352274 (W) 091 4607464.
Press Officer: Roger Phillips,2 Burnham Close, South Beach, Northumberland, NE24 3UB. Tel No: (H) 0670 362395.
Club Colours: Emerald green and black.

BRAMLEY RUFC
Ground Address: The Warrels, Grosmont Terrace, Warrels Road, Bramley, Leeds LS13 3NY. Tel No: 0532 577787.
Club Secretary: D A Nesham, 40 Water Lane, Farnley, Leeds LS12 5LX. Tel No: (H) 0532 576208 (W) 0532 478494.
Club Colours: Green with black and gold chest band.

CLECKHEATON RUFC
Ground Address: Moorend, Cleckheaton, W Yorkshire BD19 3UD. Tel No: 0274 873410.
Club Secretary: Ian Johnson, 20 St Andrews Crescent, Oakenshaw, Bradford BD12 7EL. Tel No: (H)0274 601043 (W) 0484 646816.
Press Officer: Alan Bentley, 9 Ghylroyd Drive, Birkenshaw, Bradford, Tel No: (H) 0274 682266 (W) 0924 291242.
Club Colours: Red/white hoops, white shorts, red socks.

GOOLE RUFC
Ground Address: The Clubhouse, Murham Ave, Goole, North Humberside, DN14 6PA. Tel No: 0405 762018.
Club Secretary: I R Higgins, 14 The Meadows, Howden, Goole, North Humberside, DN14 7DX. Tel No: (H) 0430 430037 (W) 0405 76821.
Press Officer: J Kaye, Plough Farm, Saltmarshe, Howden, North Humberside, Tel No: 0430 430221 (W) 0757 289191.
Club Colours: Navy and gold quarters.

FINAL TABLE

	P	W	D	L	F	A	PD	Pts
Doncaster	12	11	0	1	294	39	255	22
Driffield	12	9	2	1	265	76	189	20
Hull	12	9	1	2	280	88	192	19
Cleckheaton	12	9	1	2	260	88	172	19
Horden	12	7	0	5	259	156	103	14
Blyth	12	6	0	6	157	228	-71	12
Ripon	12	5	0	7	183	205	-22	10
Ashington	12	5	0	7	161	244	-83	10
Westoe	12	4	0	8	147	176	-29	8
Acklam	12	4	0	8	84	247	-163	6
Rockliff	12	3	0	9	90	277	-187	6
Beverley	12	2	0	10	112	226	-114	4
Bishop Auckland	12	2	0	10	121	386	-265	4

HORDEN COLLIERY WELFARE RFC
Ground Address: Welfare Park, Hordon, Tel No: 091 3501.
Club Secretary:L Applegarth. 10 Almond Ter, Horden, Co Durham SR8 4EZ. Tel No: (H) 091 5862477.
Press Officer: W Featonby, 20 Morpeth St, Horden, Co Durham, SR8 4BB. Tel No. 091 5866973.
Club Colours: Claret and sky blue.

HULL RUFC
Ground Address: Howarth Park Beverley High Road, Hull, HU6 7AB. Tel No: 0482 802119.
Club Secretary: D J Ward, 78 St Margaret'S Avenue, Cottingham, Hull, HU16 5NB. Tel: (H) 0482 842292 (W) 0482 2542.
Press Officer: J Calbby, 29 Hall Walk, Cottingham, HU16 4RL. Tel No: (H) 0482 845974.
Club Colours: Black with red and gold hoop round collar.

RIPON RUFC
Ground Address: Mallocie Park, Ripon, North Yorks, Tel No: 0765 604675.
Club Secretary: R A Bruce, 19 Littlethorpe Park, Ripon, North Yorks. Tel No: (H) 0765 603681 (W) 0535 636116.
Press Officer: Andy Renshaw.
Club Colours: Navy blue, white light blue hoops.

WESTOE RFC
Ground Address: Dean Road, South Shields, Tyne & Wear, Tel No: 091 456 1506.
Club Secretary: J R Wells, 240, Mowbury Road, South Shields, Tyne & Wear NE33 3NW. Tel No: (H) 091 2260, (W) 091 4560405.
Press Officer: J R Wells, address as above.
Club Colours: Dark blue/sky blue red hoops.

WHITBY RUFC
Ground Address: Whiteleys Road, Whitby, N Yorks. Tel No: 0947 602008.
Club Secretary: F Howarth 18 Lime Grove, Whitby, N Yorks, YO21 1LP. Tel No 0947 600692.
Press Officer: F Howarth.
Club Colours: Maroon shirt navy shorts.

WHITLEY BAY ROCKCLIFF RFC
Ground Address: Hillheads, Lovaine Avenue, Whitley Bay, Northumberland NE25 8RW. Tel No: 091 251 3704.
Club Secretary: Graham Shepherd, Bank Chambers, 31 Station Road, Wallsend, NE28 6SZ. Fax 091 234 2193 (W) 091 252 3952.
Press Officer: Ian Firth, 72 Davison Avenue, Whitley Bay, NE26 3SU. Tel No: 091 253 2303 (W) 091 252 0113.
Club Colours: Red shirts with gold collar and cuffs; white shorts.

NORTHERN DIVISION

DURHAM & NORTHUMBERLAND ONE 1993-94 FIXTURES

December 18 (Week 15)
Consett v Mowden Park
Guisborough v Sunderland
Ryton v Percy Park
Darlington R.A. v Darlington
Seaham v North Shields
Hartlepool TDSOB v Bishop Auckland

October 23 (Week 8)
Consett v Guisborough
Bishop Auckland v Sunderland
North Shields v Percy Park
North Durham v Darlington
Seaham v Darlington R.A.
Hartlepool TDSOB v Ryton

January 8 (Week 18)
Percy Park v Darlington R.A.
Sunderland v Ryton
Mowden Park v Guisborough
Bishop Auckland v Consett
North Shields v Hartlepool TDSOB
North Durham v Seaham

October 30 (Week X2)
Ryton v Consett
Darlington R.A. v Hartlepool TDSOB
Darlington v Seaham
Percy Park v North Durham
Sunderland v North Shields
Mowden Park v Bishop Auckland

January 29 (Week X5)
Consett v North Shields
Guisborough v Bishop Auckland
Ryton v Mowden Park
Darlington R.A. v Sunderland
Darlington v Percy Park
Hartlepool TDSOB v North Durham

November 13 (Week 10)
Consett v Darlington R.A.
Guisborough v Ryton
North Shields v Mowden Park
North Durham v Sunderland
Seaham v Percy Park
Hartlepool TDSOB v Darlington

February 12 (Week 22)
Sunderland v Darlington
Mowden Park v Darlington R.A.
Bishop Auckland v Ryton
North Shields v Guisborough
North Durham v Consett
Seaham v Hartlepool TDSOB

November 20 (Week 11)
Darlington R.A. v Guisborough
Darlington v Consett
Percy Park v Hartlepool TDSOB
Sunderland v Seaham
Mowden Park v North Durham
Bishop Auckland v North Shields

March 12 (Week 26)
Consett v Seaham
Guisborough v North Durham
Ryton v North Shields
Darlington R.A. v Bishop Auckland
Darlington v Mowden Park
Percy Park v Sunderland

December 4 (Week 13)
Consett v Percy Park
Guisborough v Darlington
Ryton v Darlington R.A.
North Durham v Bishop Auckland
Seaham v Mowden Park
Hartlepool TDSOB v Sunderland

March 26 (Week 28)
Mowden Park v Percy Park
Bishop Auckland v Darlington
North Shields v Darlington R.A.
North Durham v Ryton
Seaham v Guisborough
Hartlepool TDSOB v Consett

December 11 (Week 14)
Darlington v Ryton
Percy Park v Guisborough
Sunderland v Consett
Mowden Park v Hartlepool TDSOB
Bishop Auckland v Seaham
North Shields v North Durham

April 9 (Week 30)
Guisborough v Hartlepool TDSOB
Ryton v Seaham
Darlington R.A. v North Durham
Darlington v North Shields
Percy Park v Bishop Auckland
Sunderland v Mowden Park

DURHAM & NORTHUMBERLAND ONE

BISHOP AUCKLAND RUFC
Ground Address: West Mills Playing Fields, Bridge Road, off Newton Cap, Bishop Auckland, CL14 7PA. Tel: 0388 602922.
Club Secretary: K A Wilkinson, 7 Victoria Avenue, Bishop Auckland, Co. Durham, DL14 7JH. Tel: (H) 0388 605768 (W) 0388 603388.
Press Officer: D Bartle, 59 Middlehope Grove, Bishopsgate, Bishop Auckland, DL14 0SH. Tel: (H) 0388 661405 (W) 0325 300333 Ext 256.
Club Colours: Navy & sky blue.

CONSETT RUFC
Ground Address: Belle View Park, Medomsley Road, Consett, County Durham. Tel: 0207 504261.
Club Secretary: A Clarke, 18 Third Street, Crookhall, Consett, County Durham, DH8 7LT. Tel: (H) 0207 503477.
Press Officer: A Clarke, 18 Third Street, Crookhall, Consett, County Durham, DH8 7LT. Tel: (H) 0207 503477.
Club Colours: Amber & black.

DARLINGTON RFC
Ground Address: "Lingfield", McMullen road, Darlington, DL1 1BP. Tel: 0325 466974.
Club Secretary: Andrew P F Foster, "Dardogan", 45 Hartford Road, Darlington, County Durham, DL3 8HF. Tel: (H) 0325 466501(W) 0325 331818.
Press Officer: John Morgans, 22 Carnel Gardens, Darlington, County Durham. Tel: 0325 352106 (W) 0388 607511.
Club Colours: Black & white hoops, black short, scarlet socks.

DARLINGTON MOWDEN PARK RFC
Ground Address: 22 Yiewsley Drive, Darlington, County Durham, DL3 9XS. Tel: 0325 465932.
Club Secretary: M Cambell, 491 North road, Darlington, County Durham, DL1 3AB. Tel: (H) 0325 462162.
Press Officer: N G Crawford, 10 Breck Road, Darlington, County Durham, DL3 8NH.
Club Colours: Royal blue & white.

DARLINGTON RA RUFC
Ground Address: Brinkham Road, Darlington.
Club Secretary: A Thompson, 23 Westgate Crescent, Darlington, Durham DL3 0SY. Tel: (H) 0325 284354 (W) 0325 300770
Club Colours: Black and amber.

GUISBOROUGH RUFC
Ground Address: Belmangate, Guisborough, Cleveland, TS14 7BB. Tel: 0287 632966.
Club Secretary: Dennis F Childs, 32 Boston Drive, Marton, Cleveland, TS7 8LX. Tel: (H) 0642 314081.
Press Officer: Peter Griffiths, 80 Great Auk, Guisborough, Cleveland, TS14 8PQ. Tel: (H) 0287 610838 (W) 0642 532016.
Club Colours: Black with amber collar & cuffs.

NORTH DURHAM RFC
Ground Address: Alexandra Road, Gareshead, Tyne & Wear. Tel: 091 478 3071.
Club Secretary: K Jobson, 13 Lady Haugh Drive, Whicklam, Newcastle-upon-Tyne, NE16 5TL. Tel: (H) 091 488 3955.
Press Officer: Roy Thompson, c/o North Durham RFC, Alexandra Road, Gareshead, Tyne & Wear. Tel: 091 478 3071.
Club Colours: Red & white hoops.

NORTH SHIELDS RFC
Ground Address: Preston Playing Fields, Preston Village, North Shields, Tyne & Wear. Tel: 091 257 7352.
Club Secretary: David Daniels, 1 Highcross Road, North Shields, Tyne & Wear. Tel: (H) 091 252 6395 (W) 091 268 8586.

FINAL TABLE

	P	W	D	L	F	A	PD	Pts
Whitby	12	10	0	2	261	107	154	20
Darlington	12	9	0	3	251	126	125	18
W Ha'pool TDSOB	12	7	2	3	157	134	23	16
Ryton	12	7	1	4	187	105	82	15
Mowden Park	12	7	0	5	185	130	55	14
Guisborough	12	7	0	5	130	139	-9	14
Sunderland	12	6	0	6	161	155	6	12
Seaham	12	6	0	6	169	180	-11	12
Percy Park	12	5	1	6	210	207	3	11
Darlington RA	12	4	0	8	115	194	-79	8
Consett	12	3	0	9	111	190	-79	6
Hartlepool	12	3	0	9	101	186	-85	6
Seghill	12	2	0	10	112	297	-185	4

Press Officer: Alan Guy, 12 Clifton Terrace, Whitley Bay, Tyne & Wear. t(H) 091 252 6395 (W) 091 268 8586.
Club Colours: Royal blue & white hoops, white shorts.

PERCY PARK RFC
Ground Address: The Clubhouse, Preston Avenue, North Shields, Tyne & Wear. Tel: 091 2575710.
Club Secretary: A C Baker, c/o The Garth, Winlaton, Tyne & Wear, NE21 6DD. Tel: (H) 091 2577007 (W) 091 4144860.
Press Officer: F M Black, 86 Paignton Avenue, Whitley Bay, Tyne & Wear. Tel: (H) 091 2528371 (W) 091 2528371.
Club Colours: Black & white hoops, black shorts.

RYTON RUFC
Ground Address: Main Road, Ryton, Tyne & Wear, NE40 3AG. Tel: 091 413 3820.
Club Secretary: J A Trodden, 63 Horsley Avenue, Ryton, Tyne & Wear, NE40 4XQ. Tel: (H) 091 413 2700 (W) 0670 713451.
Press Officer: D Roberts, 47 Grange Drive, Rydon, Tyne & WEar. Tel: (H) 091 413 2882.
Club Colours: Royal blue & white.

SEAHAM RUFC
Ground Address: New Drive Playing Fields, Seaham. Tel: 091 581 6459.
Club Secretary: Dave Turns, 27 Cornelia Terrace, Seaham, County Durham. Tel: (H) 091 581 8560.
Press Officer: Dean Kennedy, 27 Cornelia Terrace, Seaham, County Durham. Tel: (H) 091 581 6050.
Club Colours: Red.

SUNDERLAND RFC
Ground Address: Ashbrooke, West Lawn, Sunderland, Tyne & Wear, SR2 7HH. Tel: 091 528 4536.
Club Secretary: J D Boyd, 15 Alexandra Park, Sunderland, Tyne & Wear, SR3 1XJ. Tel: (H) 091 520 1187.
Press Officer: P Foggin, 68 Park Lea, Herrington, Sunderland, Tyne & Wear. Tel: (H) 091 528 2306.
Club Colours: Gold, black & Scarlet hoops.

WEST HARTLEPOOL TECHNICAL DAY SCHOOL OLD BOYS RUFC
Ground Address: Wiltshire Way, Hartlepool, Cleveland. Tel: 0429 233548.
Club Secretary: David Bramley, 63 Hutton avenue, Hartlepool, Cleveland, TS26 9PP. Tel: (H) 0429 263157 (W) 0642 433363.
Club Colours: Royal blue & white.

NORTHERN DIVISION

DURHAM & NORTHUMBERLAND TWO 1993-94 FIXTURES

October 23 (Week 8)
Newton Ayecliffe v Ponteland
Seghill v Medicals
Seaton Carew v Winlaton Vulcans
Houghton v Hartlepool BBOB
S Tyneside Coll v Wallsend
Wensleydale v Hartlepool

October 30 (Week X2)
Hartlepool v Newton Ayecliffe
Wallsend v Wensleydale
Hartlepool BBOB v S Tyneside Coll
Winlaton Vulcans v Houghton
Medicals v Seaton Carew
Chester-le-Street v Seghill

November 13 (Week 10)
Newton Ayecliffe v Wallsend
Ponteland v Hartlepool
Seaton Carew v Chester-le-Street
Houghton v Medicals
S Tyneside Coll v Winlaton Vulcans
Wensleydale v Hartlepool BBOB

November 20 (Week 11)
Wallsend v Ponteland
Hartlepool BBOB v Newton Ayecliffe
Winlaton Vulcans v Wensleydale
Medicals v S Tyneside Coll
Chester-le-Street v Houghton
Seghill v Seaton Carew

December 4 (Week 13)
Newton Ayecliffe v Winlaton Vulcans
Ponteland v Hartlepool BBOB
Hartlepool v Wallsend
Houghton v Seghill
S Tyneside Coll v Chester-le-Street
Wensleydale v Medicals

December 11 (Week 14)
Hartlepool BBOB v Hartlepool
Winlaton Vulcans v Ponteland
Medicals v Newton Ayecliffe
Chester-le-Street v Wensleydale
Seghill v S Tyneside Coll
Seaton Carew v Houghton

December 18 (Week 15)
Newton Ayecliffe v Chester-le-Street
Ponteland v Medicals
Hartlepool v Winlaton Vulcans
Wallsend v Hartlepool BBOB
S Tyneside Coll v Seaton Carew
Wensleydale v Seghill

January 8 (Week 18)
Winlaton Vulcans v Wallsend
Medicals v Hartlepool
Chester-le-Street v Ponteland
Seghill v Newton Ayecliffe
Seaton Carew v Wensleydale
Houghton v S Tyneside Coll

January 29 (Week X5)
Newton Ayecliffe v Seaton Carew
Ponteland v Seghill
Hartlepool v Chester-le-Street
Wallsend v Medicals
Hartlepool BBOB v Winlaton Vulcans
Wensleydale v Houghton

February 12 (Week 22)
Medicals v Hartlepool BBOB
Chester-le-Street v Wallsend
Seghill v Hartlepool
Seaton Carew v Ponteland
Houghton v Newton Ayecliffe
S Tyneside Coll v Wensleydale

March 12 (Week 26)
Newton Ayecliffe v S Tyneside Coll
Ponteland v Houghton
Hartlepool v Seaton Carew
Wallsend v Seghill
Hartlepool BBOB v Chester-le-Street
Winlaton Vulcans v Medicals

March 26 (Week 28)
Chester-le-Street v Winlaton Vulcans
Seghill v Hartlepool BBOB
Seaton Carew v Wallsend
Houghton v Hartlepool
S Tyneside Coll v Ponteland
Wensleydale v Newton Ayecliffe

April 9 (Week 30)
Ponteland v Wensleydale
Hartlepool v S Tyneside Coll
Wallsend v Houghton
Hartlepool BBOB v Seaton Carew
Winlaton Vulcans v Seghill
Medicals v Chester-le-Street

DURHAM & NORTHUMBERLAND TWO

CHESTER-LE-STREET RFC
Ground Address: Riverside Park, Chester-le-Street, Co. Durham. Tel: 091 388 4121.
Club Secretary: Paul Langley, 34 Wynard, Chester-le-Street, Co. Durham DH2 2TQ. Tel: (H) 091 388 9616 (W) 091 383 3443.
Press Officer: Neil Stephenson, 5 Chatton Close, Chester-le- Street, Co. Durham. Tel: 091 389 2812.
Club Colours: Navy blue shirts & shorts, red socks.

HARTLEPOOL RFC
Ground Address: Mayfield Park, Essington Road, Hartlepool, Cleveland TS24 9BA.
Club Secretary: K Dobson, 15 Sandbanks Drive, Hart Station, Hartlepool, Cleveland. Tel: (H) 0429 261236 (W) 0429 266522.
Press Officer: John Poradley, 41 Formby Close, Hartlepool. Tel: 0429 867262.
Club Colours: Black.

HARTLEPOOL BOYS BRIGADE OLD BOYS RFC
Ground Address: Old Friarage, Headland, Hartlepool.
Club Secretary: G K Faint, 11 Nesbyt Road, Hartlepool, Cleveland TS24 9NB. Tel: (H) 0429 265674 (W) 091 477 0288.
Club Colours: White with broad black band; black shorts.

HOUGHTON RUFC
Ground Address: Dairy Lane, Houghton le Spring, Tyne & Wear. Tel: 091 584 1460.
Club Secretary: D Winthrop, "Hillcroft", 14 North Road, Hetton- le-Hole, Tyne & Wear DH5 9JU. Tel: (H) 091 526 2163 (W) 091 567 0094.
Club Colours: Black with white hoops; black shorts; black socks with white tops.

MEDICALS RFC
Ground Address: Medical Sports Ground, Cartington Terrace, Newcastle NE6 5RS. Tel: 091 265 6321.
Club Secretary: Dr Andrew Greenwood, 45 Church Road, Gosforth, Newcastle NE3 1UE. Tel: (H) 091 285 0686 (W) 091 491 5600.
Press Officer: Dr D S H Row, 50 Harley Terrace, Cosforth, Newcastle. Tel: (H) 091 284 8953 (W) 0670 812125.
Club Colours: Maroon & white.

NEWTON AYCLIFFE RUFC
Ground Address: Newton Aycliffe Sports Club, Moore Lane, Newton Aycliffe, Co. Durham. Tel:0325 312768.
Club Secretary: Dale Thomas Kelly, 1 Forresters Path, School Aycliffe, Co. Durham L5 6TA. Tel: 0325 311957.
Press Officer: Stuart McClean, 118 Falkener Road, Newton Aycliffe, Co Durham. Tel: 0325 317134.
Club Colours: Maroon, green & gold; black shorts;maroon socks.

PONTELAND RFC
Ground Address: Ponteland Leisure Centre, Callerton Lane, Ponteland, Northumberland. Tel: 0661 825441.
Club Secretary: A Jackson, 34 Collingwood Crescent, Ponteland, Northumberland NE20 9DZ. Tel: 0661 871832.
Press Officer: T Martin, 36 Woodside, Dvras Hall, Ponteland, Newcastle Upon Tyne. Tel: 0661 23625.

SEATON CAREW RUFC
Ground Address: Hornby Park, Elizabeth Way, Seaton Carew, Hartlepool, Cleveland TS25 2AZ. Tel: 0429 260945.
Club Secretary: Paul McManus, 9 Ruswarp Grove, Seaton Carew,.Hartlepool, Cleveland TS25 2BA. Tel: (H) 0429 233189 (W) 0429 268821.
Press Officer: David Brown, 146 Oxford Road, Hartlepool, Cleveland TS25 5NH. Tel: 0429 231787.
Club Colours: Maroon & amber hoops shirts & socks; black shorts.

FINAL TABLE

	P	W	D	L	F	A	PD	Pts
North Durham	12	10	0	2	197	105	92	20
North Sheilds	12	8	1	3	228	59	169	17
Wallsend	12	8	2	2	161	114	47	16
Chester-le-Street	12	7	1	4	131	102	29	15
Houghton	12	7	0	5	207	180	27	14
Medicals	12	8	0	4	159	134	25	12
Ponteland	12	6	0	6	143	132	11	12
Wensleydale	12	5	1	6	120	93	27	11
Seaton Carew	12	5	0	7	136	190	-54	10
Winlaton	12	4	0	8	122	140	-18	8
S Tyneside Coll	12	3	1	8	95	256	-161	7
Billingham	12	3	0	9	104	199	-95	4
Barnard Castle	12	1	0	11	71	265	-194	0

SEGHILL RUFC
Ground Address: Welfare Park, Seghill, Cramlington, Northumberland NE23 7ER. Tel:091 237 0414.
Club Secretary: Stewart Grainger, 16 Carrick Drive, Parklands, Blyth NE24 3SX. Tel: 0670 355 909.
Press Officer: Paul Gelling, 43 Hastings Gardens, New Hartley, Tyne & Wear NE25 0JF. Tel: (H) 091 237 3724 (W) 091 259 3000.
Club Colours: Red & black.

SOUTH TYNESIDE COLLEGE RUFC
Ground Address: Grosvenor Road, South Shields, Tyne & Wear.
Club Secretary: R Smith, 87 Colman Avenue, South Shields, Tyne & Wear NE34 9AG. Tel: (H) 091 454 2359 (W) 091 456 0403.
Club Colours: Black with red & gold hoops.

WALLSEND RUFC
Ground Address: Benfield Coomunity Association, Benfield Road, Newcastle. Tel: 091 262 9431.
Club Secretary: L Dunne, 23 Laurel Close, Walkerville, Newcastle 6 4PJ. Tel: (H) 091 263 5398 (W) 091 384 5544.
Club Colours: Green & gold tops; white shorts, green socks.

WENSLEYDALE RUFC
Ground Address: Cawkill Park, Wensleydale Road, Leyburn. Tel: 0969 23067.
Club Secretary: D Ward, 3 Kelbersdale Terrace, Leyburn, N Yorkshire DL8 5AR. Tel: (H) 0969 22046 (W) 0969 23109.
Club Colours: Black & amber hoops.

WINLATON VULCANS RUFC:
Ground Address: Axwell View Playing Fields, Winlaton, Tyne & Wear. Tel: 091 414 2502.
Club Secretary: M Roddam, 70 Silverdale Drive, Winlaton, Tyne & Wear, Tyneside. Tl: (H) 091 414 2901 (W) 0207 542935.
Club Colours: Black with white collar.

NORTHERN DIVISION

DURHAM & NORTHUMBERLAND THREE 1993-94 FIXTURES

October 23 (Week 8)
Prudhoe Hospital v Hartlepool Athletic
Billingham v Shildon Town
Belmont v Wearside
Richmondshire v Barnard Castle

October 30 (Week X2)
Jarrovians v Prudhoe Hospital
Wearside v Richmondshire
Shildon Town v Belmont
Sedgefield v Billingham

November 13 (Week 10)
Prudhoe Hospital v Washington
Hartlepool Athletic v Jarrovians
Belmont v Sedgefield
Richmondshire v Shildon Town

November 20 (Week 11)
Washington v Hartlepool Athletic
Barnard Castle v Prudhoe Hospital
Sedgefield v Richmondshire
Billingham v Belmont

December 4 (Week 13)
Prudhoe Hospital v Wearside
Hartlepool Athletic v Barnard Castle
Jarrovians v Washington
Richmondshire v Billingham

December 11 (Week 14)
Barnard Castle v Jarrovians
Wearside v Hartlepool Athletic
Shildon Town v Prudhoe Hospital
Belmont v Richmondshire

December 18 (Week 15)
Prudhoe Hospital v Sedgefield
Hartlepool Athletic v Shildon Town
Jarrovians v Wearside
Washington v Barnard Castle

January 8 (Week 18)
Wearside v Washington
Shildon Town v Jarrovians
Sedgefield v Hartlepool Athletic
Billingham v Prudhoe Hospital

January 29 (Week X5)
Prudhoe Hospital v Belmont
Hartlepool Athletic v Billingham
Jarrovians v Sedgefield
Washington v Shildon Town
Barnard Castle v Wearside

February 12 (Week 22)
Shildon Town v Barnard Castle
Sedgefield v Washington
Billingham v Jarrovians
Belmont v Hartlepool Athletic
Richmondshire v Prudhoe Hospital

March 12 (Week 26)
Hartlepool Athletic v Richmondshire
Jarrovians v Belmont
Washington v Billingham
Barnard Castle v Sedgefield
Wearside v Shildon Town

March 26 (Week 28)
Sedgefield v Wearside
Billingham v Barnard Castle
Belmont v Washington
Richmondshire v Jarrovians

April 9 (Week 30)
Washington v Richmondshire
Barnard Castle v Belmont
Wearside v Billingham
Shildon Town v Sedgefield

DURHAM & NORTHUMBERLAND THREE

BARNARD CASTLE RUFC
Ground Address: Birch Road, Barnard Castle, Co Durham. Tel: 0833 31766.
Club Secretary: Tim Worley, 17 Newgate, Barnard Castle,Co Durham DL12 8NQ. Tel: 0833 37608 (W) 0833 690305.
Club Colours: All black.

BELMONT RUFC
Ground Address: Civil Service Sports Ground, Belmont, Durham. Tel: 091 386 4615.
Club Secretary: G Nangle, 5 Winchester Road, Newton Hall, Durham DH1 5QU. Tel: (H) 091 386 0827 (W) 091 386 2621 x273.
Club Colours: Dark blue/light blue.

BILLINGHAM RUFC
Ground Address: Stadium, Central Avenue, Billingham, Cleveland. Tel: 0642 523788.
Club Secretary: J M Ker, 4 Anlaby Close, Billingham, Cleveland TS23 3RA. Tel: (H) 0642 560536 (W) 0642 560692.
Press Officer: Niall Taylor, 21 Swaledale Crescent, Billingham, Cleveland TS23 1NP. Tel: 0642 535096 (W) 0642 230505.
Club Colours: Green & white hoop shirt & socks; white shorts.

HARTLEPOOL ATHLETIC RFC
Ground Address: Oakesway Estate, Hartlepool, Cleveland TS24 0RE. Tel: 0429 274715.
Club Secretary: Jim Ainslie, 10 Regent Street, Hartlepool, Cleveland TS24 0QN. Tel: (H) 0429 260003 (W) 0836 258317.
Club Colours: Sky blue shirts, white shorts, royal blue socks.

JARROVIANS RUFC
Ground Address: Lukes Lane Estate, Hebburn, Tyne & Wear. Tel: 091 489 3291.
Club Secretary: Steve Softley, 20 Gladstone Street, Hebburn, Tyne & Wear NE31 2XJ. Tel: (H) 091 489 0789 (W) 091 477 2271.
Club Colours: Black & amber hoops.

RICHMONDSHIRE RUFC
Ground Address: Bad Boys Park, Richmondshire Leisure Centre, Barrack Hill, The Garden Village, Richmond, N Yorkshire.
Club Secretary: S Speakman, 36 Victoria Road, Richmond, N Yorkshire DL10 4AU. Tel: (H) 0748 825579 (W) 0748 850111.
Press Officer: Mr R Craig, 14 Alma Place, Richmond, N Yorkshire. Tel: 0748 826591.
Club Colours: Red, white & gold hoops.

PRUDHOE HOSPITAL RFC
Ground Address: Prudhoe Hospital, Sports & Social Club, Northumberland.
Club Secretary: Gary Bridgeware, 3 Hulcrest Court, Prudhoe, Northumberland NE42 3PQ. Tel: (H) 0661 832772 (W) 061 832501.
Club Colours: Red, white & blue checks.

FINAL TABLE

	P	W	D	L	F	A	PD	Pts
Newton Aycliffe	10	9	0	1	256	103	153	16
Hartlepool BBOB	11	7	2	2	215	165	50	16
Richmondside	10	7	0	3	289	80	209	14
Sedgefield	10	7	0	3	232	113	119	14
Prudhoe	10	6	1	3	127	89	38	13
Jarrovians	10	5	0	5	182	110	72	10
Wearside	10	5	0	5	170	145	25	8
Washington	10	4	0	6	100	242	-142	8
Hartlepool Athletic	9	0	2	7	70	165	-35	2
Durham Civil Service	10	2	0	8	115	264	-149	2
Shildon	10	0	1	9	46	381	-335	1

SEDGEFIELD RUFC
Ground Address: Sedgefield Community College, Stockton-on-Tees, Cleveland. Tel: 0740 21097.
Club Secretary: Neil Hetherington, 1 The Meadows, Sedgefield, Stockton-on-Tees, Cleveland. Tel: (H) 0740 21179 (W) 0836 292665.
Club Colours: Red & black quarters; black shorts; black socks with red tops.

SHILDON TOWN RUFC
Ground Address: Sunnydale Leisure Centre, Middridge Lane, Shildon. Tel: 0388 777340.
Club Secretary: Peter Plews, 14 Alexandra Street, Shildon, Co Durham DL4 2EY. Tel: 0388 777334.
Club Colours: Red & green quarters.

WASHINGTON RUFC
Ground Address: Northumbria Centre, Northern Area Playing Fields, Stephenson Industrial Estate, Washington, Tyne & Wear.
Club Secretay: Ian Cruickshank, 20 Martin Court, Ayton Village, Washington, Tyne & Wear NE38 0AD. Tel: 415 4655.
Club Colours: Blue & gold stripes.

WEARSIDE RUFC
Ground Address: Bede School, Durham Road, Sunderland.
Club Secretary: George Constable, 9 Violet Street, Millfield, Sunderland.
Press Officer: Gary Cuminskey, 5 Violet Street, Millfield.
Club Colours: Red & blue hoops.

NORTHERN DIVISION

YORKSHIRE ONE 1993-94 FIXTURES

October 23 (Week 8)
Malton & Norton v Leodiensians
Old Otliensians v Ilkley
North Ribblesdale v Bradford Salem
York R.I. v Wheatley Hills
Yarnbury v Wath
Sheffield Oaks v Pocklington

October 30 (Week X2)
Pocklington v Malton & Norton
Wath v Sheffield Oaks
Wheatley Hills v Yarnbury
Bradford Salem v York R.I.
Ilkley v North Ribblesdale
Hemsworth v Old Otliensians

November 13 (Week 10)
Malton & Norton v Wath
Leodiensians v Pocklington
North Ribblesdale v Hemsworth
York R.I. v Ilkley
Yarnbury v Bradford Salem
Sheffield Oaks v Wheatley Hills

November 20 (Week 11)
Wath v Leodiensians
Wheatley Hills v Malton & Norton
Bradford Salem v Sheffield Oaks
Ilkley v Yarnbury
Hemsworth v York R.I.
Old Otliensians v North Ribblesdale

December 4 (Week 13)
Malton & Norton v Bradford Salem
Leodiensians v Wheatley Hills
Pocklington v Wath
York R.I. v Old Otliensians
Yarnbury v Hemsworth
Sheffield Oaks v Ilkley

December 11 (Week 14)
Wheatley Hills v Pocklington
Bradford Salem v Leodiensians
Ilkley v Malton & Norton
Hemsworth v Sheffield Oaks
Old Otliensians v Yarnbury
North Ribblesdale v York R.I.

December 18 (Week 15)
Malton & Norton v Hemsworth
Leodiensians v Ilkley
Pocklington v Bradford Salem
Wath v Wheatley Hills
Yarnbury v North Ribblesdale
Sheffield Oaks v Old Otliensians

January 8 (Week 18)
Bradford Salem v Wath
Ilkley v Pocklington
Hemsworth v Leodiensians
Old Otliensians v Malton & Norton
North Ribblesdale v Sheffield Oaks
York R.I. v Yarnbury

January 29 (Week X5)
Malton & Norton v North Ribblesdale
Leodiensians v Old Otliensians
Pocklington v Hemsworth
Wath v Ilkley
Wheatley Hills v Bradford Salem
Sheffield Oaks v York R.I.

February 12 (Week 22)
Ilkley v Wheatley Hills
Hemsworth v Wath
Old Otliensians v Pocklington
North Ribblesdale v Leodiensians
York R.I. v Malton & Norton
Yarnbury v Sheffield Oaks

March 12 (Week 26)
Malton & Norton v Yarnbury
Leodiensians v York R.I.
Pocklington v North Ribblesdale
Wath v Old Otliensians
Wheatley Hills v Hemsworth
Bradford Salem v Ilkley

March 26 (Week 28)
Hemsworth v Bradford Salem
Old Otliensians v Wheatley Hills
North Ribblesdale v Wath
York R.I. v Pocklington
Yarnbury v Leodiensians
Sheffield Oaks v Malton & Norton

April 9 (Week 30)
Leodiensians v Sheffield Oaks
Pocklington v Yarnbury
Wath v York R.I.
Wheatley Hills v North Ribblesdale
Bradford Salem v Old Otliensians
Ilkley v Hemsworth

348

YORKSHIRE ONE

BRADFORD SALEM RFC
Ground Address: Shay Lane, Haeton, Bradford, BD9 6SL.
Tel No: O274 496430.
Club Secretary: M N Sweeney, 83 Hollybank Road,
Poradpad, BD7 4QL. Tel No: O274 573037 (W) O532
439301.
Press Officer: M Martindale, The Victoria House, 15
Salisbury St, Calverley, LS28 5PY. Tel No: O532 574412
(W) O274 370902.
Club Colours: Royal Blue/black/gold quarters.

HEMSWORTH RUFC
Ground Address: Moxon Fields, Lowfield Road, Hemsworth,
Pontefract, West Yorkshire WF9 4JT. Tel: O977 610078.
Club Secretary: Mark Roberts, "The
Elms", Stockinggate/South Kirkby/Pontefract WF9 3QX.
Tel No: (H)O977 644379 (W) same.
Club Colours: Navy blue shirts, shorts and socks.

ILKLEY RUFC
Ground Address: Stacks Field, Denton Road,Ilkley, W
Yorks. Tel No: O943 6O7037
Club Secretary: Patrick Lee, 64 Station Road, Burley-in-
Wharfedale, W Yorks. Tel No: (H) O943 862599 (W)
O532 577617.
Press Officer:Andy Munro, 15 Margerison Road, Ben
Rhydding, Ilkey. Tel No:O943 6O2579 (W) O943 6O2855.
Club Colours: Red, white and black.

LEODIENSIAN RUFC
Ground Address: Cragg Lane, Alwoodley, Leeds 17. Tel
No: O532 673409.
Club Secretary: Hugh Dorring, 17 Newlaithes Gardens,
Horsforth, Leeds, LS18 4JW. Tel No: (H) O532 59O6O7
(W) O532 444421.
Press Officer: Chris White, 2 Moor Allerton Crescent,
Alwoodley, Leeds 17. Tel No: O532 664839 (W) O532
434837.
Club Colours: Navy blue and gold.

MALTON & NORTON RUFC
Ground Address: Peasey Hill Road, Pasture Lane, Malton,
North Yorkshire. Tel No: O653 694657.
Club Secretary:C Whincup, The Aboretum Keld Head
Hall, Middleton Road, Pickering, N York YO18 8NR. Tel
No: O751 73149.
Club Colours: Black/Red/White hoops.

NORTH RIBBLESDALE RUFC
Ground Address: Grove Park, Settle. Tel No: O729 822755.
Club Secretary: R T Graveson, Attermire House, Castle
Hill, Settle, North Yorkshire, BD24 9EU. Tel No: (H)
O729 823559 (W) O729 825252.
Club Colours: Royal blue and white.

OLD OTLIENSIANS RUFC
Ground Address: Chaffers Field, Pool Road, Otley, West
Yorkshire. Tel No: O943 461476.
Club Secretary: John Kerby, 24 Meadow Lane, N Yorks,
MG3 2PH. Tel No: (H) O423 780968 (W) O423 885959
EX 3075.
Press Officer: John Kerby.
Club Colours: Royal blue, navy blue and white hoops.

POCKLINGTON RUFC
Ground Address: Percy Road, Pocklington, York. Tel No:
O759 3O3358.
Club Secretary: M B Herring, 34 Hill Rise Drive, Market
Weighton, York YO4 3JZ. Tel No: (H) O430 872156 (W)
O482 666198.
Press Officer: P G Gilbank, 48 George Street, Pocklington,
York. Tel No: (H) O759 3O5888.
Club Colours: Navy and white hoops.

FINAL TABLE

	P	W	D	L	F	A	PD	Pts
Goole	12	10	0	2	285	84	201	20
Bradford Salem	12	10	0	2	253	129	124	20
Sheffield Oaks	12	10	0	2	201	108	93	20
Wheatley Hills	12	9	0	3	260	108	152	18
Leodiensians	12	9	0	3	200	134	66	18
North Ribblesdale	12	8	0	4	183	105	78	14
Malton & Norton	12	5	0	7	228	177	51	10
Yarnbury	12	5	0	7	180	230	-50	10
Pocklington	12	4	1	7	164	158	6	9
Old Otliensians	12	3	0	9	126	255	-129	6
Hemsworth	12	2	1	9	124	231	-107	5
York RI	12	2	0	10	157	335	-178	4
Castleford	12	0	0	12	49	395	-346	0

SHEFFIELD OAKS RUFC
Ground Address: Limestone Cottage, Claywheels Lane,
Sheffield.
Club Secretary: M r K J W Mallinson, 8 Ashurst Drive,
Stannington, Sheffield S6 5LL. Tel No: (H) O742 333078
(W) O742 3O3937.
Press Officer: Mr G Davies, The Griffs Lodge, Stopes
Road,Stannington, Sheffield, S6 6BW. Tel No: O742
335829 (W) O742 63O222 EXT 6386.
Club Colours: Royal blue and gold hoops.

WATH RUFC
Ground Address: Moor Road, Wath Upon Deane,
Rotherham, S Yorkshire. Tel No: O7O9 872399.
Club Secretary: M Criddle, 45 Sandbeck Road,
Bennethorpe, Doncaster, S Yorkshire. Tel No: (H) O3O2
368518 (W) O3O2 320444.
Press Officer: G Scherdel, Newburn Hse, 63 Rig Drive,
Swinton, Rotherham. Tel No: (H)O7O9 873398 (W) O532
425994.
Club Colours: Blue with maroon gold bands.

WHEATLEY HILLS RUFC
Ground Address: Wheatley Hills Sports Ground, Brunel
Road, York Road, Industrial Estate, Doncaster DN5 8PT
Yorkshire. Tel No: O3O2 781472
Club Secretary: A R Dunkerley, 1 Mayfields Scawthorpe,
Doncaster DN5 7UA, Yorkshire. Tel No: (H) O3O2
782214 (W) O7O9 522292.
Press Officer: T Clayton, 23 Fairfield Road, York Road,
Doncaster, DN5 9BN Yorkhire. Tel NO: (H) O3O2 783471
(W) O972 581919 x 235.
Club Colours: Maroon and gold quarters, maroon shorts.

YARNBURY HORSFORTH RUFC
Ground Address: Brownberrie Lane, Horsforth, Leeds,
LS18 5HB, Tel No.O532 581346.
Club Secretary: Brian Griffiths, 27 West End Lane,
Horsforth, Leeds, LS18 5JP. Tel No: (H)587OOO.
Press Officer: Philip Baston, 35 Green Lane, Rawdon,
Leeds. Tel No: (H) 5O8494.
Club Colours: Blue, black, white.

YORK RAILWAY INSTITUTE RUFC
Ground Address: New Lane, Acomb, York. Tel No:
O9O4 79893O
Club Secretary: Sean Heslop, 98 Malvern Avenue, Acomb,
York YO2 5SG. Tel No: (h) O9O4 79793O (W) O9O4 524662
Press Officer: James Naylor, 4 Meadow Court,
Dringhouses, York, YO2 2JF. Tel No:(H) O9O4 7O4884.
Club Colours: Blue and white hooped shirts and socks,
black shorts.

NORTHERN DIVISION

YORKSHIRE TWO
1993-94
FIXTURES

December 18 (Week 15)
Dinnington v Northallerton
Old Modernians v Huddersfield YMCA
Hessle v Moortown
Halifax Vandals v West Leeds
Leeds CCSA v Barnsley
Sheffield Tigers v Scarborough

October 23 (Week 8)
Dinnington v Old Modernians
Scarborough v Huddersfield YMCA
Barnsley v Moortown
Castleford v West Leeds
Leeds CCSA v Halifax Vandals
Sheffield Tigers v Hessle

January 8 (Week 18)
Moortown v Halifax Vandals
Huddersfield YMCA v Hessle
Northallerton v Old Modernians
Scarborough v Dinnington
Barnsley v Sheffield Tigers
Castleford v Leeds CCSA

October 30 (Week X2)
Hessle v Dinnington
Halifax Vandals v Sheffield Tigers
West Leeds v Leeds CCSA
Moortown v Castleford
Huddersfield YMCA v Barnsley
Northallerton v Scarborough

January 29 (Week X5)
Dinnington v Barnsley
Old Modernians v Scarborough
Hessle v Northallerton
Halifax Vandals v Huddersfield YMCA
West Leeds v Moortown
Sheffield Tigers v Castleford

November 13 (Week 10)
Dinnington v Halifax Vandals
Old Modernians v Hessle
Barnsley v Northallerton
Castleford v Huddersfield YMCA
Leeds CCSA v Moortown
Sheffield Tigers v West Leeds

February 12 (Week 22)
Huddersfield YMCA v West Leeds
Northallerton v Halifax Vandals
Scarborough v Hessle
Barnsley v Old Modernians
Castleford v Dinnington
Leeds CCSA v Sheffield Tigers

November 20 (Week 11)
Halifax Vandals v Old Modernians
West Leeds v Dinnington
Moortown v Sheffield Tigers
Huddersfield YMCA v Leeds CCSA
Northallerton v Castleford
Scarborough v Barnsley

March 12 (Week 26)
Dinnington v Leeds CCSA
Old Modernians v Castleford
Hessle v Barnsley
Halifax Vandals v Scarborough
West Leeds v Northallerton
Moortown v Huddersfield YMCA

December 4 (Week 13)
Dinnington v Moortown
Old Modernians v West Leeds
Hessle v Halifax Vandals
Castleford v Scarborough
Leeds CCSA v Northallerton
Sheffield Tigers v Huddersfield YMCA

March 26 (Week 28)
Northallerton v Moortown
Scarborough v West Leeds
Barnsley v Halifax Vandals
Castleford v Hessle
Leeds CCSA v Old Modernians
Sheffield Tigers v Dinnington

December 11 (Week 14)
West Leeds v Hessle
Moortown v Old Modernians
Huddersfield YMCA v Dinnington
Northallerton v Sheffield Tigers
Scarborough v Leeds CCSA
Barnsley v Castleford

April 9 (Week 30)
Old Modernians v Sheffield Tigers
Hessle v Leeds CCSA
Halifax Vandals v Castleford
West Leeds v Barnsley
Moortown v Scarborough
Huddersfield YMCA v Northallerton

YORKSHIRE TWO

BARNSLEY RUFC
Ground Address: Wombwell Lane, Stairfoot, Barnsley,
South Yorkshire. Tel: 0226 284344.
Club Secretary: P M Stephens, 4 Bentham Way,
Mapplewell, Barnsley, S75 5QA. Tel: (H) 0226 386473
(W) 0924 280444.
Press Officer: D West, 10 Pollit Street, Barnsley, S71 1DJ.
Tel: (H) 0226 281783.
Club Colours: Red, white, navy blue hoops.

CASTLEFORD RUFC
Ground Address: Willowbridge Lane, Whitwood,
Castleford, West Yorkshire. Tel: 0977 554762.
Club Secretary: D M Botham, 11 Pondsfield Close,
Kippax, Leeds, LS25 7HN. Tel: (H) 0532 869591 (W)
0532 579001.
Press Officer: D M Botham, 11 Pondsfield Close, Kippax,
Leeds, LS25 7HN. Tel: (H) 0532 869591 (W) 0532 579001.
Club Colours: Red & blue hoops.

DINNINGTON RUFC
Ground Address: Lodge Lane, Dinnington, Sheffield,
South Yorkshire, S31 7PB. Tel: 0909 562044.
Club Secretary: M Burke, 5 Roon Walk, Dinnington,
Sheffield, South Yorkshire, S31 7AQ. Tel: (H) 0909
564712.
Press Officer: M Burke, 5 Troon Walk, Dinnington,
Sheffield, South Yorkshire, S31 7AQ. Tel: (H) 0909
564712.
Club Colours: Blue, white & gold hoops.

HALIFAX VANDALS RUFC
Ground Address: Warley Town Lane, Warley, Halifax,
West Yorkshire, HX2 7SA. Tel: 0422 831703.
Club Secretary: Andrew Ward, 124 Ravenstone Drive,
Greetland, Halifax, West Yorkshire, HX4 8DY. Tel: (H)
0422 371999 (W) 0422 824186.
Press Officer: Stephen C Beard, 2 Silverwood Walk,
Pellon, Halifax, West Yorkshire, HX2 0QR. Tel: (H) 0422
353099 (W) 0484 719642.
Club Colours: Blue & white thin hoops, dark blue shorts.

HESSLE RUFC
Ground Address: Livingstone Road, Hessle, North
Humberside, HU13 0EG. Tel: 0482 643430.
Club Secretary: D P Sewell, 67 Barrow Lane, Hessle,
North Humberside, HU13 0QB. Tel: (H) 0482 645191 (W)
0482 869286.
Press Officer: J C Nunns, 58 Station Road, Hessle, North
Humberside, HU13 0BG. Tel: (H) 0482 647808.
Club Colours: Green, black & white hoops, white shorts.

HUDDERSFIELD YMCA RUFC
Ground Address: Laund Hill Sports Ground, Salendine
Nook, Huddersfield. Tel: 0484 654052.
Club Secretary: Ian Leask, 3 Cheviot Way, Mirfield, West
Yorkshire, WF14 8HW. Tel: (H) 0924 496448 (W) 0706
32512.
Press Officer: Paul Hampson, 8 Fixby Park Drive, Fixby,
Huddersfield, HD2 2NN. Tel: (H) 0484 531942.
Club Colours: Black & red hoops, black shorts.

LEEDS CIVIL SERVICE RUFC
Ground Address: Civil Service Sports Ground, Newton
Road, Leeds.
Club Secretary: David G Smith, 46 Highfield Avenue,
Wortley, Leeds, LS12 4BY. Tel: (H) 0532 790365.
Press Officer: Steve sykes, 96 Leasowe Road, Leeds,
LS10 2EZ. Tel: (H) 0532 779156.
Club Colours: Red, gold & black hoops.

MOORTOWN RUFC
Ground Address: Moss Valley (off The Avenue),
Alwoodley, Leeds. Tel: 0532 678243.

FINAL TABLE

	P	W	D	L	F	A	PD	Pts
Wath	12	12	0	0	245	75	170	22
Ilkley	12	10	0	2	383	57	326	20
Old Modernians	12	9	0	3	172	121	51	18
Barnsley	12	8	0	4	268	113	155	16
Northallerton	12	6	1	5	117	153	-36	13
Scarborough	12	6	1	5	117	181	-64	13
Huddersfield YMCA	12	5	1	6	123	171	-48	11
Moortown	12	4	1	7	120	173	-53	9
Sheffield Tigers	12	4	0	8	133	159	-26	8
Dinnington	12	4	0	8	160	240	-80	8
West Leeds	12	4	0	8	105	241	-136	8
Leeds CSSA	12	2	0	10	137	286	-149	4
Knottingley	12	2	0	10	67	222	-155	2

Club Secretary: G Spark, 7 Hall Cliffe Grove, Harbury,
Wakefield, W. Green, WF4 6DE. Tel: (H) 0924 271808.
Press Officer: G Spark, 7 Hall Cliffe Grove, Harbury,
Wakefield, W. Green, WF4 6DE. Tel: (H) 0924 271808.
Club Colours: Maroon, green & white hoops.

NORTHALLERTON RUFC
Ground Address: Brompton lodge, Northallerton Road,
Brompton,Northallerton, DL6 2PZ. Tel: 0609 773496.
Club Secretary: S Hague, 14 The Stonebow,
thornton-le-Beans, Northallerton, North Yorkshire. Tel: (H)
0609 774325 (W) 0609 780780 Ext 2216.
Press Officer: Mike Beech, 2 Grange Cottages,
Breckenborough, Thirsk, North Yorkshire, YO7 4El. Tel:
(H) 0845 587328 (W) 0642 248155 Ext 3207.
Club Colours: Green, amber & white.

OLD MODERNIANS RUFC
Ground Address: Cookridge Lane, Cookridge, Leeds,
LS16 7ND. Tel: 0532 671075.
Club Secretary: Kevin R Shotton, 11 Adwalton Close,
Drighlington, Bradford, BD11 1DQ. Tel: (H) 0532
851896(W) 0484 710327.
Press Officer: Brian Doule, 74 Hall Park Avenue, Horsforth,
Leeds, LS18 5LU. Tel: (H) 0532 587478 (W) 0532 434103.
Club Colours: Red & black hoops, black shorts.

SCARBOROUGH RUFC
Ground Address: The Clubhouse, Scalby Road,
Scarborough, North Yorkshire, YO12 6EE. Tel: 0723
363039.
Club Secretary: Susan G Hanson, The Clubhouse, Scalby
Road, Scarborough, North Yorkshire, YO12 6EE. Tel: (W)
0723 363039.
Press Officer: David Campbell, 58 Scalby Avenue,
Scarborough, North Yorkshire. Tel: (H) 0723 376339(W)
0723 367431.
Club Colours: Maroon, navy & white.

SHEFFIELD TIGERS RUFC
Ground Address: Hathersage Road, Dore Moor, Sheffield,
S17 3AB. Tel: 0742 360075.
Club Secretary: Martin Caine, 20 Sandy Acres Drive,
Waterthorpe, Sheffield, S19 6LS. Tel: (H) 0742 489052
(W) 0602 620532.
Club Colours: Maroon & white hoops, black shorts.

WEST LEEDS RUFC
Ground Address: Blue Hill Lane, Wortley, leeds, LS12.
Tel: 0532 639869.
Club Secretary: G W Falding, 20 Walkers Lane, Wortley,
Leeds, LS12 4AP. Tel: (H) 0532 639989.
Club Colours: Navy, old gold & white.

NORTHERN DIVISION

YORKSHIRE THREE
1993-94
FIXTURES

December 18 (Week 15)
Wetherby v Marist
Hullensians v Old Rishworthians
Leeds YMCA v Aireborough
Leeds Corinthians v Knottingley
Burley v Rodillians
Heath v Wibsey

October 23 (Week 8)
Wetherby v Hullensians
Wibsey v Old Rishworthians
Rodillians v AireBorough
Ossett v Knottingley
Burley v Leeds Corinthians
Heath v Leeds YMCA

January 8 (Week 18)
Aireborough v Leeds Corinthians
Old Rishworthians v Leeds YMCA
Marist v Hullensians
Wibsey v Wetherby
Rodillians v Heath
Ossett v Burley

October 30 (Week X2)
Leeds YMCA v Wetherby
Leeds Corinthians v Heath
Knottingley v Burley
Aireborough v Ossett
Old Rishworthians v Rodillians
Marist v Wibsey

January 29 (Week X5)
Wetherby v Rodillians
Hullensians v Wibsey
Leeds YMCA v Marist
Leeds Corinthians v Old Rishworthians
Knottingley v Aireborough
Heath v Ossett

November 13 (Week 10)
Wetherby v Leeds Corinthians
Hullensians v Leeds YMCA
Rodillians v Marist
Ossett v Old Rishworthians
Burley v Aireborough
Heath v Knottingley

February 12 (Week 22)
Old Rishworthians v Knottingley
Marist v Leeds Corinthians
Wibsey v Leeds YMCA
Rodillians v Hullensians
Ossett v Wetherby
Burley v Heath

November 20 (Week 11)
Leeds Corinthians v Hullensians
Knottingley v Wetherby
Aireborough v Heath
Old Rishworthians v Burley
Marist v Ossett
Wibsey v Rodillians

March 12 (Week 26)
Wetherby v Burley
Hullensians v Ossett
Leeds YMCA v Rodillians
Leeds Corinthians v Wibsey
Knottingley v Marist
Aireborough v Old Rishworthians

December 4 (Week 13)
Wetherby v Aireborough
Hullensians v Knottingley
Leeds YMCA v Leeds Corinthians
Ossett v Wibsey
Burley v Marist
Heath v Old Rishworthians

March 26 (Week 28)
Marist v Aireborough
Wibsey v Knottingley
Rodillians v Leeds Corinthians
Ossett v Leeds YMCA
Burley v Hullensians
Heath v Wetherby

December 11 (Week 14)
Knottingley v Leeds Corinthians
Aireborough v Hullensians
Old Rishworthians v Wetherby
Marist v Heath
Wibsey v Burley
Rodillians v Ossett

April 9 (Week 30)
Hullensians v Heath
Leeds YMCA v Burley
Leeds Corinthians v Ossett
Knottingley v Rodillians
Aireborough v Wibsey
Old Rishworthians v Marist

352

YORKSHIRE THREE

AIREBOROUGH RUFC
Ground Address: 46 Green Lane Cricket Club, Nunrold Park, Yeadon, Leeds, L19. Tel: 0943 878299.
Club Secretary: J R Dolan, 21 Greenfell Close, Fell Lane, Keighley, BD22 6DJ. Tel: (H) 0535 606521 (W) 0532 832500.
Press Officer: J Chapman, 15 Mount Pleasant, Guiseley, Leeds L20. Tel: (H) 0943 878422 (W) 0943 878422.
Club Colours: Maroon & white.

BURLEY RUFC
Ground Address: Clubhouse, Abbey Road, Leeds, LS5 3NG. Tel: 0532 757400.
Club Secretary: Terry McCreedy, 42 Fearnville Place, Leeds, LS8 3DY. Tel: (H) 0532 655065 (W) 0274 727524.
Press Officer: Martin Gosney, 7 Blackwood Avenue, Cookeridge, Leeds, LS16 7BN. Tel: (H) 0532 679758.
Club Colours: Maroon & white.

HEATH RUFC
Ground Address: North Dean, Stainland Road, West Vale, Halifac, HX4 8LS. Tel: 0422 372920.
Club Secretary: Craig Bedford, 58 Hollins Lane, Sowerby Bridge, Halifax, HX6 2RP. Tel: (H) 0422 834473 (W) 0422 373462.
Press Officer: Dave Grayson, 61 Windmill Crescent, Northowram, Halifax. Tel: (H) 0422 206932 (W) 0422 330061.
Club Colours: Claret, gold & emerald.

HULLENSIANS RUFC
Ground Address: Springhead Lane, Anlaby, Hull. Tel: 0482 505656.
Club Secretary: Mark Bayston, 4 Park lane, West Anlaby Park, Hull, HU4 6TU. Tel: (H) 0482 54222 (W) 0482 830367.
Press Officer: Denis Stout, 28 Chestnut Avenue, Willerby, Hull, HU10 6PD. Tel: (H) 0482 651179 (W) 0482 27301.
Club Colours: Red & black.

KNOTTINGLEY RUFC
Ground Address: Howards Field, Marsh Lane, Knottingley, West Yorkshire. Tel: 0977 672438.
Club Secretary: Glen McCusker LLB, 9A Manor Earth, Riccall, Yorkshire, YO4 6QX. Tel: (H) 0757 248548.
Press Officer: Alan Brown, 9 Northfield Road, Knottingley, West yorkshire. Tel: (H) 0977 672438.
Club Colours: Blue & white regular hoops, navy shorts.

LEEDS CORINTHIANS RUFC
Ground Address: Middleton District Centre, Middleton, Leeds 10. Tel: 0532 711574.
Club Secretary: Malcolm Naylor, 9 Staithe Gardens, middleton, Leeds, LS10 3NA. Tel: (H) 0532 705919.
Press Officer: Graham Mapplebeck, 33 Oakley Street, Thorpe, Wakefield, WF3 3DX. Tel: (H) 0924 828809 (W) 0532 457205.
Club Colours: Black with gold trim. Alternative: red.

LEEDS YMCA RUFC
Ground Address: Lawnswood YMCA, Otley Road, Leeds, LS16 6HQ. Tel: 0532 678168.
Club Secretary: Paul Goodhall, 12 Carr Manor Crescent, Leeds, LS17 5DH. Tel: (H) 0532 668974 (W) 0532 629955.
Press Officer: Paul Goodhall, 12 Carr Manor Crescent, Leeds, LS17 5DH. Tel: (H) 0532 668974 (W) 0532 629955.
Club Colours: Light blue & dark blue hoops.

MARIST RUFC
Ground Address: Cranbrook Avenue, Hull. Tel: 0482 859216.
Club Secretary: Dale W Rawson, 27 St Andrews Way, James Reckitt Avenue, Hull, HU8 8JJ. Tel: (H) 0482 798339 (W) 0482 20336.

FINAL TABLE

	P	W	D	L	F	A	PD	Pts
Hessle	12	11	1	0	317	89	228	23
Halifax Vandals	12	10	1	1	213	108	105	21
Hullensians	12	8	0	4	153	119	34	16
Heath	12	7	0	5	146	106	40	14
Wetherby	12	6	1	5	179	147	32	13
Wibsey	12	6	1	5	204	174	30	13
Aireborough	12	6	1	5	140	104	36	11
Rodillians	12	5	1	6	119	142	-23	11
Old Rishworthians	12	4	1	7	107	165	-58	9
Leeds Corinthians	12	4	0	8	119	243	-124	8
Marist	12	3	1	8	123	228	-105	7
Burley	12	2	1	9	114	186	-72	3
Baildon	12	1	1	10	65	193	-128	3

Press Officer: Dale W Rawson, 27 St Andrews Way, James Reckitt Avenue, Hull, HU8 8JJ. Tel: (H) 0482 798339 (W) 0482 20336.
Club Colours: Royal blue & white.

OLD RISHWORTHIAN RUFC
Ground Address: The Clubhouse, Copley, Halifax, West Yorkshire. Tel: 0422 353919.
Club Secretary: D W Butler, Keepers, Shaw Lane, Holywell Green, Halifax. Tel: (H) 0422 371672 (W) 0484 721223.
Press Officer: R Greenwood, 19 Hammerstones Road, Elland, Halifax. Tel: (H) 0422 375706.
Club Colours: Maroon, white & black hoops.

OSSETT RUFC
Ground Address: Spring Mill, off Queens Drive, Ossett, West Yorkshire. Tel: 0924 273618.
Club Secretary: Jeremy Slack, 1 Spa Croft Road, Ossett, West Yorkshire, WF5 0EU. Tel: (H) 0924 273952.
Press Officer: Jeremy Slack, 1 Spa Croft Road, Ossett, West Yorkshire, WF5 0EU. Tel: (H) 0924 273952.
Club Colours: Red & black quarters, black shorts.

STANLEY RODILLIANS RUFC
Ground Address: Manley Park, Lee Moor Road, Stanley, Wakefield, West Yorkshire. Tel: 0924 823619.
Club Secretary: R J Matthews, 27 Newlands Walk, Stanley, Wakefield, WF3 4DT. Tel: (H) 0924 828727 (W) 0924 823135.
Club Colours: Green, black & white hoops, black shorts.

WETHERBY RUFC
Ground Address: Grange Park, Wetherby, West Yorkshire. Tel: 0937 582461.
Club Secretary: G Davies, Fellside, Langwith, Valley Road, collingham, Wetherby. Tel: (H) 0937 572405.
Press Officer: G M Jones, 1 Quarry Hill Lane, Wetherby, West Yorkshire, LS22 4RY. Tel: (H) 0937 582402 (W) 0937 581417.
Club Colours: Red & white hoops.

WIBSEY RUFC
Ground Address: Northfield Road, Wibsey. Tel: 0274 671643/274.
Club Secretary: Martin Spencer, 143 High Street, Wibsey, Bradford. Tel: (H) 0274 605566 (W) 0274 610722
Press Officer: Ian Gregson, c/o Clubhouse.
Club Colours: Red and green hoops.

NORTHERN DIVISION

YORKSHIRE FOUR
1993-94
FIXTURES

October 23 (Week 8)
B.P. Chemicals v Danum Phoenix
De La Salle v Rowntree
Baildon v Skipton
Hornsea v Yorkshire Main
Knaresborough v Phoenix Park
Castle College v Withernsea

October 30 (Week X2)
Withernsea v B.P. Chemicals
Phoenix Park v Castle College
Yorkshire Main v Knaresborough
Skipton v Hornsea
Rowntree v Baildon
Mosborough v De La Salle

November 13 (Week 10)
B.P. Chemicals v Phoenix Park
Danum Phoenix v Withernsea
Baildon v Mosborough
Hornsea v Rowntree
Knaresborough v Skipton
Castle College v Yorkshire Main

November 20 (Week 11)
Phoenix Park v Danum Phoenix
Yorkshire Main v B.P. Chemicals
Skipton v Castle College
Rowntree v Knaresborough
Mosborough v Hornsea
De La Salle v Baildon

December 4 (Week 13)
B.P. Chemicals v Skipton
Danum Phoenix v Yorkshire Main
Withernsea v Phoenix Park
Hornsea v De La Salle
Knaresborough v Mosborough
Castle College v Rowntree

December 11 (Week 14)
Yorkshire Main v Withernsea
Skipton v Danum Phoenix
Rowntree v B.P. Chemicals
Mosborough v Castle College
De La Salle v Knaresborough
Baildon v Hornsea

December 18 (Week 15)
B.P. Chemicals v Mosborough
Danum Phoenix v Rowntree
Withernsea v Skipton
Phoenix Park v Yorkshire Main
Knaresborough v Baildon
Castle College v De La Salle

January 8 (Week 18)
Skipton v Phoenix Park
Rowntree v Withernsea
Mosborough v Danum Phoenix
De La Salle v B.P. Chemicals
Baildon v Castle College
Hornsea v Knaresborough

January 29 (Week X5)
B.P. Chemicals v Baildon
Danum Phoenix v De La Salle
Withernsea v Mosborough
Phoenix Park v Rowntree
Yorkshire Main v Skipton
Castle College v Hornsea

February 12 (Week 22)
Rowntree v Yorkshire Main
Mosborough v Phoenix Park
De La Salle v Withernsea
Baildon v Danum Phoenix
Hornsea v B.P. Chemicals
Knaresborough v Castle College

March 12 (Week 26)
B.P. Chemicals v Knaresborough
Danum Phoenix v Hornsea
Withernsea v Baildon
Phoenix Park v De La Salle
Yorkshire Main v Mosborough
Skipton v Rowntree

March 26 (Week 28)
Mosborough v Skipton
De La Salle v Yorkshire Main
Baildon v Phoenix Park
Hornsea v Withernsea
Knaresborough v Danum Phoenix
Castle College v B.P. Chemicals

April 9 (Week 30)
Danum Phoenix v Castle College
Withernsea v Knaresborough
Phoenix Park v Hornsea
Yorkshire Main v Baildon
Skipton v De La Salle
Rowntree v Mosborough

YORKSHIRE FOUR

BAILDON RUFC
Ground Address: Jenny Lane, Baildon, Shipley, W Yorkshire, BD17 6RS. Tel: 0274 582644.
Club Secretary: R B Hawkins, 30 Moorfield Drive, Baildon, Shipley, W Yorkshire, BD17 6LQ. Tel: (H) 0274 580292 (W) 0831 174171.
Press Officer: J Hyde, 2 Southcliffe Drive, Baildon, BD17 5QX. Tel: (H) 0274 590598 (W) 0274 591382.
Club Colours: Red, white & white hoops.

B P CHEMICALS RUFC
Ground Address: BP Sports & Social Club, Saltend, Hedon Road, Hull, HU12 8DS. Tel: 0482 896251.
Club Secretary: Ian Batty, 349 Ings Road, Sutton, Hull, HU7 4UY. Tel: (H) 0482 77574 (W) 0482 594444.
Press Officer: Ian Batty, 349 Ings Road, Sutton, Hull, HU7 4UY.
Club Colours: Maroon & gold.

CASTLE COLLEGE RUFC
Ground Address: Ash House Lane, Dore, Sheffield 17.
Club Secretary: Andy Cook, 47 Bishop Hill, Woodhouse, Sheffield, S13 7EN. Tel: (H) 0742 696596 (W) 0742 738441 Ext 243.
Club Colours: Black & amber quarters.

DANUM PHOENIX RUFC
Ground Address: ICI Sports & Social Club, Wheatley hall Road, Doncaster. Tel: 0302 364307.
Club Secretary: Martin O'Hara, The Townhouse, 27 Bennetthorpe, Doncaster, DN2 6AA. Tel: (H) 0302 349753.
Press Officer: Richard Cooper-Holmes, 2 Dunscroft Grove, Littleworth Park, Rossington, Doncaster. Tel: 0302 864668.
Club Colours: All black with red & yellow band.

DE LA SALLE (SHEFFIELD) RUFC
Ground Address: De la Salle Association Club, Behind Beauchief Hall, Beauchief Abbey Lane, Sheffield. Tel: 367756.
Club Secretary: Maureen Buckley, 93 Ingram Road, Sheffield, S2 2SB. Tel: (H) 0742 720246.
Press Officer: Tony Buckley, , 93 Ingram Road, Sheffield, S2 2SB. Tel: (H) 0742 720246.
Club Colours: Green & gold hoops.

HORNSEA RUFC
Ground Address: Hollis Recreational Ground, Atwick Road, Hornsea, North Humberside, HU18 1ET. Tel: 0964 534181.
Club Secretary: Dr Ian Sibley-Calder, Westfield, Westwood Avenue, Hornsea, HU18 1ET. Tel: (H) 0964 534925 (W) 0964 532212.
Press Officer: John Dexter, 119 Woodall Lane, Molescroft, Beverley, HU17 7JV. Tel: h0482 872470.
Club Colours: Black with green & white hoops.

KNARESBOROUGH RUFC
Ground Address: Hay-A-Park, Knaresborough, North Yorkshire. Tel: 0423 868976.
Club Secretary: R C Stevenson, 48 Half Penny Lane, Knaresborough, HG5 0NS. Tel: (H) 0423 868976 (W) 0423 866868.
Press Officer: S Collyer, 16 Aspin Park Road, Knaresborough. Tel: (H) 0423 063335.
Club Colours: Navy blue & gold.

MOSBOROUGH RUFC
Ground Address: Westfield Sports Centre, Westfield Crescent, Mosborough, Sheffield, S19 5AQ. Tel: 0742 510376.
Club Secretary: Peter J Bishop, 18 Shaldon Grove, Aston, Sheffield, S31 0DH.

FINAL TABLE

	P	W	D	L	F	A	PD	Pts
Osset	12	12	0	0	234	47	187	24
Leeds YMCA	12	9	0	3	217	86	131	18
De la Salle (Sheff)	12	8	1	3	215	108	107	17
Phoenix Park	12	8	1	3	186	107	79	17
Skipton	12	7	0	5	216	102	114	14
Mosborough	12	7	0	5	192	119	73	14
Danum Phoenix	12	6	1	5	186	127	59	13
Hornsea	12	7	0	5	184	152	32	10
BP Chemicals	12	4	0	8	123	203	-80	8
Castle College	12	3	1	8	130	203	-73	7
Withernsea	12	3	0	9	93	178	-85	6
Yorks Main	12	1	0	11	46	325	-279	0
Yorkshire CW	12	1	0	11	48	344	-296	0

Press Officer: Lawrence Hannan, 12 Stonegravers Croft, Halfway, Sheffield, S19 5HP. Tel: (H) 0742 488425 (W) 0246 854650.
Club Colours: Black & white hoops.

PHOENIX PARK RUFC
Ground Address: Stony Royd, Farsley, Leeds. Tel: 0532 553439.
Club Secretary: Michael Ryan, 280 Whitehall Road, Wyke, Bradford BD12 9DX. Tel: (W) 0274 727886.
Press Officer: Paul Hodgson, 46 Croft Street, Farsley, Leeds. Tel: (H) 0532 550076.
Club Colours: Royal blue, gold & white.

ROWNTREE RUFC
Ground Address: Nestle Rowntree Sportsground, Mille Crux, Haxby Road, York. Tel: 0904 623933.
Club Secretary: C W Maher, 40 Kensington Street, South Bank, York, YO2 1JA. Tel: (H) 638870.
Press Officer: B Cottom, 21 Woodland Place, New Earswick, York. Tel: (H) 766122 (W) 624872 Ext 255.
Club Colours: Red, black & white hoops.

SKIPTON RFC
Ground Address: The Coulthurst Memorial Ground, Sandylands, Skipton, North Yorkshire. Tel: 0756 793148.
Club Secretary: Andrew Clark, 200 Moorview Way, Skipton, North Yorkshire, BD23 2TN. Tel: (H) 0756 798137 (W) 0836 560140.
Press Officer: Andrew Clark, 200 Moorview Way, Skipton, North Yorkshire, BD23 2TN. Tel: (H) 0756 798137 (W) 0836 560140.
Club Colours: Cardinal red.

WITHERNSEA RUFC
Ground Address: Plough Inn, Hollym, North Humberside. Tel: 0964 612049.
Club Secretary: A C Ellis, 11-17 Seaside Road, Withernsea, HU19 2DL. Tel: (H) 0964 613278 (W) 0964 613278.
Press Officer: A Moore, Hawthorne Rise, South End, Roos. Tel: (H) 0964 670429.
Club Colours: White & blue hoops.

YORKSHIRE MAIN RUFC
Ground Address: Miners Welfare, Edlington Lane, Edlington, Doncaster. Tel: 0709 864075.
Club Secretary: Stuart Kalne, 73 Fernleigh Court, Wakefield, W. Yorkshire. Tel: (H) 0924 384561.
Press Officer: S Hanson, 56 Bennetthorpe, Doncaster, S Yorkshire. Tel: 0302 322730.
Club Colours: Green, black, red & white hoops.

NORTHERN DIVISION

YORKSHIRE FIVE
1993-94
FIXTURES

October 23 (Week 8)
Menwith Hill Quakers v Garforth
Yorkshire C.W. v Aldwich le Street
Armthorpe Markham v Rawmarsh
Harlow Nomads v St James

October 30 (Week X2)
Leger v Menwith Hill Quakers
Rawmarsh v Harlow Nomads
Aldwich le Street v Armthorpe Markham
New Earswick v Yorkshire C.W.

November 13 (Week 10)
Menwith Hill Quakers v Stocksbridge
Garforth v Leger
Armthorpe Markham v New Earswick
Harlow Nomads v Aldwich le Street

November 20 (Week 11)
Stocksbridge v Garforth
St James v Menwith Hill Quakers
New Earswick v Harlow Nomads
Yorkshire C.W. v Armthorpe Markham

December 4 (Week 13)
Menwith Hill Quakers v Rawmarsh
Garforth v St James
Leger v Stocksbridge
Harlow Nomads v Yorkshire C.W.

December 11 (Week 14)
St James v Leger
Rawmarsh v Garforth
Aldwich le Street v Menwith Hill Quakers
Armthorpe Markham v Harlow Nomads

December 18 (Week 15)
Menwith Hill Quakers v New Earswick
Garforth v Aldwich le Street
Leger v Rawmarsh
Stocksbridge v St James

January 8 (Week 18)
Rawmarsh v Stocksbridge
Aldwich le Street v Leger
New Earswick v Garforth
Yorkshire C.W. v Menwith Hill Quakers

January 29 (Week X5)
Menwith Hill Quakers v Armthorpe Markham
Garforth v Yorkshire C.W.
Leger v New Earswick
Stocksbridge v Aldwich le Street
St James v Rawmarsh

February 12 (Week 22)
Aldwich le Street v St James
New Earswick v Stocksbridge
Yorkshire C.W. v Leger
Armthorpe Markham v Garforth
Harlow Nomads v Menwith Hill Quakers

March 12 (Week 26)
Garforth v Harlow Nomads
Leger v Armthorpe Markham
Stocksbridge v Yorkshire C.W.
St James v New Earswick
Rawmarsh v Aldwich le Street

March 26 (Week 28)
New Earswick v Rawmarsh
Yorkshire C.W. v St James
Armthorpe Markham v Stocksbridge
Harlow Nomads v Leger

April 9 (Week 30)
Stocksbridge v Harlow Nomads
St James v Armthorpe Markham
Rawmarsh v Yorkshire C.W.
Aldwich le Street v New Earswick

YORKSHIRE FIVE

ADWICK-LE-STREET RUFC
Ground Address: Church Lane Playing fields,
Adwick-le-Street, Doncaster, South Yorkshire. Tel: c/o
Tally Ho! 0302 722372.
Club Secretary: R J Terry, 7 Cranfield Drive, Skellow,
Doncaster, South Yorkshire DN6 8RS. Tel: (H) 0302
727580 (W) 0977 517517.
Press Officer: M A Flanagan, 31 Alexandra Road,
Bentley, Doncaster, South Yorkshire. Tel: (H) 0302 872429.
Club Colours: Light blue/dark blue hoops.

ARMTHORPE MARKHAM RUFC
Ground Address: Church Street Cricket Ground,
Armthorpe, Doncaster.
Club Secretary: Barry Jones, 98 Laburnum Drive,
Armthorpe, Doncaster DN3 3HL. (H) 0302 832804.
Club Colours: Red, black, white, blue quarters.

GARFORTH RUFC
Ground Address: Garforth Community College, Lidgett
Lane, Garforth LS25 1LJ.
Club Secretary: Mr Peter Hazledine, 90 Fairburn Drive,
Garforth, Leeds LS25 2JD. Tel: (H) 0532 866035 (W) 0532
869091.
Club Colours: Gold & royal blue hoop across chest, black
up to chest with scarlet collar & cuffs.

HARLOW NOMADS RUFC
Ground Address: Harrogate Grammar School, Arthurs
Avenue, Harrogate.
Club Secretary: S Robinson, c/o 65 Arthurs Avenue,
Harrogate, North Yorks HG2 0EB. Tel: 0423 568913.
Fixtures Secretary: A Rogerson, 13 Grosvenor Road,
Harrogate. Tel: 0423 564481.
Club Colours: Royal blue jerseys & socks, white shorts.

LEGER RUFC
Ground Address: HM Prison Lindholme, Doncaster,
South Yorkshire. Tel: 0302 846600 x241.
Club Secretary: John Ayre, PE Department, HM Prison
Lindholme, Doncaster, South Yorkshire. Tel: (H) 0302
840696 (W) 0902 846600 x241.
Press Officer: Graham Barber, PE Department, HM Prison
Lindholme, Doncaster, South Yorkshire. Tel: (H) 0302
771146 (W) 0302 846600 x241.
Club Colours: Yellow/green.

MENWITH HILL QUAKERS RUFC
Ground Address: Menwwith Hill Station, Nr Harrogate,
North Yorkshire.
Club Secretary: Richard Brent, Fitness Centre, Menwith
Hill Station, Nr Harrogate HG3 2RF. Tel: 0423 777781.
Club Colours: Green & gold quarters.

NEW EARSWICK RFC
Ground Address: White Rose Avenue, New Earswick,
York. Tel: 0904 750103.
Club Secretary: Howard Elders, 26 Priory Wood Way,
Huntington, York YO3 9TG. Tel: (H) 0904 652471.
Club Colours: Black & white hoops.

RAWMARSH RUFC
Ground Address: Rawmarsh Leisure Centre, Barbers
Avenue, Rawmarsh.
Club Secretary: Alan Parker, 3 McManus Avenue,
Rawmarsh, Rotherham S62 7RD. Tel: (H) 0709 522795.
Club Colours: Black, amber trim. Change kit: Maroon,
yellow & black hoops.

FINAL TABLE

	P	W	D	L	F	A	PD	Pts
Knaresborough	9	9	0	0	219	42	177	18
Rowntrees	9	7	1	1	178	54	124	15
Stocksbridge	9	7	0	2	112	51	61	14
Rawmarsh	9	5	0	4	163	64	99	10
Adwick-le-Street	8	4	1	3	134	71	63	9
St James	8	4	0	4	88	175	-87	8
Garforth	9	3	0	6	84	121	-37	6
New Earswick	8	2	0	6	68	174	-106	4
Armthorpe M'kham	8	1	0	7	34	178	-144	2
Leger	9	0	0	9	44	194	-150	0

ST JAMES'S UNIVERSITY HOSPITAL RUFC
Ground Address: Soldiers Field, Roundhay Road, Leeds
8. Tel: 0532 493650.
Club Secretary: Peter A Billsberry, 74 Compton Crescent,
Leeds LS9 6DQ. Tel: (H) 0532 493650.
Club Colours: Dark blue shirts & socks, white shorts.

STOCKSBRIDGE RUFC
Ground Address: 634 Manchester Road, Stocksbrudge,
Sheffield S30. Tel: 0742 885078.
Club Secretary: Reg Hirst, 2 Haigh Cottages,
Roughbirchworth Lane, Oxspring, Sheffield S30 6YQ. Tel:
(H) 0226 765921.
Club Colours: Royal blue with two white hoops.

YORKSHIRE COPPERWORKS
Ground Address: Haigh Park Road, Stourton, Leeds 10,
Yorshire. Tel: 0532 701715.
Club Secretary: Mark Coleman, PO Box 166, Leeds LS1
1RD. Tel: (H) 0532 820578 (W) 0532 701107.
Club Colours: Blue & gold jersey.

THE BEST PACK IN THE CHAMPIONSHIP.

MIDLAND DIVISION

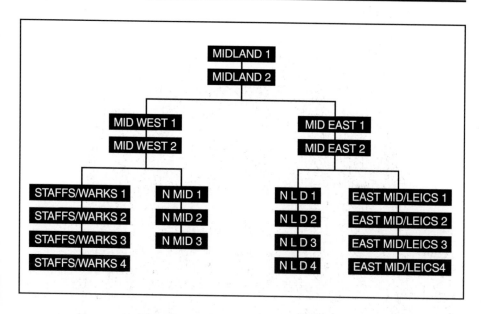

ADMINISTRATIVE RULES

NOTIFICATION OF RESULTS

Club Secretaries are responsible for their club's compliance with the rules of notification of results.

The home club shall notify the appropriate party the result of a league match by telephone by the time stated in the Administrative Instructions.

Both clubs in confirmation of the match played shall return by FIRST CLASS MAIL, the official Match Result Card, completed in all respects to the appropriate officer of the league in accordance with the Administrative Instructions.

Failure to telephone and card in the match results within the time limits laid down shall incur an immediate fine of £15. A second offence a fine of £25 and a third and subsequent offence £25 and a deduction of two league points.

Offending clubs will be notified of fines imposed. Failure to pay within 28 days will result in the offending club being deducted two league points.

There is no right of appeal.

A club with any fines outstanding after its final league game has been played will incur a recommendation to the R.F.U. that the club be suspended or expelled from the league for the following season.

ADMINISTRATIVE INSTRUCTIONS

a. League results to be telephoned to Russells by 5.00pm on the Saturday of the game. Telephone: 0533 872991, Fax: 0533 320064.

b. Match result card to be posted by first class mail on the Monday following the Saturday game.

c. Notification and collection of fines will be administered by the appropriate League Secretary.

COMPUTER PRINTOUTS FOR PLAYERS' REGISTRATIONS

If Clubs require updated printouts for new players a **stamped addressed envelope must be enclosed** with the relevant registration forms and forwarded to the Registrar, PO Box 183, Leicester LE3 8BZ. Otherwise it will be assumed that an updated printout is not required. It is essential that all Clubs appoint an officer to be responsible for all registration matters.

POSTPONED GAMES

The home club shall notify the appropriate party and the League Secretary of a postponed fixture.

Postponed games must be played on the first available non league/non cup weekend unless the club has been informed by the League Secretary of an alternative formula before the start of the season.

THE BEST PACK IN THE CHAMPIONSHIP.

MIDLAND DIVISION

CHAIRMAN
David Robins, Rugby House, Upper Chase Road, Malvern WR14 2BU (H) 0684 564826 (B) 0684 560247 (Fax) 0684 893125

HON. SECRETARY
Michael Wilson, 6 New Road, Easton-on-the-Hill, Stamford, Lincs. PE9 3NN

LEAGUE SECRETARIES
Midland One David Coe, 114 Harborough Road, Desborough, Northants NN14 2QY (H) 0536 761637 (B) 0536 402551 x 3112 (Fax) 0536 402680
Midland Two Geoff Goodall, 38 Presthills Road, Hinckley, Leics LE10 1AJ (H) 0455 238742 (B) 0203 562650 (Fax) 0203 563816
Midland East One Mike Bracy, 9 Wardown Court, New Bedford Road, Luton, Beds LU3 1LH (H) 0582 24144 (B) 021 327 3399 (Fax) 021 327 5122
Midland West One Pat Dally, 153 Masshouse Lane, Kings Norton, Birmingham B38 9AD (H) 021 459 3930 (B) 021 451 1535 (Fax) 021 433 3737
Midland East Two Brian Johnston, 9 Nursery Close, Atworth, Melksham, Wilts SN12 8HX (H) 0225 790658 (B) 0249 442771 (Fax) 0249 442865
Midland West Two Simon Peace, 12 Alfreda Avenue, Hollywood, Worcs B47 5BP (H) 021 474 4142
Staffs/Warks One Keith Dale, 14 St Anthony's Drive, Newcastle, Staffs ST5 2JE (H) 0782 615770
Staffs/Warks Two Bruce Braithwaite, 4 Badgers Croft, Eccleshall, Staffs ST21 6DS (H) 0785 851114 (B) 0785 277330
Staffs/Warks Three & Four Ray Roberts, 261 Alwyn Road, Bilston, Rugby, Warks (H) 0788 810276
North Midland One Chris Parsons, 15 Silverbirch Drive, Wythall, Worcs B47 5RB (H) 021 474 4785
North Midland Two John McNally, 490 Brook Lane, Moseley, Birmingham B13 0BZ (H) 021 604 6180 (B) 021 783 7232 (Fax) 021 789 8306
North Midland Three Jeff Hughes, 17 Lynn Brook Close, Hollywood, Worcs. (H) 021 430 3313
Notts/Lincs & Derby One Kevin Price, 14 Seagrave Road, Thrussington, Leicestershire. (H) 0664 424388
Notts/Lincs & Derby Two Paul Raymont, 10 Thornham Crescent, Kirkby-in-Ashfield, Nottinghamshire N17 9GB. (B) 0623 750990
Notts/Lincs & Derby Three David H Murphy, The Old Carpenters Arms, 32 High Street, Little Bytham, Grantham, Lincolnshire NG33 4QX (H) 0780 410692

Notts/Lincs & Derby Four Carol Godfrey, 31 George Street, Worksop, Nottinghamshire S80 1QJ. (H) 0909 482439 (B) 0909 475284 x 219
East Midland/Leicestershire One & Four Paul Adams, 323a Bedford Road, Kempston, Beds. MK42 8QB. (H) 0234 853390 (F) 0234 857552
East Midland/Leicestershire Two Michael King, 53 Kettering Road, Market Harborough, Leics. (H) 0858 467267
East Midland/Leicestershire Three Bob Ingledew, 15 Martin Close, Bedford MK41 7JY. (H) 0234 268482

MIDLAND DIVISION

MIDLAND ONE
1993-94
FIXTURES

December 18 (Week 15)
Barkers Butts v Westleigh
Campt Hill v Towcestrians
Derby v Burton
Leighton Buzzard v Leamington
Wolverhampton v Mansfield
Worcester v Bedford

October 23 (Week 8)
Bedworth v Leamington
Camp Hill v Barkers Butts
Mansfield v Westleigh
Syston v Burton
Wolverhampton v Leighton Buzzard
Worcester v Derby

January 8 (Week 18)
Bedworth v Wolverhampton
Leamington v Derby
Mansfield v Camp Hill
Syston v Worcester
Towcestrians v Barker Butts
Westleigh v Leighton Buzzard

October 30 (Week X2)
Burton v Worcester
Derby v Wolverhampton
Leamington v Syston
Leighton Buzzard v Camp Hill
Towcestrians v Mansfield
Westleigh v Bedworth

January 29 (Week X5)
Barkers Butts v Mansfield
Burton v Leamington
Camp Hill v Bedworth
Derby v Westleigh
Leighton Buzzard v Towcestrians
Wolverhampton v Syston

November 13 (Week 10)
Barkers Butts v Leighton Buzzard
Bedworth v Towcestrians
Camp Hill v Derby
Syston v Westleigh
Wolverhampton v Burton
Worcester v Leamington

February 12 (Week 22)
Bedworth v Barkers Butts
Mansfield v Leighton Buzzard
Syston v Camp Hill
Towcestrians v Derby
Westleigh v Burton
Worcester v Wolverhampton

November 20 (Week 11)
Burton v Camp Hill
Derby v Barkers Butts
Leamington v Wolverhampton
Mansfield v Bedworth
Towcestrians v Syston
Westleigh v Worcester

March 12 (Week 26)
Barkers Butts v Syston
Burton v Towcestrians
Camp Hill v Worcester
Derby v Mansfield
Leamington v Westleigh
Leighton Buzzard v Bedworth

December 4 (Week 13)
Barkers Butts v Burton
Camp Hill v Leamington
Leighton Buzzard v Derby
Syston v Mansfield
Wolverhampton v Westleigh
Worcester v Towcestrians

March 26 (Week 28)
Bedworth v Derby
Mansfield v Burton
Syston v Leighton Buzzard
Towcestrians v Leamington
Wolverhampton v Camp Hill
Worcester v Barkers Butts

December 11 (Week 14)
Bedworth v Syston
Burton v Leighton Buzzard
Leamington v Barkers Butts
Mansfield v Worcester
Towcestrians v Wolverhampton
Westleigh v Camp Hill

April 9 (Week 30)
Barkers Butts v Wolverhampton
Burton v Bedworth
Derby v Syston
Leamington v Mansfield
Leighton Buzzards v Worcester
Westleigh v Towcestrians

MIDLAND ONE

BANKERS BUTTS RFC
Ground Address: Pickford Grange Lane, Allesley, Coventry. Tel:0676 22192.
Club Secretary: B J Pearson, 61 Frobisher Road, Styveelisle, Coventry, West Midlands, CV5 9AR. Tel: (H) 0203 402121 (W) 0203 402121.
Press Officer: P J Jackson, 87 Gretna Road, Green Lane South, Coventry, CV3 6DT. Tel: (H) 0203 419595.
Club Colours: Royal Blue/Gold.

BEDWORTH RFC
Ground Address: Rectory Fields, Sharts Road, Bedworth, Warwickshire. Tel: 0203 312025.
Club Secretary: D Hatfield, 17 New Road, Ash Green, Exhall, Coventry, West Midlands. Tel: (H) 0203 365160 (W) 0203 362399.
Press Officer: N Brown, 20 Rosemerry Way, Hinckley, Leicestershire, LE10 0LH. Tel: (H) 0455 230840 (W) 0203 350505.
Club Colours: Green shirt, white shorts.

BURTON FC
Ground Address: Peel Croft, Lichfield Street, Burton on Trent, Staffordshire. Tel: 0283 64510.
Club Secretary: J D Lowe, 20 The Chevin, Stretton, Burton on Trent, Staffordshire, DE14 3RH. Tel: (H) 0283 34422.
Press Officer: Simon Archer, Burton Mail, 65-68 High Street, Burton on Trent, DE14 1LE. Tel: (W) 0283 512345
Club Colours: White shirt with black diagonal band.

CAMP HILL RFC
Ground Address: Haslucks Green Road, Shirley, Solihull, West Midlands. Tel: 021 744 4175.
Club Secretary: Russell Homer, c/o Kidsons Impey, Bank House, 8 Cherry Street, Birmingham. Tel: (H) 021 631 2631 (W) 021 705 2462.
Press Officer: Paul Twiby, 167 Rowood Drive, Solihill, B92 9LL. Tel: (H) 021 705 2462 (W) 021 705 2462.
Club Colours: Maroon & light blue.

DERBY RFC
Ground Address: Kedleston Road, Derby. Tel: 0322 44341.
Club Secretary: Jan Newbury, 3 Denver Road, Mickleover, Derby. Tel: (H) 0322 516854.
Press Officer: Gerry Sherry, 22 Brading Close, Alvaston, Derby. Tel: (H) 0322 7552319.
Club Colours: Black & amber.

LEAMINGTON RFC
Ground Address: Moorfields, Kenilworth Road, Leamington Spa, Warwickshire. Tel: 0926 425584.
Club Secretary: Sylvia Mallinson, 2 Bonneville Close, Allesley, Coventry, CV5 9QH. Tel: (H) 0676 22388.
Press Officer: John Oxlenbould, 10 Leicester Lane, Leamington Spa, Warwickshire. Tel: (H) 0926 427164.
Club Colours: Royal blue with single scarlet & gold hoop.

LEIGHTON BUZZARD RFC
Ground Address: "Wrights Meadow", Leighton Road, Stanbridge, Leighton Buzzard, Bedfordshire. Tel: 0525 371322.
Club Secretary: J McCormack, 15 Neptune Gardens, Leighton Buzzard. Tel: (H) 0525 378194 (W) 081 346 1676.
Club Colours: Blue & white hoop, blue shorts.

MANSFIELD RUFC
Ground Address: Eakring Road, Mansfields, Nottinghamshire. Tel: 0623 6498364.
Club Secretary: Keith Bingley, Lamins Lane, Bestwood Park, Nottingham, NF6 8UJ. Tel: (H) 0602 208943 (W) 0623 25821.

FINAL TABLE

	P	W	D	L	F	A	PD	Pts
Birmingham Solihull	13	11	1	1	250	107	143	23
Barkers Butts	13	10	1	2	255	128	127	21
Leamington	13	9	0	4	235	218	17	18
Syston	13	7	2	4	224	114	110	16
Camp Hill	13	7	0	6	137	204	-67	14
Bedworth	13	6	1	6	202	152	50	13
Derby	13	6	1	6	189	170	19	13
Wolverhampton	13	6	0	7	174	126	48	12
Westleigh	13	6	0	7	129	167	-38	12
Leighton Buzzard	13	6	0	7	143	209	-66	12
Mansfield	13	5	1	7	130	161	-31	11
Newark	13	4	0	9	111	248	-137	8
Paviors	13	2	1	10	104	168	-64	5
Vipers	13	1	2	10	118	229	-111	4

Press Officer: David Grummett, 10 Lingfield Close, Mansfield, Nottinghamshire, NF18 3LW. Tel: (H) 0623 654962.
Club Colours: Blue & white hoops, navy shorts.

SYSTON RFC
Ground Address: Barkby Road, Queniborough, Leicester. Tel: 0533 601223.
Club Secretary: J D Newton, 62 Fosse Way, Syston, Leicester, LE7 1NE. Tel: (H) 0533 694647.
Press Officer: M Newton, 37 Woodgate Drive, Birstall, Leicester. Tel: (H) 0533 674245 (W) 0533 538241.
Club Colours: Saxe & navy hoops, navy shorts.

TOWCESTRIANS RFC
Ground Address: Greens Norton Road, Towcester, Northamptonshire. Tel: 0327 50141.
Club Secretary: Steve Clews, Hill Cottage, The Hill, Pury End, Nr. Towcester, Northants. Tel: (H) 0327 33443 (W) 0525 376611.
Club Colours: Maroon and gold.

WESTLEIGH RFC
Ground Address: Lutterworth Road, Blaby, Leicestershire. Tel: 0533 771100.
Club Secretary: Mark Jordan, 16 Half Moon Crescent, Oadby, Leicester, LE2 4HD. Tel: (H) 0533 712549 (W) 0533 535328.
Press Officer: Mark Jordan, 16 Half Moon Crescent, Oadby, Leicester, LE2 4HD. Tel: (H) 0533 712549 (W) 0533 535328.
Club Colours: Black & white 3" hoops.

WOLVERHAMPTON RUFC
Ground Address: Castlecroft, Castlecroft Road, Wolverhampton, WV3 8NA. Tel: 0902 763900.
Club Secretary: N R Foxall, 45 Manston Drive, Perton, Wolverhampton, WV6 7LX. Tel: (H) 0902 752208 (W) 0902 791479.
Press Officer: J Phelps, 92 Woodthorne Road South, Tettenhall, Wolverhampton, WV6 8SW. Tel: (H) 0902 752208 (W) 0902 791479.
Club Colours: Black shirts, black shorts.

WORCESTER RFC
Ground Address: Sixways, Warndon Lane, Hindlip, Worcester. Tel: 0905 54183/51173.
Club Secretary: A C Harline, 6 The Grove, Laines, Worcester. Tel: (H) 0905 51900 (W) 0562 822295.
Press Officer: A C Harling, 6 The Grove, Claines, Worcester. Tel: (H) 0905 54900 (W) 0562 822295.
Club Colours: Navy & gold.

MIDLAND DIVISION

October 23 (Week 8)
Bedford Athletic v Belgrave
Peterborough v Paviours
Stafford v Matlock
Stockwood Park v Keresley
Whitchurch v Newark
Willenhall v Broad Street

October 30 (Week X2)
Broad Street v Bedford Athletic
Newark v Willenhall
Keresley v Whitchurch
Matlock v Stockwood Park
Paviours v Stafford
Vipers v Peterborough

November 13 (Week 10)
Bedford Athletic v Newark
Belgrave v Broad Street
Stafford v Vipers
Stockwood Park v Paviours
Whitchurch v Matlock
Willenhall v Keresley

November 20 (Week 11)
Newark v Belgrave
Keresley v Bedford Athletic
Matlock v Willenahall
Paviours v Whitchurch
Vipers v Stockwood Park
Peterborough v Stafford

December 4 (Week 13)
Bedford Athletic v Matlock
Belgrave v Keresley
Broad Street v Newark
Stockwood Park v Peterborough
Whitchurch v Vipers
Willenhall v Paviours

December 11 (Week 14)
Keresley v Broad Street
Matlock v Belgave
Paviours v Bedford Athletic
Vipers v Willenhall
Peterborough v Whitchurch
Stafford v Stockwood Park

December 18 (Week 15)
Bedford Athletic v Vipers
Belgrave v Paviours
Broad Street v Matlock
Newark v Keresley
Whitchurch v Stafford
Willenhall v Peterborough

January 8 (Week 18)
Matlock v Newark
Paviours v Broad Street
Vipers v Belgrave
Peterborough v Bedford Athletic
Stafford v Willenhall
Stockwood Park v Whitchurch

January 29 (Week X5)
Bedford Athletic v Stafford
Belgrave v Peterborough
Broad Street v Vipers
Newark v Paviours
Keresley v Matlock
Willenhall v Stockword Park

February 12 (Week 22)
Paviours v Keresley
Vipers v Newark
Peterborough v Broad Street
Stafford v Belgrave
Stockwood Park v Bedford Athletic
Whitchurch v Willenhall

March 12 (Week 26)
Bedford Athletic v Whitchurch
Belgrave v Stockwood Park
Broad Street v Stafford
Newark v Peterborough
Kerresley v Vipers
Matlock v Paviours

March 26 (Week 28)
Vipers v Matlock
Peterborough v Keresley
Stafford v Newark
Stockwood Park v Broad Street
Whitchurch v Belgrave
Willenhall v Bedford Athletic

April 9 (Week 30)
Belgrave v Willenhall
Broad Street v Whitchurch
Newark v Stockwood Park
Keresley v Stafford
Matlock v Peterborough
Paviours v Vipers

MIDLAND TWO

BEDFORD ATHLETIC RUFC
Ground Address: Bedford Athletic RUFC Clubhouse, Putnoe Wood, Wentworth Drive, Bedford. Tel: 0234 350874.
Club Secretary: Barry M Eynon, 122 George Street, Bedford MK40 3SH. Tel: (H) 0234 355136 (W) 0706 620220.
Club Colours: Black & white hooped jerseys, dark blue shorts, black stockings.

BELGRAVE RFC
Ground Address: Belgrave Pastures, Thurcaston Road/Abbey Lane, Leicester. Tel: 0533 663033.
Club Secretary: Michael John Goddard, Grange Court, 271A Birstall Road, Birstall, Leics LE4 4DJ. Tel: (H) 0533 677383 (W) 0880 334 886.
Press Officer: Graham Ball, 11 Springfield Close, Glenfield, Leics. Tel: (H) 0533 878973 (W) 0533 544448.
Club Colours: Red & black hoops, navy shorts.

BROADSTREET RFC
Ground Address: Ivor Preece Field, Brandon Road, Coventry. Tel: Clubhouse 0203 453982; Caretaker 0203 451706.
Club Secretary: Mr J McGinty, 60 Caludon Road, Stoke, Coventry CV2 4LP. Tel: (H) 0203 441210 (W) 0203 382167.
Press Officer: Mr G Watts, 15 Coopers Walk, Bubbenhall, Nr Coventry CV8 3JB. Tel: (H) 0203 301838 (W) 0203 633336.
League Contact: Mr Dave Wilkinson, 4 Court Leet, Binley Woods, Coventry CV3 2JR. Tel: 0203 543548.
Club Colours: Red with green & white bands, navy shorts, green socks. Green with red & white bands, navy shorts, green socks. Cup strip: white with red & green bands, white shorts, white socks.

KERESLEY RFC
Ground Address: The John Radford Fields, Burrow Hill Lane, Corley, Coventry CV7 8BE. Tel: 0676 40082.
Club Secretary: Arthur Jones, 118 Outlands Drive, Hollycroft, Hinckley, Leics LE10 0TW. Tel: (H) 0455 616905 (W) 0203 332365 x202.
Press Officer: Dean Morris, 42 Babbacombe Road, Styvechale, Coventry. Tel: (H) 0203 690242.
Club Colours: Scarlet, white & royal hoops, navy shorts.

MATLOCK RUFC
Ground Address: Cromford Meadows, Cromford, Nr Matlock, Derbyshire. Tel: 0629 822821.
Club Secretary: Sean Heathcote, H J Enthovens Ltd, Darley Dale, Matlock, Derbys DE4 3LP. Tel: (H) 0629 56809 (W) 0629 733291 x344.
Club Colours: Royal blue, gold & grey quartered shirts.

NEWARK RUFC
Ground Address: Kelham Road, Newark. Tel: 0636 702355.
Club Secretary: Edward Hine, Flat 3, Pelham Drive, The Park, Nottingham NG7 1DE. Tel: (H) 0602 475086 (W) 0602 473522.
Press Officer: Mike Bossart, The Orchard Room, South Scarle, Newark, Notts. Tel: (H) 0636 892127.
Club Colours: Navy blue shirts with white band, navy blue shorts.

PAVIOURS RFC
Ground Address: Burntstump Hill, Arnold, Nottingham NG5 8PQ. Tel: 0602 630384.
Club Secretary: D I Hudson, The School House, Eakring Road, Kneesall, Newark, Notts NG22 0AG. Tel: (H) 0623 861072.
Club Colours: Red & green shirt, blue shorts.

PETERBOROUGH RUFC
Ground Address: Second Drove, Fengate, Peterborough. Tel: 0733 69413.
Club Secretary: B A Hedges, 85 Apsley Way, Longthorpe, Peterborough PE3 9NZ. Tel: (H) 0733 332287.

FINAL TABLE

	P	W	D	L	F	A	PD	Pts
Burton	11	10	1	0	209	74	135	21
Worcester	11	9	0	2	188	89	99	18
Bedford Athletic	11	8	1	2	194	91	103	17
Stockwood Park	11	6	1	4	133	168	-35	13
Keresley	11	6	0	5	145	151	-6	12
Broad Street	11	5	1	5	169	127	42	11
Peterborough	11	5	0	6	135	133	2	10
Stafford	11	5	0	6	141	154	-13	10
Whitchurch	11	4	0	7	156	130	26	8
Matlock	11	2	0	9	102	167	-65	4
Moderns	11	2	0	9	64	206	-142	4
Biggleswade	11	2	0	9	101	247	-146	4

Press Officer: Mr A R J McGeown, 38 Lansdowne Walk, Orton Longueville, Peterborough. Tel: (H) 0733 233018 (W) 393555.
Club Colours: Red, gold, silver.

STAFFORD RUFC
Ground Address: Castlefields, Newport Rd, Stafford. Tel: 0785 211241.
Club Secretary: Peter L Hill, 39 Rising Brook, Stafford ST17 9DE. Tel: (H) 0785 59583.
Press Officer: A J Barlow, 20 Coronation Road, Stafford ST16 3JR. Tel: (H) 46810 (W) 46810.
Club Colours: Black & amber irregular hoops.

STOCKWOOD PARK RFC
Ground Address: London Road, Luton, Beds LU1 4BH. Tel: 0582 28044.
Club Secretary: Steve Askew, 152 Ventnor Gardens, Luton, Beds LU3 3SW. Tel: (H) 0582 583733.
Press Officer: Mark McKenna, 80 Willow Way, Ampthill, Beds. Tel: (H) 0525 406144 (W) 0582 572222.
Club Colours: Red shirt with yellow hoop, navy shorts.

VIPERS RFC
Ground Address: Blaby By-pass, Whetstone, Leicester. Tel: 0533 864777.
League Contact: Colin Underwood, 12 Hazel Bank Road, Countesthorpe, Leics. LE8 3RR. Tel: (H) 0533 7776269 (W) 0533 531191 x5045.
Press Officer: Richard Ford, 127 Dorchester Road, Leicester. Tel: (H) 0533 547204.
Club Colours: Black, green & gold hoops.

WHITCHURCH RFC
Ground Address: Edgeley Park, Whitchurch, Shropshire. Tel: 0948 663316.
Club Secretary: Neil Prunier, 9 St Mary's St, Whitchurch, Shropshire SY13 1QU. Tel: (H) 0948 663012 (W) 0948 663012.
Press Officer: Ian Grandfield, 2 Emmanuel Terrace, Fauls Green, Whitchurch, Shropshire SY13 2AX. Tel: (H) 0948 841033.
Club Colours: Red shirts, white shorts.

WILLENHALL RFC
Ground Address: Bognor Road, Essington, Nr Wolverhampton, West Midlands. Tel: 0922 405694.
Club Secretary: Elfyn Pugh, 9 Five-Fields Road, Willenhall, West Midlands WV12 4NZ. Tel: (H) 0902 607747 (W) 097 885 2141.
Press Officer: G Leo, c/o Willenhall RFC, Bognor Road, Essington, Nr Wolverhampton. Tel: (H) 0922 416973.
Club Colours: Maroon/black.

MIDLAND DIVISION

MIDLAND WEST ONE
1993-94
FIXTURES

October 23 (Week 8)
Nuneaton Old Eds v Kings Norton
Bromsgrove v Dudley
Old Leamingtonians v Newcastle Staffs
Longton v Newbold
Aston Old Eds v Ludlow
Sutton Coldfields v Leek

October 30 (Week X2)
Kings Norton v Bromsgrove
Leek v Nuneaton Old Eds
Ludlow v Sutton Coldfield
Newbold v Aston Old Eds
Newcastle Staffs v Longton
Old Halesonians v Old Leamingtonians

November 13 (Week 10)
Dudley v Kings Norton
Bromsgrove v Leek
Longton v Old Halesonians
Aston Old Eds v Newcastle Staffs
Sutton Coldfield v Newbold
Nuneaton Old Eds v Ludlow

November 20 (Week 11)
Leek v Dudley
Ludlow v Bromsgrove
Newbold v Neneaton Old Eds
Newcastle Staffs v Sutton Coldfield
Old Halesonians v Aston Old Eds
Old Leamingtonians v Longton

December 4 (Week 13)
Kings Norton v Leek
Bromsgrove v Newbold
Dudley v Ludlow
Aston Old Eds v Old Leamingtonians
Sutton Coldfield v Old Halesonians
Nuneaton Old Eds v Newcastle Staffs

December 11 (Week 14)
Ludlow v Kings Norton
Newbold v Dudley
Newcastle Staffs v Bromsgrove
Old Haelsonians v Nuneaton Old Eds
Old Leamingtonians v Sutton Coldfield
Longton v Aston Old Eds

December 18 (Week 15)
Kings Norton v Newbold
Bromsgrove v Old Halesonians
Dudley v Newcastle Staffs
Leek v Ludlow
Sutton Coldfield v Longton
Nuneaton Old Eds v Old Leamingtonians

January 8 (Week 18)
Newcastle Staffs v Kings Norton
Newbold v Leek
Old Halesonians v Dudley
Old Leamingtonians v Bromsgrove
Longton v Nuneaton Old Eds
Aston Old Eds v Sutton Coldfield

January 29 (Week X5)
Kings Norton v Old Halesonians
Bromsgrove v Longton
Dudley v Old Leamingtonians
Leek v Newcastle Staffs
Ludlow v Newbold
Nuneaton Old Eds v Aston Old Eds

February 12 (Week 22)
Old Leamingtonians v Kings Norton
Aston Old Eds v Bromsgrove
Longton v Dudley
Newcastle Staffs v Ludlow
Old Halesonians v Leed
Sutton Coldfield v Nuneaton Old Eds

March 12 (Week 26)
Kings Norton v Longton
Bromsgrove v Sutton Coldfield
Dudley v Aston Old Eds
Leek v Old Leamingtonians
Ludlow v Old Halesonians
Newbold v Newcastle Staffs

March 26 (Week 28)
Aston Old Eds v Kings Norton
Nuneaton Old Eds v Bromsgrove
Sutton Coldfield v Dudley
Old Halesonians v Newbold
Old Leamingtonians v Ludlow
Longton v Leek

April 9 (Week 30)
Kings Norton v Sutton Coldfield
Dudley v Nuneaton Old Eds
Leek v Aston Old Eds
Ludlow v Longton
Newbold v Old Leamingtonians
Newcastle Staffs v Old Halesonians

MIDLAND WEST ONE

ASTON OLD EDWARDIANS FC
Ground Address: Sunnybank Avenue, Perry Common, Birmingham, B44 0AP. Tel: 021 373 5746.
Club Secretary: Malcolm A Perrott, 21 Ivy Road, Sutton Coldfields, West Midlands. Tel: (H) 021 355 2639.
Press Officer: Derek A Coles, 17 Chester Road, Streetly, Sutton Coldfield, West Midlands. Tel: (H) 021 353 8077.
Club Colours: Red, white & myrtle green hoops, white shorts.

BROMSGROVE RFC
Ground Address: Finstall Park, Finstall Road, Bromsgrove, Worcestershire, B60 3DH. Tel: 0527 74690.
Club Secretary: Keith R Hirst, Worms Ash Farm, Fockbury Lane, Dodford, Bromsgrove, Worcestershire, B61 9AT. Tel: (H) 0527 33087 (W) 021 552 1541.
Press Officer: Keith Udy, The Lodge, Pipers Hill Common, Hanbury, Nr Bromsgrove, Worcestershire, B60 4AU. Tel: (H) 0527 821369 (W) 021 475 7591.
Club Colours: White with red/black/red hoop.

DUDLEY KINGSWINFORD RFC
Ground Address: Heathbrook, Swindon Road, Wall Heath, Kingswinford, West Midlands, DY6 0AW. Tel: 0384 287006.
Club Secretary: David Evans, 156 Common Road, Wombourne, West Midlands, WV5 0LX. Tel: (H) 0902 894463 (W) 0902 316327. **Press Officer:** John Challans, 12 Wheatridge Close, Wall HEath,, Kingswinford, DY6 0DE. Tel: (H) 0384 288945 (W) 021 585 6646.
Club Colours: Cambridge blue & navy hoops, black shorts.

KINGS NORTON RFC
Ground Address: Ash Lane, Hopwood, Birmingham, B48 7BB. Tel: 021 445 3340.
Club Secretary: G S C Maciver, 11 Chapel Walk, Kings Norton, Birmingham, B30 3LW. Tel: (H) 021 459 3930.
Press Officer: P Dalley, 153 Masshouse Lane, Kings Norton, Birmingham, B30. Tel: (H) 021 459 3930.
Club Colours: Red & gold hoops, white shorts.

LEEK RUFC
Ground Address: Birchall Playing Fields, Cheddleton Road, Leek, Staffordshire.
Club Secretary: John M Adams, 23 Silverstone Avenue, Brooklands Park, Cheadle, Stoke on Trent, ST10 1DD. Tel: (H) 0538 752003 (W) 0782 577575. **Press Officer:** Daniel Hunt, 22 Shirbourne Road, Leek, Staffordshire, ST13 6LE. Tel: (H) 0538 381045.
Club Colours: Blue & white narrow hoops.

LONGTON RUFC (Formerly Old Longtonian)
Ground Address: Roughcote Lane, Caverswall, Nr. Stoke on Trent. Tel: 0782 394449.
Club Secretary: Alan Miller, 5 The Dreys, Trentham, Stoke on Trent, ST4 8DU. Tel: (H) 0782 641845 (W) 0782 315188.
Press Officer: D Cartlidge, 184 Star and Garter Road, Lightwood, Longton, Stoke on Trent. Tel: (H) 0782 314803.
Club Colours: Yellow & black quarters (change - blue).

LUDLOW RFC
Ground Address: The Linney Fields, Ludlow. Tel: 0584 875762.
Club Secretary: Colin Spanner, 58 Henley Orchards, Ludlow, SY8 1TN. Tel: (H)0584 877224. **Press Officer:** John Webb, 6 New Street, Ludlow, Shropshire. Tel: (H)0584 877224.
Club Colours: Red shirts, black shorts.

NEWBOLD RFC
Ground Address: The Clubhouse, Parkfield Road, Newbold on Avon, Rugby, CV21 1EZ. Tel: 0788 565811.
Club Secretary: Alan Bale, The Club House, Parkfield Road, Newbold on Avon, Rugby, CV2 1EZ.

FINAL TABLE

	P	W	D	L	F	A	PD	Pts
Willanhall	12	9	0	3	183	97	86	18
Newbold	12	7	2	3	163	87	76	16
O. Leamingtonians	12	7	1	4	168	156	12	15
Bromsgrove	12	7	0	5	188	103	85	14
Ludlow	12	6	2	4	157	129	28	14
Old Longtonians	12	6	0	6	110	186	-76	12
Dudley	12	5	1	6	152	119	33	11
Leek	12	5	1	6	130	148	-18	11
Sutton Coldfield	12	5	1	6	138	204	-66	11
Kings Norton	12	5	0	7	147	128	19	10
Old Halesonians	12	5	0	7	120	165	-45	10
Newcastle (Staffs)	12	3	3	6	92	113	-21	9
Old Yardleians	12	2	1	9	132	245	-113	5

Press Officer: John Forman, 29 The Crescent, Brinklow, Rugby, CV23 0LG Tel: (H) 0788 832412. (W) 0788 832412.
Club Colours: Red & black quarters.

NEWCASTLE (STAFFS) RUFC
Ground Address: Lilleshall Road, Newcastle-under-Lyme. Tel: 0782 617042.
Club Secretary: R J O Websdale, 22 Carsington Close, Seabridge, Newcastle-under-Lyme, ST5 9DS. Tel: (H) 0782 638784 (W) 0782 839880. **Press Officer:** T M Kelly, Lindale, 8 Hassam Parade, Wolstanton, Newcastle-under-Lyme, ST5 9DS. Tel: (H) 0782 62362 (W) 0782 614370.
Club Colours: Maroon & white hoops, black shorts.

NUNEATON OLD EDWARDIANS RFC
Ground Address: Weddington Road, Nuneaton, Warwickshire. Tel: 0203 386778.
Club Secretary: A P Betney, 8 Sunnuyside, Hinckley, Leicestershire, LE10 1TS. Tel: (H) 0455 635715 (W) 0455 220061. **Press Officer:** R R Arnold, 9 St Nicolas Park Drive, Nuneaton, Warwickshire. Tel: (H) 0203 384305.
Club Colours: Red & white hoops.

OLD HALESONIANS RFC
Ground Address: Wassell Grove, Hagley, Worcs, West Midlands. Tel: 05623 883036.
Club Secretary: T J Wheeler, 14 Wollescote Road, Pedmore, Stourbridge, West Midlands, DY9 7JJ. Tel: (H) 0384 394627 (W) 021 423 4000. **Press Officer:** Ray Brown, 4 The Avenue, Rubery, Birmingham, B45 9UE. Tel: (H) 021 453 1466 (W) 021 4186 3486.
Club Colours: Royal blue/amber hoop, blue shorts.

OLD LEAMINGTONIANS RFC
Ground Address: "The Crofts", Bericote Road, Blackdown, Leamington Spa, Warwickshire, CV32 6QF. Tel: 0926 424991.
Club Secretary: Barry T Ames, 11 Aintree Drive, Leamington Spa, CV32 7TU. Tel: (H) 0926 338360 (W) 0926 313133. **Press Officer:** Barry T Ames, 11 Aintree Drive, Leamington Spa, CV32 7TU. Tel: (H) 0926 338360 (W) 0926 313133.
Club Colours: Blue & gold hoops, blue shorts.

SUTTON COLDFIELD RFC
Ground Address: Walmely Road, Sutton Coldfield, West Midlands. Tel: 021 351 5323.
Club Secretary: Tim Gallagher, 61 Gorge Road, Sedgley, West Midlands, DY3 1LE. Tel: (H) 0903 887605 (W) 0902 305961. **Press Officer:** K Lewis, 19 Elizabeth Road, New Oscott, Sutton Coldfield, West Midlands. Tel: (H) 021 354 6009.
Club Colours: Emerald green & white shirts, white shorts.

MIDLAND DIVISION

MIDLAND WEST TWO
1993-94
FIXTURES

December 18 (Week 15)
Newport v Selly Oak
Coventry v Old Laurentians
Dixonians v Old Yardleians
Old Coventrians v Kenilworth
West Mids Police v Stratford
Woodrush v Shrewsbury

October 23 (Week 8)
Newport v Coventry Welsh
Shrewsbury v Old Laurentians
Stratford v Old Yardleians
Tamworth v Kenilworth
West Mids Police v Old Coventrians
Woodrush v Dixonians

January 8 (Week 18)
Old Yardleians v old Coventrians
Old Laurentians v Dixonians
Selly Oak v Coventry Welsh
Shrewbury v Newport
Stratford v Woodrush
Tamworth v West Mids Police

October 30 (Week X2)
Dixonians v Newport
Old Coventrians v Woodrush
Kenilworth v West Mids Police
Old Yardleians v Tamworth
Old Laurentians v Stratford
Selly Oak v Shrewsbury

January 29 (Week X5)
Newport v Stratford
Coventry Welsh v Shrewsbury
Dixonians v Selly oak
Old Coventrians v Old Laurentians
Kenilworth v Old Yardleians
Woodrush v Tamworth

November 13 (Week 10)
Newport v Old Coventrians
Coventry Welsh v Dixonians
Stratford v Selly Oak
Tamworth v Old Laurentians
West Mids Police v Old Yardleians
Woodrush v Kenilworth

February 12 (Week 22)
Old Laurentians v Kenilworth
Selly Oak v Old Coventrians
Shrewsbury v Dixonians
Stratford v Coventry Welsh
Tamworth v Newport
West Mids Police v Woodrush

November 20 (Week 11)
Old Coventrians v Coventry Welsh
Kenilworth v Newport
Old Yardleians v Woodrush
Old Laurentians v West Mids Police
Selly Oak v Tamworth
Shrewsbury v Stratford

March 12 (Week 26)
Newport v West Mids Police
Coventry Welsh v Tamworth
Dixonaisn v Stratford
Old Coventrians v Shrewsbury
Kenilworth v Selly Oak
Old Yardleians v Old Laurentians

December 4 (Week 13)
Newport v Old Yarkleians
Coventry Welsh v Kenilworth
Dixonians v Old Coventrians
Tamworth v Shrewsbury
West Mids Police v Selly Oak
Woodrush v Old Laurentians

March 26 (Week 28)
Selly oak v Old Yardleians
Shrewsbury v Kenilworth
Stratfod v Old Coventrians
Tamworth v Dixonians
West Mids Police v Coventry Welsh
Woodrush v Newport

December 11 (Week 14)
Kenilworth v Dixonians
Old Yardlieans v Coventry Welsh
Old Laurentians v Newport
Selly Oak v Woodrush
Shrewsbury v West Mids Police
Statford v Tamworth

April 9 (Week 30)
Coventry Welsh v Woodrush
Dixonians v West Mids Police
Old Coventrians v Tamworth
Kenilworth v Stratford
Old Yardleians v Shrewsbury
Old Laurentians v Selly Oak

MIDLAND WEST TWO

COVENTRY WELSH RFC
Ground Address: Burbages lane, Longford, Coventry. Tel: 0203 360303.
Club Secretary: J P Griffiths, 44 Woodland Avenue, Earlsdon, Coventry. Tel: (H) 0203 674552 (W) 0203 562998.
Press Officer: J Price, 25 Hockett Street, Cheylesmore, Coventry. Tel: (H) 0203 504268.
Club Colours: Scarlet shirts, white shorts.

DIXONIANS RFC
Ground Address: Stanmore Road, Edgbaston, Birmingham. Tel: 021 434 3313.
Club Secretary: V Shingler, 8 Hockley Court, Stratford Road, Hockley Heath, Solihull, B94 6NW. Tel: (W) 0564 784040.
Press Officer: A J Kendrick, 94 Harborne, Oldbury, Warley, West Midlands. Tel: (H) 021 429 1619.
Club Colours: Maroon, green & black.

KENILWORTH RFC
Ground Address: Gusshouse Line, Kenilowrth, CV8 2AJ. Tel: 0926 53945.
Club Secretary: W J Whitesmith, 4 Gusshouse Line, Kenilworth, CV8 2AJ. Tel: (H) 0926 59465 (W) 0926 851113.
Press Officer: D Stephenson, 3 Moseley Road, Kenilworth, CV8 2AR. Tel: (H) 0926 57948.
Club Colours: Sky blue & amber.

NEWPORT (Salop) RFC
Ground Address: The Show Ground, Forton Road, Newport·Shropshire. Tel: 0952 810021.
Club Secretary: Simon Harris, Holly House, Stafford Road, Newport, Shropshire TF10 7NA. Tel: (H) 0952 813066 (W) 0952 606555.
Press Officer: Tim Edwards, Adeney Cottage, Adeney, Newport, Shropshire. Tel: (H) 0952 820555.
Club Colours: White and crimson hoops.

OLD COVENTRIANS RFC
Ground Address: Club Ground, Tile Hill Lane, Coventry, CV4 9DE. Tel: 0203 715273.
Club Secretary: Simon Bayliss-Stranks, 7 South Avenue, Stoke Park, Coventry, CV2 4DQ. Tel: (H) 0203 456929.
Press Officer: Graham Rossborough, c/o Club Ground, Tile Hill Lane, Coventry, CV4 9DE. Tel: (H) 0203 715273 (W) 0203 421990.
Club Colours: Black, gold & red.

OLD LAURENTIAN RFC
Ground Address: Fenley Field, Limetree Avenue, Bilton, Rugby. Tel: 0788 810855.
Club Secretary: A E Willis, 45 Frobisher Road, Rugby, CV22 7HS. Tel: (H) 0788 813481 (W) 0203 402121 x 3564.
Press Officer: M Lewis,68 Hillmorton Road, Rugby, CV22 5AF. Tel: (H) 0788 573261 (W) 0788 573261.
Club Colours: Maroon green and gold hoops.

OLD YARDLEIANS RFC
Ground Address: Tilehouse Lane, Shirley, Solihull, West Midlands. Tel: 021 743 5311.
Club Secretary: Mick Ison, 28 Quinton Close, Solihull, West Midlands B92 9BL. Tel: (H) 021 743 5311.
Press Officer: Ken Collins, 6,Watwood Road, Shirley, Solihull, West Midlands. Tel: (H) 021 733 7440.
Club Colours: Maroon, green & old gold quarters, navy shorts.

SELLY OAK RFC
Ground Address: Holders Lane Sports Ground, Moseley, Birmingham. 021 449 7950.
Club Secretary: Ian Thom, 218 Dawlish Road, Selly Oak, Birmingham, B29 7AT. Tel: (H) 021 471 1849 (W) 021 569 4245.
Press Officer: Debbie Alton, 123 Manor Farm Road, Tyseley, Birmingham. Tel: (H) 021 6081650.
Club Colours: Blue & white hoops.

FINAL TABLE

	P	W	D	L	F	A	PD	Pts
Nuneaton O Ed	12	11	1	0	245	82	163	23
Aston Ol Edward	12	11	0	1	277	92	185	22
Selly Oak	12	9	1	2	274	90	184	19
Old LAurentians	12	8	1	3	270	96	174	17
Stratford-on-Avon	12	6	1	5	126	133	-7	13
Shrewsbury	12	6	1	5	145	-207	-62	13
Kenilworth	12	6	0	6	177	204	-27	12
Dixonians	12	5	1	6	135	140	-5	11
Tamworth	12	4	1	7	158	198	-40	9
West Mids Police	12	3	1	8	90	165	-75	5
Woodrush	12	2	1	9	108	209	-101	5
Coventry Welsh	12	2	1	9	105	218	-113	5
Handsworth	12	0	0	12	67	359	-292	0

SHREWSBURY RUFC
Ground Address: Sundorne Castle, Uffington, Shrewsbury, SY4 4RR. Tel: 0743 353380.
Club Secretary: Graham S Jackson, 99 Highfields, Shrewsbury, SY2 5PJ. Tel: (H) 0743 361802.
Press Officer: Anthony McAndrew, 40 Rea Street, Belle Vue, Shrewsbury. Tel: (H) 0743 362922.
Club Colours: Light & dark blue hoops, navy shorts.

STRATFORD UPON AVON RFC
Ground Address: Pearcecroft, Lexley Road, Stratford-upon-Avon. Tel: 0789 297796.
Club Secretary: R Grant, 4 St Gregory's Road, Stratford-upon- Avon, Warwickshire, CV37 6UH. Tel: (H) 0789 266722 (W) 021 502 7116.
Press Officer: R Grant, 4 St Gregory's Road, Stratford-upon-Avon, Warwickshire, CV37 6UH. Tel: (H) 0789 266722 (W) 021 502 7116.
Club Colours: Black & white.

TAMWORTH RUFC
Ground Address: Wigginton Lodge, Wigginton Park, Tamworth, Staffordshire, B79 8ED. Tel: 0827 68794.
Club Secretary: Craig Parker, 36 Ethelfleda Road, Hockley, Tamworth, Staffordshire. Tel: (H) 0827 285471 (W) 0827 310300.
Press Officer: Craig Parker, 36 Ethelfleda Road, Hockley, Tamworth, Staffordshire. Tel: (H) 0827 285471 (W) 0827 310300.
Club Colours: Maroon, black & white hoops.

WEST MIDLANDS POLICE RFC
Ground Address: Tally Ho Police Training Centre, Pershore Road, Edgbaston, Birmingham, B57. Tel: 021 626 5479.
Club Secretary: Simon J Hussey, 67 Carol Crescent, Halesowen, West Midlands, B63 3RR. Tel: (H) 021 550 5725 (W) 021 322 6084.
Press Officer: M Joiner, Police Station, Stechford, Birmingham. Tel: 021 705 5603 (W) 021 626 7010.
Club Colours: Red shirts, black shorts.

WOODRUSH RFC
Ground Address: Icknield Street, Forhill, Birmingham, B38 0EL. Tel: 0564 822878.
Club Secretary: S H Edwards, 6 Tanwood Close, Callowhill, Redditch, B97 5YU. Tel: 0527 544281.
Press Officer: M Fenwick, 31 Birmingham Road, Alvechurch, Birmingham. Tel: (H) 021 445 2206.
Club Colours: Green & white hoops, black shorts.

MIDLAND DIVISION

STAFFORDSHIRE & WARWICKSHIRE ONE 1993-94 FIXTURES

October 23 (Week 8)
Coventry Saracens v Dunlop
Old Wheatleyans v Manor Park
Trentham v Handsworth
Trinity Guild v G E C St Leonards
Uttoxeter v G E C Coventry
Stoke Old Boys v Eccleshall

October 30 (Week X2)
G E C Coventry v Stoke Old Boys
G E C St Leonards v Uttoxeter
Handsworth v Trinity Guild
Manor Park v Trentham
Southam v Old Wheatleyans
Eccleshall v Coventry Saracens

November 13 (Week 10)
Coventry Saracens v G E C Coventry
Dunlop v Eccleshall
Trentham v Southam
Trinity Guild v Manor park
Uttoxeter v Handsworth
Stoke Old Boys v G E C St Leonards

November 20 (Week 11)
G E C Coventry v Dunlop
G E C St Leonards v Coventry Saracens
Handsworth v Stoke Old Boys
Manor Park v Uttoxeter
Southam v Trinity Guild
Old Wheatleyans v Trentham

December 4 (week 13)
Coventry Saracens v Handsworth
Dunlop v G E C St Leonards
Eccleshall v G E C Coventry
Trinity Guild v Old Wheatleyans
Uttoxeter v Southam
Stoke Old Boys v Manor Park

December 11 (Week 14)
G E C St Leonards v Eccleshall
Handsworth v Dunlop
Manor Park v Coventry Saracens
Southam v Stoke Old boys
Old Wheatleyans v Uttoxeter
Trentham v Trinity Guild

December 18 (Week 15)
Coventry Saracens v Southam
Dunlop v Manor Park
Eccleshall v Handsworth
G E C Coventry v G E C Saracens
Uttoxeter v Trentham
Stoke Old Boys v Old Wheatleyans

January 8 (Week 18)
Handsworth v G E C Coventry
Manor Park v Eccleshall
Southam v Dunlop
Old Wheatleyans v Coventry Saracens
Trentham v Stoke Old Boys
Trinity Guild v Uttoxeter

January 29 (Week X5)
Coventry Saracens v Trentham
Dunlop v Old Wheatleyans
Eccleshall v Southam,
G E C Coventry v Manor Park
G E C St Leonards v Handsworth
Stoke Old Boys v Trinity Guild

February 12 (Week 22)
Manor Park v G E C St Leonards
Southam v G E C Coventry
Old Wheatleyans v Eccleshall
Trentham v Dunlop
Trinity Guild v Coventry Saracens
Uttoxeter v Stoke Old Boys

March 12 (Week 26)
Coventry Saracens v Uttoxeter
Dunlop v Trinity Guild
Eccleshall v Trentham
Handsworth v Manor Park
G E C Coventry v Old Wheatleyans
G E C St Leonards v Southam

March 26 (Week 28)
Old Wheatleyans v G E C St Leonards
Southam v Handsworth
Trentham v G E C Coventry
Trinity Guild v Eccleshall
Uttoxeter v Dunlop
Stoke Old Boys v Coventry Saracens

April 9 (Week 30)
Dunlop v Stoke Old Boys
Eccleshall v Uttoxeter
G E C Coventry v Trinity Guild
G E C St Leonards v Trentham
Handsworth v Old Wheatleyans
Manor Park v Southam

370

STAFFS & WARWICKS ONE

COVENTRY SARACENS RFC
Ground Address:Bredon Avenue, Binley, Coventry, Tel
No. 0203 453557.
Club Secretary:Brian Craner, 71 Westhill Road, Coundon,
Coventry, West Midlands, CV6 2AD, Tel No. (H) 0203
590280, (W) 0203 832996. Press Officer:Brian Craner,
address as above.
Club Colours: Black with red green V on shirt

DUNLOP RFC
Ground Address:Burnaby Road, Radford, Coventry, Tel
No: (0203) 662394
Club Secretary:Seamus Harnett, 19, Stepping Stones
Road, Coundon, Coventry, Tel (0203)
601995, (W) 416255. Press Officer: Mrs K Challis, 19
Stepping Stones Road, Coundon, Coventry, CV5 8JT. Tel
No: (H) (0203) 337152.
Club Colours: Black and Amber Hoops.

ECCLESHALL RUFC
Ground Address: Stone Road, Nr. Eccleshall, Staffs.
Club Secretary: B Simpson, 35 Trinity Road, Eccleshall,
ST21 6AP Tel No: (H) 0785 851997 (W) 0782 264521.
Press Officer: S Law, 21 Cramer Street, Stafford, ST17
4BX. Tel No: (H) 0785 224482.
Club Colours:Black with emerald and gold hoops.

GEC (COVENTRY) RFU
Ground Address: GEC Sports Pavilion off Allard Way,
Coventry, Tel No: 0203 451157.
Club Secretary: Richard Everitt, PP16.5 Berkley House,
245 Broad Street, Birmingham B1 2HQ. Tel No: (H) 0203
456670, (W) 021230 3564. Press Officer:Phil Gaffney,
74 Cecily Road, Cheylesmore, Coventry, CV3 5LA. Tel
No: (H) 0203 504435.
Club Colours: Red/Blue/Green Hoops.

GEC ST LEONARDS RUFC
Ground Address: GEC Alstom Protection Control, St
Leonards Works, Stafford. Tel No: 0785 58070.
Club Secretary: J A Whibley, 32 Marlborough Avenue,
Stafford, Staffordshire, ST16 3SU. Tel No: (H) 0785
48932 (W) 0785 48932. Press Officer: Mr Terry Whitton,
7 Somerset Road, Highfield 8T17 9UZ. Tel No: (H) 0785
221640, (W) 0889 271000 x 176.
Club Colours: Black with gold band.

HANDSWORTH RUFC
Ground Address: 450 Birmingham Road, Walsall, WS5
3JP. Tel No: 021 357 6427.
Club Secretary: Mr Julian P Guds, 3 St Georges Court,
Persehouse St, Walsall, WS1 2AT. Tel No. (H) 0922
645856 (W) 0384 254565. Press Officer: Mr Richard
Guest, 4 Newquay Close, Park Hall, Walsall, WS5 3EP.
Tel No: (H) 0922 38542.
Club Colours: Red and white hoops, navy blus shorts.

MANOR PARK RFC
Ground Address: Griff & Coton Sports Ground, Heath
End Road, Nuneaton, Warks. Tel No: 0203 386798.
Club Secretary: S. Wilson, 88 Edward Street, Hinckley,
Leicestershire LE10 ODL. Tel No: 0455 (635858) (W)
0203 861823. Press Officer:Mr R Fulford, 25 Bentley
Road, Nuneaton, Warks, Tel No: 0203 374992.
Club Colours: Red & black hooped shirts/Black shorts and
socks

OLD WHEATLEYANS RFC
Ground Address: Norman Place Road, Coundon,
Coventry. Tel No: 0203 334888.
Club Secretary: Richard Leigh, 8, Orchard Crescent,
Coventry, CV3 6HJ, Tel No: 0203 501998 (W) 0203
688918. Press Officer: As above
Club Colours: Blue maroon gold.

FINAL TABLE

	P	W	D	L	F	A	PD	Pts
Old Coventrians	12	11	1	0	345	54	291	23
Manor Park	12	10	1	1	341	117	224	21
Dunlop	12	9	0	3	244	109	135	16
Trentham	12	8	0	4	261	161	100	16
Coventry Saracens	12	7	0	5	213*	111	102	14
Old Wheatleyans	12	7	0	5	254	154	100	14
Trinity Guild	12	7	0	5	337	160	177	12
GEC St Leonards	12	5	0	7	154	255	-101	10
GEC Coventry	12	5	0	7	141	176	-35	8
Eccleshall	12	5	0	7	158	224	-66	8
Uttoxeter	12	1	0	11	53	362	-309	0
Wednesbury	12	1	0	11	56	353	-297	0
Linley	12	1	0	11	68	441	-373	2

SOUTHAM RFC
Ground Address: Kineton Road, Southam, Nr Leamington
SPA, Warks. Tel No: 0926 813674.
Club Secretary: M S Haville, The Tanners, Church Road,
Long Itchington, Nr Rugby, Warks. Tel No: (H) 0926
814803, (W) 0788 570357. Press Officer: A Mitchell,
Feetahona, Lawford Heath Farm, Lawford Heath, Nr
Rugby. Tel No: (H) 0788 814838
Club Colours: Navy blue with white hoops.

STOKE OLD BOYS RFC
Ground Address: Brookvale Avenue, Binley, Coventry.
Tel No: 0203 453631.
Club Secretary: Brian Jose, 33, Hothorpe Close, Binley,
Coventry, CV3 2HX. Tel No. (H) 0203 457122, (W)
0203 335121. Press Officer: Brian Jose, 33 Hothorpe
Close, Binley, Coventry, CV3 2HY. Tel No: 0203 457122
(W) 0203 335121.
Club Colours: Maroon/White navy shorts.

TRENTHAM RUFC
Ground Address: Oaktree Road, Trentham,
Stoke-on-Trent. Tel No: 0782 642320.
Club Secretary: Mark Riley, 7 Waterbeck Grove,
Trentham, Stoke- on-Trent. Tel No: (H) 0782 644874 (W)
0925 824511 Press Officer: Adam Slater, 52 Flash Lane,
Stoke-on-Trent, ST4 5QZ. Tel No: (H) 0782 410912 (W)
0782 577136.
Club Colours: Green and white hoops, black shorts.

TRINITY GUILD RFC
Ground Address: Rowley Road, Baginton, Coventry, Tel
No: 0203 305928.
Club Secretary: D Williams, 122 Grange Road, Coventry,
Warks. Tel. No: (H) 360833. Press Officer: A Thomas, 6
Windmill Court, Windmill Lane, Longford, Coventry. Tel
No: (H) 684865.
Club Colours: Maroon, old gold dark blue hoops, navy
shorts.

UTTOXETER RUFC
Ground Address: Oldfields Sports Centre, Springfield
Road, Uttoxeter, Staffs. Tel No: 0889564347
Club Secretary: Simon Bailey, Stoneleigh Cottage, Great
Cubley, Nr Ashbourne, Derbys, DEG 2EY. Tel No: (H)
0335330306 (W) 0889593031. Press Officer: Les
Humphries, 14 Eaton Road, Rochester, Uttoxeter, Staffs,
ST14 5LL. Tel No: (H) 0889590604, (W) 0889593680
(After 2.30 p.m.).
Club Colours: Blue with red and gold hoops.

MIDLAND DIVISION

STAFFORDSHIRE & WARWICKSHIRE TWO 1993-94 FIXTURES

October 23 (Week 8)
Berkswell & Balsall v Cannock
St Andrews Rugby v Atherstone
Silhillians v Pinley
Linley v Old Oaks
Spartans v Earlsdon
Wednesbury v Coventrians

October 30 (Week X2)
Coventrians v Berkswell & Balsall
Earlsdon v Wednesbury
Old Oaks v Spartans
Pinley v Linley
Arwood v Silhillians
Harbury v St Andrews Rugby

November 13 (Week 10)
Berkswell & Balsall v Earlsdon
Cannock v Coventrians
Silhillians v Harbury
Linley v Atherstone
Spartans v Pinley
Wednesbury v Old Oaks

November 20 (Week 11)
Earlsdon v Cannock
Old Oaks v Berkswell & Balsall
Pinley v Wednesbury
Atherstone v Spartans
Harbury v Linley
St Andrews Rugby v Silhillians

December 4 (Week 13)
Berkewell & Balsall v Pinley
Cannock v Old oaks
Coventrians v Earlsdon
Linley v St Andrews Rugby
Spartans v Harbury
Wednesbury v Atherstone

December 11 (Week 14)
Old Oaks v Coventrians
Pinley v Cannock
Atherstone v Berkswell & Balsall
Harbury v Wednesbury
St Andrews Rugby v Spartans
Silhillians v Linley

December 18 (Week 15)
Berkswell & Bilsall v Harbury
Cannock v Atherstone
Coventrians v Pinley
Earlsdon v Old Oaks
Spartans v Silhillians
Wednesbury v St Andrews Rugby

January 8 (Week 18)
Pinley v Earlsdon
Atherstone v Coventrians
Harbury v Cannock
St Andrews Rugby v Berkswell 7 Balsall
Silhillians v Wednesbury
Linley v Spartans

January 29 (Week X5)
Berkswell & Balsall v Silhillians
Cannock v St Andrews Rugby
Coventrians v Harbury
Earsdon v Atherstone
Old Oaks v Pinley
Wednesbury v Linley

February 12 (Week 22)
Atherstopne v Old Oaks
Harbury v Earlsdon
St Andrews Rugby v Coventrians
Silhillians v Cannock
Linley v Berkswell & Balsall
Spartans v Wednesbury

March 12 (week 26)
Berkswell & Balsall v Spartans
Cannock v Linley
Coventrians v Silhillians
Earlsdon v St Andrews Rugby
Old Oaks v Harbury
Pinley v Atherstone

March 26 (Week 28)
Harbury v Pinley
St Andrews Rugby v Old oaks
Silhillians v Earlsdon
Linley v Coventrians
Spartans v Cannock
Wednesbury v Berkswell & Balsall

April 9 (Week 30)
Cannock v Wednesbury
Coventrians v Spartans
Earlsdon v Linley
Old Oaks v Silhillians
Pinley v St Andrews Rugby
Atherstone v Harbury

STAFFORDSHIRE/WARWICKSHIRE TWO

ATHERSTONE RFC
Ground Address: Ratcliffe Road, Atherstone, Warwickshire. Tel: 0827 714934.
Club Secretary: David Boal, Thurmaston House, 74 South Street, Atherstone, Warwishire, CV9 1DZ. Tel: (H) 0827 713145.
Press Officer: Andy Stubbs, 108 New Street, Raddesley Ensor, Nr Atherstone, Warwickshire. Tel: (H) 0827 711210.
Club Colours: All black.

BERKSWELL & BALSALL RFC
Ground Address: Meeting House Lane, Balsall Common, Nr. Coventry.
Club Secretary: P C Wigley, 36 Kemps Green Road, Balsall Common, Nr. Coventry, West Midlands, CV7 7QE. Tel: (H) 0676 533036 (W) 0827 710641.
Press Officer: Steve Wake, 33 Wildcroft Road, Whoberley, Coventry, CV5 8AU. Tel: (HJ) 0203 711510 (W) 021 500 6188.
Club Colours: Red jersey, black shorts.

CANNOCK RUFC
Ground Address: The Morgan Ground, Stafford Road, Huntington, Nr Cannock, Staffordshire. Tel: 0543 574165.
Club Secretary: R J Rafferty, 7 Beech Pine Close, Hednesford, Staffordshire, WS12 4RZ. Tel: (H) 0543 876040 (W) 0562 60234.
Press Officer: R J Rafferty, 7 Beech Pine Close, Hednesdford, Staffordshire, WS12 4RZ. Tel: (H) 0543 876040 (W) 0562 60234.
Club Colours: (I) Blue & gold (II) Black.

COVENTRIANS RFC
Ground Address: Black Pad, Off Yelverton Road, Radford, Coventry. Tel: 0203 682885.
Club Secretary: J H Parke, 47 High Street, Ryton-on-Dunsmore, Nr Coventry, CV8 3FJ. Tel: (H) 0203 304394 (W) 0203 539010 Ext. 6952.
Press Officer: P M Brown, 38 Arnold Avenue, Coventry, CV3 5LX. Tel: (H) 0203 415744 (W) 0203 402121 x 3060.
Club Colours: Blue & white squares.

EARLSDON RFC
Ground Address: Mitchell Avenue, Canley, Coventry. Tel: 0203 464467.
Club Secretary: J G Ward, 18 Wainbody Avenue, Green Lane, Coventry, CV3 6DB. Tel: (H) 0203 419729.
Club Colours: Red & white.

HARBURY RFC
Ground Address: Middle Road, Harbury, Warwickshire. Tel: 0926 613462.
Club Secretary: Graham Lewis, 9 Chapel Street, Harbury, Warwickshire, CV33 9HT. Tel: (H) 0926 613343.
Press Officer: Graham Lewis, 9 Chapel Street, Harbury, Warwickshire, CV33 9HT. Tel: (H) 0926 613343.
Club Colours: Cherry & white hoops.

LINLEY & KIDSGROVE RUFC
Ground Address: Birchenwood Sports Ground, Birchenwood, Kidsgrove, Stoke-on-Trent.
Club Secretary: Jason Swingewood, 6 Clandon Avenue, Tunstall, Stoke-on-Trent, Staffordshire, ST6 5UT. Tel: (H) 0782 837647 (W) 0782 266737/0836 639585.
Press Officer: Ron Tyson, 18 Derwent Close, Alsager, Stoke- on- Trent, Staffordshire. Tel: (H) 0270 878516 (W) 0782 837508.
Club Colours: Green & gold quarters.

OLD OAKS RUFC
Ground Address: Pelsall Comprehensive School, Pelsall Lane, Pelsall, Nr Walsall, West Midlands. Tel: 0922 682089.
Club Secretary: Martin Berry, 70 Charles Crescent, Pelsall, Nr Walsall, West Midlands. Tel: 0922 694839 (W) 021 360 7000.

FINAL TABLE

	P	W	D	L	F	A	PD	Pts
Stoke Old Boys	12	12	0	0	362	81	281	24
Southam	12	11	0	1	371	94	277	22
Silhillians	12	10	0	2	250	97	153	20
Pinley	12	8	0	4	227	159	68	16
Rugby St Andrews	12	7	1	4	173	134	39	15
Earlsdon	12	6	0	6	189	136	53	12
Spartans	12	7	0	5	167	123	44	12
Berkswell & Balsall	12	5	1	6	165	122	43	11
Cannock	12	4	0	8	123	337	-214	8
Coventrians	12	3	0	9	118	191	-73	6
Old Oaks	12	2	1	9	106	236	-130	5
Rubery Owen	12	1	1	10	72	273	-201	3
Rugeley	12	0	0	12	39	413	-374	-6

Press Officer: Andy Raybould, 19 Bradford Road, Brownhills, Nr Walsall, West Midlands. Tel: (H) 0543 375201 (W)021 360 7000.
Club Colours: Red & blue quarters.

PINLEY RFC
Ground Address: The Croft, Wyken Croft, Wyken, Coventry, West Midlands, CV2 3AA. Tel: 0203 602059.
Club Secretary: D J Antram, 10 Angela Avenue, Potters Green, Coventry, CV2 2GT. Tel: (H) 0203 615968 (W) 0203 602020 Ext. 8638.
Press Officer: S McKillop, 5 Tiverton Road, Wyken, Coventry, CV2 3DN. Tel: (W) 0203 602059.
Club Colours: Black with red horizontal stripe.

RUGBY ST ANDREWS RFC
Ground Address: Hillmorton Grounds, Ashlawn Road, Rugby. Tel: 542786.
Club Secretary: Jim Corry, 3 Holme Way, Barby, Nr Rugby, CV23 8UQ. Tel: (H) 0788 891039 (W) 0455 232763.
Club Colours: Blue & navy hoops, navy shorts.

SILHILLIANS RUFC
Ground Address: Warwick Road, Copt HEath, Solihull, West Midlands. Tel: 0564 777680.
Club Secretary: G R Loader, 4 Shackleton Drive, Perton, Wolverhampton, WV6 7SA. Tel: (H) 0902 742695 (W) 0902 353522.
Press Officer: D N Green, 7 Copt Heath Drive, Knowle, Solihull, West Midlands. Tel: (H) 0564 777669 (W) 0564 777680.
Club Colours: Maroon, blue & white.

SPARTANS RUFC
Ground Address: Coppice Lane, Middleton, Nr Tamworth, Staffordshire. Tel: 021 308 5857.
Club Secretary: Sarah McGrory, 33 Alexandra Mews, Victoria Road, Tamworth, Staffordshire, B79 7HT. Tel: (H) 0827 693132.
Press Officer: Nick Wood, 15 Hook Drive, Four Oaks, Sutton Coldfield, West Midlands. Tel: (H) 021 353 3388.
Club Colours: Black shirts, black shorts.

WEDNESBURY RUFC
Ground Address: Hydes Road Playing Fields, Wednesbury, West Midlands.
Club Secretary: Peter Hughes, 28 Alder Road, Wednesbury, West Midlands, WS10 9PX. Tel: (H) 021 556 5005 (W) 021 366 6303.
Press Officer: David Orme, 134 Hydes Road, Wednesbury, West Midlands, WS10 0DH. Tel: (H) 021 556 3048 (W) 021 588 2273 Ext 19.
Club Colours: Black & white hoops, black shorts.

MIDLAND DIVISION

STAFFORDSHIRE & WARWICKSHIRE THREE 1993-94 FIXTURES

October 23 (Week 8)
Alcester v Burntwood
Shipston v Old Warwicks
Standard v Michelin
Warwick v Rugeley
Wheaton Aston v Rubery Owen
Wulfrun v Claverdon

October 30 (Week X2)
Claverdon v Alcester
Rubery Owen v Wulfrun
Rugeley v Wheaton Aston
Michelin v Warwick
Old Warwicks v Standard
Warwicks Police v Shipston

November 13 (Week 10)
Alcester v Rubery Owne
Burntwood v Claverdon
Standard v Warwicks Police
Warwick v Old Warwicks
Wheaton Aston v Michelin
Wulfrun v Rugeley

November 20 (Week 11)
REubery Owen v Burntwood
Rugeley v Alcester
Michelin v Wulfrun
Old Warwicks v Wheaton Aston
Warwicks Police v Warwick
Shipston v Standard

December 4 (Week 13)
Alcester v Michelin
Burntwood v Rugeley
Claverdon v Rubery Owen
Warwick v Shipston
Wheaton Aston v Warwicks Police
Wulfrun v Old Warwicks

December 11 (Week 14)
Rugfeley v Claverdon
Michelin v Burntwood
Old Warwicks v Alcester
Warwicks Police v Wulfrun
Shipston v Wheaton Aston
Standard v Warwick

December 18 (Week 15)
Alcester v Warwicks Police
Burntwood v Old Warwicks
Claverdon v Michelin
Rubery Owen v Rugeley
Wheaton Aston v Standard
Wulfrun v Shipston

January 8 (Week 18)
Michelin v Rubery Owen
Old Warwicks v Claverdon
Warwicks Police v Burntwood
Shipston v Alcester
Standard v Wulfrun
Warwick v Wheaton Aston

January 29 (Week X5)
Alcester v Standard
Burntwood v Shipston
Claverdon v Warwickshire
Rubery Owen v Old Warwicks
Rugeley v Michelin
Wulfrun v Warwick

February 12 (Week 22)
Old Warwicks v Rugeley
Warwicks Police v Rubery Owen
Shipston v Claverdon
Standard v Burntwood
Warwick v Alcester
Wheaton Aston v Wulfrun

March 26 (Week 28)
Alcester v Wheaton Aston
Burntwood v Warwick
Claverdon v Standard
Rubery Owen v Shipston
Rugeley v Warwicks Police
Michelin v Old Warwicks

April 9 (Week 30)
Burntwood v Wulfrun
Claverdon v Wheaton Aston
Rubery Owen v Warwick
Rugeley v Standard
Michelin v Shipston
Old Warwicks v Warwicks Police

374

STAFFS & WARWICKS THREE

ALCESTER RFC
Ground Address: King's Coughton, Alcester, Warwicks, B49 5QF. Tel No: 0789 764061.
Club Secretary: M J Edwards, 8, Icknield Row, Alcester, Warks, B49 5EW. Tel No: (H) 0789 764096 (W) 0789 762285.
Press Officer: P Lewis-Jones, Mill House, Aston, Cantlow, Solihull, West Midlands. Tel No: (H) 0789 488273, (W) 0789 488273.
Club Colours: Black and red shirts, black shorts.

BURNTWOOD RUFC
Ground Address: Burntwood Recreation Centre, High Street, Chasetown, Walsall, W. Mids.
Club Secretary: Steve Pugh, 14 Telford Close, Burntwood, Walsall, W.Mids. Tel No: (H) 0543 672976.
Press Officer: Rob Forsyth, 25 Viscount Road, Holly Grove, Chase Terrace, Walsall, W.Mids. Tel No: (H) 0543 675406.
Club Colours: Emerald white red hoops, black shorts.

CLAVERDON RFC
Ground Address: Yarningale Commom, Ossetts Hole Lane, Claverdon, Warwicks. Tel No: 0926843133.
Club Secretary: Basil Sayer, The White House, 45 Station Road, Balsall Common, Coventry, CV7 7FN, Tel No: 0676532014, (W) 0933224444.
Press Officer: Jonathan Swaby, Essex House, Lye Green, Claverdon, Warwicks, CV35 8HI. Tel No: 0926842961 (W) 0527510015.
Club Colours: Red and white.

MICHELIN RUFC
Club Address: Michelin Athletic Club, Rosetree Avenue, Trent Vale, Stoke on Trent. Tel No: 0782 642369.
Club Secretary: Anthony Colclough, 36 Cookson Avenue, Dresden, Stoke on Trent. Tel No: (H) 0782 316413.
Press Officer: Mike Pellington, 29 Blakelow Road, Abbey Hulton, Stoke on Trent.
Club Colours: Yellow /Blue hoops.

OLD WARWICKIANS RUFC
Ground Address: Sports Ground, Hampton Road, Warwick. Tel No: 0926 496295
Club Secretary: G Donovan, 89 Tachbrook Street, Leamington Spa, Warwickshire CV31 2BG. Tel No: (H) 0929 330600 (W) 226243.
Press Officer: Mike Wilson, 63, St Helens Road, Leamington Spa, Warws.CV31 3QG. Tel No: 0926 428246 (W) 0926 472728.
Cub Colours: Maroons/white hoop.

RUBERY OWEN RFC
Ground Address: High Hill Centre, Upper Sneyd Road, Essington, WV11 2DW. Tel No: 0922 492795.
Club Secretary: Darren Owen, 21 Osborne Drive, Victoria Mews, Darlaston, W Mids, WS10 8YQ. Tel No: (H) 0215263431 (W) 021 5577641.
Club Colours: Red Shirts, Black shorts.

RUGELEY RUFC
Ground Address: Hagley Park, Rugeley, Staffordshire. Tel No: 0889 582266
Club Secretary: J McGuckin, 27 Birchlane, Brereton, Rugeley, Staffs.Tel No: (H) 0889 570102.
Press Officer: R Morrison, 10 Colton Road, Rugeley. Tel No: 0889 570937.
Club Colours: Amber shirts, black shorts and socks.

FINAL TABLE

	P	W	D	L	F	A	PD	Pts
Atherstone	11	10	0	1	283	64	219	20
Harbury	11	8	1	2	184	61	123	17
Warwick	11	8	0	3	221	156	65	16
Old Warwickians	11	7	0	4	219	142	77	14
Shipston-on-Stour	11	6	1	4	231	111	120	13
Standard	11	5	1	5	116	160	-44	9
Wheaton Aston	11	4	0	7	113	145	-32	8
Michelin	11	4	0	7	92	212	-120	8
Alcester	11	3	1	7	85	100	-15	7
Wulfrun	11	3	1	7	119	195	-76	7
Claverdon	11	3	0	8	162	225	-63	6
Coventry Technical	11	2	1	8	82	348	-266	5

SHIPSTON-ON-STOUR
Ground Address: Mayo Road, Shipston-on-Stour, Warks. Tel No: 0608 662107.
Club Secretary: Richard Slatter, Woodhills, Farm, Todenham, Moreton-in-Marsh, Glos. GL56 9PH. Tel No: 0608 50453 (W) same.
Press Officer: As Secretary.
Club Colours: Black shirts, shorts and stockings.

STANDARD RFC
Ground Address: Standard Triumph Rec Club, Tile Hill Lane, Coventry. Tel No: 675186.
Club Secretary: Alan Ferrar, 24 Roosevelt Drive, Tile Hill, Coventry, CV4 9LP. Tel No: (H) 469935 (W) 717683.
Press Officer: Henry Kantor, 4 Bowell Close, Coventry. Tel No: (H) 463855.
Club Colours: Dark blue, light blue and white hoops.

WARWICK RFC
Ground Address: Hampton Fields, Hampton Road, Warwick. Tel No: 0926 410972.
Club Secretary: Mr I M Joyce, 50 Monks Road, Stoke, Coventry, CV1 2BY. Tel No (H) 0203 630250 (W) 0926 452400.
Press Officer: Mr J. M. Joyce. Address as above.
Club Colours: Purple and black hoops, black shorts.

WARWICKSHIRE CONSTABULARY RFC
Ground Address: Police HQ, Leek Wootton, Warwickshire. Tel No: 0926 415000.
Club Secretary: A G Mumford, 11, Barton Road, Bedworth, Warwickshire, CV12 8HG. Tel No: 0203 640109 (W) 0926 4155000.
Press Officer: A G Mumford. Address as above.
Club Colours: Maroon/Navy.

WHEATON ASTON RUFC
Ground Address: Asleigh Fields, Wheaton Aston Sports and Social Club, Capley Road, Wheaton Aston, Staffs, Tel No: 0785/840440
Club Secretary: N Hammond, 1 Primrose, Close, Wheaton Aston, Staffs, ST19 9PX. Tel No: (H) 0785/840907
Press Officer: T Parrot, Mill House, Mill Lane, Great Heywood, Staffs. Tel No: (H) 0889/882568.
Club Colours: Black/Gold.

WULFRUN RFC
Ground Address: Wednesfield H15, Lakefield Road, Wednesfield, Wolverhampton. Tel No: 0902 732470.
Club Secretary: C Withers, 138 Old Park Road, Dudley, West Midlands DY1 3ND. Tel: (H) 0902 731325.
Club Colours: Green with black "V".

MIDLAND DIVISION

STAFFORSHIRE & WARWICKSHIRE FOUR 1993-94 FIXTURES

October 23 (Week 8)
Bloxwich v Coventry Tech
Stone v Rugby Welsh
Fife Street v Jaguar

October 30 (Week X2)
Cheadle v Bloxwich
Rugby Welsh v Fife Street
Shottery v Stone

November 13 (Week 10)
Bloxwich v Coventry PO
Coventry Tech v Cheadle
Fife Street v Shottery

November 20 (Week 11)
Coventry PO v Coventry Tech
Ford v Bloxwich
Stone v Fife Street

December 4 (Week 13)
Bloxwich v Jaguar
Coventry Tech v Ford
Cheadle v Coventry PO

December 11 (Week 14)
Ford v Cheadle
Jaguar v Coventry Tech
Rugby Welsh v Bloxwich

December 18 (Week 15)
Bloxwich v Shottery
Coventry Tech v Rugby Welsh
Cheadle v Jaguar
Coventry PO v Ford

January 8 (Week 18)
Jaguar v Coventry PO
Rugby Welsh v Cheadle
Shottery v Coventry Tech
Stone v Bloxwich

January 29 (Week X5)
Bloxwich v Fife Street
Coventry Tech v Stone
Cheadle v Shottery
Coventry PO v Rugby Welsh
Ford v Jaguar

February 12 (Week 22)
Rugby Welsh v Ford
Shottery v Coventry PO
Stone v Cheadle
Fife Street v Coventry Tech

March 12 (Week 26)
Cheadle v Fife Street
Coventry PO v Stone
Ford v Shottery
Jaguar v Rugby Welsh

March 26 (Week 28)
Shottery v Jaguar
Stone v Ford
Fife Street v Coventry PO

April 9 (Week 30)
Ford v Fife Street
Jaguar v Stone
Rugby Welsh v Shottery

STAFFS & WARWICKS FOUR

BLOXWICH RFC
Ground Address: T P Riley Community School, Lichfield Road, Bloxwich. Tel No: 0922 710463.
Club Secretary: Jim Rlidge. 5 Primpose Close, Pelsall, Walsall, WS3 5B7. Tel No: 0922 693690 (W) 0509 219990.
Press Offocer: Rob Tittley, 27 Lapwing Close, Cheslyn Hay, Staffs. Tel No: (H) 0922 416227 (W) 0922 710077.
Club Colours: Green and black quarters, black shorts and stockings.

CHEADLE RUFC
Ground Address: Stanfields Playing Ground, Tean Road, Cheadle, Stoke-on-Trent, Tel No: 0538 751476.
Club Secretary: Mrs J A Hill, Abbot's Lea, Hall Orchard, Cheadle, Stoke-on-Trent. Tel No: (H) 0538 751476.
Press Officer: As Secretary.
Club Colours: Sky blue with central white band.

COVENTRY POST OFFICE RFC
Ground Address: Telepost Club, Northbrook Road, Coundon, Coventry. Tel No: 0203 332714.
Cub Secretary: Miss Y Graham. 251 Telfer Road, Radford, Coventry, CV6 3DS. Tel No: (H) 0203 598378.
Press Officer: Miss Y Graham. Address as above.
Club Colours: Red and black hoops, black shorts.

COVENTRY TECHNICAL RFC
Ground Address: Charter Avenue, Canley, Coventry.
Club Secretary: Neil Franklin, 42, Haynestong Road, Coundon, Coventry, CV6 1GJ. Tel No: (H) 0203 335560, (W) 0203 668706.
Press Officer: Rick Rees, 47 Brackenhurst Road, Coundon, Coventry. Tel No: (H) 0203 336240.
Club Colours: Dark Green/Gold/Chocalate Hoops.

FIFE STREET WORKING MEN'S CLUB RFC
Ground Address: To be confirmed.
Club Secretary: Lynne Gillespie, 60 Bristol Road, Earlsdon, Coventry CV5 6LH. Tel: (H) 0203 675401 (W) 0203 831919
Club Colours: Green , white and red hoops.

FORD LEAMINGTON RFC
Ground Address: Newbold Comyn, Newbold Terrace, Leamington Spa, Warwickshire.
Club Secretary: Alan Clarke. 58 William Tarver Close, Warwick, Warwickshire. Tel No (H) 0926 401532.
Press Officer: Brian Butler, 14 The Greswoldes, Radford Semele, Leamington Spa, CV31 1TP. Tel No: (H) 0926 888702.
Club Colours: Navy blue, black and white hoops/Black shorts.

JAGUAR RFC
Ground Address: Sports and Social Club, Middlemarch Road, Coventry, Warwickshire. Tel No: 0203 5991118.
Club Secretary: M. Mills, 51 Dawes Close, Stoke, Coventry CV2 4LL. Tel No: (H) 0203 459314.
Press Officer: Simon Hargreaves, 10 Grangemouth Road, Radford, Coventry, CV6 3SE. Tel No: (H) 0203 592307 (W) 0203 592307.
Club Colours: Green/Gold quarters.

FINAL TABLE

	P	W	D	L	F	A	PD	Pts
Warwickshire Police	9	9	0	0	324	31	293	18
Burntwood	9	8	0	1	296	61	235	16
Shottery	9	6	1	2	194	77	117	13
Rugby Welsh	9	6	0	3	204	105	99	12
Stone	9	4	1	4	230	154	76	9
Bloxwich	9	3	2	4	65	121	-56	8
Coventry P O	9	3	0	6	94	113	-19	6
Ford	9	3	0	6	104	145	-41	6
Jaguar (Coventry)	9	0	0	9	35	261	-226	0
Cheadle	9	1	0	8	18	370	-352	0

RUGBY WELSH RFC
Ground Address: Alwyn Road, Recreation Ground, Bilton, Rugby, (Ground remote from clubhouse) Tel No: 0788 565605 (Clubhouse)
Club Secretary: Roy Thompson. 1 Heather Close, Highlands, Rugby CV22 6SB. Tel No: (H) 0788 577796 (W) 0788 545062.
Press Officer: As for Secretary.
Club Colours: Red jerseys, white shorts, red socks.

SHOTTERY RUFC
Ground Address: Shottery Fields, Shottery, Stratford-Upon-Avon, Warwickshire.
Club Secretary: Pip Whitting, 2 Hillside Road, Stratford-Upon- Avon, Warwickshire, CV37 9EB. Tel No: (H) 299022 (W) 299022.
Press Officer: As above.
Club Colours: Blue/White Jerseys and white shorts.

STONE RUFC
Ground Address: Alleynes School, Oulton Road, Stone, Staffs.
Club Secretary: David Ducmore, 1 Coombe Park Road, Walton, Stone, Staffs, ST15 0AY. Tel No: (H) (0385) 811427 (W) 0785 814930.
Club Colours: Maroon and green quarters.

MIDLAND DIVISION

NORTH MIDLAND ONE 1993-94 FIXTURES

October 23 (Week 8)
Bridgnorth v Evesham
Redditch v Old Griffs
Kidderminster v Old Centrals
Telford v Droitwich
Veseyans v Luctonians
Warley v Five Ways O E

October 30 (week X2)
Five Ways O E v Bridgnorth
Luctonians v Warley
Droitwich v Veseyans
Old Centrals v Telford
Old Griffs v Kidderminster
Pershore v Redditch

November 13 (Week 10)
Bridgnorth v Luctonians
Evesham v Five Ways O E
Kidderminster v Pershore
Telford v Old Griffs
Veseyans v Old Centrals
Warley v Droitwich

November 20 (Week 11)
Luctonians v Evesham
Droitwich v Bridgnorth
Old Centrals v Warley
Old Griffs v Veseyans
Pershore v Telford
Redditch v Kidderminster

December 4 (Week 13)
Bridgnorth v Old Centrals
Evesham v Droitwich
Five Ways O E v Luctonians
Telfrod v Redditch
Veseyans v Pershore
Warley v Old Griff

December 11 (Week 14)
Droitwich v Five Ways O E
Old Centrals v Evesham
Old Griffs v Bridgnorth
Pershore v Warley
Redditch v Veseyans
Kidderminster v Telford

December 18 (Week 15)
Bridgnorth v Pershore
Evesham v Old Griffs
Five Ways O E v Old Centrals
Luctonians v Droitwich
Veseyans v Kidderminster
Warley v Redditch

January 8 (week 18)
Old Centrals v Luctonians
Old Griffs v Five Ways O E
Pershore v Evesham
Redditch v Bridgnorth
Kidderminster v Warley
Telford v Veseyans

January 29 (Week X5)
Bridgnorth v Kidderminster
Evesham v Redditch
Five Ways O E v Pershore
Luctonians v Old Griffs
Droitwich v Old Centrals
Warley v Telford

February 12 (Week 22)
Old Griffs v Droitwich
Pershore v Luctonians
Redditch v Five Ways O E
Kidderminster v Evesham
Telford v Bridgnorth
Veseyans v Warley

March 12 (Week 26)
Bridgnorth v Beseyans
Evesham v Telford
Five Ways O E v Kiddermister
Luctonians v Redditch
Droitwich v Pershore
Old Centrals v Old Griffs

March 26 (Week 28)
Pershore v Old Centrals
Redditch v Droitwich
Kidderminster v Luctonians
Telford v Five Ways O E
Veseyans v Evesham
Warley v Bridgnorth

April 9 (Week 30)
Evesham v Warley
Five Ways O E v Veseyans
Luctonians v Telford
Droitwich v Kidderminster
Old Centrals v Redditch
Old Griffs v Pershore

NORTH MIDLAND ONE

BRIDGNORTH RFC
Ground Address: The Bull, Bridge Street, Bridgnorth, Shropshire, WV15 5AA. Tel No: O746 762796.
Club Secretary: Pete Shimmin, 7, Buck Cottage, Sheinton, Cressage, Shropshire, SY5 6OJ. Tel No: O952 51O6O4 (W) O746 766488.
Press Officer: Geoff Davis. 11 Love Lane, Bridgnorth, Shropshire. Tel No:O766 763252.
Club Colours: Black shirts/black shorts.

DROITWICH RFC
Ground Address: The Clubhouse, Hanbury Road. Droitwich Spa, Worcs. Tel No: O9O5 77O384.
Club Secretary: R A Willetts, 23 Hawford Place, Droitwich Spa, Worcs, WR9 8NG. Tel No: O9O5 774341.
Press Officer: As Secretary.
Club Colours: Gold and black hoops

EVESHAM RFC
Ground Address: Off Albert Road, Evesham, Worcs. Tel No: O386 446469.
Club Secretary: J P Hartley, Nightingale House, Bishampton, Pershore, Worcs. Tel No: O386 82325 (W) O527 76776.
Press Officer: Ms. Carol Horseman, 3 Greenhill Gardens, Evesham, Worcs. Tel No: O386 49563 (W) O386 765888.
Club Colours: Navy and maroon hoops.

FIVE WAYS FC
Ground Address: "Masshouse", Ash Lane, Hopwood, Birmingham B48 7BD. Tel No: O21 445 49O9
Club Secretary: Richard Lisseter, 138 Chatsworth Road, Malesowen, W Mids B62 8TH. Tel No: O21-559-6549 (W) O21-55O-1724.
Press Officer: As Secretary
Club Colours: Navy blue, amber.

KIDDERMINSTER CAROLIANS RFC
Ground Address: Marlpool Lane, Kidderminster, Worcs, DY11 3JH. Tel No: O562 74OO43.
Club Secretary: Mr Wallace Bond, 7, Belvedere Crescent, Meadow Rise, Bewdley, Worcs, DY12 1JX. Tel No: (H) O299 4O4171 (W) O21 233 4466, FAX O21 233 2376.
Press Officer: Mr Brian Gittins, 16 Chaddesley Road, Kidderminster, Worcs, DY1O 3AD. Tel No: O562 745429 (W) O562 745429.
Club Colours: Black with gold hoops.

LUCTONIANS RFC
Ground Address: Mortimer Park, Hereford Road, Kingsland, Derefordshire. Tel No: O568-7O8345.
Club Secretary: Huw Davies, The Bell House, Kingsland, Leominster, Herefordshire, HR6 9RU. Tel No: (H) O568-7O845O (W) O432-36213O.
Press Officer: Robin East, 4O2 Buckfield Road, Leominster, Herefordshire. Tel No: (H) O568-614436.
Club Colours: Jerseys: Black and white rings, shorts black.

OLD CENTRALS RFC
Ground Address: Moundsley Hall, Walkers Heath Road, Kings Norton, Birmingham, B3O. Tel No: O21 458 24O8.
Club Secretary: M Harris, 32, Barker Road, Sutton Coldfield, W. Mids, B74 2NZ. Tel No: (H) O21-3549876 (W) O2O3 855538.
Club Colours: Green maroon gold.

OLD GRIFFINIANS
Ground Address: Moundsley Hall, Kings Norton, Birmingham B3O. Tel No: O21 458 24O8.
Club Secretary: R Adie, 33 Middlemore Road, Northfield, Birmingham, B31. Tel No: (H) O21 4774894 (W) O21 453 1778.

FINAL TABLE

	P	W	D	L	F	A	PD	Pts
Newport	12	11	0	1	382	81	301	22
Five Ways Old Ed	12	11	0	1	252	70	182	22
Luctonians	12	10	0	2	400	76	324	20
Pershore	12	6	0	6	188	159	29	12
Telford	12	6	0	6	196	178	18	12
Evesham	12	6	1	5	170	153	17	11
Veseyans	12	6	1	5	141	141	0	11
Old Centrals	12	5	0	7	154	181	-27	10
Warley	12	4	0	8	143	155	-12	8
Old Griffinians	12	5	0	7	188	212	-18	8
Bridgnorth	12	3	0	9	92	338	-246	6
Redditch	12	2	0	10	98	360	-262	4
Ross-on-Wye	12	2	0	10	102	427	-322	2

Press Officer: Mr M Giles, 122 Middlehall Road, Northfield, Birmingham B3O Tel No: O21 4585131.
Club Colours: Black.

PERSHORE RFC
Ground Address: Mill Lane, Wyre Piddle, Pershore, Worcs. Tel No: O386 5541O5.
Club Secretary: Mr A K Jenkinson, 12 Eltric Road, Claines, Worcester. Tel No. O9O5 54346
Press Officer: Mr A Brunyee, 55 Oldbury Road, St. Johns, Worcester, Tel No: O9O5 42277O8.
Club Colours: Black with two scarlet hoops.

REDDITCH RFC
Ground Address: Bromsgrove Road, Redditch.
Club Secretary: Bryn Richards, 29 Ladbrook Close, Oakenshaw, Redditch, Worcs, B98 7XR. Tel No: (H) O527 54287O
Press Officer: Will McKay, 55 Mount Street, Smallwood, Redditch. Tel No: (H) O527 59531O.
Club Colours: Light/Dark Blue

TELFORD HORNETS RFC
Ground Address: Town Park, Hinkshay Road, Dawley, Telford, Shropshire, TF4 3NZ. Tel No: O952 5O544O.
Club Secretary: Martin Dolphin, 1O Canonbie Lea Madeley, Telford, Shropshire TF7 5RL. Tel No: (H) O952 68494O (W) O952 294987.
Press Officer: Dave Mann, 364 Holyhead Road, Wellington, Telford, Shropshire TF1 2DD. Tel No: (H) O952-223O44, (W) O952 253511, O952-243O51 (FAX).
Club Colours: Black with gold chestband.

VESEYANS RFC
Ground Address: Little Hardwick Road, Streetly, Sutton Coldfield, West Midlands. Tel No: O21 353 5388.
Club Secretary: Gavin Humphreys, 496 Lichfield Road, Sutton Coldfield, West Mids B74 4EL, Tel No: (H) O21-3O8-1135 (W) O21- 631-3232.
Club Colours: Black & white shirts, black shorts and socks.

WARLEY RFC
Ground Address: Broomfield, The Uplands, Smethwick, Warley, West Midlands, B67 6BJ. Tel No: O21 558 OO84.
Club Secretary: Mr K Ward, 72 Oak Road, Oldbury, Warley, B68 OBD Tel No: O21 422 4639.
Press Officer: M Hancox, 36 Marlborough Road, Smethwick, Warley Tel No: (H) O21 4296647.
Club Colours: Red & white hooped shirts, black shorts.

MIDLAND DIVISION

NORTH MIDLAND TWO
1993-94
FIXTURES

October 23 (Week 8)
Birmingham Welsh v Birmingham C O
Kynoch v Erdington
Malvern v Edwardians
Market Drayton v Old Salts
Old Moselians v Bromyard
Tenbury v Bournville

October 30 (Week X2)
Bournville v Birmingham Welsh
Bromyard v Tenbury
Old Salts v Old Moselians
Edwardians v Market Drayton
Erdington v Malvern
Ross v Kynoch

November 13 (Week 10)
Birmingham Welsh v Bromyard
Birmingham C O v Bournville
Malvern v Ross
Market Drayton v Erdington
Old Moselians v Edwardians
Tenbury v Old Salts

November 20 (Week 11)
Old Salts v Birmingham Welsh
Bromyard v Birmingham C O
Edwardians v Tenbury
Erdington v Old Moselians
Ross v Market Drayton
Kynoch v Malvern

December 4 (Week 13)
Birmingham Welsh v Edwardians
Birmingham C O v Old Salts
Bournville v Bromyard
Market Drayton v Kynoch
Old Moselians v Ross
Tenbury v Erdington

December 11 (Week 14)
Erdington v Birmingham Welsh
Old Salts v Bournville
Edwardians v Birmingham C O
Ross v Tenbury
Kynoch v Old Moselians
Malvern v Market Drayton

December 18 (Week 15)
Birmingham Welsh v Ross
Birmingham C O v Erdington
Bournville v Edwardians
Bromyard v Old Salts
Old Moselians v Malvern
Tenbury v Kynoch

January 8 (Week 18)
Kynoch v Birmingham Welsh
Malvern v Tenbury
Edwardians v Bromyard
Erdington v Bournville
Ross v Birmingham C O
Market Drayton v Old Moselians

January 29 (Week X5)
Birmingham Welsh v Malvern
Bournville v Ross
Bromyard v Erdington
Old Scotts v Edwardians
Birmingham C O v Kynoch
Tenbury v Market Drayton

February 12 (Week 22)
Market Drayton v Birmingham Welsh
Erdington v Old Salts
Ross v Bromyard
Kynoch v Bournville
Malvern v Birmingham C O
Old Moselians v Tenbury

March 12 (Week 26)
Birmingham Welsh v Old Moselians
Birmingham C O v Market Drayton
Bournville v Malvern
Bromyard v Kynoch
Old Salts v Ross
Edwardians v Erdington

March 26 (Week 28)
Tenbury v Birmingham Wells
Ross v Edwardian
Kynoch v Old Salts
Malvern v Bromyard
Market Drayton v Bournville
Old Moselians v Birmingham C O

April 9 (Week 30)
Birmingham C O v Tenbury
Bournville v Old Moselians
Bromyard v Market Drayton
Old Salt v Malvern
Edwardians v Kynoch
Erdington v Ross

380

NORTH MIDLAND TWO

BIRMINGHAM CITY OFFICIALS RFC
Ground Address: Kenryck Road, Shard End, Birmingham.
Club Secretary: Mick Hancox, 16 Newcroft Grove,
Yardley, Birmingham, B26 1SN. Tel: (H) 021 783 1124.
Press Officer: Mick Hancox, 16 Newcroft Grove, Yardley,
Birmingham, B26 1SN. Tel: (H) 021 783 1124.
Club Colours: Navy blue with maroon & gold hoops.

BIRMINGHAM WELSH RFC
Ground Address: Catherine de Barnes Lane, Bickenhill,
Solihull, West Midlands. Tel: 0675 442995.
Club Secretary: Jon Poole, 39 Stanton Road, Shirley,
Solihull, West Midlands, B90 2DU. Tel: (H) 021 745 9570
(W) 021 445 2356.
Press Officer: Jon Poole, 39 Stanton Road, Shirley,
Solihull, West Midlands, B90 2DU. Tel: (H) 021 745 9570
(W) 021 445 2356.
Club Colours: Red & green quarters, black shorts.

BOURNVILLE RFC
Ground Address: Rowheath Playing Fields, Heath Road,
Bournville, Birmingham. Tel: 021 458 1711.
Club Secretary: Harry Tempest, 29 Bell Hill, Northfield,
Birmingham, B31 1LB. Tel: (H) 021 604 9845.
Press Officer: Peter Gurvill, 52 Watford Road, Cotteridge,
Birmingham, B30 1PD. Tel: (H) 021 458 2538 (W) 021
475 5187.
Club Colours: Maroon, gold & blue.

BROMYARD RFC
Ground Address: Mintridge, Bromyard, Herefordshire.
Tel: 0885 488152.
Club Secretary: M Warren, The Chestnuts, Munderfield,
Bromyard, Herefordshire, HR7 4JT. Tel: (H) 0885 4790684
(W) 0885 490480.
Club Colours: Green & gold.

EDWARDIAN FC
Ground Address: Streetsbrook Road, Solihull, West
Midlands, B90 3PF. Tel: 021 744 6821.
Club Secretary: Tog Isaacs, 72 Rectory Park Road,
Sheldon, Birmingham, B26 3LH. Tel: (H) 021 624 1045
(W) 0527 36363.
Press Officer: Tog Isaacs, 72 Rectory Park Road, Sheldon,
Birmingham, B26 3LH. Tel: (H) 021 624 1045 (W) 0527
36363.
Club Colours: Old gold, claret, navy irregular hoops.

ERDINGTON RFC
Ground Address: Birches Green Playing Fields, Kingsbury
Road, Erdington, Birmingham. Tel: 021 373 7597.
Club Secretary: Derek owen, 129 Bradbury Road,
Solihull, West Midlands, B92 8AL. Tel: (H) 021 706 4699
(W) 0527 64252.
Press Officer: Graham Rhodes, 26 Lakeside Drive,
Monkspath, Solihull, West MIdlands. Tel: (H) 021 745
7792 (W) 021 331 5355.
Club Colours: White with blue hoop, blue shorts.

KYNOCH RFC
Ground Address: Holford Drive, Perry barr, Birmingham,
B42 2TU. Tel: 021 356 4369.
Club Secretary: J K Ross, 127 Leopold Avenue,
Handsworth Wood, Birmingham, B20 1EX.
Press Officer: T Groom, 6 Moore Court, Jeffrey Road,
Erdington, Birmingham C24 8AY. Tel: (H) 021 384 1824.
Club Colours: Black & white hoops.

MALVERN RFC
Ground Address: Spring Lane, Malvern, Worcestershire,
WR14. Tel: 0684 573728.
Club Secretary: M G Davies, 102 Friut Lands, Malvern,
Worcestershire, WR14 4XB. Tel: (H) 0684 567835 (W)
021 456 3663.

FINAL TABLE

	P	W	D	L	F	A	PD	Pts
Droitwich	12	11	0	1	248	133	115	22
Kidderminster	12	10	1	1	244	91	153	21
Edwardians	12	10	0	2	291	39	252	20
Erdington	12	8	1	3	260	91	169	17
B'mingham City Off	12	8	1	3	259	116	143	17
Malvern	12	6	1	5	278	145	133	13
Market Drayton	12	5	0	7	201	197	4	10
Bournville	12	5	0	7	125	260	-135	10
Old Moseleians	12	4	0	8	169	278	-109	8
Bromyard	12	3	1	8	132	192	-60	7
Tenbury	12	2	1	9	96	216	-120	5
Kynoch	12	2	0	10	92	364	-272	4
Birchfield	12	1	0	11	95	368	-273	2

Press Officer: M G Davies, 102 Fruit Lands, Malvern,
Worcestershire, WR14 4XB. Tel: (H) 0684 56783 (W) 021
456 3663.
Club Colours: Maroon with light blue & gold hoops.

MARKET DRAYTON RFC
Ground Address: Greenfield, Market Drayton, Shropshire.
Club Secretary: R Davies, 73 Longslow Road, Market
Drayton, Shropshire, BF9 3BP. Tel: (H) 0630 655069.
Press Officer: R Davies, 73 Longslow Road, Market
Drayton, Shropshire, BF9 3BP. Tel: (H) 0630 655069.
Club Colours: Black with emerald collars.

OLD MOSELIANS RFC
Ground Address: Lugtrot Lane, Solihull, West Midlands.
Tel: 021 705 7847.
Club Secretary: John Stefani, 6 Stand Street, Warwick,
CV34 6HR. Tel: (H) 0926 497275 (W) 0926 464511.
Press Officer: John Stefani, 6 Stand Street, Warwick,
CV34 6HR. Tel: (H) 0926 497275 (W) 0926 464511.
Club Colours: Black with red & white chest band, black
shorts.

OLD SALTLEIANS RFC
Ground Address: Watton lane, Water Orton, Birmingham.
Tel: 021 748 3380.
Club Secretary: Derek Bolton, 50 Emmanuel Road,
Wyldegreen, Sutton Coldfield. Tel: (H) 021 350 7027.
Press Officer: Terry Beuan, 17 Hawksford Close, Castle
Bromwich, B36. Tel: (H) 021 748 6405.
Club Colours: Red & yellow hoops.

ROSS ON WYE RFC
Ground Address: Ross Sports Centre, Wilton Road, Ross
on Wye, Herefordshire. Tel: 0989 63256.
Club Secretary: J Long, Marsh Farm, Hildersley, Ross on
Wye. Tel: (H) 0989 62380 (W) 0989 62380.
Press Officer: J Boaden, Ross RFC, Station Street, Ross on
Wye, Herefordshire.
Club Colours: Blue and white hoops.

TENBURY RFC
Ground Address: Palmers Meadow, Tenbury Wells,
Worcestershire. Tel: 0584 810456.
Club Secretary: Roger Bowkett, The Laurels, Worcester
Road, Great Witley, Worcestershire, WR6 6HR. Tel: (H)
0299 896676 (W) 0584 810351.
Press Officer: Roger Bowkett, The Laurels, Worcester
Road, Great Witley, Worcestrshire, WR6 6HR. Tel: (H)
0299 896676 (W) 0584 810351.
Club Colours: Black & green quarters.

NORTH MIDLAND THREE
1993-94
FIXTURES

October 23 (Week 8)
Stourport v Birmingham C S
Yardley & District v Birchfield
Upton v Ledbury
Witton v Bishops Castle
W M Police v Cleobury

October 30 (Week X2)
Birchfield v Stourport
Bishops Castle v Yardley & District
Ledbury v W M Police
Oswestry v Thimblemill
Cleobury v Witton

November 6 (Week 9)
Stourport v Bishops Castle
Birmingham C S v Birchfield
Upton v Oswestry
Witton v Ledbury
Yardley & District v Cleobury

November 13 (Week 10)
Bishops Castle v Birmingahm C S
Ledbury v Yardley & District
Oswestry v W M Police
Thimblemill v Upton
Cleobury v Stourport

November 20 (Week 11)
Stourport v Ledbury
Birchfield v Bishops Castle
W M Police v Thimblemill
Witton v Oswestry
Birmingham C S v Cleobury

December 4 (Week 13)
Ledbury v Birmingham C S
Oswestry v Yardley & District
Thimblemill v Witton
Upton v W M Police
Cleobury v Birchfield

December 11 (Week 14)
Stourport v Oswestry
Birchfield v Ledburty
Witton v Upton
Yardley & District v Thimblemill
Bishops Castle v Cleobury

December 18 (Week 15)
Thimblemill v Stourport
Oswestry v Birmingham C S
Ledbury v Bishops Castle
Upton v Yardley & District
W M Police v Witton

January 8 (Week 18)
Stourport v Upton
Birmingham C S v Thimblemill
Birchfield v Oswestry
Yardley & District v W M Police
Cleobury v Ledbury

January 22 (Week 20)
W M Police v Stourport
Upton v Birmingham C S
Oswestry v Bishops Castle
Thimblemill v Birchfield
Witton v Yardley & District

January 29 (Week X5)
Stourport v Witton
Birmingham C S v W M Police
Birchfield v Upton
Bishops Castle v Thimblewell
Cleobury v Oswestry

February 12 (Week22)
Yardley & District v Stourport
Witton v Birmingham C S
Oswestry v Ledbury
Upton v Birchfield
Thimblemill v Cleobury

February 26 (Week 24)
Cleobury v Upton
Birmingham C S v Yardley & District
Birchfield v Witton
Bishops Castle v W M Police
Ledbury v Thimblewell

NORTH MIDLAND THREE

BIRCHFIELD RFC
Ground Address: Moor Lane, Witton, Birmingham, Tel No: O21 356 2142
Club Secretary: John Wingate, 125 Parkfield Drive, Castle, Bromwich, B36 9TY. Tel No: O21 749 244O, (W) O527 O23O5.
Press Officer: John Wingate. Address as above.
Club Colours: Green and black hoops.

BIRMINGHAM CIVIL SERVICE
Ground Address: Civil Service Sports Ground, Old Damson Lane, Elmdon, Solihull, West Midlands. Tel No: O21 782 2151 O21 782 O423.
Club Secretary: R G Webb, 51 Ladbrook Road, Solihull, West Midlands B91 3RW. Tel No: (H) O217O52812.
Press Officer: As Secretary.
Club Colours: Red shirts, with 5" white hoop, navy blue shorts, red socks.

BISHOP'S CASTLE & ONNY VALLEY RUFC
Ground Address: Love Lane, Bishop's Castle.
Club Secretary: Mr Paul Middleton, Tregaron, 7 Shrewsbury Road, Longden, Shrewsbury, SY5 8ER, Tel No: (H) O743 86O141 (W) O743 79O336.
Press Officer: Mr Sam Jones, IvyHouse, Habberley, Pontesbury, Shrewsbury, Shropshire. Tel No: O743 79OO35.
Club Colours: Red & green shirts, black shorts, green socks.

CLEOBURYMORTIMER RFC
Ground Address: Lacon Childe School, Cleobury Mortimer, Shropshire. Tel: 0299 270085
Club Secretary: Richard Redfern, 43 Furlongs Road, Cleobury Mortimer, Shropshire DY14 9YE. Tel: (H) 0299 270472.
Press Officer: Dave Hinves, 7, Simon Evans Close, Cleobury Mortimer, Shropshire. Tel: 0299 271059.
Club Colours: Green and red quarters.

LEDBURY RFC
Ground Address: Ross Road Playing Fields, Ledbury. Tel No: O531 631788.
Club Secretary: David Kerr, Flat 1, 5 Worcester Road, Ledbury, Herfordshire, HR8 1PL. Tel No: (H) O531 632375 (W) O531632665.
Press Officer: As Secretary.
Club Colours: Black with white hoops.

OSWESTRY RUFC
Ground Address: Park Hall, Oswestry, Shropshire S711 4AS. Tel No: O691 652949.
Club Secretary: Miss Debbie Maddocks, 69 Cherry Tree Drive, St Martin, Oswestry Shrops SY11 3HX. Tel No: (H) O691 773863 (W) O244 35O377.
Press Officer: W Howell, Bryn offer the Racecourse, Oswestry, Shropshire 7HW. Tel No: (H) O691 654552 (W) O691 654551.
Club Colours: Red and black hoops.

STOURPORT RFC
Ground Address: The Playing Fields, Watshes, Stourport-on-Severn, Worcs.
Club Secretary: A Foster, Lime Kilns, Pensax, Abberley, Worcester, WR6 Tel No: O299 896631.
Press Officer: A Foster, The Lime Kilns, Pensax, Great Whitley, Worcs. Te; No: O299 89631.
Club Colours: Blue/Amber band.

FINAL TABLE

	P	W	D	L	F	A	PD	Pts
Birmingham Welsh	11	10	0	1	296	112	184	20
Old Saltleians	11	9	0	2	217	99	118	18
Birmingham Civil S	11	8	1	2	250	80	170	17
Upton-on-Severn	11	7	1	3	163	113	50	15
Yardley & District	11	6	1	4	137	75	62	13
Bishops Castle	11	6	0	5	165	77	88	12
Bewdley	11	4	1	6	191	131	60	9
Oswestry	11	4	0	7	117	151	-34	8
Ledbury	11	4	0	7	129	189	-60	8
Witton	11	4	0	7	129	221	-92	8
West Mercia Pol	11	2	0	9	84	243	-159	4
Thimblemill	11	0	0	11	21	408	-387	0

THIMBLEMILL RFC
Ground Address: Thimblemill Recreation Centre, Thimblemill Road, Smethwick, West Midlands. Tel No: O21 429 2459.
Club Secretary: David Davis, 78 Wilmington Road, Quinton, Birmingham, B32 1DU. Tel No:(H) O21 422 4693.
Press Officer: As Secretary.
Club Colours: (1) Green/Blue quarters. (2) Red/White quarters.

UPTON-UPON-SEVERN
Ground Address: Collinghurst Meadow, Old St, Upton-upon-Severn, Tel No: O684 594445.
Club Secretary: Peter Barker, Tiltridge Farm, Upper Hook Road, Upton-Upon-Severn, Worcs, WR8 OSA. Tel No: (H) O684 59290O.
Press Officer: As Secretary.
Club Colours: Black and white quarters.

WEST MERCIA CONSTABULARY RFC
Ground Address: Police Headquarters, Hindlip Hall, Worcester, Tel No: O9O5 72300O.
Club Secretary: Paul Crofts, 16, Node Hill, Studley, Warks B8O 7RR. Tel No: (H) O527 854287 (W) O527 584888.
Press Officer: As Secretary
Club Colours: Light blue, dark blue quarters.

WITTON RFC
Ground Address: Ansells Sports and Social Club, Aldridge Road, Perry Barr, Birmingham. Tel No: O21 356 4296.
Club Secretary: P S Jones, 1O8 Grindleford Road, Great Barr, Birmingham, B42 2SQ. Tel No: O21 36O 1831, (W) O21 632 4381.
Press Officer: Barry Underwood, Flat 1, 323 Birmingham Road, Great Barr, Birmingham B43 7AP. Tel No: (H) O21 358 484O.
Club Colours: Yellow/Black shirts, black shorts.

YARDLEY & DIST RFC
Ground Address: Colehall Lane, Yardley, Birmingham, Tel No: O21 781 845O.
Club Secretary: Ms J Thornton, 45 St Gerrards Road, Solihull, W Midlands B91 1UB. Tel No. (H) O21 7O4 2973 (W) O21 212 2362.
Press Officer: As above
Club Colours: Blue and gold hoops.

MIDLAND DIVISION

MIDLAND EAST ONE
1993-94
FIXTURES

December 18 (Week 15)
Amber Valley v Moderns
Ampthill v Luton
Biggleswade v Hinckley
Chesterfield v Kettering
Stoneygate v Spalding
Northampton BBOB v Scunthorpe

October 23 (Week 8)
Amber Valley v Ampthill
Northampton BBOB v Bigglesade
Scunthorpe v Luton
Spalding v Hinckley
Stewart & Lloyds v Kettering
Stoneygate v Chesterfield

January 8 (Week 18)
Hinckley v Chesterfield
Luton v Biggleswade
Moderns v Ampthill
Scunthorpe v Amber Valley
Spalding v Northampton BBOB
Stewarts & Lloyds v Stoneygate

October 30 (Week X2)
Biggleswade v Amber Valley
Chesterfield v Northampton BBOB
Kettering v Stoneygate
Hinckley v Stewarts & Lloyds
Luton v Spalding
Moderns v Scunthorpe

January 29 (Week X5)
Amber Valley v Spalding
Ampthill v Scunthorpe
Biggleswade v Moderns
Chesterfield v Luton
Kettering v Hinckley
Northampton BBOB v Stewarts & Lloyds

November 13 (Week 10)
Amber Valley v Chesterfield
Ampthill v Biggleswade
Spalding v Moderns
Stewarts & Lloyds v Liston
Stoneygate v Hinckley
Northampton BBOB v Kettering

February 12 (Week 22)
Luton v Kettering
Moderns v Chesterfield
Scunthorpe v Bigglesade
Spalding v Ampthill
Stewarts & Lloyds v Amber Valley
Stoneygate v Northampton BBOB

November 20 (Week 11)
Chesterfield v Ampthill
Kettering v Amber Valley
Hinckley v Northampton BBOB
Luton v Stoneygate
Moderns v Stewarts & Lloyds
Scunthorpe v Spalding

March 12 (Week 26)
Amber Valley v Stoneygate
Ampthill v Stewarts & Lloyds
Biggleswade v Spalding
Chesterfield v Scunthorpe
Kettering v Moderns
Hinckley v Luton

December 4 (Week 13)
Amber Valley v Hinckley
Ampthill v Kettering
Biggleswade v Chesterfield
Stewarts & Lloyds v Scunthorpe
Stoneygate v Moderns
Northampton BBOB v Luton

March 26 (Week 28)
Moderns v Hinckley
Northampton BBOB v Amber Valley
Scunthorpe v Kettering
Spalding v Chesterfield
Stewarts & Lloyds v Biggleswade
Stoneygate v Ampthill

December 11 (Week 14)
Kettering v Bigglswade
Hinckley v Ampthill
Luton v Amber Valley
Moderns v Northampton BBOB
Scunthorpe v Stoneygate
Spalding v Stewarts & Lloyds

April 9 (Week 30)
Ampthill v Northampton BBOB
Biggleswade v Stoneygate
Chesterfield v Stewarts & Lloyds
Kettering v Spalding
Hinckley v Scunthorpe
Luton v Moderns

MIDLAND EAST ONE

AMBER VALLEY RUFC
Ground Address: The Recreation Ground, Swanwick, Derbyshire. Tel: 0773 605072.
Club Secretary: John Colbourne, 37 Boughton Drive, Swanwick, Derbyshire. Tel: (H) 0773 605601.
Press Officer: B Whitfield, The Delves, Swanwick, Derbyshire. Tel: (H) 0773 603335.
Club Colours: Amber & black.

AMPTHILL & DISTRICT RUFC
Ground Address: Dillingham Park, Woburn Road, Ampthill, Bedford. Tel: 0525 403303.
Club Secretary: Richard Churchill, The Bungalow, Park Gardens, Blechley, Milton Keynes, MK3 6HT. Tel: (H) 0908 379089.
Press Officer: Eric Turner, 34 Dunstable Stret, Ampthill, Bedford, MK45 2JT. Tel: (H) 0525 403128.
Club Colours: Maroon & amber shirts, black shorts.

BIGGLESWADE RUFC
Ground Address: Langford Road, Biggleswade, Bedfordshire, SG18 9RA. Tel: 0767 312463.
Club Secretary: Mike Williams, 8 Laurel Way, Ickleford, Hitchin, Herts, SG5 3UP. Tel: (H) 0462 454782.
Press Officer: Nigel Aldis, 7 Mayfield Court, Sandy, Bedfordshire, SG19 1NF. Tel: (H) 0767 681340.
Club Colours: Navy blue with red hoop.

CHESTERFIELD RUFC
Ground Address: Stonegravels, Sheffield Road, Chesterfield. Tel: 0242 232321.
Club Secretary: P I Jackson, 396 Old Road, Chesterfield, S40 3QF. Tel: (H) 568287 (W) 270112.
Press Officer: N Jackson, 20Mendip Crescent, Ashgate, Chesterfield. Tel: (H) 0246 207269 (W) 0742 583120.
Club Colours: Red with white hoops, white shorts.

HINKLEY RFC
Ground Address: Leicester Road, Hinckley. Tel: 0455 615010.
Club Secretary: F J Swift, 8 The Rills, Hinckley, LE10 1NA. Tel: (H) 0455 250270.
Press Officer: F J Swift, 8 The Rills, Hinckley, LE10 1NA. Tel: (H) 0455 250270.
Club Colours: Black & amber shirts, black shorts.

KETTERING RFC
Ground Address: Waverley Road, Kettering. Tel: 0536 85588.
Club Secretary: Mike Evans, 40 Brooksdale Close, Kettering, NN16 9BJ. Tel: (H) 0536 517625 (W) 0933 225445.
Press Officer: David Newman, 31 Ise View Road, Desborough, Northamptonshire. Tel: (H) 0536 760126 (W) 0536 710422.
Club Colours: Blue & white hoops, navy shorts.

LUTON RFC
Ground Address: Newlands Road, Luton. Tel: 0582 20355.
Club Secretary: P J Wilson, 17 Burghley Close, Flitwick, Bedford, MK45 1TF. Tel: (H) 0525 713409 (W) 071 218 4077.
Press Officer: Bryn Hughs, Luton RFC, Newlands Road, Luton. Tel: 0582 20355.
Club Colours: Green with red & white band, black shorts.

MODERNS RFC
Ground Address: Ferryfield, Main Road, Wilford, Nottingham. Tel: 0602 811374.
Club Secretary: David Hargreaves, 21 Orpean Way, Banks Road, Toton, Nottingham, NG9 6LE. Tel: (H) 0602 461779 (W) 0602 507577.
Press Officer: David Hargreaves, 21 Orpean Way, Banks Road, Toton, Nottingham, NG9 6LE. Tel: (H) 0602 461779 (W) 0602 507577.
Club Colours: Red & white.

FINAL TABLE

	P	W	D	L	F	A	PD	Pts
Belgrave	12	11	0	1	245	77	168	22
Hinckley	12	10	1	1	296	119	177	21
Ampthill	12	8	0	4	204	200	4	16
Stoneygate	12	6	2	4	251	108	143	14
Scunthorpe	12	6	2	4	234	155	79	14
Chesterfield	12	6	1	5	151	187	-36	13
Amber Valley	12	4	3	5	148	125	23	11
Stewart & Lloyds	12	5	1	6	123	196	-73	11
Spalding	12	6	0	6	156	196	40	10
Luton	12	3	3	6	147	144	3	9
Mellish	12	2	2	8	97	241	-144	4
West Bridgford	12	2	0	10	121	288	-167	4
Dronfield	12	1	1	10	84	262	-178	1

NORTHAMPTON BOYS BRIGADE OLD BOYS RFC
Ground Address: St Andrews Road, Semilong, Northampton. Tel: 0604 32460.
Club Secretary: Barry Clark, 50 Reedway, Spinney Hill, Northampton. Tel: (H) 0664 699661.
Press Officer: Richard White, 30 Granary Road, East Hunsbury, Northampton, NN4 0XA. Tel: (H) 0604 702427 (W) 0604 250151.
Club Colours: Light blue, dark blue & maroon hoops.

SCUNTHORPE RUFC
Ground Address: Helsam Park, Ashby road, Scunthorpe. Tel: 0724 843013.
Club Secretary: A Bagshaw, 51 Old Brumby Street, Scunthorpe, DN16 1AJ. Tel: (H) 0724 849838 (W) 0724 280666.
Press Officer: L Clayton, 2 LAngley Drive, Bottesford, Scunthorpe. Tel: (H) 0724 848855 (W) 0724 280280 x 2785.
Club Colours: Green shirt, white shorts, green socks.

SPALDING RFC
Ground Address: Memorial Field, St Thomas Road, Spalding, Lincs. Tel: 0775 725191.
Club Secretary: S Barber, 28 The Terrace, London Road, Spalding, Lincs, PE11 2TA. Tel: (H) 0775 722073 (W) 0775 724261.
Press Officer: A Aistrup, 15 Crowson Way, Peeping St James, Peterborough, Cambridgeshire, PE6 8EY. Tel: (H) 0778 345163 (W) 0775 759091.
Club Colours: Maroon & navy blue.

STEWARTS & LLOYDS RFC
Ground Address: Occupation Road, Corby, NN17 1EH. Tel: 0536 400317.
Club Secretary: J M Thompson, 5 Howe Crescent, Corby, Northamptonshire, NN17. Tel: (H) 0536 202433.
Press Officer: D Murdoch, 12 Deene Close, Corby, Northamptonshire, NN17 1HY. Tel: (H) 0536 204930 (W) 0536 203381.
Club Colours: Black.

STONEYGATE FC
Ground Address: Covert Lane, Scraptoft, Leicestershire, LE7 9SP. Tel: 0533 419188.
Club Secretary: Steve Morris, 23 Bankart Avenue, Oadby, Leicestershire, lE2 2AD. Tel: (H) 0533 705857 (W) 0533 628596.
Press Officer: Bruce Cooper, Brookview Main Street, Peatling, Parva, Leicestershire. Tel: (H) 0533 478554 (W) 0533 593848.
Club Colours: Cardinal red & white hoops, navy blue shorts.

MIDLAND DIVISION

MIDLAND EAST TWO
1993-94
FIXTURES

October 23 (Week 8)
Coalville v Dronfield
South Leicester v Lutterworth
Mellish v Long Buckby
West Bridgford v Lincoln
Wellingborough v Grimsby
Worksop v Kesteven

October 30 (Week X2)
Kesteven v Coalville
Grimsby v Worksop
Lincoln v Wellingborough
Long Buckby v West Bridgford
Lutterworth v Mellish
Kibworth v South Leicester

November 13 (Week 10)
Coalville v Grimsby
Dronfield v Kesteven
Mellish v Kibworth
West Bridgford v Lutterworth
Wellingborough v Long Buckby
Worksop v Lincoln

November 20 (Week 11)
Grimsby v Dronfield
Lincoln v Coalville
Long Buckby v Worksop
Lutterworth v Wellingborough
Kibworth v West Bridgford
South Leicester v Mellish

December 4 (Week 13)
Coalville v Long Buckby
Dronfield v Lincoln
Kesteven v Grimsby
West Bridgford v South Leicester
Wellingborough v Kibworth
Worksop v Lutterworth

December 11 (Week 14)
Lincoln v Kesteven
Long Buckby v Dronfield
Lutterworth v Coalville
Kibworth v Worksop
South Leicester v Wellingborough
Mellish v West Bridgford

December 18 (Week 15)
Coalville v Kibworth
Dronfield v Lutterworth
Kesteven v Long Buckby
Grimsby v Lincoln
Wellingborough v Mellish
Worksop v South Leicester

January 8 (Week 18)
Long Buckby v Grimsby
Lutterworth v Kesteven
Kibworth v Dronfield
South Leicester v Coalville
Mellish v Worksop
West Bridgford v Wellingborough

January 29 (Week X5)
Coalville v Mellish
Dronfield v South Leicester
Kesteven v Kibworth
Grimsby v Lutterworth
Lincoln v Long Buckby
Worksop v West Bridgford

February 12 (Week 22)
Lutterworth v Lincoln
Kibworth v Grimsby
South Leicester v Kesteven
Mellish v Dronfield
West Bridgford v Coalville
Wellingborough v Worksop

March 12 (Week 26)
Coalville v Wellingborough
Dronfield v West Bridgford
Kesteven v Mellish
Grimsby v South leicester
Lincoln v Kibworth
Long Buckbuy v Lutterworth

March 26 (Week 28)
Kibworth v Long Buckby
South Leicester v Lincoln
Mellish v Grimsby
West Bridgford v Kesteven
Wellingborough v Dronfield
Worksop v Coalville

April 9 (Week 30)
Dronfield v Worksop
Kesteven v Wellingborough
Grimsby v West Bridgford
Lincoln v Mellish
Long Buckby v South Leicester
Lutterworth v Kibworth

MIDLAND EAST TWO

COALVILLE RFC
Ground Address: Memorial Ground, Broomleys Road, Coalville, Leicestershire. Tel: 812090.
Club Secretary: P Smith, 50 Parkdale, Ibstock, Leicestershire, LE671JW. Tel: (H) 0530 262113 (W) 0530 832085.
Press Officer: A frost, "Drybrook", 3 Langton Close, Whitwick, Leicestershire. Tel: (H) 0530 832526.
Club Colours: Navy with 4" amber chest band.

DRONFIELD RUFC
Ground Address: Dronfield (Gosforth) School, Stubley Lane, Dronfield Woodhouse, Nr Sheffield. Tel: 0742 890913.
Club Secretary: Richard Nixon, 129 Rideway Road, Sheffield S12 2SQ. Tel: (H) 0742 398510 (W) 0709 828500.
Press Officer: Steve Bertram, 20 Wentworth Road, Dronfield Woodhouse, NR Sheffield, S18 5ZU. Tel: (H) 0246 410899 (W) 0742 765646.
Club Colours: Red, black & green hoops.

GRIMSBY RUFC
Ground Address: Springfield Road, Grimsby, South Humberside. Tel: 0472 878594.
Club Secretary: D T Foulkes, 18 Amesbury Avenue, Grimsby, South Humberside, DN33 3HT. Tel: (H) 0472 826078 (W) 0472 887117.
Press Officer: D T Foulkes, 18 Amesbury Avenue, Grimsby, South Humberside, DN33 3HT. Tel: (H) 0472 826078 (W) 0472 887117.
Club Colours: Royal blue shirts, white shorts.

KESTEVEN RFC
Ground Address: Woodnook, Near Grantham. Tel: 0476 64887.
Club Secretary: N J Pert, 8 High Street, Ropsley, Near Grantham. Tel: (H) 0476 85352 (W) 0476 61631/4.
Press Officer: Michael Money, 29 Pastures Road, Barrowby, Near Grantham. Tel: (H) 0476 68028.
Club Colours: Black shirts, white shorts.

KIBWORTH RUFC
Ground Address: Northampton Road, Market Harborough, Leicestershire.
Tel: 0858 464210.
Club Secretary: David R Coe, 114 Harborough Road, Desborough, Northamptonshire, NN14 2QY. Tel: (H) 0536 761637 (W) 05436 402551 Ext. 3114.
Press Officer: C J Knights, 12 Farndon Road, Market Harborough, Leicestershire. Tel: (H) 0858 4646776 (W) 0858 432222.
Club Colours: Black shirts, black shorts.

LINCOLN RFC
Ground Address: Lindum Sports Club, St Giles Avenue, Coragby Road, Lincoln, LN2 4PE. Tel: 0522 526592.
Club Secretary: J Grove, 11 Broadway Close, Broadway, Lincoln, LN2 1SW. Tel: (H) 0522 525724 (W) 0522 513434.
Press Officer: Sid Gott, Lindum Sports Club, St Giles Avenue, Coragby Road, Lincoln, LN2 4PE. Tel: (W) 0522 526592.
Club Colours: White jersey, red collar, white shorts.

LONG BUCKBY RFC
Ground Address: Station Road, Long Buckby, Northamptonshire. Tel: 0327 842222.
Club Secretary: Philip Osborne, Ashthorne, Teeton Road, Ravensthorpe, Northampton, NN6 8EJ. Tel: (H) 0604 770772 (W) 0327 705785.
Press Officer: Bob Eales, 22 Grasscroft, Long Buckby, Northamptonshire. Tel: (H) 0327 843135.
Club Colours: Emerald green.

FINAL TABLE

	P	W	D	L	F	A	PD	Pts
Kettering	13	12	0	1	351	66	285	24
Northampton B B	13	11	0	2	264	87	177	22
Long Buckby	13	10	1	2	357	116	241	21
South Leicester	13	8	0	5	171	178	-7	16
Worksop	13	7	0	6	205	149	56	14
Lincoln	13	8	0	5	152	148	4	14
Wellingborough	13	6	1	6	191	192	-1	13
Coalville	13	6	1	6	88	164	-76	13
Kesteven	13	3	2	8	129	302	-173	8
Lutterworth	13	3	1	9	144	199	-55	7
Stamford	13	4	1	8	102	215	-113	7
Mkt Rasen & Louth	13	3	1	9	139	269	-130	7
Southwell	13	3	0	10	146	248	-102	6
Glossop	13	3	0	10	96	237	-141	6

LUTTERWORTH RFC
Ground Address: Ashby Lane, Bitteswell, Nr Lutterworth, Leicestershire. Tel: 0455 557329.
Club Secretary: Colin Hudson, Mason & Bowns Cottage, Ashby Parva, Nr Lutterworth, Leicestershire, LE17 5HY. Tel: (H) 0455 209053 (W) 0788 5771914.
Press Officer: Colin Hudson, Mason & Bowns Cottage, Ashby Parva, Nr Lutterworth, Leicestershire, LE17 5HY. Tel: (H) 0455 209053 (W) 0788 5771914.

MELLISH RFC
Ground Address: Plains Road, Mapperley, Nottingham,. NG3 5RT. Tel: 0602 266653.
Club Secretary: M Wrench, 1 Arndale Road, Sherwood, Nottingham. Tel: (H) 0602 264991.
Press Officer: M Wrench, 1 Arndale Road, Sherwood, Nottingham. Tel: (H) 0602 264991.
Club Colours: Black, yellow & green.

SOUTH LEICESTER RFC
Ground Address: Welford Road,Wigston Magna, Leicester LE18 1TE. Tel: 0533 882066.
Club Secretary: Richard Dowdall, 4 Bodmin Ave, Wigston Magna, Leicester LE18 2HB. Tel: (H) 0533 885606.
Press Officer: John Cooke, 89 Mere Road, Wigston. Tel: (W) 0533 881234.
Club Colours: Green and white hoops.

WELLINGBOROUGH RFC
Ground Address: Cut Throat Lane, Great Doddington, Wellingborough, Northamptonshire. Tel: 0933 222260.
Club Secretary: Bob Stevenson, 12 South Street, Wollaston, Northants, NN9 7RX. Tel: (H) 0933 664538 (W) 0933 226077.
Club Colours: White shirts with red hoop, navy shorts.

WEST BRIDGFORD RFC
Ground Address: The Memorial Ground, Stamford Road, West Bridgford, Nottingham. Tel: 0602 232506.
Club Secretary:L K Howells, 117 Mount Pleasant, Keyworth, Nottingham, NG12 5ES. Tel: (H) 0602 374468.
Press Officer: I Bellamy, 17 Knights Close, West Bridgford, Nottingham. Tel: (H) 0602 846414.
Club Colours: Black with red & gold hoops, black shorts.

WORKSOP RUFC
Ground Address: Stubbing Meadows, Stubbing Lane, Worksop, Nottinghamshire. Tel: 0909 484247.
Club Secretary: John H Gibson, 31 George Street, Worksop, Notts, S80 1QJ. Tel: (H) 0909 482439 (W) 0909 482439.
Press Officer: Keith Billam, 19 Masefield Place, Worksop, Nottinghamshire S81 0HB. Tel: (H) 0909 477974.
Club Colours: Black & white hoops, black shorts.

MIDLAND DIVISION

NOTTS, LINCS & DERBY ONE 1993-94 FIXTURES

December 18 (Week 15)
Ashbourne v Glossop
Bakewell Mannerians v Stamford
Long Eaton v Meden Vale
Nottingham Casuals v Keyworth
Sleaford v Ilkeston
Southwell v East Leake

October 23 (Week 8)
Bakewell Mannerians v Ashbourne
Ilkeston v Glossop
Keyworth v East Leake
Market Rasen & Louth v Meden Vale
Nottingham Casuals v Long Eaton
Sleaford v Southwell

January 8 (Week 18)
Stamford v Ashbourne
East Leake v Long Eaton
Ilkeston v Bakewell Mannerians
Keyworth v Sleaford
Market Rasen & Louth v Nottingham Casuals
Glossop v Southwell

October 30 (Week X2)
Stamford v Ilkeston
East Leake v Market Rasen & Louth
Long Eaton v Sleaford
Glossop v Keyworth
Meden Vale v Nottingham Casuals
Southwell v BakewellMannerians

January 29 (Week X5)
Ashbourne v Ilkeston
Bakewell Mannerians v Keyworth
Long Eaton v Glossop
Sleaford v Market Rasen & Louth
Meden Vale v East Leake
Southwell v Stamford

November 13 (Week 10)
Ashbourne v Southwell
Bakewell Mannerians v Long Eaton
Keyworth v Stamford
Market Rasen & Louth v Glossop
Nottingham Casuals v East Leake
Sleaford v Meden Vale

February 12 (Week 22)
Stamford v Long Eaton
Ilkeston v Southwell
Keyworth v Ashbourne
Market Rasen & Louth v Bakewell Mannerians
Glossop v Meden Vale
Nottingham Casuals v Sleaford

November 20 (Week 11)
Stamford v Market Rasen & Louth
East Leake v Sleaford
Ilkeston v Keyworth
Long Eaton v Ashbourne
Glossop v Nottingham Casuals
Meden Vale v Bakewell Mannerians

March 12 (Week 26)
Ashbourne v Market Rasen & Louth
Bakewell Mannerians v Nottingham Casuals
East Leake v Glossop
Long Eaton v Ilkeston
Meden Vale v Stamford
Southwell v Keyworth

December 4 (Week 13)
Ashbourne v Meden Vale
Bakewell Mannerians v East Leake
Market Rasen & Louth v Ilkeston
Nottingham Casuals v Stamford
Sleaford v Glossop
Southwell v Long Eaton

March 26 (Week 28)
Stamford v East Leake
Ilkeston v Meden Vale
Keyworth v Long Eaton
Market Rasen & Louth v Southwell
Nottingham Casuals v Ashbourne
Sleaford v Bakewell Mannerians

December 11 (Week 14)
Stamford v Sleaford
East Leake v Ashbourne
Ilkeston v Nottingham Casuals
Keyworth v Market Rasen & Louth
Glossop v Bakewell mannerians
Meden Vale v Southwell

April 9 (Week 30)
Ashbourne v Sleaford
East Leake v Ilkeston
Long Eaton v Market Rasen & Louth
Glossop v Stamford
Meden Vale v Keyworth
Southwell v Nottingham Casuals

NOTTS, LINCS & DERBY ONE

ASHBOURNE RUFC
Ground Address: The Recreation Ground, Ashbourne, Derbyshire.
Club Secretary: Steve Jones, 20 North Leys, Ashbourne, Derbyshire. Tel No: (H) 0335-344753, (W) 0335 343821.
Press Officer: Andrew Birch, 19 New Derby Road, Ashbourne, Derbyshire. Tel No: (H) 0335 343789.
Club Colours: Old gold/navy hoops.

BAKEWELL MANNERIANS RUFC
Ground Address: The Showground, Coombs Road, Bakewell, Derbyshire.
Club Secretary Tom Furness, Fern Bank, Brookfield Lane, Bakewell, Derbyshire, DE45 1AN. Tel No: 0629 812863 (W) 0629 580000 EXT 7186.
Press Officer: David Gray, Coromandel, Hassop Road, Bakewell, Derbyshire, DE45 1NP. Tel No: (H) 0629 812435 (W) 0629 815007.
Club Colours: Shirts: Dark blue, light blue and white hoops. Shorts: Navy.

EAST LEAKE RFC
Ground Address: East Leake Leisure Centre, Lantern Lane, East Leake, Nottinghamshire. Tel No: 0509 852956.
Club Secretary: Mr Paul Cobbin, 15 Old Way, Hathern, Nr Loughborough, Leics, LE12 5NH. Tel No.(H) 0509 646354 (W) 0850 375313.
Press Officer: Mr Graham Hey, 13 Cheviot Drive, Shepshed, Leics, LE12 9ED. Tel No: (H) 0509 503723.
Club Colours: Maroon and white hoops, black shorts.

GLOSSOP RUFC
Ground Address: Hargate Hill Lane, Charlesworth, Glossop, Derbyshire. Tel No: 0457 864553.
Club Secretary: Alastair May, 6 Kinder, Grove, Romiley, Stockport, SK6 4EU. Tel No: (H) 061 427 5774 (W) 0457 861216.
Press Officer: Mark Harris, 3 Duke Street, Glossop, Derbyshire. Tel No: (H) 0457 852116.
Club Colours: Blue and white quartered shirts.

ILKESTON RUFC
Ground Address: Gallows Inn Fields, Ilkeston.
Club Secretary: Ean Wykes, 8 Carman Close, Watnall, Notts, NG 16 1JX. Tel No: (H) 0602 384307 (W) 0602 384093.
Press Officer: John O'Mahoney, 219 Nottingham Road, Ilkeston, Derby, DE7 5AL. Tel No: (H) 0602 325531.
Club Colours: Emerald Green, white and blue hoops.

KEYWORTH RFC
Ground Address: The Pavilion, Willoughby Lane, Widmerpool, Nottts. Tel: 0602 375579.
Club Secretary: Mr A Stimpson, The Grange, 48 Main Street, Willoughby on the Wolds, Loughborough LE12 6SZ. Tel: (H) 0509 880122 (W) 0509 881253.
Club Colours: Black shirt with 2 amber stripes.

LONDON EATON
Ground Address: West Park, Long Eaton, Nottinghamshire, Tel No: 0602 460907.
Club Secretary: Clive Lobley, 7 George Street, Arnold, Nottingham, NG5 6LD. Tel No: (H) 0602 21105, (W) 0602 670012.
Press Officer: As above.
Club Colours: Royal blue.

MARKET RASEN AND LOUTH RUFC
Ground Address: Willingham Road, Market Rasen. Tel No: 0673 843162.
Club Secretary: B N Harper, Nongoby, Church Lane, Manby, Louth, Lincs, LN11 8HL. Tel No:(H) 0507 327318.

FINAL TABLE

	P	W	D	L	F	A	PD	Pts
Grimsby	11	9	1	1	239	112	127	19
Ilkeston	11	9	0	2	332	122	210	18
Sleaford	11	9	0	2	225	100	125	18
Nottingham Cas	11	7	1	3	166	131	35	15
Ashbourne	11	7	0	4	200	104	96	14
Bakewell Manner	11	7	0	4	195	130	65	14
Long Eaton	11	5	0	6	153	171	-18	10
Keyworth	11	4	0	7	130	174	-44	6
All Spartans	11	2	1	8	103	196	-93	5
East Retford	11	2	0	9	76	293	-217	4
Nottinghamians	11	1	0	10	89	238	-149	2
Notts Cons	11	2	1	8	70	241	104	1

Press Officer: J Reynolds, Sanderlings,Willingham Road, Market Rasen. Tel No:(H) 0673 842588.
Club Colours: Red and green hooped jerseys and stockings and white shorts.

MEDEN VALE RUFC
Ground Address: Welbeck Colliery Miners Welfare Inst, Elkesley Road, Meden Vale,Notts. No: 0623 842267.
Club Secretary: David Ellison, 50 Forest Street, Kirkby-in- Ashfield, Nottingham, NG17 7DT. Tel No: (H) 0623 751086, (W) 0623 791281.
Press Officer: Edward Davison, 25 Eamanton Road, Meden Vale, Notts. Tel No: 0623 842018.
Club Colours: Red and black quarters, black shorts and socks.

NOTTINGHAM CASUALS RFC
Ground Address: Canal Side, Meadow Road, Beeston, Rylands, Nottingham. Tel No: 0602 250135.
Club Secretary: A Rothera, Flat 3, 11 Hamilton Drive, The Park, Nottingham, NG7 1DF. Tel No: (H) 0602 470058 (W) 0602 514489.
Press Officer: L. M. W. Kluk, 40 Hemlock Avenue, Stapleford, Nottingham NG9 8DN. Tel No: 0602 393127 (W) 0773 570137.
Club Colours: White with maroon hoops.

SLEAFORD RFC
Ground Address: East Road, Sleaford, Tel No: 0529 303335.
Club Secretary: Andrew Sharpe, 5 Pinewood Drive, Grantham, Lincs NG31 8QQ. Tel No: (H) 0476 70976 (W) 0476 66363.
Press Officer: Andrew Sharpe. Address as above.
Club Colours: Red and black hoops, black shorts, red socks.

SOUTHWELL RUFC
Ground Address: Pentelowes Park Lane, Southwell, Notts. Tel No:0636 812576
Club Secretary: Tim Brooks, 116 Westgate, Southwell, Notts NG25 0LT. Tel No: (H) 0636 816189 (W) 0602 812125.
Press Officer: Tony Morris, Landseer Road, Southwell, Notts. Tel No: (H) 0636 815013.
Club Colours: Maroon jerseys, navy blue shorts.

STAMFORD RUFC
Ground Address: Mambleton Road, Stamford, Lincs. Tel No: 0780 52180.
Club Secretary: N M Jolly, 21 Chatsworth Road, Stamford, Lincs. Tel No: (H) 0780 52134(W) 0780 720501.
Press Officer: N M Jolly. 21 Chatsworth Road, Stamford, Lincs. Tel No: (H) 0780 52134 (W) 0780 720501.
Club Colours: Purple/black/white.

MIDLAND DIVISION

NOTTS, LINCS & DERBY TWO 1993-94 FIXTURES

October 23 (Week 8)
East ReTford v Stamford College
Boots Athletic v Ashfield Swans
Boston v Buxton
Notts Constabulary v Rolls Royce
MelbournE v All Spartans
Nottinghamians v Leesbrook

October 30 (Week X2)
Bingham v Boots Athletic
Ashfield Swans v East Retford
Leesbrook v Boston
All Spartans v Nottinghamians
Rolls Royce v Melbourne
Stamford College v Notts Constabulary

November 13 (Week 10)
East Retford v Bingham
Boston v All Spartans
Buxton v Leesbrook
Notts Constabulary v Ashfield Swans
Melbourne v Stamford College
Nottinghamians v Rolls Royce

November 20 (Week 11)
Bingham v Notts Constabulary
Ashfield Swans v Melbourne
Boots Athletic v East Retford
All Spartans v Buxton
Rolls Royce v Boston
Stamford College v Nottinghamians

December 4 (Week 13)
Boston v Stamford College
Buxton v Tolls Royce
Notts Constabulary v Boots Athletic
Leesbrook v All Spartans
Melbourne v Bingham
Nottinghamians v Ashfield Swans

December 11 (Week 14)
Bingham v Nottinghamians
Ashfield Swans v Boston
East Retford v Notts Constabulary
Boots Athletic v Melbourne
Rolls Royce v Leesbrook
Stamford College v Buxton

December 18 (Week 15)
Boston v Bingham
Buxton v Ashfield Swans
Leesbrook v Stamford College
Melbourne v East Retford
All Spartans v Rolls Royce
Nottinghamians v Boots Athletic

January 8 (Week 18)
Bingham v Buxton
Ashfield Swans v Leesbrook
East Retford v Nottinghamians
Boots Athletic v Boston
Notts Constabulary v Melbourne
Stamford College v All Spartans

January 29 (Week X5)
Boston v East Retford
Buxton v Boots Athletic
Leesbrook v Bingham
All Spartans v Ashfield Swans
Nottinghamians v Notts Constabulary
Rolls Royce v Stamford College

February 12 (Week 22)
Bingham v All Spartans
Ashfield Swans v Rolls Royce
East Retford v Buxton
Boots Athletic v Leesbrook
Notts Constabulary v Boston
Melbourne v Nottinghamians

March 12 (Week 26)
Boston v Melbourne
Buxton v Notts Constabulary
Leesbrook v East Retford
All Spartans v Boots Athletic
Rolls Royce v Bingham
Stamford College v Ashfield Swans

March 26 (Week 28)
Bingham v Stamford College
East Retford v All Spartans
Boots Athletic v Rolls Royce
Notts Constabulary v Leesbrook
Melbourne v Buxton
Nottinghamians v Boston

April 9 (Week 30)
Ashfield Swans v Bingham
Buxton v Nottinghamians
Leesbrook v Melbourne
All Spartans v Notts Constabulary
Rolls Royce v East Retford
Stamford College v Boots Athletic

NOTTS, LINCS & DERBY TWO

ALL SPARTANS RUFC
Ground Address: Lawn Pleasure Gardens, Sutton Lawn, Sutton in Ashfield, Notts. Tel No: O623 554554.
Club Secretary: Joe Higgins, 7 Blenheim Close, Forest Town, Mansfield, Notts NG19 OPN. Tel No: O623 641985.
Press Officer: A Upton, 111 Corn Close, South Normanton, Derbyshire DE55 2JE. Tel No: (H) O773 581738.
Club Colours: Blue with broad amber hoop.

ASHFIELD SWANS RUFC
Ground Address: Asfield School, Sutton Road. Kirkby-in-Ashfield, Notts. Tel No: O623 752403.
Club Secretary: S Trainer, 12 Belfry Close, Broadlands Park, Kirkby-in-Ashfield, Notts NG17 8NS. Tel No: O623 443744, (W) O6O2 657271.
Press Officer: P Raymont, 18 Longhill Rise, Kirby in Ashfield, Notts. Tel No: (H) O623 75O99O.
Club Colours: Red and black quarters.

BINGHAM RUFC
Ground Address: Town Pavilion, Brendon Grove, Wynhill, Bingham, Notts. Tel No: O949 839 874.
Club Secretary: Mr J Mitton, 1O Dark Lane, Whatton, Notts, NG13 9FE. Tel No: (H) O949 51238 (W) O6O2 483500.
Press Officer: J Fuchs, 44 Chaworth Road, Bingham, Notts, NG13 8EU. Tel No: (H) O94983936.
Club Colours: Green and red loops.

BOOTS ATHLETIC RUFC
Ground Address: Boots Sports Ground and Lady Bay, West Bridgford, Nottingham. Tel No: O6O2 492388.
Club Secretary: David Bright. 121 Rutland Road, West Bridgford, Nottingham, NG2 5DY. Tel No: (H) O6O2 455623 (W) O6O2 592294.
Press Officer: Chris Harries, 218 Rutland Road, West Bridgford, Nottingham. Tel No: (H)82262O.
Club Colours: Navy and sky blue quarters.

BOSTON RFC
Ground Address: Great Fen Road, Wyberton, Baston, Lincs. PE21 7PB Tel No: O2O5 362683.
Club Secretary: Mrs L Creasey. 28 Fieldfare Croft, Boston, Lincs, PE21 8ED. Tel No: (H) O2O5 356753 (W) O2O5 313036.
Press Officer: Mr S Cooper, 56 Brand End Road, Butterwick, Boston, Lincs. PE22 OJD. Tel No: (H) O2O5 76O787.
Club Colours: Blue and white hoops.

BUXTON RUFC
Ground Address: Fairfield Centre, Victoria Park Road, Fairfield, Buxton. Tel No: O298 24081.
Club Secretary: David Redford Allsop, Corbiere, 2O Green Lane, Buxton, Derbyshire. Tel No: (H) O298 22517.
Club Colours: Jerseys and socks. blue/gold/red hoops. Shorts blue.

EAST RETFORD RUFC
Ground Address: Ordsall Road, Retford. Tel No: O777 7O3243
Club Secretary: Mick Storey, 3 Bankside Ordsall, Retford, Notts DN22 7UW. Tel No: O777 7O6O72.
Club Colours: Emerald Amber hoops.

LEESBROOK ASTERDALE RUFC
Ground Address: Asterdale Club, Borrowash Road, Spondon, Derby. Tel No: O332 668656.
Club Secretary: Leon Davies, c/o D.R.S. Victoria Chambers, 6O London Road, Derby DE1 2PA. Tel No: (H)

FINAL TABLE

	P	W	D	L	F	A	PD	Pts
East Leake	12	11	0	1	281	95	186	22
Meden Vale	12	9	0	3	250	112	138	18
Leesbrook	12	8	1	3	181	117	64	17
Rolls Royce	12	8	0	4	238	145	93	16
Buxton	12	8	0	4	242	124	118	14
Boston	12	6	1	5	170	181	34	13
Melbourne	12	7	0	5	223	144	79	12
Boot Athletic	12	5	1	6	103	128	-25	11
Ashfield Swans	12	5	0	7	148	181	-33	10
North Kesteven	12	5	1	6	235	195	40	9
Belper	12	3	0	9	112	288	-176	4
Tupton	12	1	0	11	128	365	-237	2
Cleethorpes	12	0	0	12	118	400	-282	0

O332 519221 (W) O332 29O188.
Press Officer: Leon Davies, Address as above.
Club Colours: Green blue white black quarters, black shorts and socks.

MELBOURNE RFC
Ground Address: Recreation Ground, Cockshut Lane, Melbourne, Derbyshire, DE73 1DG
Club Secretary: Mrs C Millington, 6 Jubilee Close, Melbourne, Derbyshire, DE73 1GR. Tel No: (H) O332 863422 (W) O332 863422.
Press Officer: Mrs C Millington, 6 Jubilee Close, Melbourne, Derbyshire, DE73 1GR. Tel No: (H) O332 863422 (W) O332 863422.
Club Colours: Bottle green shirts, white shorts.

NOTTINGHAMIANS RFC
Ground Address: Adbolton Lane, West Bridgford, Nottingham. Tel No: 811372.
Club Secretary: Martin Jones, 1 Hilside Avenue, Mapperley, Nottingham NG3 6DP. Tel No: (H) 261866 (W) 358565.
Press Officer: Jeff Teece, 7O Hallfields, Edwalton, Nottingham. Tel No: (H) 233498.
Club Colours: Black white purple hoops.

NOTTINGHAMSHIRE CONSTABULARY
Ground Address: c/o Mellish RFC, Memorial Grounds, Plaine Road, Mapperley, Nottingham. Tel No: O6O2 622O52.
Club Secretary: I Winton. Old Breck Hall Mews, Main Street, Papplewick, Nottinghamshire. Tel No. (H) O6O2 64O364 (W) O6O2 482O999.
Press Officer: I Winton. Address as above
Club Colours: Green/Black.

ROLLS-ROYCE RFC
Ground Address: Merrill Way, Derby. Tel No: O332 249167
Club Secretary: Mr N Coleman, 4O Farneworth Road,, Mickleover, Derby DE3 5ER. Tel No: (H) O332 51850S (W) O332 245576.
Club Colours: Maroon/Sky blue quarters, black shorts.

STAMFORD COLLEGE
Ground Address: Drift Road, Stamford, Lincs, Tel No: O78O 64141
Club Secretary: Brian Lonslow. 6 Park View, Barnack Road, Stamford, Lincs, PE9 2NG. Tel No: (H) O78O 66195.
Club Colours: Red and Green Hoops.

MIDLAND DIVISION

NOTTS, LINCS & DERBY THREE 1993-94 FIXTURES

December 18 (Week 15)
Barton & District v Cotgrave
Bourne v Hope Valley
Cleethorpes v University of Derby
Gainsborough v Belper
Skegness v Tupton
North Kesteven v Horncastle

October 23 (Week 8)
Cleethorpes v Barton & District
Horncastle v Cotgrave
Tupton v Hope Valley
Ollerton v Belper
Skegness v Gainsborough
North Kesteven v Bourne

January 8 (Week 18)
Cotgrave v Bourne
University of Derby v Barton & District
Hope Valley v Gainsborough
Horncastle v Cleethorpes
Tupton v North Kesteven
Ollerton v Skegness

October 30 (Week X2)
Belper v Skegness
Bourne v Cleethorpes
Cotgrave v Tupton
University of Derby v Horncastle
Gainsborough v North Kesteven
Hope Valley v Ollerton

January 29 (Week X5)
Barton & District v Horncastle
Belper v Hope Valley
Bounre v University of Derby
Cleethorpes v Tupton
Gainsborough v Cotgrave
North Kesteven v Ollerton

November 13 (Week 10)
Barton & District v Bourne
Cleethorpes v Gainsborough
Tupton v University of Derby
Ollerton v Cotgrave
Skegness v Hope Valley
North Kesteven v Belper

February 12 (Week 22)
Cotgrave v Belper
Derby College v Gainsborough
Horncastle v Bourne
Tupton v Barton & District
Ollerton v Cleethorpes
Skegness v North Kesteven

November 20 (Week 11)
Belper v Cleethorpes
Cotgrave v Skegness
University of Derby v Ollerton
Gainsborough v Barton & District
Hope Valley v North Kesteven
Horncastle v Tupton

March 12 (Week 26)
Barton & District v Ollerton
Belper v University of Derby
Bourne v Tupton
Cleethorpes v Skegness
Gainsborough v Horncastle
Hope Valley v Cotgrave

December 4 (Week 13)
Barton & District v Belper
Bourne v Gainsborough
Cleethorpes v Hope Valley
Ollerton v Horncastle
Skegness v University of Derby
North Kesteven v Cotgrave

March 26 (Week 28)
University of Derby v Hope Valley
Horncastle v Belper
Tupton v Gainsborough
Ollerton v Bourne
Skegness v Barton & District
North Kesteven v Cleethorpes

December 11 (Week 14)
Belper v Bourne
Cotgrave v Cleethorpes
Derby College v North Kesteven
Hope Valley v Barton & District
Horncastle v Skegness
Tupton v Ollerton

April 9 (Week 30)
Barton & District v North Kesteven
Belper v Tupton
Bourne v Skegness
Cotgrave v University of Derby
Gainsborough v Ollerton
Hope Valley v Horncastle

NOTTS, LINCS & DERBY THREE

BARTON & DISTRICT RUFC
Ground Address: Mill Lane, Barrow on Humber, South Humberside. Tel: 0469 31119.
Club Secretary: T Phipps, 4 West Acidge, Barton on Humber, South Humberside, DN18 5AN. Tel: (H) 0652 632373 (W) 0724 847888.
Press Officer: T Phipps, 4 West Acidge, Barton on Humber, South Humberside, DN18 5AN. Tel: (H) 0652 632373 (W) 0724 847888.
Club Colours: Red & white hoops.

BELPER RFC
Ground Address: Eyes Meadows, Duffield, Derbyshire.
Club Secretary: Chris Smith, Hillcrest, Hillcliff Lane, Turnditch, Derbyshire, DE5 2EA. Tel: (H) 0773 550702 (W) 0332 32248.
Press Officer: Mike Ryan, 6 Oakwood Drive, Oakwood, Derby. Tel: (H) 0322 665377.
Club Colours: Black & white hoops.

BOURNE RUFC
Ground Address: Milking Nook Drove, Spalding Road, Bourne. Tel: 0778 393346.
Club Secretary: Andrew J Rowe, 54 North Road, Bourne, Lincs, PE10 9BT. Tel: (H) 0778 424353 (W) 0933 57511.
Press Officer: Andrew J Rowe, 54 North Road, Bourne, Lincs, PE10 9BT. Tel: (H) 0778 424353 (W) 0933 57511.
Club Colours: Navy with gold band.

CLEETHORPES RUFC
Ground Address: Wilton Road, Cleethorpes. Tel: 0472 812936.
Club Secretary: Alan Clark, 10 Cambridge Street, Cleethorpes, South Humberside, DN37 8HB. Tel: (H) 0472 692716 (W) 0469 572464.
Press Officer: Alan Clark, 10 Cambridge Street, Cleethorpes, South Humberside, DN37 8HB. Tel: (H) 0472 692716 (W) 0469 572464.
Club Colours: Gold with blue hoops.

COTGRAVE COLLIERY RUFC
Ground Address: Cotgrave Community Centre, Cotgrave, Nottinghamshire.
Club Secretary: Mr Robinson, 10 Fosse Walk, Cotgrave, Nottinghamshire, NG12 3NZ. Tel: (H) 0602 892501.
Press Officer: Mr Robinson, 10 Fosse Walk, Cotgrave, Nottinghamshire, NG12 3NZ. Tel: (H) 0602 892501.
Club Colours: Maroon & blue quarters.

GAINSBOROUGH RUFC
Ground Address: Rose leisure, North Warren Road, Gainsborough, Lincs. Tel: 0427 612915.
Club Secretary: A C Lobley, Church View Cottage, Gringley Road, Walkeringham, Doncaster, DN10 4HW. Tel: (H) 0427 890951.
Press Officer: Paul Bell, 55 Tooley Street, Gainsborough, Lincs. Tel: (H) 0427 616828.
Club Colours: Black.

HORNCASTLE RFC
Ground Address: Playing Fields, Horncastle, Lincs.
Club Secretary: Lorna Longmuir, 6 Wesselow Road, Coningsby, Lincoln LN4 4RN. Tel: 0526 344160.
Press Officer: Bill Laing, 12 Allen Road, Coningsby, Lincoln, LN4 4RN. Tel: (H) 0526 342992.
Club Colours: Green 7 gold quarters, black shorts.

HOPE VALLEY RUFC
Ground Address: Castleton Playing Fields, Hollowford Lane, Castleton. Tel: 0433 620247.
Club Secretary: Ian Broad, 8 Hagg Lane, Den Bank, Sheffield, S10 5PJ. Tel: (H) 0742 308409.

FINAL TABLE

	P	W	D	L	F	A	PD	Pts
Bingham	11	10	0	1	229	97	132	20
Stamford College	11	9	0	2	226	76	150	18
Gainsborough	11	9	0	2	186	106	80	18
Barton & District	11	7	0	4	110	99	11	14
Ollerton & Beverc't	11	6	0	5	175	164	11	12
Hope Valley	11	5	0	6	252	141	111	10
Bourne	11	5	0	6	146	169	-23	10
Skegness	11	5	0	6	123	184	-61	10
Derby College	11	4	0	7	123	169	-46	8
Yarborough Bees	11	3	0	8	114	228	-114	6
Bolsover	11	2	0	9	31	133	-102	4
Rainworth	11	1	0	10	58	207	-149	2

Press Officer: Ian Broad, 8 Hagg Lane, Den Bank, Sheffield, S10 5PJ. Tel: (H) 0742 308409.
Club Colours: Purple, green & white quarters, black shorts.

NORTH KESTEVEN
Ground Address: Memorial Playing Fields, Newark Road, North Hykeham, Lincoln. Tel: 0522 680193.
Club Secretary: Kevin Flynn, 20 Stenigot Close, Doddington Park, Lincoln, LN6 3PB. Tel: (H) 0522 692409 (W) 0526 20472 Ext 7247.
Press Officer: Kevin Flynn, 20 Stenigot Close, Doddington Park, Lincoln, LN6 3PB. Tel: (H) 0522 692409 (W) 0526 20472 Ext 7247.
Club Colours: Black with white, emerald & scarlet bands, black shorts.

OLLERTON RUFC
Ground Address: Boughton Sports Field, Boughton, Newark, Nottinghamshire, NG22 9JZ. Tel: (H) 0623 860871.
Club Secretary: D G Price, Lathkill, Harrow Farm, Tuxford Road, Boughton, Newark, Nottinghamshire, NG22 9JZ. Tel: (H) 0623 860871.
Press Officer: Jeff Raine, 9 Dovecroft, New Ollerton, Newark, Nottinghamshire. Tel: (H) 0623 862697.
Club Colours: Yellow & blue hoops.

SKEGNESS RFC
Ground Address: Hainfleet Road, Skegness, Lincs. Tel: 0754 765699.
Club Secretary: Alan Hawkes, Grunters Grange, East Keal, Spilsby, Lincs, PE23 4AY. Tel: (H) 0790 52788.
Press Officer: Chris Otty, 7 Lifeboat Avenue, Skegness, PE25 3EW. Tel: (H) 0754 766816.
Club Colours: Royal blue/white hoops.

TUPTON RUFC
Ground Address: North Side, Tupton, Chesterfield.
Club Secretary: S Robinson, 7 Gladstone Road, Chesterfield, S40 4TE. Tel: (H) 0246 202857 (W) 0246 217713.
Press Officer: S Robinson, 7 Gladstone Road, Chesterfield, S40 4TE. Tel: (H) 0246 202857 (W) 0246 217713.
Club Colours: Blue with three yellow hoops.

UNIVERSITY OF DERBY RUFC
Ground Address: Cuddles Road, Derby, DE22 1GB.
Club Secretary: D R French, 73 Cedar Street, Derby, DE22 1GE. Tel: (H) 0332 371275 (W) 0332 47181.
Press Officer: D R French, 73 Cedar Street, Derby, DE22 1GE. Tel: (H) 0332 371275 (W) 0332 47181.
Club Colours: Red & royal blue quarters.

MIDLAND DIVISION

NOTTS, LINCS & DERBY FOUR 1993-94 FIXTURES

October 23 (Week 8)
Yarborough Bees v Rainworth
Bilsthorpe v Castle Donington
Sutton Bonington v Whitwell

October 30 (Week X2)
Bolsover v Bilsthorpe
Rainworth v Sutton Bonington
Castle Donington v Yarborough Bees

November 13 (Week 10)
Yarborough Bees v Bolsover
Sutton Bonington v Castle Donington
Whitwell v Rainworth

November 20 (Week 11)
Bilsthorpe v Yarborough Bees
Bolsover v Sutton Bonington
Castle Donington v Whitwell

December 4 (Week 13)
Rainworth v Castle Donington
Sutton Bonington v Bilsthorpe
Whitwell v Bolsover

December 11 (Week 14)
Yarborough Bees v Sutton Bonington
Bilsthorpe v Whitwell
Bolsover v Rainworth

December 18 (Week 15)
Rainworth v Bilsthorpe
Whitwell v Yarborough Bees
Castle Donington v Bolsover

January 8 (Week 18)
Rainworth v Yarborough Bees
Whitwell v Sutton Bonington
Castle Donington v Bilsthorpe

January 29 (Week X5)
Yarborough Bees v Castle Donington
Bilsthorpe v Bolsover
Sutton Bonington v Rainworth

February 12 (Week 22)
Bolsover v Yarborough Bees
Rainsworth v Whitwell
Castle Donington v Sutton Bonington

February 19 (Week 23)
Yarborough Bees v Bilsthorpe
Sutton Bonington v Bolsover
Whitwell v Castle Donington

March 12 (Week 26)
Bilsthorpe v Sutton Bonington
Bolsover v Whitwell
Castle Donington v Rainworth

March 26 (week 28)
Rainworth v Bolsover
Sutton Bonington v Yarborough Bees
Whitwell v Bilsthorpe

April 9 (Week 30)
Yarborough Bees v Whitwell
Bilsthorpe v Rainworth
Bolsover v Castle Donington

NOTTS, LINCS & DERBY FOUR

BILSTHORPE RUFC
Ground Address: Bilsthorpe Sports Ground, Eakring Road, Bilsthorpe.
Club Secretary: Peter G Steffen, 55 Crompton Road, Bilsthorpe, Newark, Notts, NG22 8PS. Tel No: (H) 0623 870906 (W) 0623 24895.
Press Officer: Darren Wilford, 18 Sixth Avenue, Edwinstowe, Mansfield, Notts, NG21 9PN. Tel No: 0623 824120.
Club Colours: (1st) Black and yellow reversed quarters. (2nd Strip) Blue (Plain).

BOLSOVER RUFC
Ground Address: Bolsover School, Welbeck Road, Bolsover, Chesterfield.
Club Secretary: Lynda Knight, 224 Shuttlewood Road, Bolsover, Chesterfield, Derbyshire, Tel No. (H) 0246 822418.
Club Colours: Blue, gold and white hoops.

CASTLE DONINGTON RUFC
Ground Address: The Pavillion, The Spittal Castle, Donington, Derbyshire. Tel No: N/A via pub 0332 812214.
Club Secretary: Adrian C. E. Hackett, The Old Bakery, Thringstone, Leicestershire, LE67 6AP. Tel No:0530 223599 or 0831 675987.
Press Officer: Mr P G Parry, Flat 1, St Anne's Lane, 4-6 Borough Street, Castle Donington, Derby. DE7 2LA. Tel No: 0832 521645 (W) 0332 756041.
Club Colours: Red/black quarters, black shorts, red/back hooped socks.

RAINWORTH RUFC
Ground Address: Joseph Whitaker School, Walsop Lane, Rainworth.
Club Secretary: Nigel Dunn, 102 Rulford Avenue, Rainworth, Mansfield, Notts. Tel No: (H) 0623 797698.
Press Officer: As above.
Club Colours: Red/White.

SUTTON BONINGTON RFC
Ground Address: University of Nottingham, Facalty of Agriculture, Sutton Bonnington, Loughborough, Leic. LE12 5RD. Tel No: 0602 515151 EXT 8648.
Club Secretary: James Dunthorne. As above during term time.
Club Colours: Black and green quarters, black shorts.

WHITWELL RUFC
Ground Address: Southfield Lane, Primary School, Whitwell, Worksop, Notts.
Club Secretary: Mrs J Marshall, 3 Duke St, Whitwell, Workshop, Notts, S80 4TH. Tel No: 0909 722060.
Club Colours: Black/Green.

YARBOROUGH BEE'S RUFC
Ground Address: Yarborough Sports Centre, Riseholme Road, Lincoln.
Club Secretary: Mr H. Sampson, 7 Shannon Ave., Lincoln LN6 7JG. Tel No:(H) 0522 691631.
Club Colours: Maroon and amber.

FINAL TABLE

	P	W	D	L	F	A	PD	Pts
Cotgrave	10	9	0	1	263	68	195	18
Horncastle	10	7	0	3	193	106	87	14
Sutton Bonn Sc	10	6	0	4	225	105	120	12
Castle Donington	10	4	0	6	145	152	-7	8
Whitwell	10	4	0	6	132	193	-61	8
Bilsthorpe	10	0	0	10	37	371	-334	0

MIDLAND DIVISION

EAST MIDLAND & LEICESTERSHIRE ONE 1993-94 FIXTURES

December 18 (Week 15)
Aylestone St James v Northampton Old Scouts
Brackley v Old Bosworthians
Daventry v Northampton Mens Own
Dunstablians v Huntingdon
Melton Mowbray v Market Bosworth
St Neots v Oadby Wyggestonians

October 23 (Week 8)
Aylestone St James v St Neots
Dunstablians v Brackley
Huntingdon v Northampton Mens Own
Loughborough v Old Bosworthians
Market Bosworth v Oadby Wyggestonians
Melton Mowbray v Daventry

January 8 (Week 18)
Huntingdon v Melton Mowbray
Loughborough v Dunstablians
Market Bosworth v Aylestone St James
Northampton Mens Own v Brackley
Northampton Old Scouts v St Neots
Oadby Wyggestonians v Daventry

October 30 (Week X2)
Brackley v Melton Mowbray
Daventry v Aylestone St James
Northampton Mens Own v Loughborough
Northampton Old Scouts v Markets Bosworth
Oadby Wyggestonians v Huntingdon
Old Bosworthians v Dunstablians

January 29 (Week X5)
Aylestone St James v Huntingdon
Brackley v Oadby Wyggestonians
Daventry v Northampton Old Scouts
Melton Mowbray v Loughborough
Old Bosworthians v Northampton Mens Own
St Neots v Market Bosworth

November 13 (Week 10)
Aylestone St James v Brackley
Dunstablians v Northampton Mens Own
Huntingdon v Northampton Old Scouts
Loughborough v Oadby Wyggestonians
Melton Mowbray v Old Bosworthians
St Neots v Daventry

February 12 (Week 22)
Dunstablians v Melton Mowbray
Huntingdon v St Neots
Loughborough v Aylestone St James
Market Bosworth v Daventry
Northampton Old Scouts v Brackley
Oadby Wyggestonians v Old Bosworthians

November 20 (Week 11)
Brackley v St Neots
Market Bosworth v Huntingdon
Northampton Mens On v Melton Mowbray
Northampton old Scouts v Loughborough
Oadby Wyggestonians v Dunstablians
Old Bosworthians v Ayleston St James

March 12 (Week 26)
Aylestone St James v Dunstablians
Brackley v Market Bosworth
Daventry v Huntington
Northampton Mens Own v Oadby Wyggestonians
Old Bosworthians v Northampton Old Scouts
St Neots v Loughborough

December 4 (Week 13)
Aylestone St James v Northampton Mens Own
Daventry v Brackley
Dunstablians v Northampton Old Scouts
Loughborough v Market Bosworth
Melton Mowbray v Oadby Wyggestonians
St Neots v Old Bosworthians

March 26 (Week 28)
Dunstablians v St Neots
Huntingdon v Brackley
Loughborough v Daventry
Market Bosworth v Old Bosworthians
Melton Mowbray v Aylestone St James
Northampton Old Scouts v Northampton Mens Own

December 11 (Week 14)
Huntingdon v Loughborough
Market Bosworth v Dunstablians
Northampton Mens Own v St Neots
Northampton Old Scouts v Melton Mowbray
Oadby Wyggestonians v Aylestone St James
Old Bosworthians v Daventry

April 9 (Week 30)
Brackley v Loughborough
Daventry v Dunstablians
Northampton Mens Own v Market Bosworth
Oadby Wyggestonians v Northampton Old Scouts
Old Bosworthians v Huntingdon
St Neots v Melton Mowbray

EAST MIDLAND & LEICESTER ONE

AYLESTONE ST JAMES RFC
Ground Address: The Clubhouse, Covert Lane, Scraptoft, Leicester. Tel: 0533 419202.
Club Secretary: K W I Ridge, 5 Cannons Close, Narborough, Leicestershire. Tel: (H) 0533 866481 (W) 608187. **Press Officer:** R Angel, 6 Foxglove Close, East Goslote, Leicestershire. Tel: (H) 0533 607359 (W) 0533 531964.
Club Colours: Royal blue & white hoops.

BRACKLEY RUFC
Ground Address: Pavilions Way, Brackley, Northamptonshire. Tel: 0280 700685.
Club Secretary: Alan Jukes, 61 Martial Daire Boulevard, Brackley, Northamptonshire, NN13 6LS. Tel: (H) 0280 701011. **Press Officer:** Alan Jukes, 61 Martial Daire Boulevard, Brackley, Northamptonshire, NN13 6LS. Tel: (H) 0280 701011.
Club Colours: Royal blue & white quarters, blue shorts.

DAVENTRY RFC
Ground Address: Stefen Hill, Western Avenue, Daventry, Northamptonshire, NN11 4ST. Tel: 0327 703802.
Club Secretary: Derek Oakes, 47 Staverton Road, Daventry, Northamptonshire, NN11 4EY. Tel: (H) 0327 72333. **Press Officer:** Paul Wilson, Gable End Cottage, 22 High Street, Greens Norton, towcester, Northamptonshire, NN12 8BA. Tel: (H) 0327 51304 (W) 0788 521595.
Club Colours: All black.

DUNSTABLIANS RUFC
Ground Address: Bidwell Park, Bedford Road, Houghton Regis, Dunstable, Bedfordshire, LU50 6JW. Tel: 0582 866555.
Club Secretary: Paul Freeman, 19 Preston Road, Toddington, Near Dunstable, Bedfordshire, LU5 6EG. Tel: (H) 0525 874550 (W) 0234 328111 Ext 3165. **Press Officer:** Martin Coulter, 36 Derwent Drive, Dunstable, Bedfordshire, LU6 3PB. Tel: (H) 0582 600248 (W) 0582 23652.
Club Colours: Red, black & silver.

HUNTINGDON RUFC
Ground Address: The Racecourse, Brampton, Huntingdon.
Club Secretary: N F Whitsey, The Vines, Bridge Road, Broughton, Huntingdon, PE17 3AY. **Press Officer:** T Parratt, 4 High Street, Kimbolton, Huntingdon. Tel: (H) 0480 860776 (W) 0480 495090.
Club Colours: Emerald Green.

LOUGHBOROUGH RFC
Ground Address: The Clubhouse, Derby Road Playing Fields, Derby Road, Loughborough. Tel: 0509 216093.
Club Secretary: Anne Murphy, 51 Park Road, Loughborough, LE11 2ED. Tel: (H) 0509 231575. **Press Officer:** Paul Hilder.
Club Colours: Navy blue & old gold.

MARKET BOSWORTH RFC
Ground Address: Cadeby lane, Cadeby, Market Bosworth. Tel: 0455 291340.
Club Secretary: G Donnelly, 23 Norfolk Road, Desford, Leicester, LE9 9HR. Tel: (H) 0455 823522 (W) 0455 232328. **Press Officer:** B Godfrey, 6 Lyndene Close, Earl Shilton, Leicestershire, LE9 7FE. Tel: (H) 0455 846720 (W) 0455 843017.
Club Colours: Blue, gold & white hoops, black shorts.

MELTON MOWBRAY RUFC
Ground Address: All England Ground, Saxby Road, Melton Mowbray, Leicestershire.
Club Secretary: Act Middleton, 13 Birch Close, Melton Mowbray, Leicestershire, LE13 0QA. Tel: (H) 0664 67042 (W) 0664 63484. **Press Officer:** Act Middleton, 13 Birch Close, Melton Mowbray, Leicestershire, LE13 0QA. Tel: (H) 0664 67042 (W) 0664 63484.
Club Colours: Maroon & white.

FINAL TABLE

	P	W	D	L	F	A	PD	Pts
Kibworth	12	12	0	0	320	116	204	24
Loughborough	12	10	0	2	238	138	100	20
Northampton MO	12	9	0	3	221	122	99	18
Northampton OS	12	8	1	3	306	156	150	17
Market Bosworth	12	7	1	4	241	124	117	15
Oadby Wygg'ians	12	6	0	6	159.	130	29	12
St Neots	12	5	1	6	184	161	23	11
Old Bosworthians	12	5	0	7	173	221	-48	10
Melton Mowbray	12	4	1	7	143	173	-30	9
Huntingdon	12	4	1	7	131	225	-94	9
Aylestone St James	12	3	0	9	103	227	-124	6
Brackley	12	2	0	10	203	272	-69	4
St Ives	12	0	1	11	84	441	-357	1

NORTHAMPTON MENS OWN RFC
Ground Address: Stoke Road, Ashton, Northampton,, NN7 2JN. Tel: 0604 862463.
Club Secretary: David Edwards, 1A Landcross Drive, Abington vale, northampton, NN3 3NA. Tel: (H) 0604 28972 (W) 0604 252837. **Press Officer:** James Attwood, Miles Well House, 90 Lumbertubs Lane, Northampton, NN3 1AH. Tel: (H) 0604 644638.
Club Colours: White with single royal blue hoop, navy blue shorts.

NORTHAMPTON OLD SCOUTS RFC
Ground Address: Rushmere Road, Northampton. Tel: 0604 33639.
Club Secretary: R Letty, 49 Barley Hill Road, Southfields, Northampton. Tel: (H) 0604 758383 (W) 0604 252837. **Press Officer:** R Letty, 49 Barley Hill Road, Southfields, Northampton, Tel: (H) 0604 758383 (W) 06047 252837.
Club Colours: Red, gold, emerald green with navy blue hoops.

OADBY WYGGESTONIAN RFC
Ground Address: Oval Park, Wigston Road, Oadby, Leicester. Tel: 0533 714848.
Club Secretary: Jim Kilgallen, 75 Leicester Road, Dadby, Leicester, LE2 4DF. Tel: (H) 0533 713987. **Press Officer:** Andrew Beevers, 1 Steeple Close, Wigston, Leicester, LE18 3QN. Tel: (H) 0533 883480 (W) 0533870621.
Club Colours: Black, white & gold hoops, black shorts.

OLD BOSWORTHIANS RFC
Ground Address: Hinckley Road, Leicester Forest East, Leicester. Tel: 0533 387136.
Club Secretary: Grahame David Spendlove-Mason, Croft House Farm, Post Office Lane, Newton Harcourt, Leicestershire, LE8 0FN. Tel: (H) 0533 592965 (W) 0533 557803. **Press Officer:** Michael Willcox, 27 Bambrook Close, Desford, Leicestershire, LE9 9FY. Tel: (H) 0455 824277 w0530 414281.
Club Colours: Navy & sky blue.

ST NEOTS RUFC
Ground Address: The Common, St Neots. Tel: 0480 474285.
Club Secretary: Ray London, 14 James Court, Euynesbury, St Neots. Tel: (H) 0480 475392 (W) 0480 812202 Ext 249. **Press Officer:** John Grosvenor, 1 Silvan Close, Little Paxton, St Neots, PE19 4PJ. Tel: (H) 0480 219812.
Club Colours: Sky with broad navy hoop, navy shorts.

MIDLAND DIVISION

EAST MIDLAND & LEICESTERSHIRE TWO 1993-94 FIXTURES

December 18 (Week 15)
Aylestonians v Bugbrooke
Bedford Queens v Old Ashbeians
Birstall v Oakham
Northampton Casuals v New Parks Old Boys
St Ives v Rushden & Higham
Wigston v Wellingborough Old G

October 23 (Week 8)
Bedford Queens v Wigston
Birstall v Aylestonians
Oakham v New Parks Old Boys
Old Northamptonians v Bugbrooke
Rushden & Higham v Wellingborough Old G
St Ives v Northampton Casuals

January 18 (Week 18)
New Parks Old Boys v Aylestonians
Oakham v St Ives
Old Ashbeians v Wigston
Old Northamptonians v Birstall
Rushden & Higham v Bedford Queens
Wellingborough Old G v Northampton Casuals

October 30 (Week X2)
Aylestonians v St Ives
Bugbrooke v Birstall
New Parks Old Boys v Old Northamptonians
Northampton Casuals v Bedford Queens
Old Ashbeins v Rushden & Higham
Wellingborough Old G v Oakham

January 29 (Week X5)
Aylestonians v Wellingborough Old G
Bedford Queens v Oakham
Bugbrooke v New Parks Old Boys
Northampton Casuals v Old Ashbeians
St Ives v Old Northamptonians
Wigston v Rushden & Higham

November 13 (Week 10)
Bedford Queens v Aylestonians
Birstall v New Parks Old Boys
Oakham v Old Ashbeians
Old Northamptonians v Wellingborough Old G
St Ives v Bugbrooke
Wigston v Northampton Casuals

February 12 (Week 22)
Birstall v St Ives
Oakham v Wigston
Old Ashbeians v Aylestonians
Old Northamptonians v Bedford Queens
Rushden & Higham v Northampton Casuals
Wellingborough Old G v Bugbrooke

November 20 (Week 11)
Aylestonians v Wigston
Bugbrook v Bedford Qyeens
New Parks Old Boys v St Ives
Rushden & Higham v Oakham
Old Ashbeians v Old Northamptonians
Wellingvorough Old G v Birstall

March 12 (Week 26)
Aylestonians v Rushden & ghigham
Bedford Queens v Birstall
Bugbrooke v Old Ashbeians
New Parks Old Boys v Wellingborough Old G
Northampton Casuals v Oakham
Wigston v Old Northamptonians

December 4 (week 13)
Bedford Queens v New Parks Old Boys
Birstall v Old Ashbeians
Northampton Casuals v Aylestonians
Old Northamptonians v Rushden & Higham
St Ives v Wellingborough Old G
Wigston v Bugbrooke

March 26 (Week 28)
Birstall v Wigston
Oakham v Aylestonians
Old Ashbeians v New Parks Old Boys
Old Northamptonians v Northampton Casuals
Rushden & Ghigham v Bugbrooke
St Ives v Bedford Queens

December 11 (Week 14)
Bugbooke v Northampton Casuals
New Parks Old Boys v Wigston
Oakham v Old Northamptonians
Old Ashbeians v St Ives
Rushden & Higham v Birstall
Wellingborough Old G v Bedford Queens

April 9 (Week 30)
Aylestonians v Old Northamptonians
Bugbrooke v Oakham
New Parks Old Boys v Rushden & Higham
Northampton Casuals v Birstall
Wigston v St Ives
Wellingborough Old G v Old AShbeians

398

EAST MIDLAND & LEICESTER TWO

AYLESTONIANS
Ground Address: Knighton Lane East, Leicester. Tel: 0533 834899.
Club Secretary: C Cooper, 84 Vaughan Street, Leicester, LE3 5JP. Tel: (H) 0533 530282 (W) 0533 834899.
Press Officer: C Cooper, 84 Vaughan Street, Leicester, LE3 5JP. Tel: (H) 0533 530282 (W) 0533 834899.
Club Colours: Red, white & blue hoops.

BEDFORD QUEENS RUFC
Ground Address: Allen Park, Old Ford End Road, Bedford. Tel: 0234 271172.
Club Secretary: James Cunningham, 16 Adelaide Square, Bedford. Tel: (H) 02334 269085 (W) 0234 347111.
Press Officer: J Radnor, 133 Ireland Shefford, Bedfordshire, SG17 5QL. Tel: (H) 0462 816175.
Club Colours: Maroon & white hoops.

BIRSTALL RFC
Ground Address: Longslade Community College, Wadilip Lane, Birstall, Leicestershire. Tel: 05233 674211.
Club Secretary: R G Offley, 46 Barons Way, Market Cross, Mountsorrel, Leicestershire, LE12 7EA. Tel: (H) 0533 302424.
Press Officre: P Russell.
Club Colours: Green, white & black hoops, black shorts.

BUGBROOKE RUFC
Ground Address: Playing Fields, Pilgrim Lane, Bugbrooke, Northamptonshire. Tel: 0604 831137.
Club Secretary: John Gowen, 46 Granary Road, East Hunsbury, Northampton, Northanmptonshire, NN4 0XA. Tel: (H) 0604 705273 (W) 0604 671176.
Press Officer: John Gowen, 45 Granary Road, east Hunsbury, Northampton, Northamptonshire, NN4 0XA. Tel: (H) 0604 705273 (W) 0604 671176.
Club Colours: Bottle green shirt with gold collar, green shorts.

NEW PARKS (OLD BOYS) RFC
Ground Address: New Parks Community College, Greencoat Road, Leicester.
Club Secreaty: John Cluer, 50 Babingley Drive, Leicester, LE4 0HH. Tel: (H) 0533 352457 (W) 0533 482451.
Press Officer: John Cluer, 50 Babingley Drive, Leicester, LE4 0HH. Tel: (H) 0533 352457 (W)0533 482451.
Club Colours: Sky blue, black shorts.

NORTHAMPTON CASUALS RFC
Ground Address: Rushmills House, Rushmills, Bedford Road, Northampton. Tel: 0604 36716.
Club Secretary: S M Tee, 32 Duston Wildes, Duston, Northampton, NN5 6ND. Tel: (H) 0604 587982 (W) 021 440 5151.
Press Officer: P S Franklin, Rushmills Hoiuse, Rushmills, Bedford Road, Northampton. Tel: (W) 0604 36716.
Club Colours: Black with amber band.

OAKHAM RFC
Ground Address: The Showground, Barleythorpe Road, Oakham, Rutland. Tel: 0570 724206.
Club Secretary: Peter Bateman, 26 Well Street, Langham, Oakham, Rutland, LE15 7JS. Tel: (H) 0572 756143 (W) 0533 550020.
Press Officer: Peter Bateman, 26 Well Street, Langham, Oakham, Rutland, LE15 7JS. Tel: (H) 0572 756143 (W) 0533 550020.
Club Colours: Black shirts with amber hoop.

OLD ASHBEINAS RFC
Ground Address: New Field, Lower, Packington Road, Ashby de la Zouch, Leicestershire. Tel: 0530 413998.
Club Secretary: John Mitchell, 50 Pennine Way, Ashby, Leicestershire, LE63 1EW. Tel: (H) 0530 415284.

FINAL TABLE

	P	W	D	L	F	A	PD	Pts
Daventry	11	8	1	2	172	82	90	17
Dunstablians	11	8	0	3	215	131	84	16
Wigston	11	8	0	3	173	113	60	16
Oakham	11	7	1	3	180	97	83	15
Rushden & Higham	11	6	1	4	162	115	47	13
Bedford Queens	11	6	0	5	149	175	-26	11
Aylestonians	11	5	1	5	149	175	-26	11
Birstall	11	4	1	6	155	142	13	9
Wellingborough OG	11	3	2	6	135	165	-30	8
Old Ashbeians	11	3	2	6	103	168	-65	8
Northampton Cas	11	3	0	8	130	185	-55	6
New Parks O B	11	0	1	10	75	353	-278	1

Press Officer: Phil Dyer, 18 Cambrian Way, Ashby, Leicestershire. Tel: (H) 0830 416500.
Club Colours: Maroon & sky blue hoops, navy shorts.

OLD NORTHAMPTONIANS RFC
Ground Address: Sports Field, Billing Road, Northampton. Tel: 0604 340456.
Club Secretary: N Pickerill, 232 Billing Road, Northampton, NN1 5AR. Tel: (H) 0604 30711.
Press Officer: J Bull, 24 Peregrine Place, East Hunsbury, Northampton. Tel: (H) 0604 763265.
Club Colours Cardinal, navy, & gold hoops.

RUSHDEN AND HIGHAM RUFC
Ground Address: Manor Park, Bedford Road, Rushden, Northamptonshire, NN10 0SA. Tel: 0933 312071.
Club Secretary: Steve Miles, 9 Grange Road, Little Cransley, Kettering, Northamptonshire, NN14 1PH. Tel: (H) 0536 790429 (W) 0604 235410.
Press Officer: Steve Miles, 9 Grange Road, Little Cransley, Kettering, Northamptonshire, NN14, 1PH. Tel: (H) 0536 790429 (W) 0604 235410.
Club Colours: Black & white hoops.

ST IVES (CAMBS) RUFC
Ground Address: St Ives Outdoor Complex, California Road, St Ives, Huntingdon, Cambridgeshire, PE17 4SJ.
Club Secretary: Alison Gough, 9 Stubbs Close, St Ives, Huntingdon, Cambridgeshire, PE17 6HQ. Tel: (H) 0480 495359 (W) 0487 710393.
Press Officer: Adrian Lewis, Flat 4, Lorna Court, St Ives, Huntington, Cambridgeshire, PE17 4FD. Tel: (H) 0480 494603.
Club Colours: Royal blue shirts, black shorts.

WELLINGBOROUGH OLD GRAMMARIANS RFC
Ground Address: Memorial Sports Field, Saunders Road, Finedon Road Industrial Estate, Wellingborough, Northamptonshire. Tel: 0933 279316.
Club Secretary: Paul Bush, 33 Newtown Road, Little Irchester, Wellingborough, Northamptonshire, NN8 2QX. Tel: (H) 0933 441663 (W) 0933 277432.
Press Officer: Adrian Howes, 4 Orwell Close, Wellingborough, Northamptonshire, NN8 5WX. Tel: (H) 0933 401361 (W) 0933 440077.
Club Colours: Claret & white hoops, black shorts.

WIGSTON RFC
Ground Address: Leicester Road, Countesthorpe, Leicestershire. Tel: 0533 771153.
Club Secretary: Steve Benton, 5 Ramsden Avenue, Wigston, Leicestershire, LE18 1DX.
Press Officer: Steve Redferry, c/o Wigson RFC, Leicester Road, Countesthorpe, Leicestershire.
Club Colours: Purple with black/silver & gold arm.

MIDLAND DIVISION

EAST MIDLAND & LEICESTERSHIRE THREE 1993-94 FIXTURES

Decmeber 18 (Week 15)
Corby v West Leicester
Old Newtonians v Deepings
Anstey v Kempston
Old Wellingburians v Burbage
Westwood v Colworth
Bedford Swifts v Shepshed

October 23 (Week 8)
Corby v Old Newtonians
Colworth v Deepings
Burbage v Shepshed
Oundle v Kempston
Old Wellingburians v Anstey
Westwood v Bedford Swifts

October 30 (Week X2)
Bedford Swifts v Corby
Anstey v Westwood
Kempston v Old Wellingburians
Shepshed v Oundle
Deepings v Burbage
West Leicester v Colworth

November 13 (Week 10)
Corby v Anstey
Old Newtonians v Bedford Swifts
Burbage v West Leicester
Oundle v Deepings
Old Wellingburians v Shepshed
Westwood v Kempston

November 20 (Week 11)
Anstey v Old Newtonians
Kempston v Corby
Shepshed v Westwood
Deepings v Old Wellingburians
West Leicester v Oundle
Colworth v Burbage

December 4 (Week 13)
Corby v Shepshed
Old Newtonians v Kempston
Bedford Swifts v Anstey
Oundle v Colworth
Old Wellingburians v West Leicester
Westwood v Deepings

December 11 (Week 14)
Kempston v Bedford Swifts
Shepshed v Old Newtonians
Deepings v Corby
West Leicesters v Westwood
Colworth v Old Wellingburians
Burbage v Oundle

January 8 (Week 18)
Shepshed v Anstey
Deepiongs v Bedford Swifts
West Leicester v Old Newtonians
Colworth v Corby
Burbage v Westwood
Oundle v Old Wellingburians

January 29 (Week X5)
Corby v Burbage
Old Newtonians v Colworth
Bedford Swifts v West Leicester
Anstey v Deepings
Kempston v Shepshed
Westwood v Oundle

February 12 (week 22)
Deepings v Kempston
West Leicester v Anstey
Colwworth v Bedford Swifts
Burbage v Old Newtonians
Oundle v Corby
Old Wellingburians v Westwood

March 12 (Week 26)
Corby v Old Wellingburians
Old Newtonians v Oundle
Bedford Swifts v Burbage
Anstey v Colworth
Kempston v West Leicester
Shepshed v Deepings

March 26 (Week 28)
West Leicester v Shepshed
Colworth v Kempston
Biurbage v Anstey
Oundle v Bedford Swifts
Old Wellingburians v Old Newtonians
Westwood v Corby

April 9 (Week 30)
Old Newtonians v Westwood
Bedford Swifts v Old Wellingburians
Anstey v Oundle
Kempston v Burbage
Shepshed v Colworth
Deepings v West Leicester

ANSTEY RFC
Ground Address: Link Road Playing Field, Link Road, Anstey, Leicester.
Club Secretary: Tony Duffield, 10 Pinewood Close, Leicester, LE4 1ER. Tel: (H) 0533 355986.
Club Colours: Black shirts & shorts.

BEDFORD SWIFTS RUFC
Ground Address: Bedford Athletics Stadium, Barkers Lane, Bedford, MK41 9SA. Tel: 0234 351115.
Club Secretary: Trevor n Stewart, 64 Ravensden Road, Renhold, Bedford, MK41 0JY. Tel: (H) 0234 771828 (W) 0767 681491.
Press Officer: Steve Toner, 17 Swift Close, Beford, MK41 7HS. Tel: (H) 0234 214850 (W) 0234 272700.
Club Colours: Royal Blue with amber hoops, navy shorts.

BURBAGE RFC
Ground Address: John Cleveland College, Butt Lane, Hinckley, Leicestershire.
Club Secretary: G M Startin, 102 Strathmore Road, Hinckley Leicestershire, LE10 0LR. Tel: (H) 0455 634073 (W) 0455 637841.
Press Officer: G M Startin, 102 Strathmore Road, Hinckley, Leicestershire, LE10 0LR. Tel: (H) 0455 634073 (W) 0455 637841.
Club Colours: Green & white hoops.

COLWORTH HOUSE RUFC
Ground Address: Colworth house Club, Unilever Research, Sharnbrook, Bedford, MK44 1LQ. Tel: 0234 222221.
Club Secretary: Dr Paul Dunnett, Barden Cottage, 37 Sandy Road, Willington, Bedford, MK44 2QS. Tel: (H) 0234 838671 (W) 0234 222857.
Press Officer: Dr Paul Dunnett, Barden Cottage, 37 Sandy Road, Willington, Bedford, MK44 2QS. Tel: (H) 0234 838671 (W) 0234 222857.

CORBY RFC
Ground Address: Northen Park, Rockingham Triangle, Corby, Northamptonshire. Tel: 0536 204466.
Club Secretary: George A Ewen, Northen Park, Rockingham Triangle, Corby, Northamptonshire. Tel: 0536 204466.
Press Officer: Gary Chisolm, Northen Park, Rockingham Triangle, Corby, Northamptonshire. Tel: 0536 204466.
Club Colours: Red & white.

DEEPINGS RUFC
Ground Address: Linchfield Road, Deeping St James, Peterborough. Tel: 0778 345228.
Club Secretary: Brian Kirby, 14 Woodcroft Close, Market Deeping, Peterborough, PE6 8BT. Tel: (H) 0778 343048 (W) 0733 68989 Ext 4173.
Press Officer: Marcus Lawday, 21 Wade Park Avenue, Market Deeping, Peterborough, PE6 8JL. Tel: (H) 0778 344907 (W) 0733 239977.
Club Colours: Yellow, green & black hoops.

KEMPSTON RUFC
Ground Address: 134 High Street, Kempston, Bedfordshire, c/o Cutler Hammer Sports & Social Club. Tel: 0234 852499.
Club Secretary: Will Hunt, 5 Vyne Close, Kempston, Bedfordshire, MK42 8RH. Tel: (H) 0234 852072 (W) 0525 404305.
Press Officer: Mark Duke, 21 Gulliver Close, Kempston, Bedfordshire, MK42 9RH. Tel: (H) 0234 855426.
Club Colours: Red & black quarters.

OLD NEWTONIANS RFC
Ground Address: Hinkley Road, Leicester Forest East, Leicester. Tel: 392389.
Club Secretary: G A Clark, 250 Wigston lane, Ayleston, Leicester, LE2 8DH. Tel: 832309.

FINAL TABLE

	P	W	D	L	F	A	PD	Pts
O. N'thamptonians	12	12	0	0	504	50	454	24
Bugbroke	12	11	0	1	584	75	509	22
Bedford Swifts	12	9	0	3	326	172	154	18
Westwood	12	7	1	4	313	169	144	15
Oundle	12	7	1	4	205	187	18	15
Anstey	12	6	2	4	251	104	147	14
Colworth House	12	7	1	4	325	180	127	13
Deepings	12	5	2	5	183	254	-71	12
Old Newtonians	12	4	1	7	130	206	-76	9
Shepshed	12	3	0	9	87	457	-370	6
West Leicester	12	2	0	10	88	366	-278	4
Old Wellingburians	12	1	0	11	75	388	-313	2
Burbage	12	0	0	12	63	508	-445	0

Press Officer: Stuart Prior, 21 Great Meadow Road, Groby, Leicester. Tel: (H) 878435 (W) 530066 Ext 5133.
Club Colours: Navy with white, green, red, white hoops.

OLD WELLINGBURIANS RFC
Ground Address: The Embankment Club, Wellingborough.
Club Secretary: Mark Thompson, 60 Glenfield Drive, South Doddington, Northants, NN9 7TE. Tel: (W) 0234 343221.
Press Officer: Nick Ellis, 2 Gillam Butts, Coutesthorpe, Leicester. Tel: (H) 0533 772066 (W) 021 233 9070.
Club Colours: Green, Gold, mauve.

OUNDLE RFC
Ground Address: Occupation Road, Oundle, Northants. Tel: 0832 273101.
Club Secretary: Roger Smith, 6 Pheasant Way, Yaxley, Peterborough, Cambs. PE7 3HN. Tel: (H) 0733 242344 (W) 0733 556610.
Press Officer: Nigel Howe, Highgate House, Bulwick, Nr Corby, Northamptonshire. Tel: (H) 078085 285.
Club Colours: Black with red & white stripe.

SHEPSHED RFC
Ground Address: Hind Leys Campus, Forest Street, Shepshed, Leicestershire. Tel: 0509 503592.
Club Secretary: Mick Steven, 121 Cossington Road, Sileby, Leicestershire, LE12 7RP. Tel: (H) 0509 816199 (W) 0533 484131.
Press Officer: Mick Steven, 121 Cossington Road, Sileby, Leicestershire, LE12 7RP. Tel: (H) 0509 816199 (W) 0533 484131.
Club Colours: Red & black quarters.

WEST LEICESTER RFC
Ground Address: St Mary's Fields, Narborough Road, Leicester. Tel: 0533 540634.
Club Secretary: G E Topley, 8 Hillsborough Road, Parva, Leicester, LE2 9PL. Tel: (H) 0533 774119 (W) 0533 888951.
Press Officer: G E Topley, 8 Hillsborough Road, Parva, Leicester, LE2 9PL. Tel: (H) 0533 774119 (W) 0533 888951.
Club Colours: Red with white shorts, black socks.

WESTWOOD RUFC
Ground Address: Phorpnes Club, London Road, Peterborough. Tel: 0733 343501.
Club Secretary: Jim McCrowie, 3 Laurel Close, Yaxley, Peterborough, PE17 3LQ.
Press Officer: E Malaczek, 307 Eastfield Road, Peterborough. Tel: (H) 0733 349820.
Club Colours: Red & white hoops.

MIDLAND DIVISION

EAST MIDLAND & LEICESTERSHIRE FOUR 1993-94 FIXTURES

October 2 (Week 5)
Braunstone v Clapham
Cosby v Littlehey
Northampton Heathens v Potton
Thorney v Vauxhall Motors

October 23 (Week 8)
Clapham v Cosby
Littlehey v Northampton Heathens
Potton v Thorney
Vauxhall Motors v Braunstone

October 30 (Week X2)
Braunstone v Potton
Cosby v Vauxhall Motors
Northampton Heathens v Clapham
Thorney v Littlehey

November 13 (Week 10)
Clapham v Thorney
Littlehey v Braunstone
Potton v Cosby
Vauxhall Motors v Northampton heathens

November 20 (Week 11)
Clapham v Vauxhall Motors
Cosby v Bruanstone
Potton v Cosby
Vauxhall Motors v Northampton Heathens

December 4 (Week 13)
Braunstone v Northampton Heathens
Potton v Clapham
Thorney v Cosby
Vauxhall Motors v Littlehey

December 18 (Week 15)
Clapham v Braunstone
Littlehey v Cosby
Potton v Northampton heathens
Vauxhall Motors v Thorney

January 8 (Week 18)
Braunstone v Northampton Heathens
Littlehey v Thorney
Potton v Brausntone
Vauxhall Motors v Cosby

February 12 (Week 22)
Braunstone v Littlehey
Cosby v Potton
Northampton Heathens v Vauxhall motors
Thorney v Clapham

March 12 (Week 26)
Braunstone v Cosby
Littlehey v Potton
Northampton Heathens v Thorney
Vauxhall Motors v Clapham

March 26 (Week 28)
Clapham v Littlehey
Cosby v Northampton Heathens
Potton v Vauxhall Motors
Thorney v Braunstone

April 9 (Week 30)
Clapham v Potton
Cosby v Thorney
Littlehey v Vauxhall Motors
Northampton Heathens v Braunstone

402

EAST MIDLAND & LEICESTER FOUR

BRAUNSTONE TOWN RFC
Ground Address: Mossdale Meadows, The Kingsway, Braunstone, Leicester.
Club Secretary: P S Clarke, 28 Park Road, Wisston, Leicester, LE18 4QD. Tel: (H) 0533 773507 (W) 0455 822441.
Press Officer: P S Clarke, 28Park Road, Wisston, Leicester, LE18 4QD. Tel: (H) 0533 773507 (W) 0455 822441.
Club Colours: Maroon & gold, black shorts.

CLAPHAM RUFC
Ground Address: Twinwoods Road, Clapham, Bedfordshire.
Club Secretary: D R Tough, Millbrook house, 109 High Street, Riseley, Bedfordshire MK44 1DF. Tel: 0234 708453 (W) 0438 314281.
Press Officer: G Dear, 8 Sidney Road, Bedford, Bedfordshire.
Club Colours: Blue & gold quarters, blue shorts.

COSBY RFC
Ground Address: c/o Wigston RFC, Leicester Road, Countersthorpe, Leicestershire. Tel: 0533 771153.
Club Secretary: Clive W Elliott, 9 Wanertree Close, Cosby, Leicestershire, LE9 5TN. Tel: (H) 0533 841746 (W) 0530 510051.
Press Officer: Clive W Elliott, 9 Wanertree Close, Cosby, Leicestershire, LE9 5TN. Tel: (H) 0533 841746 (W) 0530 510051.
Club Colours: Black shirts & shorts.

LITTLEHEY RUFC
Ground Address: HMP Littlehey, Crown Spinney Lane, Perry, Huntingdon, Cambridgeshire, PE18 0SR. Tel: 0480 812212 Ext 248.
Club Secretary: Stephen Fagan, Physics Education Department, HMP Littlehey, Perry, Huntingdon, Cambridgeshire, PE18 0SR. Tel: (H) 1733 559063 (W) 0480 812202 Ext 248.
Press Officer: Andy Curtis, HMP Littleheyu, Crown Spinney Lane, Perry, Huntingdon, Cambridgeshire, PE18 0SR. Tel: (W) 0480 812202.
Club Colours: Blue & white halves, blue shorts.

NORTHAMPTON HEATHENS RFC
Ground Address: The Racecourse, East Park Parade, Northampton. Tel: 0604 39250 or 33660 (Victoria Inn)
Club Secretary: Derek Hodgkinson, 5 Pine Trees, Weston Favell, Northampton, NN3 3ET. Tel: (H) 0604 416442 (W) 0708 731100.
Press Officer: Derek Hodgkinson, 5 Pine Trees, Weston Favell, Northampton, NN3 3ET. Tel: (H) 0604 416442 (W) 0708 731100.
Club Colours: 3" black hoops, 1" amber hoops, black shorts.

POTTON RUFC
Ground Address: CIV Club, Station Road, Potton, Bedfordshire, SG19 2PU. Tel: 0767 261465.
Club Secretary: Alan Young, 4 Chapel Street, Potton, Bedfordshire, SG19 2PT. Tel: (H) 0767 262252.
Press Officer: Alan Young, 4 Chapel Street, Potton, Bedfordshire, SG19 2PT. Tel: (H) 0767 262252.
Club Colours: White with amber & gold band.

FINAL TABLE

	P	W	D	L	F	A	PD	Pts
Kempston	8	7	1	0	267	23	244	15
Corby	8	7	1	0	262	27	235	15
Vauxhall Motors	8	6	0	2	199	82	117	12
Littlehey	8	4	0	4	125	75	50	8
N'hamptn Heathens	8	4	0	4	130	118	12	8
Potton	8	3	0	5	66	205	-139	6
Thorney	8	2	0	6	60	170	-110	4
Clapham Twinw'ds	8	2	0	6	56	225	-169	4
Braunstone Town	8	0	0	8	13	253	-240	0

THORNEY RUFC
Ground Address: Thorney Park, Wisbech Road, Thorney, Peterborough.
Club Secretary: Paul Smith, 154 Wisbech Road, Thorney, Peterborough, Cambridgeshire, PE6 0SE. Tel: (H) 0733 270552.
Press Officer: Paul Smith, 154 Wisbech Road, Thorney, Peterboprough, Cambridgeshire, PE6 0SE. Tel: (H) 0733 270552.
Club Colours: Navy & gold quarters, change - navy.

VAUXHALL MOTORS RUFC
Ground Address: The Brache Estate, Osbourne Road, Luton.
Club Secretary: Paul McIntyre, 5 Tracey Courts, 76 Hibbert Street, Luton, Bedfordshire, LU1 3XH. Tel: (H) 0582 23168.
Press Officer: Steve MacLoughlin, 30- Catesby Green, Luton. Tel: (H) 0582 502260 (W) 0582 411685.
Club Colours: Blue shirt, 3 gold bands, black shorts.

THE BEST PACK IN THE CHAMPIONSHIP.

LONDON SOUTH EAST DIVISION

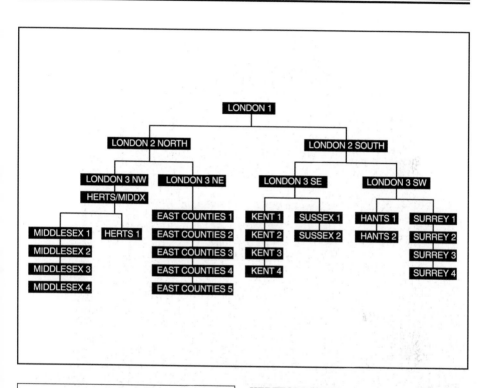

CHAIRMAN
R. Tennant, 57 Boveney Road, Forest Hill, London SE23 3NL (H) 081 699 9025.

SECRETARY
M.A. Ward, 3 Rookery Close, Oulton Broad, Lowestoft, Suffolk NR33 9NZ (H) 0502 566169 (B) 0502 566169 (F) 0502 501135.

EASTERN COUNTIES
F.A.G. Ford, "Fairhaven", 36 Haynes Road, Hornchurch, Essex RM11 2HT (H) 0708 457807 (B) 0708 345533 Ext 2210.

HAMPSHIRE
Lt. Cl. D. McF. Hathorn, 3 Broomacres, Fleet, Aldershot, Hampshire GU13 9UU (H) 0252 621565 (B) 0904 662459.

HERTFORDSHIRE
D.J. Williams, 7 Sadlers Way, Hertford, Herts SG14 2DZ (H) 0992 586744 (B) 0920 830011.

KENT
D. Attwood, 6 Somerset Gardens, Lewisham, London, SW13 7SY (H) 081 691 2820.

MIDDLESEX
D.C. Ransom, 2 Powls Court, The Rutts, Bushey Heath, Hertfordshire WD2 1LL (H) 081 950 5871 (B) 081 848 8744.

SURREY
H. Brady, 16 Selwood Terrace, London SW7 3QG (H) 071 370 1078.
A. Manly, 7 Burgoyne Road, South Norwood, London SE 25 6SI. (H) 081 653 4585 (B) 081 760 0200

SUSSEX
P Sealey, 15 Hart Close, Uckfield, Sussex TN22 2DA (H) 0825 763293 (B) 0732 863868.

THE BEST PACK IN THE CHAMPIONSHIP.

LONDON SOUTH EAST DIVISION

Officials contd.

LEAF MANAGER (CO-OPTED)
A.T.T. Street, 27 Chaucer Court, Lawn Road, Guildford, Surrey GU2 5DB (H) 0483 575742.

RFU REPRESENTATIVES
L.C.K. Angel, 1 Rochford Road, Basingstoke, Hampshire RG21 1TQ (H) 0256 27935 (B) 0256 844844 Ext 4584.
D.M. Robinson, Robinson Young Ltd, Ibson House, Eastern Way, Bury St. Edmunds, Suffolk (H) 0359 30608 (B) 0284 766261.
G.G. Smith, The Old Rectory, Provender Lane, Norton, Faversham, Kent ME13 0SU (H) 0795 521166 (B) 071 316 4411

LEAGUE SECRETARIES
London One George Ford, "Fairhaven", 36 Haynes Road, Hornchurch, Essex RM11 2HT (H) 0708 457807 (W) 0708 345533 Ext 2210.
London Two North David Williams, 7 Sadlers Way, Hertford, Herts SG14 2DZ (H) 0992 586744 (B) 0992 830011.
London Two South & London Three South-West Lt. Col. D. McF. Hathorn, 3 Broomacres, Fleet, Aldershot, Hampshire, GU13 9UU (H) 0252 621565 (W) 0904 662459.
London Three North-West Chris Poole, 24 Firs Walk, Tewin Wood, Welwyn, Hertfordshire, AL6 0NZ (H) 0438 79469 (W) 071 609 8004.
London Three North-East M. J. Stott, Brick Kiln Farm, North Walsham, Norfolk (H) 0692 403096.
London Three South-East Dennis Attwood, 6 Somerset Gardens, Lewisham, London SW13 7SY. (H) 081 691 2820.
Middlesex/Herts D. Gershlick, 20a The Avenue, Potters Bar, Hertfordshire EN6 1EB (H) 0707 44433 (W) 0234 214412.
Herts One C Poole, 24 Firs Walk, Tewin Wood, Welwyn, Herts AL6 0NZ. (H) 0438 79469 (W) 071 609 8004
Middlesex One G. Sykes, 11 Ivy Close, Eastcote, Pinner, Middlesex (H) 081 866 5430.
Middlesex Two P. Astbury, 32 Kneller Gardens, Isleworth, Middlesex (H) 081 989 5372.
Middlesex Three A. Rabjohn, 62 Central Avenue, Hounslow, Middlesex (H) 081 894 1850.
Middlesex Four Brian East, 17 Waterloo Road, London, N19 5NJ (H) 071 272 5686 (W) 071 485 4100 Ext211.
Hampshire One and Two J Sneezum, Bursledon Lodge, Salterns LAne, Old Bursledon, Southampton, Hampshire SO3 8DH (H) 0703 402286

Surrey One Greer Kirkwood, 63 Shaftesbury Way, Strawberry Hill, Twickenham TW2 5RW (H) 081 898 1767.
Surrey Two J.S. Laidman, 2 West Dene, Park Lane, Cheam, Surrey (H) 081 643 2919.
Surrey Three A. O'Shea, 37 Headington Road, Earlsfield, London SW18 3PR (H) 081 947 3924.
Surrey Four R.V. Miller, Flat 3, 127 Barnet Wood Road, Ashtead, Surrey (H) 0372 278486.
Eastern Counties One, Two and Five Mike Tuck, 51 Highfield Road, Billericay, Essex CM11 2PE (H) 0277 655483.
Eastern Counties Three and Four Ron Hatch, 99 Ernest Road, Wivenhoe, Essex CO7 9LJ (H) 0206 825882.
Sussex One and Two J.M. Carrington, 1 Graftons, Christ's Hospital, Horsham, Sussex (H) 0403 260556.
Kent One and Two J. Carley, 11 Vlissingen Drive, Deal, Kent, CT14 6TZ (H) 0304 381273 (W) 0304 812520.
Kent Three and Four R. Fisher, 7 Manwood Close, Sittingbourne, Kent ME10 4QL (H) 0795 471433 (W) 0634 388765.

LONDON & SOUTH EAST DIVISION

LONDON ONE
1993-94
FIXTURES

December 18 (Week 15)
Old Mid-Whitgiftians v Ealing
Camberley v Eton Manor
Harlow v Streatham-Croydon
Barking v Sutton & Epsom
Guildford & God'ming v Thurrock
Old Colfeians v Old Alleynian

October 23 (Week 8)
Old Mid-Whitgiftians v Camberley
Old Alleynian v Eton Manor
Thurrock v Streatham-Croydon
Dorking v Sutton & Epsom
Guildford & God'ming v Barking
Old Colfeians v Harlow

January 8 (Week 18)
Streatham-Croydon v Barking
Eton Manor v Harlow
Ealing v Camberley
Old Alleynian v Old Mid-Whitgiftians
Thurrock v Old Colfeians
Dorking v Guilford & God'ming

October 3O (Week X2)
Harlow v Old Mid-Whitgiftians
Barking v Old Colfeians
Sutton & Epsom v Guildford & God'ming
Streatham-Crodon v Dorking
Eton Manor v Thurrock
Ealing v Old Alleynian

January 29 (Week X5)
Old Mid-Whitgiftians v Thurrock
Camberley v Old Alleynian
Harlow v Ealing
Barking v Eton Manor
Sutton & Epsom v Streatham-Croydon
Old Colfeians v Dorking

November 13 (Week 1O)
Old Mid-Whitgiftians v Barking
Camberley v Harlow
Thurrock v Ealing
Dorking v Eton Manor
Guildford & God'ming v Streatham-Croydon
Old Colfeians v Sutton & Epsom

February 12 (Week 22)
Eton Manor v Sutton & Epsom
Ealing v Barking
Old Alleynian v Harlow
Thurrock v Camberley
Dorking v Old Mid-Whitfiftians
Guildford & God'ming v Old Colfeians

November 2O (Week 11)
Barking v Camberley
Sutton & Epsom v Old Mid-Whitgiftians
Streatham-Croydon v Old Colfeians
Eton Manor v Guildford & God'ming
Ealing v Dorking
Old Alleynian v Thurrock

March 12 (Week 26)
Old Mid-Whitgiftians v Guildford & God'ming
Camberley v Dorking
Harlow v Thurrock
Barking v Old Alleynian
Sutton & Epsom v Ealing
Streatham-Croydon v Eton Manor

December 4 (Week 13)
Old Mid-Whitgiftians v Streatham-Croydon
Camberley v Sutton & Epsom
Harlow v Barking
Dorking v Old Alleynian
Guildford & God'ming v Ealing
Old Colfeians v Eton Manor

March 26 (Week 28)
Ealing v Streatham-Croydon
Old Alleynian v Sutton & Epsom
Thurrock v Barking
Dorking v Harlow
Guildford & God'ming v Camberley
Old Colfians v Old Mid-Whitfiftians

December 11 (Week 14)
Sutton & Epsom v Harlow
Streatham-Croydon v Camberley
Eton Manor v Old Mid-Whitgiftians
Ealing v Old Colfeians
Old Alleynian v Guildford & God'ming
Thurrock v Dorking

April 9 (Week 3O)
Camberley v Old Colfeians
Harlow v Gildford & God'ming
Barking v Dorking
Sutton & Epsom v Thurrock
Streatham-Croydon v Old Alleynian
Eton Manor v Ealing

LONDON ONE

BARKING RUFC
Ground Address: "Goresbrook", Gale Street, Dagenham, Essex, RM9 4TY. Tel: 081 595 7324.
Club Secretary: David Arnold, 19 Hepworth Gardens, Barking, Essex, IG11 9BA. Tel: (H) 081 591 0031.
Press Officer: David Arnold, 19 Hepworth Gardens, Barking, Essex, IG11 9BA. Tel: (H) 081 591 0031.
Club Colours: Cardinal and grey.

CAMBERLEY RFC
Ground Address: Watchetts Recreation Cround, Park Road, Camberley, Surrey, GU15 2SR. Tel: 0276 25395.
Club Secretary: Bill Fletcher, 63 Rockwood Avenue, Owlsmoor, Camberley, Surrey, GU15 4TY. Tel: (H) 0344 777701 (W) 0344 51555.
Press Officer: Bill Fletcher, 63 Rockwood Avenue, Owlsmoor, Camberley, Surrey, GU15 4TY. Tel: (H) 0344 777701 (W) 0344 51555.
Club Colours: Black & amber hoops.

DORKING RFC
Ground Address: The Pavilion, The Big Field, Brockham, Betchworth, Surrey. Tel: 0787 843928.
Club Secretary: Peter Curran, Silver Acre, Camilla Drive, Westhumble. Tel: (H) 0306 884649 (W) 081 643 7221.
Press Officer: Andrew Probert, 32 The Orchard, St Johns, North Holmwood, Dorking, Surrey. Tel: (H) 0306 888731 (W) 0306 886661.
Club Colours: Red & white hoops, blue or white change.

EALING RUFC
Ground Address: Berkeley Avenue, Greenford, Middlesex. Tel: 081 422 0868.
Club Secretary: Damian Bugeja, 7 Bradley Gardens, Ealing, London, W13 8HE. Tel: (H) 081 997 9982 (W) 0344 872677.
Press Officer: Charles Miller, 5 Southdown Avenue, London, W7 2AG. Tel: (H) 081 579 6233 (W) 081 297 4248.
Club Colours: Dark green & white hoops, white shorts.

ETON MANOR RUFC
Ground Address: Eastway Sports Centre, Quarter Mile Lane, Leyton, London, E10. Tel: 081 519 0017.
Club Secretary: John Auyling, 44 Lytton Road, Leytonstone, London, E11 2JH. Tel: (H) 081 558 1800.
Press Officer: Frank Overland, 105 Whitehart Lane, Collier Row, Romford, Essex, RM7 RLX. Tel: (H) 07087 40342.
Club Colours: Dark blue with one light blue hoop.

GUILDFORD & GODALMING RFC
Ground Address: Guildford Road, Broadwater, Godalming, Surrey. Tel: 0483 416199.
Club Secretary: Alan Bird, The Old Barn, Gernhurst Green, Haslemere, Surrey, GU27 3HY. Tel:(H) 0428 653359.
Press Officer: D Roberts, 37 Manor Way, Onslow Village, Guildford, Surrey, GU2 5RP. Tel: (H) 0483 60016.
Club Colours: Green & white hoops.

HARLOW RUFC
Ground Address: Ram Gorse, Elizabeth Way, Harlow, Essex. Tel: 0279 429750.
Club Secretary: Jo Riddell, 5 Maple Avenue, Bishop's Stortford, Herts, CM23 2RP. Tel: (H) 0279 657596 (W) 071 465 5555.
Press Officer: Marcus Russell, 50 Broadfield, Broadhurst Gardens, London,m NW6 3BN. Tel: (H) 071 372 2339 (W) 071 706 2234.
Club Colours: Red with green collars and cuffs.

OLD ALLEYNIAN FC
Ground Address: Dulwich Common, London, SE21 7HA. Tel: 081 693 2402.

FINAL TABLE

	P	W	D	L	F	A	PD	Pts
Tabard	12	10	1	1	230	127	103	21
Ealing	12	10	0	2	212	118	94	20
Sutton & Epsom	12	6	3	3	177	145	32	15
Streatham-Croydon	12	6	2	4	169	138	31	14
Guildford & G'ming	12	7	0	5	185	168	17	14
Eton Manor	12	6	2	4	156	147	9	14
Barking	12	6	1	5	183	171	12	13
Old Colfeians	12	5	2	5	198	203	-5	12
Old Mid Whitgiftian	12	5	0	7	197	185	12	10
Old Alleynian	12	5	0	7	183	186	-3	10
Dorking	12	2	1	9	111	230	-119	5
Old Gaytonians	12	1	2	9	169	245	-76	4
Sidcup	12	2	0	10	134	241	-107	4

Club Secretary: D R Branscombe, 13 Gable Court, Lawrie Park Avenue, London, SE26 6HR. Tel: (H) 081 778 2868.
Press Officer: R A Crow, 13 Gable Court, Lawrie Park Avenue, London, SE26 6HR. Tel: (H) 081 778 2868.
Club Colours: Dark blue, light blue and black.

OLD COLFEIANS RFC
Ground Address: Horn Park, Eltham Road, Lee, London, SE12. Tel: 081 852 1181.
Club Secretary: D J Andrew, 80 Dallinger Road, Lee, London, SE12 0TH. Tel: (H) 081 857 4036 (W) 081 680 9011.
Press Officer: F Whiting, 31 Foxearth Road, Selsdon, Croydon, Surrey. Tel: (H) 081 657 5447.
Club Colours: Maroon, navy blue, old gold & black.

OLD MID-WHITGIFTIAN RFC
Ground Address: Lime Meadow Avenue, Sanderstead, Surrey, CR2 9AS. Tel: 081 657 2014.
League Contact: Andy Hillburn, 47A Foxearth Road, Selsdon, South Croydon, surrey, CR2 8EL. Tel: (H) 081 657 1825 (W) 071 917 8888 Ext 4435.
Press Officer: Terry McLaren, "The Stables", Old Surrey Hall, Nr East Grinstead, West sussex, RH19 3PR. Tel: (H) 0342 325 197.
Club Colours: Dark blue jerseys, shorts & socks.

STREATHAM & CROYDON RFC
Ground Address: Rosedale, 159 Bigstock Road, Thornton Heath, Surrey. Tel: 081 684 1502.
Club Secretary: R Towers, 24 Ernest Grove, Beckenham, Kent, BR3 3JF. Tel: (H) 081 658 2333.
Press Officer: Colin Ashton, 109 Tarp Road, Wallington, Surrey, SM6 8LQ. Tel: (H) 669 6092.
Club Colours: Maroon.

SUTTON & EPSOM RFC
Ground Address: Cuddington Court, Rugby Lane, West Drive, Cheam, Surrey, SM2 7NF. Tel: 081 642 0280.
Club Secretary: Brian A Moore, The Bungalow, Coulsdon Lane, Chipstead, Surrey, CR5 3QL. Tel: (H) 0737 553350.
Press Officer: John Ashton, 86 Wickham Avenue, Cheam, Surrey. Tel: (H) 081 644 9664.
Club Colours: Black & white hoops.

THURROCK RFC
Ground Address: "Oakfield", Long Lane, Grays, Essex. Tel: 0375 371887/0375 380641.
Club Secretary: K E Schooling, 10 School Lane, Orsett, Essex, RM16 3JS. Tel: 0375 891635 (W) 0375 390100.
Press Officer: E Pugh, 85 Gordon Road, Corringham, Essex. Tel: (H) 0375 676625.
Club Colours: Black & white hoops.

LONDON & SOUTH EAST DIVISION

LONDON TWO NORTH
1993-94
FIXTURES

October 23 (Week 8)
Brentwood v Norwich
Cheshunt v Old Edwardians
Ruislip v Finchley
Bishop's Stortford v Old Gaytonians
Upper Clapton v Woodford
Old Verulamians v Chingford

October 3O (Week X2)
Chingford v Brentwood
Woodford v Old Verulamians
Old Gaytonians v Upper Clapton
Finchley v Bishop's Stortford
Old Edwardians v Ruislip
Cambridge v Cheshunt

November 13 (Week 1O)
Brentwood v Woodford
Norwich v Chingford
Ruislip v Cambridge
Bishop's Stortford v Old Edwardians
Upper Clapton v Finchley
Old Verulamians v Old Gaytonians

November 2O (Week 11)
Woodford v Norwich
Old Gaytonians v Brentwood
Finchley v Old Verulamians
Old Edwardians v Upper Clapton
Cambridge v Bishop's Stortford
Cheshunt v Ruislip

December 4 (Week 13)
Brentwood v Finchley
Norwich v Old Gaytonians
Chingford v Woodford
Bishop's Stortford v Cheshunt
Upper Clapton v Cambridge
Old Verulamians v Old Edwardians

December 11 (Week 14)
Old Gaytonians v Chingford
Finchley v Norwich
Old Edwardians v Brentwood
Cambridge v Old Verulamians
Cheshunt v Upper Clapton
Ruislip v Bishop's Stortford

December 18 (Week 15)
Brentwood v Cambridge
Norwich v Old Edwardians
Chingford v Finchley
Woodford v Old Gaytonians
Upper Clapton v Ruislip
Old Verulamians v Cheshunt

January 8 (Week 18)
Finchley v Woodford
Old Edwardians v Chingford
Cambridge v Norwich
Cheshunt v Brentwood
Ruislip v Old Verulamians
Bishop's Stortford v Upper Clapton

January 29 (Week X5)
Brentwood v Ruislip
Norwich v Cheshunt
Chingford v Cambridge
Woodford v Old Edwardians
Old Gaytonians v Finchley
Old Verulamians v Bishop' Stortford

February 12 (Week 22)
Old Edwardians v Old Gaytonians
Cambridge v Woodford
Cheshunt v Chingford
Ruislip v Norwich
Bishop's Stortford v Brentwood
Upper Clapton v Old Verulamians

March 12 (Week 26)
Brentwood v Upper Clapton
Norwich v Bishop's Stortford
Chingford v Ruislip
Woodford v Cheshunt
Old Gaytonians v Cambridge
Finchley v Old Edwardians

March 26 (Week 28)
Cambridge v Finchley
Cheshunt v Old Gaytonians
Ruislip v Woodford
Bishop's Stortford v Chingford
Upper Clapton v Norwich
Old Verulamians v Brentwood

April 9 (Week 3O)
Norwich v Old Verulamians
Chingford v Upper Clapton
Woodford v Bishop's Stortford
Old Gaytonians v Ruislip
Finchley v Cheshunt
Old Edwardians v Cambridge

410

LONDON TWO NORTH

BISHOP'S STORTFORD RFC
Ground Address: Silver Leys, Hadham Road, Bishop's
Stortford, Herts, CM23 2QE. Tel: 0279 6520925.
Club Secretary: John Robinson, 193 Heath Row, Bishop's
Stortford, Herts, CM23 5BX. Tel: (H) 0279 657104 (W)
0582 24182.
Press Officer: Mike Howatson, 14 The Stewarts, Bishop's
Stortford, Herts, CM23 2NT. Tel: (H) 0279 659278 (W)
0923 245991.
Club Colours: Royal blue & white.

BRENTWOOD RFC
Ground Address: King George's Playing Field, Ingrave
Road, Brentwood, Essex Tel: 0277 210267.
Club Secretary: RW Glasby, 30 Painwick Road,
Stanford-le-Hope, Essex SS17 8HR. Tel: (H) 0375 671755
(W) 0702 74496.
Press Officer: E Shaw, 32 Wellesley Road, Brentwood,
Essex. Tel: (H) 0277 232548 (W) 081 861 0500.
Club Colours: Claret, grey and white hoops.

CAMBRIDGE RUFC
Ground Address: Grantchester Road, Cambridge, CB3
9ED. Tel: 0223 312437.
Club Secretary: DJ Martin, 45 York Street, Cambridge,
CB1 2PZ. Tel: (H) 0223 314705 (W) 0223 355682.
Press Officer: K Walker, 7 Lucketts Close, Histon,
Cambridge. Tel: (H) 0223 234874 (W) 081 967 2024.
Club Colours: Scarlet & amber hoops, white shorts.

CHESHUNT RFC
Ground Address: Rosedale Sports Club, Andrews Lane,
Cheshunt, Herts. Tel: 0992 623983.
Club Secretary: Roland Jackson, 18 Churchbury Road,
Enfield, Middlesex, EN1 3HR. Tel: (H) 0814 342 0329 (W)
071 283 6293.
Press Officer: Peter Goodwin, 20 Wavel Close, Cheshunt,
Herts, EN8 0LA. Tel: (H) 0992 633161.
Club Colours: Green & white jerseys, white shorts, red socks.

CHINGFORD RFC
Ground Address: Lea Valley Playing Fields, Waltham
Way, Chingford, London, E4 7SR. Tel: 081 529 4879.
Club Secretary: J M Carratt, 24 Alpha Road, Chingford,
London, E4 6TB. Tel: (H) 081 524 2005 (W) 081 876 3434
Ext 2426.
Press Officer: M Fulbrook, 35 Lower Park Road,
Loughton, Essex. Tel: (H) 081 508 3093.
Club Colours: Black with blue & white hoops, white shorts.

FINCHLEY RFC
Ground Address: Summers Lane, Finchley, N12 0PD.
Tel: 081 445 7568.
Club Secretary: S Clough, 91 Arcadian Gardens, London,
N22 5AG. Tel: (H) 081 888 6526 (W) 081 472 1450.
Press Officer: M Clark, 224 Long Lane, Finchley, London,
N3 2RN. Tel: (H) 081 349 7915 (W) 071 379 7900.
Club Colours: Red & white hoops.

NORWICH RFC
Ground Address: Beeston Hyrne, North Walsham Road,
Norwich, NR12 7BW. Tel: 0603 426259.
Club Secretary: Chris Gilham, Eversheds, Paston house,
Princes Street, Norwich, NR5 1BD. Tel: (H) 0603 58439
(W) 0603 660241.
Press Officer: Roy Bishop, 29 Henby Way, Avenue Green,
Thorpe St Andrew, Norwich. Tel: (H) 0603 36504.
Club Colours: Maroon, green & gold jerseys, blue shorts.

OLD EDWARDIANS RFC
Ground Address: Westlands Playing Fields, London
Road, Romford, Essex.
Club Secretary: P J Hensher, 108 Stanley Avenue, Gidea
Park, Romford, Essex. Tel: (H) 0708 764474 (W) 081 597 1126

FINAL TABLE

	P	W	D	L	F	A	PD	Pts
Harlow	12	11	1	0	327	124	203	23
Cheshunt	12	8	1	3	238	167	71	17
Ruislip	12	8	0	4	209	180	29	16
Finchley	12	8	0	4	196	140	56	14
Norwich	12	6	2	4	182	131	51	14
Bishop's Dtortford	12	7	0	5	176	131	45	14
Cambridge	12	5	1	6	109	141	-32	11
Chingford	12	4	0	8	121	182	-61	8
Upper Clapton	12	3	0	9	125	164	-39	6
Old Edwardians	12	2	1	9	110	319	-209	5
Lensbury	12	4	0	8	127	193	-66	2
Ipswich	12	1	0	11	100	252	-152	2

Press Officer: Robert Brittle, 79 Maldmay Road, Romford,
Essex. Tel: (H) 0708 767209 (W) 0277253233.
Club Colours: Navy shirts, white shorts, red socks.

OLD GAYTONIANS RFC
Ground Address: South Vale, Harrow, Middlesex, HA1
3PN. Tel: 081 423 4133.
Club Secretary: A P Usher, 9 Paynesfield Road, Bushey
Heath, Herts, WD2 1PQ. Tel: (H) 081 950 2956 (W) 081
866 8062.
Press Officer: Chris Cone, 17 Fairholme Road, Harrow,
Middlesex, HA1 2LT. Tel: (H) 081 863 3369.
Club Colours: White with broad band of chocolate, light
blue & green.

OLD VERULAMIAN RFC
Ground Address: Cottlandswick, London Colney, Nr St
Albans, Herts. Tel: 0727 822929.
Club Secretary: Tony Charlwood, 12 Waverley Road, St
Albans, Herts. Tel: (H) 0727 846923 (W) 071 782 2207.
Press Officer: Phil Greenwood, 37 Claydown Way, Slip
End, Near Luton, Beds, LU9 4DU. Tel: (H) 0582
33758(W) 0727 824546.
Club Colours: Royal blue with yellow "v", white shorts.

RUISLIP RFC
Ground Address: West End Road, Ruislip, Middlesex.
Tel: 08956 33102.
Club Secretary: Michael Searls, 16 Parkway,
Rickmansworth, Herts, WD3 2AT. Tel: (H) 0923 773903.
Press Officer: Michael Searls, 16 Parkway,
Rickmansworth, Herts, WD3 2AT. Tel: (H) 0923 773903.
Club Colours: Maroon & white hoops, white shorts.

UPPER CLAPTON FC
Ground Address: The Clubhouse, Upland Road, Thornwood
Common, Nr Epping, Essex, CM16 6NL. Tel: 0992 572588.
Club Secretary: David Miller, 13 Rushfield, Sawbridgworth,
Herts, CM21 9NF.Tel: (H) 0279 724849 (W) 081 309 6398.
Press Officer: Richard Hookham, 1 Newtown Road,
Bishop's Stortford, Herts. Tel: (H) 0279 757704 (W) 0279
420333.
Club Colours: Red & white 7" hoops.

WOODFORD RFC
Ground Address: Highams, Woodford High Road,
Woodford Green, Essex, IG8 9LB. Tel: 081 504 6769.
Club Secretary: R F Perryman, 7 Brancepeth Gardence,
Buckhurst Hill, Essex, IG9 5JL. Tel: (H) 081 505 5973 (W)
081 556 9721.
Press Officer: N Levis, Imerton road, Walthamstow, 9DE
E17. Tel: (H) 081 521 9336 (W) 071 956 1802.
Club Colours: white, lavender & black.

LONDON & SOUTH EAST DIVISION

LONDON THREE
NORTH WEST
1993-1994 FIXTURES

December 18 (Week 15)

Letchworth v Kingsburians
Old Meadonians v Old Albanians
London New Zealand v Old Merchant Taylors
Grasshoppers v Fullerians
Old Elizabethans v Staines
Lenbury v Welwyn

October 23 (Week 8)

Letchworth v Old Meadonians
Welwyn v Old Albanians
Staines v Old Merchant Taylors
Hertford v Fullerians
Old Elizabethans v Grasshoppers
Lensbury v London New Zealand

January 8 (Week 18)

Old Merchant Taylors v Grasshoppers
Old Albanians v London New Zealand
Kingsburians v Old Meadonians
Welwyn v Letchworth
Staines v Lensbury
Hertford v Old Elizabethans

October 3O (Week X2)

London New Zealand v Letchworth
Grasshoppers v Lensbury
Fullerians v Old Elizabethans
Old Merchant Taylors v Hertford
Old Albanians v Staines
Kingsburians v Welwyn

January 29 (Week X5)

Letchworth v Staines
Old Meadonians v Welwyn
London New Zealand v Kingsburians
Grasshoppers v Old Albanians
Fullerians v Old Merchant Taylors
Lensbury v Hertford

November 13 (Week 1O)

Letchworth v Grasshoppers
Old Meadonians v London New Zealand
Staines v Kingsburians
Hertford v Old Albanians
Old Elizabethans v Old Merchant Taylors
Lensbury v Fullerians

February 12 (Week 22)

Old Albanians v Fullerians
Kingsburians v Grasshoppers
Welwyn v London New Zealand
Staines v Old Meadonians
Hertford v Letchworth
Old Elizabethans v Lensbury

November 2O (Week 11)

Grasshoppers v Old Meadonians
Fullerians v Leychworth
Old Merchant Taylors v Lensbury
Old Albanians v Old Elizabethans
Kingsburians v Hertford
Welwyn v Staines

March 12 (Week 26)

Letchworth v Old Elizabethans
Old Meadonians v Hertford
London New Zealand v Staines
Grasshoppers v Welwyn
Fullerians v Kingsburians
Old Merchant Taylors v Old Albanians

December 4 (Week 13)

Letchworth v Old Merchant Taylors
Old Meadonians v Fullerians
London New Zealand v Grasshoppers
zHertford v Welwyn
Old Elizabethans v Kingsburians
Lensbury v Old Albanians

March 26 (Week 28)

Kingsburians v Old Merchant Taylors
Welwyn v Fullerians
Staines v Grasshoppers
Hertford v London New Zealand
Old Elizabethans v Old Meadonians
Lensbury v Letchworth

December 11 (Week 14)

Fullerians v London New Zealand
Old Merchant Taylors v Old Meadonians
Old Albanians v Letchworth
Kingsburians v Lensbury
Welwyn v Old Elizabethans
Staines v Hertford

April 9 (Week 3O)

Old Meadonians v Lensbury
London New Zealand v Old Elizabethans
Grasshoppers v Hertford
Fullerians v Staines
Old Merchant Taylors v Welwyn
Old Albanians v Kingsburians

LONDON THREE NORTH WEST

GRASSHOPPERS RFC
Ground Address: MacFarlane Sports Field, MacFarlane Lane, Off Syon Lane, Osterley, Middlesex. Tel: 081 568 0010. **Club Secretary:** A J Huckle, 142 West Drayton Road, Hillingdon,Middlesex, UB8 3LF. Tel: (H) 081 561 6164 (W) 07535 31261 Ext 3583.

FULLERIANS RFC
Ground Address: Watford Grammar School, New Field, Coningesby Drive, Watford, Hertfordshire. Tel: 0923 224483. **Club Secretary:** Ernest Coombs, 53 Wren Crescent, Bushey, Watford, WD2 1AN. Tel: (H) 081 950 3453. **Press Officer:** John Ayres, 9 Church Grove, Little Chalfont, Buckinghamshire, HP6 6SH. Tel: (H) 0494 763266 (W) 081 469 2244.
Club Colours: Black red & green hoops, white shorts.

HERTFORD RFC
Ground Address: Highfields Hoe Lane, Ware, Herts, SG12 9NZ. Tel: 0920 462975.
Club Secretary: A K Sparks, 29 Wilton Crescent, Hertford, SG13 8JS. Tel: (H) 0992 589364 (W) 0279 439161. **Press Officer:** A Bouaird, 45 Byde Street, Hertford, Hertfordshire. Tel: (H) 0992 589498.
Club Colours: Black, royal blue & gold jerseys, black shorts.

KINGSBURIANS RFC
Ground Address: Northwick Park Pavillion, Northwick Park Open Space, The Fairway, South Kenton, Middlesex. Tel: 081 904 4414.
Club Secretary: Bruce Bland, 10 Clitheroe Avenue, Rayners Lane, Harrow, HA2 9UX. Tel: (H) 081 868 5244 (W) 081 204 4442. **Press Officer:** Brian Jones, 46 Woodcock Hill, Kenton, Harrow, Middlesex. Tel: (H) 081 907 8220 (W) 081 907 8220.
Club Colours: Black & amber hoops, black shorts and socks.

LENSBURY RFC
Ground Address: Broom Road, Teddington, Middlesex. Tel: 081 977 8821.
Club Secretary: Sandy Riach, 51 Keswick Avenue, Kingston Vale, London, SW15 3QH. Tel: (H) 081 546 8267 (W) 0784 245058.
Club Colours: Purple, gold & black hoops.

LETCHWORTH GARDEN CITY RUFC
Ground Address: Baldock Road, Letchworth, Hertfordshire. Tel: 0462 682554.
Club Secretary: John Donegan, 9 Byrd Walk, Baldock, Hertfordshire, SG7 6LN. Tel: (H) 0462 491360 (W) 0462 442800.
Club Colours: Black & amber hoops, black shorts.

LONDON NEW ZEALAND RFC
Ground Address: Osterley Sports & Social Club, Tentglow Lane, Norwood Green, Southall, Middlesex. Tel: 081 574 3774.
Club Secretary: Tudor Oavies, 46 Lamorna Grove, Stanmore, HA7 1PQ. Tel: (H) 081 952 6822 (W) 071 723 0022. **Press Officer:** Wendy Whitchurch, 25 Cansury Avenue, Kingston, Surrey, KT2 6JP. Tel: (H) 081 546 3647 (W) 071 630 9696.
Club Colours: Black.

OLD ALBANIAN RFC
Ground Address: Beech Bottom, Old Harpenden Road, St Albans, Hertfordshire. Tel: 0727 864476.
Club Secretary: Peter Lipscomb, 35 Gurney Court Road, St Albans, Herfordshire, AL1 4QU. Tel: (H) 0727 863621 (W) 081 784 5924. **Press Officer:** Robin Hardwick, 11 Heath Road, St Albans, Hertfordshire. Tel: 0727 831476.
Club Colours: Red, blue & gold hoops, white shorts.

FINAL TABLE

	P	W	D	L	F	A	PD	Pts
Old Verulamians	12	11	0	1	312	108	204	22
Letchworth	12	11	0	1	268	102	166	22
Staines	12	9	0	3	252	129	123	18
Old Elizabethians	12	7	1	4	168	128	40	15
Welwyn	12	6	0	6	141	125	16	12
Old Merch Taylors	12	6	0	6	191	196	-5	12
Fullerians	12	5	1	6	177	203	-26	11
Grasshoppers	12	5	0	7	172	1168	4	10
Kinsburians	12	5	0	7	165	196	-31	10
Old Albanians	12	4	1	7	135	171	-36	9
Hertford	12	4	1	7	141	187	-46	9
Old Millhillians	12	2	0	10	77	274	-197	4
Harpenden	12	1	0	11	109	321	-212	2

OLD ELIZABETHAN'S (BARNET) RFC
Ground Address: Gibpsy Corner, Hays Lane, Barnet, Hertfordshire. Tel:081 449 9481.
Club Secretary: Nigel Ward, 82 Barnet Road, Potters Bar, Hertfordshire, EN6 2RD. Tel: (H) 0707 658066 (W) 071 753 1871. **Press Officer:** Peter Yates, 3 Manor Court, Mutton Lane, Potters Bar, Hertfordshire, EN6 2AA. Tel: 0707 644046 (W) 0707 662222.
Club Colours: Light & dark blue hoops.

OLD MEADONIANS RFC
Ground Address: Riverside Lands, Chiswick, London, W4. Tel: 081 994 6956.
Club Secretary: Robert Udwin, 62 Somerset Road, Chiswick, London, SE23. Tel: (H) 081 994 6623 (W)081 994 6623. **Press Officer:** Jack Sane, 17 Paxton Road, Forest Hill, London, SE23. Tel: (H) 081 291 9233 (W) 081 871 4611.
Club Colours: Maroon & blue hoops.

OLD MERCHANT TAYLORS' FC
Ground Address: "Durrants", Lincoln Way, Croxley Green, Hertfordshire, WD3 3ND. Tel: 0923 773014.
Club Secretary: M G Foster, The White House, 16 New Road, Croxley Green, Hertfordshire, WD3 3EL. Tel: (H) 0923 775793. **Press Officer:** M G Foster, The White House, 16 New Road, Croxley Green, Hertfordshire, WD3 3EL. Tel: (H) 0923 775793.

STAINES RFC
Ground Address: "The Reeves", Feltham Hill Road, Hanworth, Middlesex, TW13 7NB. Tel: 081 890 3051.
Club Secretary: W R Johnston, 4 April Close, Feltham, Middlesex, TW13 7JQ. Tel: (H) 081 890 1844 (W) 081 759 2141 Ext 233. **Press Officer:** John King, 24 Ailsa Avenue, St Margarets, Twickenham, TW1 1NG. Tel: (H) 081 892 9056. (W) 081 892 3637.
Club Colours: Red & blue hoops, white shorts.

WELWYN RFC
Ground Address: Hobbs Way, Colgrove, Wlwyn Garden City, Hertfordshire. Tel: 0707 329116.
Club Secretary: J M Sargeant, 67 Woodhall Lane, Welwyn Garden City, Herts, AL7 3TG. Tel: (H) 0707 331186 (W) 0707 326318. **Press Officer:** P Edgerley, 7 The Reddings, Welwyn Garden City, Hertfordshire. Tel: (H) 0707 325248.
Club Colours: Maroon & white hoops, blue shorts.

LONDON & SOUTH EAST DIVISION

HERTFORDSHIRE/ MIDDLESEX ONE 1993-94 FIXTURES

October 23 (Week 8)
Harrow v Hemel Hempstead
Hitchin v Centaurs
Barnet v St. Mary's Hospital
Hampstead v Hendon
Antlers v Harpenden
Old Millhillians v Haringey

October 3O (Week X2)
Haringey v Harrow
Harpenden v Old Milhillians
Hendon v Antlers
St.Mary's Hospital v Hampstead
Centaurs v Barnet
Uxbridge v Hitchin

November 13 (Week 1O)
Harrow v Harpenden
Hemel Hempstead v Haringey
Barnet v Uxbridge
Hampstead v Centaurs
Antlers v St Mary's Hospital
Old Millhillians v Hendon

November 2O (Week 11)
Harpenden v Hemel Hempstead
Hendon v Harrow
St. Mary's Hospital v Old Millhillians
Centaurs v Antlers
Uxbridge v Hampstead
Hitchin v Barnet

December 4 (Week 13)
Harrow v St. Mary's Hospital
Hemel Hempstead v Hendon
Haringey v Harpenden
Hampstead v Hitchin
Antlers v Uxbridge
Old Millhillians v Centaurs

December 11 (Week 14)
Hendon v Haringey
St. Mary's Hospital v Hemel Hempstead
Centaurs v Harrow
Uxbridge v Old Millhillians
Hitchin v Antlers
Barnet v Hampstead

December 18 (Week 15)
Harrow v Uxbridge
Hemel Hempstead v Centaurs
Haringey v St. Mary's Hospital
Harpenden v Hendon
Antlers v Barnet
Old Millhillians v Hitchin

January 8 (Week 18)
St Mary's Hospital v Harpenden
Centaurs v Haringey
Uxbridge v Hemel Hempstead
Hitchin v Harrow
Barnet v Old Millhillians
Hampstead v Antlers

Jnauary 29 (Week X5)
Harrow v Barnet
Hemel Hempstead v Hitchin
Haringey v Uxbridge
Harpenden v Centaurs
Hendon v St.Mary's Hospital
Old Millhillians v Hampstead

Febrary 12 Week 22)
Centaurs v Hendon
Uxbridge v Harpenden
Hitchin v Haringey
Barnet v Hemel Hempstead
Hampstead v Harrow
Antlers v Old Millhillians

March 12 (Week 26)
Harrow v Antlers
Hemel Hempstead v Hampstead
Haringey v Barnet
Harpenden v Hitchin
Hendon v Uxbridge
St. Mary's Hospital v Centaurs

March 26 (Week 28)
Uxbridge v St Mary's Hospital
Hitchin v Hendon
Barnet v Harpenden
Hampstead v Haringey
Antlers v Hemel Hempstead
Old Millhillians v Harrow

April 9 (Week 3O)
Hemel Hempstead v Old Mllhillians
Haringey v Antlers
Harpenden v Hampstead
Hendon v Barnet
St. Mary's Hospital v Hitchin
Centaurs v Uxbridge

HERTFORDSHIRE AND MIDDLESEX ONE

ANTLERS RFC
Ground Address: Bushy Park, Teddington, Middlesex.
Tel: 081 977 4989.
Club Secretary: Peter Woolgar, 114 Elfin Avenue,
Ashford, Middlesex, TW15 1QG. Tel: (H) 0784 259734.
Press Officer: G Lambourn, 12 Manygate Lane,
Shepperton, TW17 9ED. Tel: (H) 0932 225195.
Club Colours: Dark Blue.

BARNET RFC
Ground Address: Byng Road, Barnet, Hertfordshire. Tel:
081 449 0040.
Club Secretary: Nigel Oram, Salisbury Cottage, Essendon,
Hertfordshire, AL9 6AU. Tel: (H) 07072 68481 (W) 071
621 1224.
Press Officer: Maurice Martin, 20 North Mount,
1147/1161 High Road, Whetstone, London, N20 0PH. Tel:
(H) 081 446 4401 (W) 081 343 7748.
Club Colours: Dark blue & claret.

CENTAURS RFC
Ground Address: Gower Road, Syon Lane, Osterley,
Middlesex. Tel: 560 4500.
Club Secretary: Alan G Tucker, 38 Haven Lane, Ealing,
London, W5 2HN. Tel: (H) 081 997 2894 (W) 071 628 3844.
Press Officer: Simon East, 29 Mount Park Road, Ealing,
W5 2RS. Tel: (H) 081 997 3339 (W) 081 567 2242.
Club Colours: Light blue & dark blue hoops.

HAMPSTEAD RFC
Ground Address: Hampstead Heath Extension,
Hampstead Way, London, NW11.
Club Secretary: Stephen Loffler, 14 Grey Close, London,
NW11 6QG. Tel: (H) 081 458 6512(W) 081 759 4822.
Press Officer: Rowley Hill, Jack Straws Castle, North End
Way, London, NW3. Tel: (H) 071 435 8885 (W) 071 435
8885.
Club Colours: Yellow, claret & white.

HARINGEY RFC
Ground Address: New River Sports Centre, White Hart
Lane, Wood Green, London, N22 5QW. Tel: 081 888 9299
(Clubhouse) 081 881 1926 (Reception).
Club Secretary: Glynne Jones, 44 Park Hall Road, East
Finchley, London, N2 9PX. Tel: (H) 081 883 8091.
Club Colours: Green, scarlet & white.

HARPENDEN RFC
Ground Address: Redbourn Lane, Harpenden,
Hertfordshire. Tel: 0582 460711.
Club Secretary: Mike Aldous-Ball, 4 Wells Close,
Harpenden, Hertfordshire, AL5 3LQ. Tel: (H) 0582 461527.
Club Colours: Brown & white quartered shirts.

HARROW RUFC
Ground Address: Grove Field, Wood Lane, Stanmore
Hill, Stanmore, Middlesex. Tel: 081 954 2615.
Club Secretary: David Niccol, 3 Coledale Drive,
Stanmore, Middlesex, HA7 2QB. Tel: (H) 081 907 5867.
Press Officer: John Church, 110 Villiers Road, Oxhey,
Watford, Hertfordshire, WD1 4AJ. Tel: (H) 0923 240348.
Club Colours: Navy blue & white.

HEMEL HEMPSTEAD (CAMELOT) RUFC
Ground Address: The Clubhouse, Chaulden Lane, Hemel
Hempstead, Hertfordshire, HP1 2BS. Tel: (Admin) 0442
230353 (Public) 0442 213408.
Club Secretary: John Clapham, 49 Brook Court, Watling
Street, Radlett, Hertfordshire, WD7 7JA. Tel: (H) 0923
852104.
Press Officer: Johnm Bartholomew, "Badgers Hollow",
Shenstone Hill, Berkhamsted, HP4 2PA. Tel: (H) 0442
871091 (W) 0442 63871.
Club Colours: Royal blue with white hoop.

FINAL TABLE

	P	W	D	L	F	A	PD	Pts
Old Meadonians	12	10	2	0	162	88	74	22
London N Zealand	12	8	3	1	183	68	115	19
Centaurs	12	7	0	5	258	169	89	14
Hendon	11	7	0	4	128	94	34	14
Haringey	12	8	0	4	165	142	23	14
Antlers	12	5	1	6	160	184	-24	11
Uxbridge	11	5	0	6	99	116	-17	10
Harrow	12	5	0	7	120	154	-34	10
St Mary's Hospital	12	5	0	7	156	222	-66	10
Hemel Hempstead	12	4	0	8	169	191	-22	8
Hitchin	12	3	1	8	175	184	-9	7
Twickenham	12	4	1	7	145	197	-52	7
Stevenage	12	2	0	10	68	241	-173	4

HENDON RFC
Ground Address: Copthall Playing Fields, Great North
Way, Hendon, London NW4. Tel: 081 203 1737.
Club Secretary: R J Brown, 36 Oldhill, Dunstable,
Bedfordshire. Tel: (H) 0582 6000.
Press Officer: M Wood, 60 Stafford Road, Barnet, Herts,
EN5 4LR.
Club Colours: Bottle green, black, white.

HITCHIN RFC
Ground Address: King George V Playing Field, Old Hale
Way, Hitchin. Tel: 0462 432679.
Club Secretary: Steve Ward, 73 Millstream Close,
Hitchin, Hertfordshire, SG4 0DB. Tel: (H) 0462 455358.
Press Officer: Steve Pike, 63 Grays Lane, Hitchin,
Hertfordshire. Te;l: (H) 0462 420107.
Club Colours: Maroon jerseys, white shorts.

OLD MILLHILLIANS RFC
Ground Address: Pinner Park, Headstone Lane, Harrow,
Middlesex HA2 6BR. Tel: 081 428 2281.
Club Secretary: M Leon, Wildacre, Bushfield Road,
Bovingdon, Hertfordshire, HP3 0DR. Tel: 0442 833665.
Club Colours: Chocolate & white hoops.

ST MARY'S HOSPITAL RFC
Ground Address: Udney Park Road, Teddington,
Middlesex. Tel: 081 977 3100.
Club Secretary: R Young, West Middlesex hospital,
Twickenham Road, Isleworth, Middlesex, TW7 6AF. Tel:
(H) 081 891 0638 (W) 081 565 5768.
Press Officer: Dr M Poulter, 149 Park Road, Chiswick,
W4 3EX. Tel: (H) 081 747 0248 (W) 071 380 7606.
Club Colours: Blue shirts & shorts, white fleur de lys on
breast.

UXBRIDGE RFC
Ground Address: Uxbridge Cricket Club, Park Road,
Uxbridge, UB8 1NR. Tel: 0895 237571.
Club Secretary: Richard Jones, 103 Swakeleys Road,
Ickenham, Middlesex UB10 8DH. Tel: (H) 0895 675387
(W) 071 356 8806.
Press Officer: Malcolm NIcholson, 103 Clyfford Road,
Ruislip, Middlesex, HA4 6PX. Tel: (H) 0895 632067 (W)
0426 91479.
Club Colours: Red, black & white hooped shirts, black
shorts.

LONDON & SOUTH EAST DIVISION

MIDDLESEX ONE
1993-94
FIXTURES

October 23 (Week 8)
Roxeth Manor O B v Twickenham
Old Actonians v Wembley
Old Hamptonians v Old Abbotstonians
Hammersmith & F'm v Old Haberdashers
Mill Hill v Civil Service
Hackney v Sudbury Court

October 30 (Week X2)
Sudbury Court v Roxeth Manor O B
Civil Service v Hackney
Old Haberdashers v Mill Hill
Old Abbotstonians v Hammersmith & F'm
Wembley v Old Hamptonians
Old Isleworthian v Old Actonians

November 13 (Week 10)
Roxeth Manor O B v Civil Service
Twickenham v Sudbury Court
Old Hamptonians v Old Isleworthians
Hammersmith & F'm v Wembley
Mill Hill v Old Abbotstonians
Hackney v Old Haberdashers

November 20 (Week 11)
Civil Service v Twickenham
Old Haberdashers v Roxeth Manor O B
Old Abbotstonians v Hackney
Wembley v Mill Hill
Old Isleworthians v Hammersmith & F'm
Old Actonians v Old Hamptonians

December 4 (Week 13)
Roxeth Manor O B v Old Abbotstonians
Twickenham v Old Haberdashers
Sudbury Court v Civil Service
Hammersmith & F'm v Old Actonians
Mill Hill v Old Isleworthians
Hackney v Wembley

December 11 (Week 14)
Old Haberdashers v Sudbury Court
Old Abbotstonians v Twickenham
Wembley v Roxeth Manor O B
Old Isleworthians v Hackney
Old Actonians v Mill Hill
Old Hamptonians v Hammersmith & F'm

December 18 (Week 15)
Roxeth Manor O B v Old Isleworthians
Twickenham v Wembley
Sudbury Court v Old Abbotstonians
Civil Service v Old Haberdashers
Mill Hill v Old Hamptonians
Hackney v Old Actonians

January 8 (Week 18)
Old Abbotstonians v Civil Service
Wembley v Sudbury Court
Old Isleworthians v Twickenham
Old Actonians v Roxeth Manor O B
Old Hamptonians v Hackey
Hammersmith & F'm v Mill Hill

January 29 (Week X5)
Roxeth Manor O B v Old Hamptonians
Twickenham v Old Actonians
Sudbury Court v Old Isleworthians
Civil Service v Wembley
Old Haberdashers v Old Abbotstonians
Hackney v Hammersmith & F'm

February 12 (Week 22)
Wembley v Old Haberdashers
Old Isleworthians v Civil Service
Old Actonians v Sudbury Court
Old Hamptonians v Twickenham
Hammersmith & F'm v Roxeth Manor O B
Mill Hill v Hackney

March 12 (Week 26)
Roxeth Manor Old Bo v Mill Hill
Twickenham v Hammersmith & F'm
Sudbury Court v Old Hamptonians
Civil Service v Old Actonians
Old Haberdashers v Old Isleworthians
Old Abbotstonians v Wembley

March 26 (Week 28)
Old Isleworthians v Old Abbotstonians
Old Actonians v Old Haberdashers
Old Hamptonians v Civil Service
Hammersmith & F'm v Sudbury Court
Mill Hill v Twickenham
Hackney v Roxeth Manor O B

April 9 (Week 30
Twickenham v Hackney
Sudbury Court v Mill Hill
Civil Service v Hammersmith & F'm
Old Haberdashers v Old Hamptonians
Old Abbotstonians v Old Actonians
Wembley v Old Isleworthians

MIDDLESEX ONE

CIVIL SERVICE RUFC
Ground Address: Civil Service Sports Ground, Dukes Meadows, Riverside Drive, London, W4. Tel: 081 994 1202/2343.
Club Secretary: N G Alway, 20 Herndon Road, London, SW18 2DG. Tel: (H) 081 870 6818 (W) 071 583 5333./
Press Officer: Steve Barry, 149 Village Way, Beckenham, BR3 3WL. Tel: (H) 081 650 2945.
Club Colours: White shirts, blue shorts.

HACKNEY RFC
Ground Address: Springhill Ground, Springhill, Hackney, London, E5. Tel: 081 806 5289.
Club Secretary: H Gross, 41 Norlington Road, Leytonstone, London, E11 4BE. Tel: (H) 081 558 9543 (W) 081 558 9543.
Press Officer: F Harris, 36 Crosby Road, Dagenham, Essex, RM10 9AS. Tel: (W) 0831 625682.
Club Colours: Gold, green & blue quarters.

HAMMERSMITH & FULHAM RFC
Ground Address: Hurlingham Stadium, Hurlingham Park, London, SW6. Tel: 071 736 5186.
Club Secretary: Chris Cuthbertson, 17 Wheatshife Wharf, Wheatsheaf Lane, London, SW6 6LS. Tel: (H) 071 381 5064 (W) 0252 875075.
Press Officer: Andrew Barrett, 22 Cornwall Gardens, South Kensington, London, SW7. Tel: (H) 071 937 7862 (W) 071 258 0066.
Club Colours: Red with blue & white bands.

MILL HILL RFC
Ground Address: Page Street, Mill Hill, London, NW7. Tel: 081 203 0685.
Club Secretary: P J Braddock, 43 Winstre Road, Boreham Wood, Hertfordshire, WD6 5DR. Tel: (H) 081 953 6500 (W) 081 953 6500.
Press Officer: D Munro, 193 Woodcote Avenue, Mill Hill, London, NW7. Tel: (H) 081 906 0327 (W) 081 906 0327.
Club Colours: Chocolate & gold hoops.

OLD ABBOTSTONIANS RFC
Ground Address: Pole Hill Open Spaces, Raeburn Road, Hayes, Middlesex. Tel: 081 845 1452.
Club Secretary: Glen Baptista, 72 Sutton Court Road, Hillingdon, Middlesex, UB10 9HR. Tel: 0895 231748 (W) 071 798 7699.
Press Officer: Michael Harper, 42 Sussex Road, Ickenham,. Middlesex, UB10 8PN.
Club Colours: Blue & red quarters.

OLD ACTONIANS RFC
Ground Address: Gunnersbury Drive, Popes Lane, Ealing, London W5 4LL. Tel: 081 567 4556.
Club Secretary: J Hambly, 70A Oaklands Road, Hanwell, London, W7 2DU. Tel: (H) 081 567 1764 (W) 081 543 6533.
Press Officer: P Robinson, Flat 2, 36 Creffield Road, London, W5. Tel: (H) 081 993 1936.
Club Colours: Blue & white hoops, red collars.

OLD HABERDASHERS RFC
Ground Address: Croxdale Road, Theobald Street, Borehamwood, Hertfordshire, WD6 4PY. Tel: 081 953 1987.
Club Secretary: A J S Alexander, 26 Little Bushey Lane, Bushey Heath, Hertfordshire. Tel: (H) 081 950 1495.
Press Officer: J Hanson, The Castle, School Lane, Old Bricket Wood, Nr St Albans, Hertfordshire. Tel: (H) 0923 673267 (W) 081 953 2178.
Club Colours: Blue, white & magenta.

OLD HAMPTONIANS RFC
Ground Address: Dean Road, Hampton, Middlesex. Tel: 081 979 2784.

FINAL TABLE

	P	W	D	L	F	A	PD	Pts
Hampstead	12	11	0	1	371	71	300	22
Mill Hill	12	10	1	1	343	107	236	21
Roxeth Manor OB	12	9	0	3	192	120	72	18
Old Haberdashers	12	8	0	4	221	101	120	16
Wembley	12	8	0	4	196	138	58	16
Civil Service	12	6	1	5	160	138	22	13
Old Abbotsonians	12	5	1	6	155	179	-24	11
Hackney	12	5	1	6	100	166	-66	9
Sudbury Court	12	4	0	8	105	140	-35	8
Ham'smlth & Fulhm	12	4	0	8	104	246	-142	8
Old Isleworthians	12	3	0	9	121	184	-63	6
Old Grammarians	12	2	0	10	89	251	-162	2
Orleans FP	12	1	0	11	78	411	-333	0

Club Secretary: M M Fegan, 85 Park Road, Teddington, Middlesex, TW11 0AW. Tel: (H) 081 977 5341 (W) 071 624 1822.
Club Colours: Black, gold & silver hoops, black shorts.

OLD ISLEWORTHIANS RFC
Ground Address: The Memorial Ground, Wood Lane, Isleworth, Middlesex. Tel: 081 560 7949.
Club Secretary: Kevin Tighe, 40 Douglas Lane, Wraysbury, Staines, Middlesex. Tel: (H) 0784 482622 (W) 071 696 6684.
Club Colours: Blue with horizontal red bank & grey stripe.

ROXETH MANOR OLD BOYS RFC
Ground Address: City of Westminster, Harrow College of Further Education, Watford Road, Harrow, Middlesex.
Club Secretary: D R Pearham, 26 Yeading Avenue, Harrow, Middlesex, HA2 9RN. Tel: (H) 081 868 1799.
Press Officer: D R Pearham, 26 Yeading Avenue, Harrow, Middlesex, HA2 9RN. Tel: (H) 081 868 1799.
Club Colours: All black.

SUDBURY COURT RFC
Ground Address: The Pavilion, East Lane, North Wembley, Middlesex. Tel: 081 904 8485.
Club Secretary: Derek Gray, 33 Northwick Park Road, Harrow, Middlesex, HA1 2NY. Tel: 081 427 4155.
Press Officer: John Hennessy, 59 Norral Road, North Wembley. Tel: (H) 081 904 6694.
Club Colours: Dark blue, red & white.

TWICKENHAM RFC
Ground Address: Park Fields, South Road, Hampton. Tel: 081 979 2427.
Club Secretary: Tony Kay, 29 Grange Avenue, Twickenham, Middlesex, TW2 5TW. Tel: (H) 081 898 7210 (W) 081 898 7210.
Press Officer: Tony Kay, 29 Grange Avenue, Twickenham, Middlesex, TW2 5TW. Tel: (H) 081 898 7210 (W) 081 898 7210.
Club Colours: Red & black irregular hoops.

WEMBLEY RFC
Ground Address: Roger Bannister Playing Field, Uxbridge Road, Hatch End, Middlexex. Tel: 081 420 1789.
Club Secretary: Noreen Conlon, 62 Canterbury Way, Croxley Green, Rickmansworth, Hertfordshire, WD3 3SS. Tel: (H) 0923 230640.
Press Officer: Noreen Conlon, 62 Canterbury Way, Croxley Green, Rickmansworth, Hertfordshire, WD3 3SS. Tel: (H) 0923 230640.
Club Colours: Maroon & amber.

LONDON & SOUTH EAST DIVISION

MIDDLESEX TWO
1993-94
FIXTURES

December 18 (Week 15)
Osterley v H.A.C.
London Cornish v Orleans F.P.
Old Paulines v Barclays Bank
Feltham v Enfield Ignatians
Belsize Park v Thamesians
Hayes v Old Grammarians

October 23 (Week 8)
Osterley v London Cornish
Old Grammarians v Orleans F.P
Thamesians v Barclays Bank
Pinner & Gramms v Enfield Ignatians
Belsize Park v Feltham
Hayes v Old Paulines

January 8 (Week 18)
Barclays Bank v Feltham
Orleans F.P. v Old Paulines
H.A.C. v London Cornish
Old Grammarians v Osterley
Thamesians v Hayes
Pinner & Gramms v Belsize Park

October 3O (Week X2)
Old Paulines v Osterley
Feltham v Hayes
Enfield Ignatians v Belsize Park
Barclays Bank v Pinner & Gramms
Orleans F. P. v Thamesians
H.A.C v Old Grammarians

January 29 (Week X5)
Osterley v Thamesians
London Cornish v Old Grammarians
Old Paulines v H.A.C.
Feltham v Orleans F.P
Enfield Ignatians v Barclays Bank
Hayes v Pinner & Gramms

November 13 (Week 1O)
Osterley v Feltham
London Cornish v Old Paulines
Thamesians v H.A.C.
Pinner& Gramms v Orleans F.P.
Belsize Park v Barclays Bank
Hayes v Enfield Ignatians

February 12 (Week 22)
Orleans F.P. v Enfield Ignatians
H.A.C. v Feltham
Old Grammarians v Old Paulines
Thamesians v London Cornish
Pinner & Gramms v Osterley
Belsize Park v Hayes

November 2O (Week 11)
Feltham v London Cornish
Enfield Ignatians v Osterley
Barclays Bank v Hayes
Orleans F.P. v Belsize Park
H.A.C. v Pinner & Gramms
Old Grammarians v Thamesians

March 12 (Week 26)
Osterley v Belsize Park
London Cornish v Pinner & Gramms
Old Paulines v Thamesians
Feltham v Old Grammarians
Enfield Ignatians v H.A.C.
Barclays Bank v Orleans F.P.

December 4 (Week 13)
Osterley v Barclays Bank
London Cornish v Enfield Ignatians
Old Paulines v Feltham
Pinner & Gramms v Old Grammarians
Belsize Park v H.A.C.
Hayes v Orleans F.P.

March 26 (Week 28)
H.A.C. v Barclays Bank
Old Garmmarians v Enfield Ignatians
Thamesians v Feltham
Pinner & Gramms v Old Paulines
Belsize Park v London Cornish
Hayes v Osterley

December 11 (Week 14)
Enfield Ignatians v Old Paulines
Barclays Bank v London Cornish
Orleans F.P v Osterley
H.A..C. v Hayes
Old Grammarians v Belsize Park
Thamesians v Pinner & Gramms.

April 9 (Week 3O)
London Cornish v Hayes
Old Paulines v Belsize Park
Feltham v Pinner & Gramms
Enfield Ignatians v Thamesians
Barclays Bank v Old Grammarians
Orleans F.P. v H.A.C.

418

MIDDLESEX TWO

BARCLAYS BANK RFC
Ground Address: Park View Road, Ealing, London, W5 2JF. Tel: 081 998 4904.
Club Secretary: Mike Allen, 12 Laburnum Way, Bromley, Kent, BR2 8BZ. Tel: (H) 081 467 2097 (W) 071 491 8687 Ext 4757.
Press Officer: Mike Allen, 12 Laburnum Way, Bromley, Kent, BR2 8BZ. Tel: (H) 081 467 2097 (W) 071 491 8687 x 4757.
Club Colours: Maroon, silver & gold shirts, black shorts.

BELSIZE PARK RFC
Ground Address: C/O Hendon RFC, Copthall Stadium, Barnet. Tel: 081 203 1737.
Club Secretary: S Colquhoun, 9 Regency Lawns, Croetdown Road, London, NW5 1HF. Tel: (H) 071 485 5767 (W) 071 477 5548.
Press Officer: Mark Batchelor, 53 Atheldene Road, London, SW18 4BN. Tel: (H) 081 877 0402 (W) 081 818 4601.
Club Colours: Lavender & black.

ENFIELD IGNATIANS RFC
Ground Address: Donkey Lane, Enfield, Middlesex. Tel: 081 363 2877.
Club Secretary: Bernard Ainger, 85 Uvedale Road, Enfield, Middlesex, EN2 6HD. Tel: (H) 081 363 2307 (W) 0860 234328.
Press Officer: Gerry Davis, 58 Tillotson Road, London, N9. Tel: (H) 081 807 7811 (W) 0992 717835.
Club Colours: Blue & gold.

FELTHAM RFC
Ground Address: Park Road, Hanworth, Middlesex, TW13 7EY. Tel: 081 894 3609.
Club Secretary: B J Wilkins, 29 Gibbon Road, Kingston Upon Thames, Surrey, KT2 6AD.
Press Officer: Kevin Skinner, 15 Edinburgh Road, Hanwell, London, W7.
JClub Colours: Light blue, dark blue, gold hoop.

HAYES RFC
Ground Address: Grosvenor Field, Kingmill Avenue, Hayes, Middlesex. Tel: 081 845 4963.
Club Secretary: 2 Fulwood Close, Church Road, Hayes, Middlesex, UB3 2NF. Tel: (H) 081 573 7133.
Press Officer: 2 Fulwood Close, Church Road, Hayes, Middlesex, UB3 2NF. Tel: (H) 081 573 7133.
Club Colours: Navy.

HONOURABLE ARTILLERY COMPANY RFC
Ground Address: Artillery Garden, ArmouryHouse, City Road, London, EC1Y 2BQ. Tel: 071 604 4644.
Club Secretary: 31 Bedford Avenue, Little Chalfont, Buckinghamshire, HP6 6PS. Tel: (H) 0494 762982.
Press Officer: Colin Pritchard, 31 Bedford Avenue, Little Chaleont, HP6 6PS. Tel: (H) 0494 762982.
Club Colours: Maroon & dark blue hoops.

LONDON CORNISH RFC
Ground Address: Richardson Evans Memorial Ground, (by Robin Hood Roundabout) Roehampton Vale, Kingston. Tel: 081 788 3638.
League Contact: Antony Lander, 297 Latymer Court, Hammersmith Road, London, W6. Tel: (H) 081 746 3413 (W) 071 256 6411.
Press Officer: Luke Coombs, 49 Oldfield Road, Hampton, Middlesex, TW12 2AJ.
Club Colours: Black with narrow gold hoops.

OLD GRAMMARIANS RFC
Ground Address: Selby Site, Selby Road, Tottenham, London, N17. Tel: 081808 7697.
League Contact: B Calderwood, 17 Birch Crescent, Aylesford, Kent, ME20 7QE. Tel: (H) 0622 718350.

FINAL TABLE

	P	W	D	L	F	A	PD	Pts
Old Hamptonians	12	11	0	1	266	107	159	22
Old Actonians	12	10	0	2	181	117	64	20
Barclays Bank	12	7	1	4	189	116	73	15
Old Paulines	12	7	0	5	196	114	82	14
Belsize Park	12	5	1	6	138	135	3	11
Osterley	12	3	3	6	146	158	-12	9
H.A.C.	12	6	1	5	145	186	-41	9
Feltham	12	5	0	7	145	188	-43	8
Thamesians	12	4	0	8	115	169	-54	8
London Cornish	12	6	2	4	204	177	27	7
Enfield Ignatians	12	3	3	6	124	118	6	7
Old Tottonians	12	3	1	8	78	206	-128	5
St Barts Hospital	12	2	0	10	115	293	-178	2

Press Officer: S Abbott, 63 The Ridings, Thorley Park, Bishops Stortford, Hertfordshire, CM23 4EJ.
Club Colours: Navy, light blue & red.

OLD PAULINE FC
Ground Address: Speer Road, Thames Ditton, Surrey, KT7 0PW. Tel: 081 398 1858/9069.
Club Secretary: Tim J D Cunis, 62 Derby Road, London, SW14 7DP. Tel: (H) 081 878 3099.
Press Officer: John A Howard, 93A Richmond Park Road, Kingston, KT2 6AF. Tel: (H) 081 541 3817 (W) 081 941 4431.
Club Colours: Red, white & black hoops.

ORLEANS FRFC
Ground Address: Off Richmond Road, Twickenham. Tel: 081 892 5743.
Club Secretary: Martin Riddett, 8 Moor Mead Road, Twickenham, TW1 1JS. Tel: (H) 081 892 9663 (W) 081 745 7636.
Press Officer: Brian Smith, 35 Andover Road, Twickenham, TW2 6PD. Tel: (H) 081 894 4270 (W) 081 745 7636
Club Colours: Gold, maroon, white hoops.

OSTERLEY RFC
Ground Address: Tenterow Lane, Norwood Green, Middlesex. Tel: 081 574 3774.
Club Secretary: A Matthew, 22 Elthorne Park Road, Hanwell, Middlesex, W7 2JB. Tel: (H) 081 579 2046 (W) 081 754 1010.
Press Officer: Andy Lobb, 39 Lyndhurst Avenue, Twickenham, Middlesex. Tel: (H) 081 894 3714 (W) 071 922 3460.
Club Colours: Black & white hoops.

PINNER & GRAMMARIANS RFC
Ground Address: Shaftesbury Playing Fields, Grimsdyke Road, Hatch End, Harrow, Middlesex. Tel: 081 428 3136.
Club Secretary: Dave Hiles, 31 Lulworth Close, South Harrow, Middlesex, HA2 9NR. Tel: (H) 081 864 0787.
Press Officer: Jeremuy Whiting, 82 Wyatt Close, High Wycombe, Buckinghamshire, HP13 5YY. Tel: (H) 0494 510384 (W) 081 902 8887.
Club Colours: Navy with 1" horizontal scarlett hoops.

THAMESIANS RFC
Ground Address: Richmond upon Thames College, Egerton Road, Twickenham, Middlesex. Tel: 081 8943110.
Club Secretary: Eric Burrows, 133 Cranleigh Road, Lower Feltham, Middlesex, TW13 4QA. Tel: (H) 081 890 7162 (W) 081 893 8888.
Press Officer: David Butler, 136 Lincoln Avgenue, Twickenham, Middlesex, TW2 6NP. Tel: (H) 081 898 8544 (W) 081 570 9658.
Club Colours: Maroon, green & white.

LONDON & SOUTH EAST DIVISION

MIDDLESEX THREE
1993-94
FIXTURES

October 23 (Week 8)
Bank of England v Northolt
London Nigerian v St. Nicholas Old Boys
Royal Free Hospital v Quintin
London Exiles v U.C.S. Old Boys
St. Bart's Hospital v Old Tottonians

October 3O (Week X2)
U.C.S. Old Boys v Bank of England
Old Tottonians v London Nigerian
St. Nicholas Old Boys v Royal Free Hospital
Quintin v London Exiles
St. Bart's Hospital v Northolt

November 13 (Week 1O)
Bank of England v Quintin
Northolt v U.C.S. Old Boys
London Nigerian v St. Bart's Hospital
London Exiles v St. Nicholas Old Boys
Royal Free Hospital v Old Tottonians

November 2O (Week 11)
Quintin v Northolt
St. Nicholas Old Boys v Bank of England
Old Tottonians v London Exiles
U.C.S. Old Boys v St. Bart's Hospital
London Nigerian v Royal Free Hospital

December 4 (Week 13)
Bank of England v Old Tottonians
Northolt v St. Nicholas Old Boys
U.C.S. Old Boys v Quintin
St. Bart's Hospital v Royal Free Hospital
London Exiles v London Nigerian

December 11 (Week 14)
St.Nicholas Old Boys v U.C.S. Old Boys
Old Tottonians v Northolt
London Nigerian v Bank of England
Royal Free Hospital v London Exiles
St. Bart's Hospital v Quintin

January 29 (Week X5)
Bank of England v Royal Free Hospital
Northolt v London Nigerian
U.C.S. Old Boys v Old Tottonians
Quintin v St. Nicholas Old Boys
London Exiles v ST. Bart's Hospital

February 12 (Week 22)
Old Tottonians v Quintin
London Nigerian v U.C.S. Old Boys
Royal Free Hospital v Northolt
London Exiles v Bank of England
St. Nicholas Old Boys v St. Bart's Hospital

March 12 (Week 26)
Bank of England v St. Bart's Hospital
Northolt v London Exiles
U.C.S. Old Boys v Royal Free Hospital
Quintin v London Nigerian
St. Nicholas Old Boys v Old Tottonians

MIDDLESEX THREE

BANK OF ENGLAND RFC
Ground Address: Priory Lane, Roehampton, London SW15 5JQ. Tel: 081 876 8417.
Club Secretary: B S Brown. Tel: (H) 081 878 3396 (W) 081 876 8417.
League Contact: Mark Lewis, Flat 8, 413 Upper Richmond Road, Putney, London SW15. Tel: (H) 081 878 7790 (W) 071 380 9879.
Club Colours: Blue, gold, white hoops.

NORTHOLT RFC
Ground Address: Kensington & Chelsea Playing Fields, Dolphin Road, Northolt, Middlesex. Tel: 081 841 3088.
Club Secretary: Colin Nicholl, 43 Columbia Avenue, Ruislip, Middlesex HA4 9SU. Tel: (H) 081 866 8201 (W) 081 975 3923.
Press Officer: Geoff Payne, 16 Brackenbridge Drive, South Ruislip, Middlesex HA4 0NG. Tel: (H) 081 845 0874 (W) 071 937 5464 x2642.
Club Colours: Light blue & dark blue hoops (away, white)

LONDON EXILES RUFC
Ground Address: Regents Park, London N1.
Club Secretary: Tim Edghill, 114 Rannoch Road, London W6 9SW. Tel: (H) 081 948 3167 (W) 071 493 6040.
Club Colours: Claret, navy & white hoops & socks, white shorts.

LONDON NIGERIANS RFC
Ground Address: Copthall Playng Fields, Great North Way, Hendon, London NW4. Tel: 081 203 1737.
Club Secretary: B. Akin-Olugbemi, 3 Glebe Road, Hornsea, London N8 7DA. Tel: (H) 081 341 2371.
Club Colours: Black.

OLD TOTTONIANS RFC
Ground Address: Churchfields, Great Cambridge Road (A10)/Harrow Drive, Edmonton, London N9. Tel: 081 364 3099.
Club Secretary: Trevor de la Salle, 55 Welsummer Way, Le Motte Chase, Cheshunt, Herts EN5 0UG. Tel: (H) 0992 638492 (W) 0494 444811.
Press Officer: Peter Wafford, 33 Cotswold Way, Enfield EN2 7HD. Tel: (H) 081 363 4384 (W) 081 368 8345.
Club Colours: Blue and amber hoops.

QUINTIN RFC
Ground Address: The Quintin Hogg Memorial Ground, Harteignton Road, Chiswick, London W4. Tel: 081 994 1554.
Club Secretary: Nigel Smith, 4 Australia Avenue, Maidenhead, Berks SL6 7DJ. Tel: (H) 0628 75899 (W) 0628 822166 x5971.
Club Colours: Scarlet & green hoops.

ROYAL FREE HOSPITAL AND SCHOOL OF PHARMACY RFC
Ground Address: Myddleton House, Turkey St, Bulls Cross, Enfield. Tel: 081 976 2867.
Club Secretary: Rob Poulter, 19 Lambolle Place, Belsize Park, Hampstead, London NW3. Tel: (H) 071 483 3934 (W) 071 794 0500 x4241.
Club Colours: Black & gold.

FINAL TABLE

	P	W	D	L	F	A	PD	Pts
Pinner & Gramms	9	7	0	2	138	52	86	14
Hayes	9	6	0	3	167	93	74	12
Bank of England	9	8	0	1	146	85	61	12
UCS Old Boys	9	6	0	3	160	116	44	12
St Nicholas O B	9	5	0	4	170	114	56	10
Northolt	9	5	0	4	102	74	28	10
Quintin	8	2	0	6	61	138	-77	4
Royal Free Hosp	9	3	0	6	84	179	-95	2
London French	8	2	0	6	75	132	-57	0
Meadhurst	9	0	0	9	37	198	-161	0

ST BARTHOLOMEW'S HOSPITAL RFC
Ground Address: St Bartholomew's Hospital Athletic Ground, Perry Street, Foxbury, Chislehurst, Kent. Tel: 081 467 9452/3453.
Club Secretary: Andy Steel, MSCR, St Bartholomew's Hospital, West Smithfield, London EC1A 7BE. Tel: (H) 071 254 8439 (W) 071 253 1100 (leave message).
Club Colours: White with thin black hoops.

ST NICHOLAS OLD BOYS RFC
Ground Address: c/o Ickenham CC, Oak Avenue, Ickenham, Middlesex. Tel: 0895 639366.
Club Secretary: Mr R Maynard, 27 Haslam Close, Ickenham, Middlesex UB10 8JT. Tel: (H) 0895 679371.
Club Colours: Red shirts, white shorts, black socks.

UCS OLD BOYS RFC
Ground Address: University College School Playing Fields, Ranulf Road, London NW2. Tel: 081 452 4337.
Club Secretary: Paul Gee, 63 Blackhorse Lane, South Mimms, Herts, EN6 3PS. Tel: (H) 0707 643156 (W) 081 807 9332 x4643.
Press Officer: Geoff Boxer, 19 Queens Road, London N3 2AG. Tel: (H) 081 346 7189 (W) 071 794 0510 x5491.
Club Colours: Maroon, black & white.

Congratulations and thanks to the clubs of Middlesex Three who were the first complete league to submit their information for this book.

LONDON & SOUTH EAST DIVISION

<table>
<tr><td>

MIDDLESEX FOUR

1993-94

FIXTURES

</td><td>

March 12 (Week 26)
Middlesex Hospital v University College
St. George's Hospital v Southgate
Kodak v London French
British Airways v Meadhurst

</td></tr>
</table>

October 23 (Week 8)
G.W.R. v Middlesex Hospital
London French v British Airways
Southgate v Kodak
University College v St George's Hospital

October 3O (Week X2)
St George's Hospital v G.W.R.
Meadhurst v London French
British Airways v Southgate
Kodak v University College

November 13 (Week 1O)
G.W.R. v Kodak
Middlesex Hospital v St. George's Hospital
University College v British Airways
Southgate v Meadhurst

November 2O (Week 11)
Kodak v Middlesex Hospital
British Airways v G.W.R.
Meadhurst v University College
London French v Southgate

December 4 (Week 13)
G.W.R. v Meadhurst
Middlesex Hospital v British Airways
St. George's Hospital v Kodak
University College v London French

December 11 (Week 14)
British Airways v St. George's Hospital
Meadhurst v Middlesex Hospital
London French v G.W.R.
Southgate v University College

January 29 (Week X5)
G.W.R. v Southgate
Middlesex Hospital v London French
St. George's Hospital v Meadhurst
Kodak v British Airways

February 12 (Week 22)
Meadhurst v Kodak
London French v St. George's Hospital
Southgate v Middlesex Hospital
University College v G.W.R.

MIDDLESEX FOUR

BRITISH AIRWAYS RUFC
Ground Address: The Clubhouse, Crane Lodge Road, Cranford, Middlesex. Tel: 081 562 0291.
Club Secretary: Kieran Donaghy, 36 Welland Close, Langley, Berkshire, SL3 8UP. Tel: (H) 0753 545916 (W) 081 502 2130.
Press Officer: Kieran Donaghy, 36 Welland Close, Langley, Berkshire, SL3 8UP. Tel: (H) 0753 545916 (W) 081 502 2130.
Club Colours: Blue, red & white quarters.

THE GREAT WESTERN RAILWAY RFC
Ground Address: Castlebar Park, Vallis Way, Argyle Road, West Ealing, London, W13 0DD. Tel: 081998 7928.
Club Secretary: R J W Sullivan, 100 Westcott Crescent, Hanwell, London, W7 1PB. Tel: (H) 081 575 6074.
Press Officer: T V Shorey, 32 Croyde Avenue, Greenford, Middlesex, UB6 9LS. Tel: (H) 081 578 8706 (W) 081 813 5711.
Club Colours: Cardinal red & black.

KODAK RFC
Ground Address: Kodak Sports Ground, Harrow View, Harrow, Middlesex, HA1 4TY. Tel: 081 427 2642.
Club Secretary: Paul Childs, 44 Roe Green, Kingsbury, London, NW9 0PE. Tel: (H) 061 206 0199 (W) 081 982 4502.
Press Officer: Nick Wilson, 70 Whitchurch Avenue, Edgware, Middlesex, HA8 6HS. Tel: (H) 081 951 0184 (W) 081 868 8899 Ext 5469.
Club Colours: Green & gold.

LONDON FRENCH RFC
Ground Address: Barn Elms Playing Fields, Rocks Lane, Barnes, London, SW13.
Club Secretary: A James, 28 Priory Road, Chiswick, London, W4 5JB. Tel: (H) 081 994 1090 (W) 071 629 8191.
Club Colours: French bule shirts, white shorts, red socks.

MEADHURST RFC
Ground Address: BP Meadhurst Club, Chertsey Road, Sunbury-on- Thames. Tel: 0932 763500.
Club Secretary: Dr Thomas Knox, BP Oil, Oil Technology Centre, Chertsey Road, Sunbury-on-Thames, Middlesex, TW16 7LN. Tel: (H) 0932 223802 (W) 0932 763284.
Press Officer: Brian Messenger, BP Chemicals Limited, Research Laboratory, Poplar House, Chertsey Road, Sunbury-on-Thames, Middlesex, TW16 7LL. Tel: (H) 081 332 7635 (W) 0932 774054.
Club Colours: Green/yellow reverse quarters.

MIDDLESEX HOSPITAL RUFC
Ground Address: Athletic Ground, Perry Street, Chislehurst, Kent.. Tel: 081 467 3859.
Club Secretary: c/o Students Union. Tel: 071 580 7310.

SOUTHGATE RFC
Ground Address: Norther Telecom plc, Oakleigh Road, New Southgate, London, N11 1HB. Tel: 081 945 2655.
Club Secretary: D Hockley, 5 The Vineries, Enfield, Middlesex, EN1 3DQ. Tel: (H) 081 342 0262 (W) 071 270 3874.
Press Officer: Geoff Potter, 1 Arlow Road, Winchmore Hill, London, N21 3JS. Tel: (H) 081 342 0262 (W) 071 270 3874.
Press Officer: Geoff Potter, 1 Arlow Road, Winchmore Hill, London, N21 3JS. Tel: (H) 081 342 0262 (W) 071 270 3874.
Club Colours: Navy blue, light blue & gold.

FINAL TABLE

	P	W	D	L	F	A	PD	Pts
LondonNigerians	8	8	0	0	240	54	186	16
London Exiles	8	7	0	1	249	82	167	14
Southgate	8	5	0	3	172	123	49	10
Kodak	8	3	0	5	121	125	-4	6
Middlesex Hospital	7	3	0	4	91	161	-70	6
G.W.R.	7	3	1	3	52	93	-41	5
University College	5	2	0	3	84	73	11	4
British Airways	8	1	0	7	27	168	-141	2
St Georges Hospital	7	0	1	6	32	201	-169	1

ST GEORGES HOSPITAL RFC
Ground Address: Royal Dental Hospital Ground, Stoke Road, Cobham, Surrey. t0932 864341.
Club Secretary: Dr W Landells, Histopathology Dept, St Helier, Wrythe Lane, Carsholton, Surrey. Tel: (H) 081 946 9408 (W) 081 644 4343.
Press Officer: Dr W Landells, Histopathology Dept, St Helier, Wrythe Lane, Carsholton, Surrey. Tel: (H) 081 946 9408 (W) 081 644 4343.
Club Colours: Green & gold hoops.

UNIVERSITY COLLEGE LONDON RFC
Ground Address: Shenley Sports Grounds, Bell Lane, London Colney, Shenley, Hertfordshire. Tel: 0727 22215.
Club Secretary: Richard A M Newberry, UCLRFC, Student's Union, 25 Gordon Street, London, WC1H 0AH. Tel: (H) 071 387 3611.
Club Colours: Purple, black, blue quarters, black shorts.

LONDON & SOUTH EAST DIVISION

HERTFORDSHIRE ONE 1993-94 FIXTURES

October 23 (Week 8)
Bacavians v St. Albans
Royston v Q.E.II
Watford v Tring
Old Ashmoleans v Stevenage
Datchworth v Hatfield

October 3O (Week X2)
Hatfield v Bacavians
Stevenage v Datchworth
Tring v Old Ashmoleans
Q.E.II v Watford
Old Stanfordians v Royston

November 13 (Week (1O)
Bacavians v Stevenage
St. Albans v Hatfield
Watford v Old Stanfordians
Old Ashmoleans v Q.E.II
Datchworth v Tring

November 2O (Week 11)
Stevenage v St Albans
Tring v Bacavians
Q.E.II v Datchworth
Old Stanfordians v Old Ashmoleans
Royston v Watford

December 4 (Week 13)
Bacavians v Q.E.II
St. Albans v Tring
Hatfield v Stevenage
Old Ashmoleans v Royston
Datchworth v Old Stanfordians

December 11 (Week 14)
Tring v Hatfield
Q.E.II v St Albans
Old Stanfordians v Bacavians
Royston v Datchworth
Watford v Old Ashmoleans

January 8 Week 18)
Bacavians v Royston
St. Albans v Old Stanfordians
Hatfield v Q.E.II
Stevenage v Tring
Datchworth v Watford

January 29 (Week X5)
Q.E. II v Stevenage
Old Stanfordians v Hatfield
Royston v St. Albans
Watford v Bacavians
Old Ashmoleans v Datchworth

February 12 (Week 22)
Bacavians v Old Ashmoleans
St Albans v Watford
Hatfield v Royston
Stevenage v Old Stanfordians
Tring v Q.E.II

March 12 (Week 26)
Old Stanfordians v Tring
Royston v Stevenage
Watford v Hatfield
Old Ashmoleans v St Albans
Datchworth v Bacavians

March 26 (Week 28)
St Albans v Datchworth
Hatfield v Old Ashmoleans
Stevenage v Watford
Tring v Royston
Q.E. II v Old Stanfordians

HERTFORDSHIRE ONE

BACAVIANS RFC
Ground Address: BAe Sports and Social Club, Bragbury End, Stevenage, Hertfordshire. Tel: 0438 812985/812366.
Club Secretary: Richard Stephens, 18 Russell Close, Stevenage, SG2 8PB. Tel@: (H) 0438 351971. (W) 043 355751.
Press Officer: Allan Harris, 6 Collenswood Road, Stevenage. Tel: (H) 0438 367048 (W) 0992 556129.
Club Colours: Green with amber hoop, white shorts.

DATCHWORTH RFC
Ground Address: Datchworth Green, Datchworth, Hertfordshire. Tel: 0438 812490.
Club Secretary: L D Wyatt, 7 Hazeldell, Watton-at-Stone, HErtford, SG14 3SL. Tel: (H) 0920 830407.
Press Officer: Angus Watt, 25, Deards End Lane, Knebworth, Hertfordshire. Tel: (H) 0438 813240 (W) 0582 478888.
Club Colours: Green shirts, black shorts.

HATFIELD RFC
Ground Address: Roe Hill Sports Ground, Briars Lane, Hatfield, Hertfordshire. Tel: 0707 269814.
Club Secretary: Mark Gates, Flat 1, Carneal, Park Lane, Knebworth, Kerts, SG3 6PD. Tel: (H) 0438 816527.
Press Officer: Ian Wint, 8 Cheyne CLose, 8 Ware, Herts, SG12 0QF. Tel: (H) 0920 463307.
Club Colours: Brown, gold, green & white quarters.

OLD ASHMOLEANS RFC
Ground Address: Ashmole School, Burleigh Gardens, Southgate, London N14. Tel: 081 368 4984.
League Contact: J W Byrne, 85A Burford Gardens, Palmers Green, London N13 4LR. Tel: (H) 081 886 25995.
Press Officer: D PErks, 41 Raleigh Road, Enfield, EN2 6UD. Tel: (H) 081 367 4052 (W) 071 242 5242.
Club Colours: Scarlet & emerald hoops.

OLD STANFORDIANS RFC
Ground Address: Old Kents Lane, Standon, Hertfordshire, SG11 1LG.
Club Secretary: T Moody, 2 Rose Cottage, Hadham Road, Standon, Hertfordshire, SG11 1LG. Tel: (H) 0920 822368.
Press Officer: T Moody, 2 Rose Cottage, Hadham Road, Standon, Hertfordshire, SG11 1LG. Tel: (H)0920 822368.
Club Colours: Black with a purple hoop.

QUEEN ELIZABETH II RFC
Ground Address: Hatfield Hyde Sports Club, King George V Playing Fields, Beehive Lane, Welwyn Garden City, Hertfordshire, AL7 4BP. Tel: 0707 326700.
Club Secretary: Steve Murray, 227 Colebrook Lane, Loughton, Essex IG10 2HG. Tel: (H) 081 508 5532 (W) 071 918 3712.
Press Officer: Wayune Gorringe, 29 Boundary House, BoundaryLane, Welwyn Garden City, Hertfordshire. Tel: (H) 0707 326371.
Club Colours: Myrtle green & amber.

ROYSTON RUFC
Ground Address: The Heath Sports Club, Therfield, Heath, Baldock Road, Royston, Hertfordshire, SG8 5BG. Tel: 0763 243613.
League Contact: P Copmpton, 12 Abbotts Close, Litlington, Royston, Hertfordshire, SG8 0QQ. Tel: (H) 0763 852788 (W) 0763 852788.
Press Officer: Phil Hastings, Fieldview House, 7 Hillside, Orwell, Royston, Hertfordshire, SG8 5QZ. Tel: (H) 0223 207753 (W) 0223 207753.
Club Colours: Black & white hoops, black shorts.

FINAL TABLE

	P	W	D	L	F	A	PD	Pts
Barnet	10	10	0	0	370	48	322	20
Tring	10	9	0	1	241	88	153	18
Bacavians	10	7	1	2	172	98	74	13
Datchworth	10	6	0	4	180	127	53	12
St Albans	10	7	1	2	280	64	216	11
Old Ashmoleans	10	5	0	5	169	178	-9	10
Royston	10	4	0	6	103	269	-166	8
Hatfield	10	2	0	8	88	257	-169	4
Watford	10	2	1	7	82	176	-94	3
QE II Hospital	10	1	0	9	56	279	-223	2
Old Stanfordians	10	0	1	9	40	242	-202	1

ST ALBANS RFC
Ground Address: Boggeymidd Spring, Oaklands Lane, Smallford, St Albans, Hertforshire, AL4 0HR. Tel: 0727 869945.
Club Secretary: John Gregory, 58 Luton lane, Redbourn, Hertfordshire, AL3 7PY. Tel: (H) 0582 792798 (W) 081 205 1213 Ext 285.
Club Colours: Royal blue & gold hoops.

STEVENAGE RUFC
Ground Address: North Road, Old Town, Stevenage, Hertfordshire. Tel: 0438 359788.
Club Secretary: Chris Welch, "Holmwood", Todds Green, Stevenage, Hertfordshire, SG1 2JE. Tel: (H) 0438 353753 (W) 0438 720955.
Press Officer: Andy Pert, 48 Alleynes Road, Stevenage, Hertfordshire, SG1 3PP. Tel: (H) 0438 353753 (W) 0438 720955.
Club Colours: Green with gold hoops.

TRING RUFC
Ground Address: Pendley Sports Centre, Cew Lane, Tring, Hertfordshire. Tel: 0442 825710.
Club Secretary: Malcom Rose, 25 Grenadine Way, Tring, Hertfordshire, HP23 5EA. Tel: (H) 0442 827165 (W) 0628 486969.
Club Colours: Black & gold.

WATFORD RFC
Ground Address: Radlett Road, Watford, Hertfordshire. Tel: 243292.
Club Secretary: Keven Tagg, 13 Cannon Road, Watford, Hertfordshire, WD1 8BB. Tel: (H) 0923 252637 (W) 081 953 9922 Ext 257.
Press Officer: Gary Bridge, 18 Westfield Avenue, Watford, Hertfordshire. Tel: (H) 0923 220036.
Club Colours: Red, white & blue hoops.

LONDON & SOUTH EAST DIVISION

LONDON THREE NORTH EAST 1993-94 FIXTURES

December 18 (Week 15)
Rochford v Bury St. Edmunds
Romford v Colchester
Westcliff v Ipwich
Shelford v Saffron Walden
Woodbridge v Braintree
Campion v Basildon

October 23 (Week 8)
Rochford v Romford & G.P
Basildon v Colchester
Braintree v Ipswich
Chelmsford v Saffron Walden
Woodbridge v Shelford
Campion v Westcliff

January 8 (Week 18)
Ipswich v Shelford
Colchester v Westcliff
Bury St. Edmunds v Romford & G.P
Baildon v Rochford
Braintree v Campion
Chelmsford v Woodbridge

October 3O (Week X2)
Westcliff v Rochford
Shelford v Campion
Saffron Walden v Woodbridge
Ipswich v Chelmsford
Colchester v Braintree
Bury St. Edmunds v Basildon

January 29 (Week X5)
Rochford v Braintree
Romford & G.P. v Basildon
Westcliff v Bury St. Edmunds
Shelford v Colchester
Saffron Walden v Ipswich
Campion v Chelmsford

November 13 (Week 1O)
Rochford v Shelford
Romford & G.P v Westcliff
Braintree v Bury St. Edmunds
Chelmsford v Colchester
Woodbridge v Ipswich
Champion v Saffron Walden

Febuary 12 (Week 22)
Colchester v Saffron Walden
Bury St. Edmunds v Shelford
Basildon v Westcliff
Braintree v Romford & G.P
Chelmford v Rochford
Woodbridge v Campion

November 2O (Week (11)
Shelford v Romford & G.P.
Saffron Walden v Rochford
Ipswich v Campion
Colchester v Woodbridge
Bury St. Edmunds v Chelmsford
Basildon v Braintree

March 12 (Week 26)
Rochford v Woodbridge
Romford & G.P. v Chelmford
Westcliff v Braintree
Shelford v Basildon
Saffron Walden v Bury Sf. Edmunds
Ipswich v Colchester

December 4 (Week 13)
Rochford v Ipswich
Romford & G.P. v Saffron Walden
Westcliff v Shelford
Chelmsford v Basildon
Woodbridge v Bury St. Edmunds
Campion v Colchester

March 26 (Week 28)
Bury St. Edmunds v Ipswich
Basildon v Saffron Walden
Braintree v Shelford
Chelmsford v Westcliff
Woodbridge v Romford & G.P
Campion v Rochford

December 11 (Week 14)
Saffron Walden v Westcliff
Ipswich v Romford & G.P
Colchester v Rochford
Bury St. Edmunds v Campion
Basildon v Woodbridge
Braintree v Chelmsford

April 9 (Week 3O)
Romford & G.P v Campion
Westcliff v Woodbridge
Shelford v Chelmsford
Saffron Walden v Braintree
Ipswich v Basildon
Colchester v Bury St. Edmunds

LONDON THREE NORTH EAST

BASILDON RFC
Ground Address: Gardiners Close, Basildon, Essex.
Tel:0268 533136.
Club Secretary: L A Hymans, 32 Devon Way, Cawnvey
Island, Essex, SS8 9YD. Tel: (H) 0268 693899 (W) 0850
500159.
Press Officer: K Jefferson, 265 Key Wak, Hockley, Essex,
SS5 4UG. Tel: (H) 0702 207203.
Club Colours: Green & white hoops.

BRAINTREE RUFC
Ground Address: The Clubhouse, Robbswood, Beckers
Green Road, Braintree, Essex. Tel: 0376 322282.
Club Secretary: M Olley, 77 Kings Road, Halstead, Essex,
CO9 1HA. Tel: (H) 0787 473474.
Press Officer: D Nightingale, 6 Hereward Way,
Wethersfield, Braintree, Essex. Tel: (H) 0371 850013.
Club Colours: Black & amber quarters.

BURY ST EDMUNDS RFC
Ground Address: The Harberden Southgate Green, Bury
St Edmunds, Suffolk. Tel: 0284 753920.
Club Secretary: Mervyn Jefferey, 13 Raynesford Road,
Great Wenham, Suffolk. Tel (H) 0284 386386.
Press Officer: J Cross, 9 Malin Close, Haverhill. Tel: (H)
0440 712737.
Club Colours: Green & yellow.

CAMPION RFC
Ground Address: Cottons Park, Cottons Approach,
Romford, Essex RM7 7AA. Tel: 0708 753209.
Club Secretary: P O'Brien, 68 Lancaster Drive, Elm Park,
Hornchurch, Essex. RM12 5ST. Tel: (H) 0708 446980 (W)
0708 342827.
Club Colours: Red & black hoops.

CHELMSFORD RFC
Ground Address: Coronation Park, Timsons Lane,
Chelmsford, Essex. Tel: 0245 261159.
Club Secretary: Ian Stuart, 49 Hillside Grove, Chelmsford,
Essex, CM2 9DA. Tel: (H) 0245 352790 (W) 0279 647366.
Press Officer: Philip Suggitt, 9 Sheely Close, Macdon,
Essex, CM9 6DD. Tel: (H) 0621 857736.
Club Colours: Navy blue shirts and shorts.

COLCHESTER RFC
Ground Address: Mill Road, Mile End, Colchester, Essex,
CO4 5JF. Tel: 0206 851610.
Club Secretary: Ron Hatch, 99 Ernest Road, Wivenhoe,
Colchester, CO7 9LJ. Tel: (H) 0206 823548 (W) 0206
825882.
Press Officer: Bill Thornill, 16 Thornwood, Mile End,
Cochester, CO4 5LR. Tel: (H) 0206 845703.
Club Colours: Black.

IPSWICH RUFC
Ground Address: Humber Doucy Lane, Ipswich, Suffolk.
Tel: 0473 724072.
Club Secretary: Chris Gray, Park Farm, Park Road,
Grundisburgh, Woodbridge, Suffolk, IP13 6TR. Tel: (H)
0473 735333 (W) 0473 232000.
Press Officer: Stuart Jarropld, Downbridge Farm, Hoxne,
Eye, Suffolk. Tel: (H) 037975 317 (W) 0603 619261.
Club Colours: Black & amber hoops.

ROMFORD AND GIDEA PARK RFC
Ground Address: "Crowlands", Crow Lane, Romford,
Essex. Tel:0708 760068.
Club Secretary: D G E Davies, 25 Stanley Avenue, Gidea
Park, Romford, Essex. Tel: (H) 0708 724870 (W) 081 592
6305.
Press Officer: P D Ridley, 72 Dorset Avenue, Romford,
Essex. Tel: (H) 0708 765379.
Club Colours: Black with purple & white hoops.

FINAL TABLE

	P	W	D	L	F	A	PD	Pts
Brentwood	12	10	0	2	266	102	164	20
Rochford	12	10	0	2	210	129	81	20
Romf'd & Gidea Pk	12	9	1	2	340	91	249	19
Colchester	12	8	0	4	203	98	105	16
Campion	12	8	0	4	167	139	28	16
Basildon	12	7	0	5	159	146	13	14
Woodbridge	12	5	1	6	172	144	28	11
Braintree	12	5	1	6	147	130	17	11
Chelmsford	12	5	1	6	187	192	-5	11
Westcliff	12	5	0	7	163	140	23	10
Saffron Walden	12	2	0	10	80	265	-185	4
Canvey Island	12	2	0	10	77	294	-217	4
Cantabrigian	12	0	0	12	65	366	-301	0

ROCHFORD HUNDRED RFC
Ground Address: The Clubhouse, Magnolia Road,
Hawkwell, Essex. Tel:0702 544021.
Club Secretary: R Simon Wakefield, 54 Parklands Drive,
Springreild, Chelmsford, Essex, CM1 5SP. Tel: (H) 0245
266158 (W) 0702 541581.
Press Officer: Don Faulkner, 128 WEst Road,
Westcliff-on-Sea, Essex, SS0 9DD. Tel: (H) 0702 331850.
Club Colours: Black shirts & shorts, black socks with
white top.

SAFRON WALDEN RFC
Ground Address: Springate, Henham, Essex. Tel: 0279
850791.
Club Secretary: John Hamilton, Smith's Cottage, Smith's
Gardens, Takley, Bishops Stortford. Tel: (H) 0279 870828.
Press Officer: Chris Edwards, 93 Radwinter Road, Saffron
Walden, Essex. Tel: (H) 0799 522107.
Club Colours: Saffron gold & green.

SHELFORD RUFC
Ground Address: Davey Field, Cambridge Road, Great
Shelford, Cambridge. Tel: 0223 843357
Club Secretary: Christine Jeffery, 58 Macaulay Avenue,
Great Shelford, Cambridge, CB2 5AE. Tel: (H) 0223
844605 (W) 0223 415814.
Press Officer: Colin AStin, 40 Hauxton Road, Little
Shelford, Cambridge. Tel: (H) 0223 842154.

WESTCLIFF RFC
Ground Address: "The Gables", Aviation Way,
Southend-on-Sea, Essex, SS2 6UN. Tel: 0702 72140.
Club Secretary: Richard J Davies, 88 Flemming Avenue,
Leigh-on- Sea, Essex, SS9 3AX. Tel: (H) 0702 72140 (W)
0375 .390000 Ext 2025.
Press Officer: Geoffrey Sawyer, 30 Lascelles Gardens,
Rochford, Essex, SS4 3BP. Tel: (H) 0702 544434.
Club Colours: Maroon & old gold.

WOODBRIDGE RUFC
Ground Address: Hatchley Barn, Bromeswell, Nr
Woodbridge, IP12 2PP. Tel: 0394 460630.
Club Secretary: John Blake, Brackendale, Bromeswell,
Woodbridge, IP12 2PP. Tel: (H) 0394 460447.
Press Officer: Steve Henry, 9 Old Rectory Court, Melton,
Woodbridge, IP12 1NL. Tel: (H) 0394 387906 (W) 0473
613998.
Club Colours: Tide blue.

LONDON & SOUTH EAST DIVISION

EASTERN COUNTIES ONE
1993-94
FIXTURES

October 23 (Week 8)
Cantabrigian v Harwich & Dovercourt
Ely v West Norfolk
Ravens v Newmarket
Wanstead v Wymondham
Upminster v Canvey Island
Lowestoft & Yarmouth v Bancroft

October 3O (Week X2)
Bancroft v Cantabrigian
Canvey Island v Lowestoft & Yarmouth
Wymondham v Upminster
Newmarket v Wanstead
West Norfolk v Ravens
Maldon v Ely

November 13 (Week 1O)
Cantabrigian v Canvey Island
Harwich & Dovercourt v Bancroft
Ravens v Maldon
Wanstead v West Norfolk
Upminster v Newmarket
Lowestoft & Yarmouth v Wymondham

November 2O (Week 11)
Canvey Island v Harwich & Dovercourt
Wymondham v Cantabrigian
Newmarket v Lowestoft & Yarmouth
West Norfolk v Upminster
Maldon v Wanstead
Ely v Ravens

December 4 (Week 13)
Cantabrigian v Newmarket
Harwich & Dovercourt v Wymondham
Bancroft v Canvey Island
Wanstead v Ely
Upminster v Maldon
Lowestoft & Yarmouth v West Norfolk

December 11 (Week 14)
Wymondham v Bancroft
Newmarket v Harwich & Dovercourt
West Norfolk v Cantabrigian
Maldon v Lowestoft & Yarmouth
Ely v Upminster
Ravens v Wanstead

December 18 (Week 15)
Cantabrigian v Maldon
Harwich & Dovercourt v West Norfolk
Bancroft v Newmarket
Canvey Island v Wymondham
Upminster v Ravens
Lowestoft & Yarmouth v Ely

January 8 (Week 18)
Newmarket v Canvey Island
West Norfolk v Bancroft
Maldon v Harwich & Dovercourt
Ely v Cantabrigian
Ravens v Lowestoft & Yarmouth
Wanstead v Upminster

January 29 (Week X5)
Cantabrigian v Ravens
Harwich & Dovercourt v Ely
Bancroft v Maldon
Canvey Island v West Norfolk
Wymondham v Newmarket
Lowestoft & Yarmouth v Wanstead

February 12 (Week 22)
West Norfolk v Wymondham
Maldon v Canvey Island
Ely v Bancroft
Ravens v Harwich & Dovercourt
Wanstead v Cantabrigian
Upminster v Lowestoft & Yarmouth

March 12 (Week 26)
Cantabrigian v Upminster
Harwich & Dovercourt v Wanstead
Bancroft v Ravens
Canvey Island v Ely
Wymondham v Maldon
Newmarket v West Norfolk

March 26 (Week 28)
Maldon v Newmarket
Ely v Wymondham
Ravens v Canvey Island
Wanstead v Bancroft
Upminster v Harwich & Dovercourt
Lowestoft & Yarmouth v Cantabrigian

April 9 (Week 3O)
Harwich & Dovercourt v Lowestoft & Yarmouth
Bancroft v Upminster
Canvey Island v Wanstead
Wymondham v Ravens
Newmarket v Ely
West Norfolk v Maldon

428

EASTERN COUNTIES ONE

BANCROFT RFC
Ground Address: Buckhurst Way, Buckhurst Hill, Essex IG9 6JD. Tel: 081 504 0429.
Club Secretary: S J Thirsk, 4 Bentley Way, Woodford Green, Essex, TG8 0SR. Tel: (H) 081 564 1468 (W) 0279 441111.
Club Colours: Blue, black, cherry, light blue hoops.

CANTABRIGIAN RUFC
Ground Address: Sedley Taylor Road, Cambridge, CB2 2PW. Tel: 0223 213061.
Club Secretary: R L Ladds, 4 Flamsteed Road, Cambridge, CB1 3QU. Tel: (H) 0223 249008 (W) 0223 61111.
Club Colours: Navy blue & white hoops.

CANVEY ISLAND RUFC
Ground Address: Tewkes Creek, Dovervelt Road, Canvey Island, Essex. Tel: 0268 681881.
Club Secretary: Martin Powell, 7 Chichester Close, Canvey Island, Essex, SS8 0DZ. Tel: (H) 0268 695130 (W) 0265 584522.
Press Officer: Richard Crewe.
Club Colours: Red & blue.

HARWICH AND DOVERCOURT RUFC
Ground Tel: 0255 240225.
Club Secretary: Gary Brazier, Great Oakley, Harwich, Essex, CO12 5AX. Tel: (H) 0255 886233 (W) 0255 222200.
Press Officer: P Armstrong, 103 Clarkes Road, Dovercourt, Harwich, Essex. Tel: (H) 0255 241501.
Club Colours: Black & white hoops.

ELY RUFC
Ground Address: Ely RUFC, The Clubhouse, Downham Road, Ely, Cambridgeshire, CB6 2SH. Tel: 0353 662363.
Club Secretary: R Wilding, 12 West End, Eay, Cambridgeshire. Tel: (H) 0353 665963.
Press Officer: B Sullivan, Ley Clerks Farm, Nornea Lane, Stuntney, Ely, Cambgridgshire. Tel: (H) 0353 662285.
Club Colours: Black & gold hoops.

LOWESTOFT & YARMOUTH RUFC
Ground Address: Gunton Park, Old Lane, Corton, Nr Lowestoft. Tel: Lowestroft 730350.
Club Secretary: Keith Nelson, 70 Upper Cliff Road, Gorleston, Great Yarmouth, Norfolk, NR31 6AJ. Tel: (H) Great Yarmouth 653095 (W) Great Yarmouth 332038.
Press Officer: Keith Nelson, 70 Upper Cliff Road, Gorleston, Great Yarmouth, Norfolk, NR31 6AJ. Tel: (H) Great Yarmouth 653095 (W) Great Yarmouth 332038.
Club Colours: Royal blue & white hoops.

MALDON RUFC
Ground Address: Drapers Farm, Drapers Chase, Goldhanger Road, Heybridge, Maldon, Essex. Tel: 0621 852152.
League Contact: Norman John Manning, 57 Larch Walk, Heybridge, Maldon, Essex, CM9 7TS. Tel: (H) 0621 856073.
Press Officer: Steve Willcocks, Faith, Bridgemarsh Lane, Althorne, Essex, CM3 6DH. Tel: (H) 0621 743102.
Club Colours: Royal blue & white hoops, navy shorts.

NEWMARKET RUFC
Ground Address: Scaltrack School, Elizabeth Avenue, Newmarket, Suffolk, CB8 0DJ. Tel: 0638 663082.
Club Secretary: J W Paxton, 7 Beechwood Close, Exning, Newmarket, Suffolk, CB8 7EL. Tel: (H) 0638 577251 (W) 0638 577251.
Press Officer: Andy Downing, 107 George Lambton Avenue, Newmarket. Tel: (H) 0638 669152.
Club Colours: Green & Black hoops.

FINAL TABLE

	P	W	D	L	F	A	PD	Pts
Bury St Edmunds	12	10	0	2	301	79	222	20
Shelford	12	9	0	3	256	148	108	18
Newmarrket	12	8	1	3	247	126	121	17
Maldon	12	7	1	4	234	147	87	15
West Norfolk	12	8	2	2	255	107	148	14
Ely	12	7	0	5	249	135	114	14
Lowestoft & Y'm'th	12	7	0	5	207	148	59	14
Upminster	12	4	0	8	156	175	-19	8 .
Bancroft	12	4	0	8	160	215	-55	8
Wanstead	12	4	0	8	113	204	-91	8
Ravens	12	5	0	7	148	265	-117	8
Crusaders	12	3	0	9	91	283	-192	4
Met Pol Chigwell	12	0	0	12	34	494	-460	0

RAVENS RFC
Ground Address: c/o Fords Sports & Socail Club, Aldorough Road South, Newbury Park, Ilford, Essex. Tel: 081590 3797.
Club Secretary: Gerard Vallely, Flat 3, 18 Vernham Road, Plumstead, London, SE18 3EZ. Tel: (H) 081 855 8355 (W) 081 858 8001.
Press Officer: Richard Swan, 199 Gipsy Road, Welling, Kent, DA16 1HY. Tel: (H) 081 304 9549 (W) 081 858 8001.
Club Colours: Navy blue & gold hoops.

UPMINSTER RFC
Ground Address: Hall Lane Playing Fields, Hall Lane, Upminster, Essex. Tel:0708 220320.
Club Secretary: M Eve, 142 Cranston Park Avenue, Upminster, Essex, RM14 3XJ. Tel: 0708 225383 (W) 0708 858036.
Press Officer: V McEvoy, 16 Carlton Close, Upminster, Essex. Tel: (H) 0708 224307.
Club Colours: Blue & amber stripes.

WANSTEAD RFC
Ground Address: Roding Lane North, Ilford, Essex, IG8 8LY. Tel: 081 550 1561.
Club Secretary: M J Curry, 48, Wellesley Road, Wanstead, London, E11 2HF. Tel: (H) 081 989 0507 (W) 0850 801877.
Club Colours: Royal blue & white.

WEST NORFOLK RUFC
Ground Address: Gatehouse lane, North Wootton, King's Lynn, Norfolk. Tel: 0553 631307.
Club Secretary: J A Williams, 11 Silver Hill, Springwood, king's lynn, PE30 4TL. Tel: (H) 0553 760986 (W) 0603 627107.
Press Officer: M Ballman, 10 Shipdham Road, Toftwood, Dereham, Norfolk. Tel: (H) 0362 698289 (W) 0553 773393.
Club Colours: French grey with cerise band, navy blue shorts.

WYMONDHAM RUFC
Ground Address: Foster Harrison Memorial Ground, Tutles Lane, Wymonham, Norfolk. Tel: 0953 607332.
Club Secretary: M Warren, 67 Hawkes Lane, Bracon Ash, Norfolk. Tel: (H) 0508 70669 (W) 0603 616112.
Press Officer: S Dinneen, 108 West End, Old Costessey, Norwich, Norfolk. Tel: (H) 0603 742324 (W) 0603 212655.
Club Colours: Red & black.

LONDON & SOUTH EAST DIVISION

October 23 (Week 8)
Diss v Clacton
Loughton v Thetford
Ipswich Y.M.C.A v Crusaders
Holt v Lakenham-Hewett
Met. Police v Thames
East London v Old Bealonians

October 3O (Week X2)
Old Bealonians v Diss
Thames v East London
Lakenham-Hewett v Met. Police
Crusaders v Holt
Thetford v Ipswich Y.M.C.A.
Old Palmerians v Loughton

November 13 (Week (1O)
Diss v Thames
Clacton v Old Bealonians
Ipswich Y.M.C.A. v Old Palmerians
Holt v Thetford
Met. Police v Crusaders
East London v Lakenham-Hewett

November 2O (Week 11)
Thames v Clacton
Lakenham-Hewett v Diss
Crusaders v East London
Thetford v Met. Police
Old Palmerians v Holt
Loughton v Ipswich Y.M.C.A.

December 4 (Week 13)
Diss v Crusaders
Clacton v Lakenham-Hewett
Ols Bealonians v Thames
Holt v Loughton
Met. Police v Old Palmerians
East London v Thetford

December 11 (Week 14)
Lakenham-Hewett v Old Bealonians
Crusaders v Clacton
Thetford v Diss
Old Palmerians v East London
Loughton v Met. Police
Ipswich Y.M.C.A. v Holt

December 18 (Week 15)
Diss v Old Palmerians
Clacton v Thetford
Old Bealonians v Cruaders
Thames v Lakenham-Hewett
Met. Police v Ipswich Y.M.C.A.
East London v Loughton

January 8 (Week 18)
Crusaders v Thames
Thetford v Old Bealonians
Old Palmerians v Clacton
Loughton v Diss
Ipswich Y.M.C.A. v East London
Holt v Met. Police

January 29 (Week X5)
Diss V Ipwich Y.M.C.A.
Clacton v Loughton
Old Bealonians v Old Palmerians
Thames v Thetford
Lakenham-Hewett v Crusaders
East London v Hol

February 12 (Week 22)
Thetford v Lakenham-Hewett
Old Palmerians v Thames
Loughton v Old Bealonians
Ipswich Y.M.C.A v Clacton
Holt v Diss
Met. Police v East London

March 12 (Week 26)
Diss v Met. Police
Clacton v Holt
Old Bealonians v Ipswich Y.M.C.A.
Thames v Loughton
Lakenham-Hewett v Old Palmerians
Crusaders v Thetford

March 26 (Week 28)
Old Palmerians v Crusaders
Loughton v Lakenham-Hewett
Ipswich Y.M.C.A. v Thames
Holt v Old Bealonians
Met. Police v Clacton
East London v Diss

April 9 (Week 3O)
Clacton v East London
Old Bealonians v Met. Police
Thames v Holt
Lakenham-Hewett v Ipswich Y.M.C.A
Crusaders v Loughton
Thetford v Old Palmerians

CLACTON RUFC
Ground Address: Valley Road Recreation Ground, Clacton on Sea, Essex, CO15. Tel: 0255 421602.
Club Secretary: B W White, 80 Vista Road, Clacton on Sea, Essex, CO15 6JD. Tel: (H) 0255 432270 (W) 0255 222606.
Press Officer: B W White, 80 Vista Road, Clacton on Sea, Essex, CO15 6JD. Tel: (H) 0255 432270 (W) 0255 222606.
Club Colours: Maroon shirts, navy shorts.

CRUSADERS RFC
Ground Address: Little Melton, Norwich. Tel: 0603 811157.
Club Secretary: N D Loone, 24 St Clements Hill, Norwich, NR3 4BQ. Tel: (H) 0603 787943 (W) 0603 423429.
Press Officer: Darren Marsh, 43 The Lizard, Wymondham, Norfolk, NR18 9BH.
Club Colours: Gold & green hoops.

DISS RFC
Ground Address: Bellrope Lane, Roydon, Norfolk, Diss, QP22 3RG. Tel: 0379 642891.
Club Secretary: S R W Smith, East Cottage, 27 Scole Road, Brome Eye, Suffolk, IP23 8AS. Tel: (H) 0379 871084 (W) 0379 651931.
Press Officer: C N Potter, Mill Lane Farm, Mill Lane,Weybread, Diss, Norfolk. Tel: (H) 0379 86288.
Club Colours: Royal blue & white.

EAST LONDON RFC
Ground Address: Holland Road, West Ham, London, E15 3BP. Tel: 071 474 6761.
Club Secretary: R J Hames, 84 Forest ALpproach, Woodford Green, Essex. Tel: (H) 081 504 1477 (W) 0342 410166.
Press Officer: Brian Clos, 96A Rutland Road, Forest Gate, London, E7. Tel: (H) 081 552 4999 (W) 071 911 7127.
Club Colours: Maroon & navy hoops or quarters.

HOLT RFC
Ground Address: Bridge Road, High Kelling, Holt, Norfolk, NR25 6QT. Tel: 0263 712191.
Club Secretary: M D Bush, "The Warren", Sir Williams Lane, Aylsham, Norwich, NR11 6AW. Tel: (H) 0263 732051 (W) 0263 511264.
Club Colours: Black shirts, shorts & socks.

IPSWICH YM RUFC
Ground Address: The Street, Rushmere, Ipswich, Suffolk. Tel: 0473 713807.
Club Secretary: Steve Nunn, 7 Westwood Avenue, Ipswich, Suffolk, IP1 4EQ. Tel: (H) 0473 211865 (W) 0473 211865.
Press Officer: Mark Vaughan, 68 Levington Road, Ipswick, Suffolk, IP3 0HN. Tel: (H) 0473 718992 (W) 0473 240017.
Club Colours: Maroon & amber hoops.

LAKENHAM HEWETT RFC
Ground Address: Hill Tops Sports Ground, Main Road, Swardeston, Norwich. Tel: 05087 78826.
Club Secretary: Burnaby, Mill road, Hempnall, Norwich, Norfolk, NR15 2LP. Tel: (H) 0508 499342 (W) 0508 499342.
Press Officer: Steven Lacey, 51 Tinity Street, Norwich, NR2 2BH. Tel: (H) 0603 660803.
Club Colours: Red.

LOUGHTON RFC
Ground Address: Squirrels Lane, Hornbeam Road, Buckhurst Hill, Essex. Tel: 081 504 0065.
Club Secretary: Stephen King, 290 Blackhorse Lane, Walthamstow, London, E17 5QH. Tel: (H) 081 531 4466 (W) 071 792 1200.

FINAL TABLE

	P	W	D	L	F	A	PD	Pts
Wymondham	12	12	0	0	440	61	379	24
Harwich & Doverc't	12	9	1	2	323	52	271	19
Diss	12	9	0	3	236	75	161	16
Thames Sports	12	7	1	4	139	158	-19	15
Old Palmerians	12	8	1	3	102	136	-34	15
Thetford	12	7	0	5	173	169	4	14
Holt	12	7	0	5	141	154	-13	10
East London	12	5	0	7	116	197	-81	10
Old Bealonians	12	4	0	8	90	242	-152	8
Ipswich YMCA	12	3	0	9	95	167	-72	6
Lakenham Hewett	12	2	0	10	112	264	-152	4
S W'dham Ferrers	12	2	1	9	112	230	-118	3
Redbridge	12	1	0	11	88	311	-223	2

Press Officer: Michael Wardle, 61 The Drive, Loughton, Essex. Tel: (H) 081 508 2771.
Club Colours: White with black hoop between green hoops.

METROPOLITAN POLICE CHIGWELL RFC
Ground Address: Metropolitan Police Sports Club, Chigwell Hall, High Road, Chigwell, Essex. Tel: 081 500 2735.
Club Secretary: Malcolm Bartlett, 11 Fairfield Road, Ongar, Essex. Tel: (H) 0277 364206.
Club Colours: Royal blue shirts, black shorts, red socks.

OLD BEALONIANS RFC
Ground Address: Beal High School, Woodford Bridge Road, Ilford, Essex.
Club Secretary: N Dollie, 14A Electric Parade, George Lane, Soputh Woodford, E18 2LY. Tel: (H) 081 530 6366.
Press Officer: Mark Higginson, 5 Osprey Close, Hermon Hill, Wanstead, E11 1Sv. Tel: (H) 081 989 3617.
Club Colours: Scarlet.

OLD PALMERIANS RUFC
Ground Address: Palmers College, chadwell, Road, Grays, Essex. Tel: 0375 370121.
Club Secretary: Peter Slaughter, 77 Hope Avenue, Stanford-le- Hope, Essex, SS17 8DH. Tel: (H) 0375 361232 (W) 071 83 3267.
Press Officer: Andrew Busby, 76 Kiln Way, Badgers Dene, Grays, Essex. Tel: (H) 0375 386478.
Club Colours: Light blue & dark blue hoops.

THAMES RUFC
Ground Address: Thurrock Management Centre, Long Lane, Aveley, South Ockendon, Essex.
Club Secretary: Dave Northfield, 179 Blackshots Lane, Grays, Essex. Tel: (H) 0375 371125.
Press Officer: John Huckstepp, 136 Marlborough Gardens, Upminster, Essex. Tel: (H) 0708 228662.
Club Colours: Emerald & black hoops.

THETFORD RFC
Ground Address: Two Mile Bottom, Mundford Road, Thetford, Norfolk. Tel: 0842 755176.
Club Secretary: Paul Luml;ey, 2 Dial House, Old Market Street, Thetford, Norfolk, IP24 2EQ.
Press Officer: Andy Luckhurst, Thetford RFC, Two Mile Bottom, Mundford Road, Thetford, Norfolk. Tel: (H) 0953 83414 (W) 0847 755176.
Club Colours: Red & white hoops.

LONDON & SOUTH EAST DIVISION

EASTERN COUNTIES THREE
1993-94 FIXTURES

December 18 (Week 15)
Felixstowe v Sth. Woodham Ferrers
Fakenham v Haverhill
Thurston v Southwold
Stowmarket v Old Cooperians
London Hospital v Redbridge
Old Brentwoods v Beccles

October 23 (Week 8)
Felixstowe v Fakenham
Beccles v Haverhill
Redbridge v Southwold
Ilford Wanderers v Old Cooperians
London Hospital v Stowmarket
Old Brentwoods v Thurston

January 8 (Week 18)
Southwold v Stowmarket
Haverhill v Thurston
Sth. Woodham Ferrers v Fakenham
Beccles v Felixstowe
Redbridge v Old Brentwoods
Ilford Wanderers v London Hospital

October 3O (Week X2)
Thurston v Felixstow
Stowmarket v Old Brentwoods
Old Cooperians v London Hospital
Southwold v Ilford Wanderers
Haverhill v Redbridge
Sth. Woodham Ferrers v Beccles

January 29 (Week X5)
Felixstowe v Redbridge
Fakenham v Beccles
Thurston v Sth. Woodham Ferrers
Stowmarket v Haverhill
Old Cooperians v Southwold
Old Brentwoods v Ilford Wanderers

November 13 (Week 1O)
Felixstowe v Stowmarket
Fakeham v Thurston
Redbridge v Sth. Woodham Ferrers
Ilford Wanderers v Haverhill
London Hospital v Southwold
Old Brentwoods v Old Cooperians

February 12 (Week 22)
Haverhill v Old Cooperians
Sth. Woodham Ferrers v Stowmarket
Beccles v Thurston
Redbridge v Fakenham
Ilford Wanderers v Felixstowe
London Hospital v Old Brentwoods

November 2O (Week 11)
Stowmarket v Fakenham
Old Cooperians v Felixstowe
Southwold v Old Brentwoods
Haverhill v London Hospital
Sth. Woodham Ferrers v Ilford Wanderers
Beccles v Redbridge

March 12 (Week 26)
Felixstowe v London Hospital
Fakenham v Ilford Wanderers
Thurston v Redbridge
Stowmarket v Beccles
Old Cooperians v Sth. Woodham Ferrers
Southwold v Haverhill

December 4 (Week 13)
Felixstowe v Southwold
Fakenham v Old Cooperians
Thurston v Stowmarket
Ilford Wanderers v Beccles
London Hospital v Sth. Woodham Ferrers
Old Brentwoods v Haverhill

March 26 (Week 28)
Sth. Woodham Ferrers v Southwold
Beccles v Old Cooperians
Redbridge v Stowmarket
Ilford Wanderers v Thurston
London Hosptial v Fakeham
Old Brentwoods v Felixstowe

December 11 (Week 14)
Old Cooperians v Thurston
Southwold v Fakenham
Haverhill v Felixstowe
Sth. Woodham Ferrers v Old Brentwoods
Beccles v London Hospital
Redbridge v Ilford Wanderers

April 9 (Week 3O)
Fakenam v Old Brentwoods
Thurston v London Hospital
Stowmarket v Ilford Wanderers
Old Cooperians v Redbridge
Southwold v Beccles
Haverhill v Sth. Woodham Ferrers

EASTERN COUNTIES THREE

BECCLES RFC
Ground Address: Beef Meadow, Common Lane, Beccles, Suffolk. Tel: 0502 712016.
Club Secretary: David Smith, 4 The New Shipmeadow, Beccles, Suffolk, NR34 1HL. Tel: (H) 0502 711941 (W) 0502 715790. **Press Officer:** Michael Penneyu, 5 Hillcrest Close, Worlingham, Beccles, Suffolk.Tel: (H) 0502 715790.
Club Colours: Black & emerald quarters.

FAKENHAM RUFC
Ground Address: Old Wells Road, Fakenham, Norfolk. Tel: 0328 851007. **Club Secretary:** Alie Vogel, 2 Constitution Hill, Fakenham, Norfolk, NR1 9EF. Tel: (H) 0328 851218. **Press Officer:** Andy Buck, Old Wells Road, Fakenham, Norfolk. Tel: 0328 851007.
Club Colours: Black & light blue.

FELIXSTOWE RUFC
Ground Address: Coronation Sports Ground, Mill Lane, Felixstowe, Suffolk, IP11 8LN. Tel: 0394 270150.
Club Secretary: D A Richardson, 5 Estuary Drive, Felixstowe, Suffolk, IP11 9TL. Tel: (H) 0394 282423 (W) 0394 670845. **Press Officer:** D A Richardson, 5 Estuary Drive, Felixstowe, Suffolk, IP11 9TL. Tel: (H)0934 282423 (W) 0394 670845.
Club Colours: Black & white hooped shirt, black shorts.

HAVERHILL & DISTRICT RUFC
Ground Address: Castle Playing Fields, School Lane, Camps Road, Haverhill, Suffolk. Tel: 0440 702871.
Club Secretary: Clive D Farrow, 27 Broad Street, Haverhill, Suffolk, CB9 9HD. Tel: (H) 0440 63766. (W) 0440703551. **Press Officer:** Amdu Carr. 28 Bartlow Place, Haverhill, Suffolk. Tel: (H) 0440 61318.
Club Colours: Maroon & blue quarters, black shorts and socks.

ILFORD WANDERERS RFC
Ground Address: Ilford Wanderers RFC Sports Ground, Forest Road, Barkingside, Ilford, Essex. Tel: 081 500 4622. **Club Secretary:** Alan Lewis, 161A Aldborough Road, Seven Kings, Ilford, Essex, IG3 3HU. Tel: (H) 081 597 1158. **Press Officer:** D J Cutter, 41A Rose Valley, Brentwood, Essex. Tel: (H) 0277 222209.
Club Colours: Red, green & white.

LONDON HOSPITAL RFC
Ground Address: Hale End, London Hospital sports Ground, Wadham Road, Walthamstow, London, E17. Tel: 081 527 8996. **Club Secretary:** Dr P Colvin, 4 Hardy Road, Blackheath, London, SE3 7NR. Tel: (H) 081 858 0373 (W) 071 377 7793. **Press Officer:** Patrick Rea, London Hospital RFC, Clubs Union, Stedney Way, London, E1 2AD. Tel: (H) 071 790 4401 (W) 071 377 7641.
Club Colours: Navy & white chequers.

OLD BRENTWOODS RFC
Ground Address: Old Brentwoods Clubhouse, Ashwells Road, Bertley, Brentwood. Tel: 0277 374070.
Club Secretary: T J Faiers, "Archdale", 1 Woodway, Shenfield, Brentwood, Essex, CM15 8LP. Tel: (H) 0277 214503 (W) 081 592 4193. **Press Officer:** P Stroud, "Walden", Frog Street, Kelvedon Hatch, Brentwood, essex. Tel: (H) 0277 372974.
Club Colours: Light blue & dark blue hoops.

OLD COOPERIANS
Ground Address: Eastbrooke School, Dagenham Road, Dagenham, Essex.
Club Secretary: John C Green, Greenlow House, Royston Road, Melbourn, Hertfordshire, SG8 6DG. Tel: (H) 0763 260642 (W) 0279 652214. **Press Officer:** Geoff Brown, 12 Fairlawn Park, Woking, Surrey, GU21 4HT. Tel: (H) 0483 751176.
Club Colours: Dark blue with light blue & gold hoops.

FINAL TABLE

	P	W	D	L	F	A	PD	Pts
Loughton	12	12	0	0	298	111	187	24
Clacton	12	9	0	3	308	153	155	18
Old Cooperians	12	9	0	3	192	113	79	16
Ilford Wanderers	12	9	0	3	204	107	97	14
Fakenham	12	6	0	6	171	136	35	12
Stowmarket	12	6	0	6	158	146	12	12
Beccles	12	6	0	6	177	182	-5	12
Southwold	12	5	0	7	166	150	16	8
Haverhill	12	6	0	6	214	150	64	6
London Hospital	12	4	0	8	205	200	5	6
Old Brentwoods	12	2	0	10	79	525	-446	4
Wisbech	12	3	0	9	92	242	-150	4
Dereham	12	1	0	11	98	319	-221	2

REDBRIDGE RUFC
Ground Address: Blake Hall Sports Centre, Blake Hall Road, Wanstead. Tel: 081 989 1673.
Club Secretary: Graham King, 2 Old Fortune Cottages, Wash Road, Laindon, Essex. Tel: 0268 790536. **Press Officer:** Damion Crilley, Blake Hall Sports Centre, Blake HAll Road, Wanstead.
Club Colours: Navy blue & white quarters.

SOUTHWOLD RFC
Ground Address: The Pavillion, The Common, Southwold, Suffolk. **Club Secretary:** Andy Toone, 17 Portsck Close, Carlton Colville, Lowestoft, Suffolk, NR33 8TY. Tel: 0502 515649. **Press Officer:** Andy Toone, 17 Portsck Close, Carlton Colville, Lowestoft, Suffolk, NR33 8TY. Tel: 0502 515649.
Club Colours: Black with singleold gold hoop.

SOUTH WOODHAM FERRERS RFC
Ground Address: Saltcoats Park, Ferrers Road, South Woddham,. Ferrers, Essex. Tel: 0245 320041.
Club Secretary: S Williams, 2 Tusk Drive, South Woodham Ferrers, Essex, CM3 5RL. Tel: (H) 0245 325987. **Press Officer:** Christopher Bowers, 86 Hull Bridge Road, South Woodham, Ferrers, Essex, CM3 5LJ. Tel: (H) 0245 320014.
Club Colours: All black.

STOWMARKET RUFC
Ground Address: Chilton Fields Sports Club, Chilton Fields, Chilton Way, Stowmarket, Suffolk. Tel: 0449 613181.
Club Secretary: N A Pearman, 1 Semer Close, Stowmarket, Suffolk, IP14 2PB. Tel: (H) 0449 677288. (W) 0449 612401. **Press Officer:** M Barnard, The Old School House, Badwell ASh, Elmswell, suffolk. Tel: (H) 0359 259523.
Club Colours: Navy blue with white/red/white central band.

THURSTON RUFC
Ground Address: Robinson Field, Ixworth Road, Thurston, Suffolk. Tel: 0395 32450.
Club Secretary: Mark Abbas, The Fieldings, New Green, Thurston, Suffolk, IP31 3SD. Tel: (H) 0359 32546 (W) 0245 358522. **Press Officer:** Mark Abbas, The Fieldings, New Green, Thurston, Suffolk, IP31 3SD. Tel: (H) 0359 32546 (W) 0245 358522.
Club Colours: Navy blue shirts, blue shorts.

LONDON & SOUTH EAST DIVISION

EASTERN COUNTIES FOUR 1993-94 FIXTURES

December 18 (Week 15)
Dereham v Brightlingsea
Wisbech v Broadland
Swaffham v Essex Police
March v May & Baker
Burnham-on-Crouch v Billericay
Witham v Ongar

October 23 (Week 8)
Dereham v Wisbech
Ongar v Broadland
Billericay v Essex Police
Hadleigh v May & Baker
Burnham-on-Crouch v March
Witham v Swaffham

Janauary 8 (Week 18)
Essex Police v March
Broadland v Swaffham
Brightlingsea v Wisbech
Ongar v Dereham
Billericay v Witham
Hadleigh v Burnham-on-Crouch

October 3O (Week X2)
Swaffham v Dereham
March v Witham
May & Baker v Burnham-on-Crouch
Essex Police v Hadleigh
Broadland v Billericay
Brightlingsea v Ongar

January 29 (Week X5)
Dereham v Billericay
Wishbeck v Ongar
Swaffham v Brightlingsea
March v Broadland
May & Baker v Essex Police
Witham v Hadleigh

November 13 (Week 1O)
Dereham v March
Wishbeck v Swaffham
Billericay v Brightlingsea
Hadleigh v Broadland
Burnham-on-Crouch v Essex Police
Witham v May & Baker

February 12 (Week 22)
Broadland v May & Baker
Brightlingsea v March
Ongar v Swaffham
Billericay v Wisbech
Hadleigh v Dereham
Burnham-on-Crouch v Witham

November 2O (Week 11)
March v Wisbeck
May & Baker v Dereham
Essex Police v Witham
Broadland v Burnham-on-Crouch
Brightlingsea v Hadleigh
Ongar v Billericay

March 12 (Week 26)
Dereham v Burnham-on-Crouch
Wisbech v Hadleigh
Swaffham v Billericay
March v Ongar
May & Baker v Brightlingsea
Essex Police v Broadland

December 4 (Week 13)
Dereham v Essex Police
Wisbech v May & Baker
Swaffham v March
Hadleigh v Ongar
Burham-on-Crouch v Brightlingsea
Witham v Broadland

March 26 (Week 28)
Brightlingsea v Essex Police
Ongar v May & Baker
Billericay v March
Hadleigh v Swaffham
Burnham-on-Crouch v Wisbech
Witham v Dereham

December11 (Week 14)
May & Baker v Swaffham
Essex Police v Wisbech
Broadland v Dereham
Brightlingsea v Witham
Ongar v Burnham-on-Crouch
Billericay v Hadleigh

April 9 (Week 3O)
Wisbech v Witham
Swaffham v Burnham-on-Crouch
March v Hadleigh
May & Baker v Billericay
Essex Police v Ongar
Broadland v Brightlingsea

434

EASTERN COUNTIES FOUR

BILLERICAY RFC
Ground Address: Willowbrook, Stock Road, Billericay, Essex. Tel: 0277 841442.
Club Secretary: G J Buggle, 96 Norsey View Drive, Billericay, Essex, CM12 0QU. Tel: (W) 0375 677777.
Press Officer: R Best, 150 Seamore Avenue, Benfleet, Essex, SS7 4LA. Tel: (H) 0268 751800 (W) 0268 402080.
Club Colours: Black & gold.

BRIGHTLINGSEA RFC
Ground Address: Stranger Corner, Brightlingsea, Essex.
Club Secretary: J A McClure, 10 Pertwee Close, Brightlingsea, Essex, CO7 0RT. Tel: (H) 0206 304761 (W) 0268 525631.
Press Officer: J A McClure, 10 Pertwee Close, Brightlingsea, Essex, CO7 0RT. Tel: (H) 0206 304761 (W) 0268 525631.
Club Colours: Red shirts, black shorts.

BROADLAND RFC
Ground Address: Cobholm Pavillion, Cobholm Playing Fields, Cobholm, Great Yarmouth, Norfolk.
Club Secretary: Annette Blizzard, 30 Wolseley Road, Southtown, Great Yarmouth, Norfolk, NR31 0EJ. Tel: (H) 0493 440143 (W) 0493 657052.
Press Officer: Annette Blizzard, 30 Wolseley Road, Southtown, Great Yarmouth, Norfolk, NR31 0EJ. Tel: (H) 0493 440143 (W) 0493 657052.
Club Colours: Red, white & blue hoops.

BURNHAM-ON-CROUCH RFC
Ground Address: Dengie Hundred Sports Centre Playing Fields, Station Road, Burnham-on-Crouch, Essex, CM0 7BA. Tel: 0621 784633 (office) 0621 784656 (bar).
Club Secretary: Warwick H Bridge, 12 Glendale Road, Burnham-on- Crouch, Essex, CM0 8LY. Tel: (H) 0621 783807.
Press Officer: Phil Mounsey, 118 Maldon Road, Burnham,-on-Crouch, Essex, CM0 8DB. Tel: (H) 0621 783739.
Club Colours: Navy blue & amber hoops.

ESSEX POLICE RFC
Ground Address Police Headquarters, Chelmsford, Essex, CM2 6DA. Tel: 0245 452429.
Club Secretary: Mike Hall, 18 Queens Road, Chelmsford, Essex, CM2 6HA. Tel: (H) 0245 265794 (W) 0245 452429.
Press Officer: Mike Hall, 18 Queens Road, Chelmsford, Essex, CM2 6HA. Tel: (H) 0245 265794 (W) 0245 452429.
Club Colours: Royal blue & white.

DEREHAM RUFC
Ground Address: Moorgate, Dereham, Norfolk.
Club Secretary: Barbara Endersen, 1 Bayfield Avenue, Dereham, Norfolk, NR19 1PH. Tel: (H) 0362 691487.
Press Officer: Barbara Endersen, 1 Bayfield Avenue, Dereham, Norfolk, NR19 1PH. Tel: (H) 0362 691487.
Club Colours: Maroon with black & white hoops.

MARCH BRASA RUFC
Ground Address: Nesle-Wade Community College, Wimblington Road, March. Tel: 0354 56703.
Club Secretary: B Feetham, 13 Cherrywood Avenue, March, Cambridgeshire, PE15 9ST. Tel: (H) 0354 56703.
Club Colours: Maroon with white hoops.

MAY AND BAKER RUFC
Ground Address: Dagenaham Road, Dagenham, Essex. Tel: 081 919 3156.
Club Secretary: Terry Simmons, 105 Albion Road, Dagenham, Essex, RM10 8DE. Tel: (H) 081 593 2630 (W) 081 919 3564.
Club Colours: Black with single red hoop, black shorts.

FINAL TABLE

	P	W	D	L	F	A	PD	Pts
Felixtowe	11	10	1	0	208	70	138	19
Thurston	11	8	1	2	236	79	157	17
Hadleigh	11	8	1	2	209	130	83	15
Ongar	11	6	1	4	186	144	42	13
Billericay	11	6	0	5	198	163	35	12
Burnham-on-Crouch	11	4	2	5	254	160	94	10
Essex Polica	11	6	2	3	124	189	-65	10
Brightlingsea	11	5	1	5	165	152	13	9
March	11	4	0	7	137	165	-28	8
Witham	11	2	0	9	109	195	-86	4
Swaffham	11	1	1	9	82	274	-192	3
Norwich Union	11	1	0	10	73	331	-258	2
Stanford								0

HADLEIGH RUFC
Ground Address: Layham Road Sports Ground, Layham Road, Hadleigh, Ipswich, Suffolk. Tel: 0473 824217.
Club Secretary: Terry Sands, 4 Birch Road, Onehouse, Stowmarket, Suffolk. Tel: (H) 0449 67795 (W) 0473 658272.
Press Officer: Neil Farrow, 81 Angel Street, HAdleigh, Ipswich, Suffolk. Tel: (H) 0473 828385.
Club Colours: Maroon & white hoops.

ONGAR RUFC
Ground Address: Love Lane, High Street, Ongar. Tel: 0277 363888.
Club Secretary: Nigel Dourway, 105 Roundhills, Waltham Abbey, Essex. Tel: (H) 0992 763950 (W) 0992 788557.
Press Officer: Peter Hodgson, 16 Northcourt, Summerfields, Ingatestone, Essex, CM4 0BD. Tel: (H) 0277 354404 (W) 0836 615535.
Club Colours: Dark blue with amber band.

SWAFFHAM RUFC
Ground Address: North Pickenham Road, Swaffham, Norfolk. Tel: 0760 724829.
Club Secretary: H C Green, Gemini Cottage, Wearenham St Peter, Kings Lynn, PE32 2TD. Tel: (H) 0328 74269 (W) 0760 721281.
Press Officer: H C Green, Gemini Cottage, Wearenham St Peter, Kings Lynn, PE32 2TD. Tel: (H) 0328 74269 (W) 0760 721281.
Club Colours: Amber shirts, blue shorts & socks.

WISBECH RUFC
Ground Address: Chapel Lane, Harecroft Road, Wisbech, Cambridgeshire, PE13 1RG. Tel: 0945 63666.
Club Secretary: Jeremy Pallant, 139 Lynn Road, Wisbech, Cambridgeshire, PE13 3DH. Tel: (H) 0945 588147 (W) 0354 54321.
Press Officer: Jeremy Pallant, 139 Lynn Road, Wisbech, Cambridgeshire, PE13 1RG. Tel: (H) 0945 588147 (W) 0354 54321.
Club Colours: Red jersey, dark blue shorts.

WITHAM RUFC
Ground Address: Spa Road, Witham, Essex, CM8 1UN. Tel: 0376 511066.
Club Secretary: Tom Whelan, Shorlands, Highfields Road, Witham, Essex, CM8 2HJ. Tel: (H) 0326 515871.
Press Officer: Heather Turner, 1 Siward Road, Witham, Essex, CM8 1PL. Tel: (H) 0376 513883 (W) 0245 493444.
Club Colours: Brown & white hoops, navy shorts.

LONDON & SOUTH EAST DIVISION

EASTERN COUNTIES FIVE
1993-94
FIXTURES

December 18 (Week 15)
Watton v Norwich Union
Essex University v Chigwell
Leiston v Mersea Island
Mayfield Old Boys v Sawston
Dagenham v Burwell
Essex County Council v Mistley

October 23 (Week 8)
Watton v Essex University
Mistley v Chigwell
Burwell v Mersea Island
Stanford v Sawston
Dagenham v Mayfield Old Boys
Essex County Council v Leiston

January 8 (Week 18)
Mersea Island v Mayfield Old Boys
Chigwell v Leiston
Norwich Union v Essex University
Mistley v Watton
Burwell v Essex County Council
Stanford v Dagenham

October 3O (Week X2)
Leiston v Watton
Mayfield Old Boys v Essex County Council
Sawston v Dagenham
Mersea Island v Stanford
Chigwell v Burwell
Norwich Union v Mistley

January 29 (Week X5)
Watton v Burwell
Essex University v Mistley
Leiston v Norwich Union
Maygield Old Boys v Chigwell
Sawston v Mersea Island
Essex County Council v Stanford

November 13 (Week 1O)
Watton v Mayfield Old Boys
Essex University v Leiston
Burwell v Norwich Union
Stanford v Chigwell
Dagenham v Mersea Island
Essex County Council v Sawston

February 12 (Week 22)
Chigwell v Sawston
Norwich Union v Mayfield Old Boys
Mistley v Leiston
Burwell v Essex University
Stanford v Watton
Dagenham v Essex County Council

November 2O (Week 11)
Mayfield Old Boys v Essex University
Sawston v Watton
Mersea Island v Essex County Council
Chigwell v Dagenham
Norwich Union v Stanford
Mistley v Burwell

March 12 (Week 26)
Watton v Dagenham
Essex University v Stanford
Leiston v Burwell
Mayfield Old Boys v Mistley
Sawston v Norwich Union
Mersea Island v Chigwell

December 4 (Week 13)
Watton v Mersea Island
Essex University v Sawston
Leiston v Mayfield Old Boys
Stanford v Mistley
Dagenham v Norwich Union
Essex County Council v Chigwell

March 26 (Week 28)
Norwich Union v Mersea Island
Mistley v Sawston
Burwell v Mayfield Old Boys
Stanford v Leiston
Dagenham v Essex University
Essex County Council v Watton

December 11 (Week 14)
Sawston v Leiston
Mersea Island v Essex University
Chigwell v Watton
Norwich Union v Essex County Council
Mistley v Dagenham
Burwell v Stanford

April 9 (Week 3O)
Essex University v Essex County Council
Leiston v Dagenham
Mayfield Old Boys v Stanford
Sawston v Burwell
Mersea Island v Mistley
Chigwell v Norwich Union

436

BURWELL RFC
Ground Address: Fen Edge, The Recreation Ground, Hythe Lane, Burnwell, Cambridge.
Club Secretary: G J Humphris, 27 Casburn Lane, Burnwell. Tel: (H) 0638 741918 (W) 0638 741918.
Club Colours: Scarlet.

NELP (CHIGWELL) RUFC
Ground Address: High View, Lambourne Road, Chigwell, Essex.
Club Secretary: S Walters, 139 Femepiece Road, Hainault, Ilford, Essex, IG6 2LE. Tel: (H) 081 501 3863 (W) 071 265 4510.
Press Officer: S Walters, 139 Femepiece Road, Hainault, Ilford, Essex, IG6 2LE. Tel: (H) 081 501 3863 (W) 071 265 4510.
Club Colours: Black & maroon quarters.

DAGENHAM RUFC
Ground Address: Central Park, Dagenham, Essex.
Club Secretary: RJ Moreton, 21 Central Park Avenue, Dagenham, Essex RM10 7DA. Tel: (H) 081 984 8444 (W) 081 984 7505.
Press Officer: Gill Rogers, 2 Ashbrook Drive, Dagenham, Essex/ Tel: (H) 081 592 2053.
Club Colours: Red and white quarters.

ESSEX COUNTY COUNCIL RFC
Ground Address: Lordship Road, Writtle, Chelmsford, Essex. Tel: 0245 420400.
Club Secretary: D Sharp, 78 Albert Road, South Woodham Ferrers, Chelmsford, Essex. Tel: (H) 0245 323490 (W) 0268 702336.
Press Officer: Mark Boyden, 57 Fawkner Close, Chelmer Village, Chelmsford, CM2 6UP. Tel: (H) 0245 259196.
Club Colours: Red & white quarters.

ESSEX UNIVERSITY RUFC
Ground Address: University of Essex, Wivenhoe Park, Colchester. Tel: 0206 863211.
Club Secretary: James Woolin, Sports Fed Corridor, University of Essex, Wivenhoe Park, Colchester. Tel: (H) 0206 863211.
Press Officer: Jim Phillips, Sports Fed Corridor, University of Essex, Wivenhoe Park, Colchester. Tel: (H) 0206 8963211.
Club Colours: Red, white & black hoops.

DAGENHAM RUFC
Ground Address: Central Park, Dagenham, Essex.
Club Secretary: R J Moreton, 21 Cntral Park Avenue, Dagenham, Essex, RM10 7DA. Tel: (H) 081 984 8444 (W) 081 984 7505.
Press Officer: Gill Rogers, 2 Ashbrook Drive, Dagenham, Essex. Tel: (H) 081 592 2053.
Club Colours: Red & white quarters.

LEISTON RUFC
Club Secretary: Jim Robinson, 93 Saxmundham Road, Aldeburgh, Suffolk, IP15 5JF. Tel: (H) 0728 453774.
Press Officer: Jim Robinson, 93 Saxmundham Road, Aldeburgh, Suffolk, IP15 5JF. Tel: (H) 0728 453774.
Club Colours: Green shirts, black shorts, red socks.

MAYFIELD RUFC
Ground Address: Whitbread Playing Fields, Durham Avenue, Off Prospect Road, Woodford Green, Essex.
Club Secretary: Alan Gold, 6 Buxted Close, Buckhurst Hill, Essex, IG9 6BX. Tel: (H) 081 505 7084 (W) 0708 764083.
Press Officer: Alan Gold, 6 Buxted Close, Buckhurst Hill, Essex, IG9 6Bx. Tel: (H) 081 505 7084 (W) 0708 764083.
Club Colours: Green & white quarters.

FINAL TABLE

	P	W	D	L	F	A	PD	Pts
May & Baker	8	8	0	0	379	18	361	16
Broadland	8	6	0	2	295	56	239	12
Leiston	8	6	0	2	159	97	62	12
Burwell	8	4	0	4	91	164	-73	8
Sawston	8	3	1	4	68	113	-45	7
Mersea Island	8	3	0	5	123	159	-36	4
Mayfield Old Boys	8	3	0	5	102	178	-76	4
Chigwell	8	1	1	6	56	196	-140	1
Mistley	8	1	0	7	44	351	-307	0
Watton								0
Essex University,								0

MERSEA ISLAND RFC
Ground Address: Youth Camp, East Road, East Mersea, Essex.
Club Secretary: T Eves, Dormy House, Lower Road, Peldon, Essex, CO5 7QR. Tel: (H) 0206 735537.
Press Officer: T Eves, Dormy House, Lower Road, Peldon, Essex, CO5 7QR. Tel: (H) 0206 735537.
Club Colours: Blue & white quarters.

MISTLEY RUFC
Ground Address: Furze Hill, Mistley, Manningtree, Essex, CO11 2QL.
Club Secretary: D Ross, 27 Birch Avenue, Great Bentley, Essex, CO7 8LR. Tel: (H) 0206 250800 (W) 0376 321044.
Press Officer: R Wilson, 40 Pegasus Way, Colchester, Essex, CO4 4QE. Tel: (H) 0206 842174
Club Colours: Red & purple quarters.

NORWICH UNION RFC
Ground Address: Pinbanks, White Farm Lane, Harvey lane, Norwich, Norfolk. Tel: 0603 33752.
League Contact: Mark L Howell, 45 Belvozer Street, Earlham Road, Norwich, Norfolk. Tel: (H) 0603 614280 (W) 0603 681474.
Press Officer: Gareth Davis, 136 Gertrude Road, Norwich, NR3 4SF. Tel: (H) 0603 402159.
Club Colours: Green & white quarters, white shorts.

SAWSTON RUFC
Ground Address: Sawston Village College, New Road, Sawston, Cambridge, CB2 4BP. Tel: 0223 836615.
League Contact: Rene Genillard, 58 Lantree Crescent, Trumpington, Cambridge. Tel: (H) 0223 843985 (W) 071 620 2339 Ext 2253.
Press Officer: Rene Genillard, 58 Lantree Crescent, Trumpington, Cambridge. Tel: (H) 0223 843985 (W) 071 620 2339 Ext 2253.
Club Colours: Navy, black & white quarters.

STANFORD RFC
Ground Address: Billet Lane, Stanford Le Hope, Essex.
Club Secretary: Arlan Roach, 159 Lodge Lane, Grays, Essex, RM17 5PS. Tel: (H) 0375 377798 (W) 0860 790093.
Press Officer: Russel Jackson, 11 Fernside Close, Corringham, Essex. Tel: (H) 0375 644319.
Club Colours: Red & white hoops.

WATTON RFC
Ground Address: Watton RAF Station, Watton, Thetford.
Club Secretary: S Blackwood, 36 Queensway, Watton, Thetford, Norfolk, IP25 6BL. Tel: (W) 0953 884103 Ext 249.
Press Officer: Mike Bailey, 7 St Georges Close, Saham Toney, Watton, Norfolk.
Club Colours: Red & black quarters.

LONDON & SOUTH EAST DIVISION

LONDON TWO SOUTH 1993-94 FIXTURES

December 18 (Week 15)
Old Wimbledonians v Lewes
Thanet Wanderers v Worthing
Old Juddian v Westcombe Park
Old Blue v Carlton Park
K.C.S. Old Boys v Horsham
Old Reigatian v Sidcup

October 23 (Week 8)
Old Wimbledonians v Thanet Wanderers
Sidcup v Worthing
Horsham v Westcombe Park
Esher v Charlton Park.
K.C.S. Old Boys v Old Blues
Old Reigatian v Old Juddian

January 8 (Week 18)
Westcombe Park v Old Blues
Worthing v Old Juddian
Lewes v Thanet Wanderers
Sidcup v Old Wimbleonians
Horsham v Old Reigation
Esher v K.C.S. Old Boys

October 3O (Week X2)
Old Juddian v Old Wimbledonians
Old Blues v Old Reigatian
Charlton Park v K.C.S. Old Boys
Westcombe Park v Esher
Worthing v Horsham
Lewes v Sidcup

January 29 (Week X5)
Old Wimbledonians v Horsham
Thanet Wanderers v Sidcup
Old Juddian v Lewes
Old Blues v Worthing
Carlton Park v Westcombe Park
Old Reigation v Esher

November 13 (Week 1O)
Old Wimbledonians v Old Blues
Thanet Wanderers v Old Juddian
Horsham v Lewes
Esher v Worthing
K.C.S. Old Boys v Westcombe Park
Old Reigatian v Charlton Park

February 12 (Week 22)
Worthing v Charlton Park
Lewes v Old Blues
Sidcup v Old Juddian
Horsham v Thanet Wanderers
Esher v Old Wimbledonians
K.C.S. Old Boys v Old Reigatian

November 2O (Week 11)
Old Blues v Thanet Wanderers
Charlton Park v Old Wimbledonians
Westcombe Park v Old Reigatian
Worthing v K.C.S. Old Boys
Lewes v Esher
Sidcup v Horsham

March 12 (Week 26)
Old Wimbledonians v K.C.S. Old Boys
Thanet Wanderers v Esher
Old Juddian v Horsham
Old Blues v Sidcup
Charlton Park v Lewes
Westcombe Park v Worthing

December 4 (Week13)
Old Wimbledonians v Westcombe Park
Thanet Wanderers v Charlton Park
Old Juddian v Old Blues
Esher v Sidcup
K.C.S. Old Boys v Lewes
Old Reigatian v Worthing

March 26 (Week 28)
Lewes v Westcombe Park
Sidcup v Charlton Park
Horsham v Old Blues
Esher v Old Juddian
K.C.S. Old Boys v Thanet Wanderers
Old Reigatian v Old Wimbledonians

December 11 (Week 14)
Charlton Park v Old Juddian
Westcombe Park v Thanet Wanderers
Worthing v Old Wimbledonians
Lewes v Old Reigatian
Sidcup v K.C.S. Old Boys
Horsham v Esher

April 9 (Week 3O)
Thanet Wanderers v Old Reigatian
Old Juddian v K.C.S. Old Boys
Old Blues v Esher
Charlton Park v Horsham
Westcombe Park v Sidcup
Worthing v Lewes

438

LONDON TWO SOUTH

CHARLTON PARK RFC
Ground Address: Pippin Hall Sports Ground, Footscray Road, Eltham, London SE9. Tel: 850 0408.
Club Secretary: Andy Jackson, 45 Queenscroft Road, Eltham, London SE9 5EG. Tel: (H) 081 859 5727.
Press Officer: G Redman, 6 Glen Esk Road, Eltham, London SE9 1AG. Tel: (H) 081 859 0462.
Club Colours: Red & white shirts, dark blue shorts, red socks.

ESHER RFC
Ground Address: 369 Molesey Road, Hersham, Surrey KT12 3PF. Tel: 0932 220295.
Club Secretary: A R Till, 25 Motspur Park, New Malden, Surrey KT3 6PS. Tel: (H) 081 942 1380/
Club Colours: Black & amber.

HORSHAM RUFC
Ground Address: Hammer Pond Road, Coolhurst, Horsham, West Sussex. Tel: 0403 265027.
Club Secretary: Miss Debbie Pinchin, 13 Purton Road, Horsham, West Sussex RH12 2HB. Tel: (H) 0403 234614 (W) Answerphone 0403 270145.
Club Captain: Rod Merry, 3 Hernbrook Drive, Horsham, West Sussex. Tel: (H) 0403 251865.
Club Colours: Emerald green shirts & socks, white shorts.

K.C.S. OLD BOYS RFC
Ground Address: Arthur Road, Motspur Park, Surrey.
League Contact: John Hamilton, 1 Conway Road, Wimbledon, London SW20 8PB. Tel: (H) 081 946 7009 (W) 071 936 3000.
Club Secretary/Press Officer: Neil Crockford, 78 Claygate Lane, Hinchley Wood, Surrey KT10 0BJ. Tel: (H) 081 398 7474 (W) 081 547 2698.
Club Colours: Red, blue & old gold.

LEWES RFC
Ground Address: Stanley Tuner Ground, Kingston Road, Lewes, East Sussex. Tel: 0273 473732.
Club Secretary: Arthur Powell, 29 Cradle Hill Road, Seaford, East Sussex.
Press Officer: Phil Clark, 24 Cranedown, Lewes, East Sussex BN7 3NA. Tel: (H) 0273 476672 (W) 0273 209590.
Club Colours: Royal blue & white hoops.

OLD BLUES RFC
Ground Address: Arthur Road, Motspur Park, Surrey KT3 6PT. Tel: 081 542 1361.
League Contact: Giles Simons Club Secretary: Ian Hoskins, 1 Oak Tree Drive, Englefield Green, Surrey TW20 0NR. Tel: (H) 0784 436707.
Press Officer: John D Williams, 9 Lion Gate Gardens, Richmond, Surrey TW9 2DW. Tel: (H) 081 940 5579 (W) 081 684 0011.
Club Colours: Navy, cardinal & old gold.

OLD JUDDIAN RFC
Ground Address: Tonbridge Sports Ground, The Slade, Tonbridge, Kent. Tel: 0732 358548.
Club Secretary: Steve Davey, 35 Dowgate Close, Tonbridge, Kent TN9 2EH. Tel: (H) 0732 357429 (W) 0732 866066.
League Contact/Press Officer: Tony Russell, 28 Whistler Road, Tonbridge, Kent TB10 4RD. Tel: (H) 0732 355582.
Club Colours: Claret & light blue hooped jerseys, navy blue shorts.

OLD REIGATIAN RFC
Ground Address: ORS Field, Park Lane, Evigate, Surrey RH2 8JX. Tel: 0737 245634.
Club Secretary: T Budgen. League Contact: John Buchanan, 37 Greenwood Drive, White Bushes, Redhill, Surrey RH1 5PH. Tel: (H) 0737 762 330 (W) 0737 765 040.
Club Colours: Green, blue, white hoops.

FINAL TABLE

	P	W	D	L	F	A	PD	Pts
Camberley	12	10	2	0	241	94	147	22
Westcombe Park	12	9	1	2	279	135	144	19
Esher	12	7	0	5	201	189	12	14
KCS Old Boys	12	7	0	5	170	176	-6	14
Old Juddian	12	6	1	5	274	299	-25	13
Old Blues	12	6	0	6	269	141	128	12
Old Reigatian	12	6	0	6	242	165	77	12
Charlton Park	12	6	0	6	238	182	56	10
Worthing	12	5	0	7	178	228	-50	10
Thanet Wands	12	5	0	7	182	234	-52	10
Lewes	12	5	0	7	134	226	-32	10
Gravesend	12	3	0	9	146	218	-72	6
US Portsmouth	12	1	0	11	110	390	-380	2

OLD WIMBLEDONIANS RFC
Ground Address: 104 Cottenham Park Road, Raynes Park, London SW20 0TZ. Tel: 081 879 0700.
Club Secretary: Charlie O'Rourke, 103 Cannon Hill Lane, Merton Park, London SW20 9LE. Tel: (H) 081 540 6615 (W) 081 424 0382.
Press Officer: John Morey, 60 Burwood Road, Hersham, Walton on Thames KT12 4AJ. Tel: (H) 0932 222707.
Club Colours: Maroon, green & gold hoops.

SIDCUP FC (RFU)
Ground Address: Crescent Farm, Sydney Road, Main Road, Sidcup, Kent DA14 6RA. Tel: 081 300 2336.
Club Secretary: Allan Jones, 53 Goodwin Drive, Sidcup, Kent DA14 4NX. Tel: (H) 081 302 2382.
Press Officer: A H Marsh, 25 Broomfield Road, Sevenoaks, Kent TN13 3EL. Tel: (H) 0732 453964.
Club Colours: White (Change: Maroon).

THANET WANDERERS RUFC
Ground Address: St Peters Recreation Ground, Callis Court Road, Broadstairs, Kent. Tel: 0843 861499.
Club Secretary: Peter Hawkins, 51 Park Road, Ramsgate, Kent CT11 9TL. Tel: (H & W) 0843 593142.
Press Officer: Julian Sowden, 164 Grange Road, Ramsgate, Kent CT11 9PR. Tel: (H) 0843 590028.
Club Colours: Blue, black & yellow hoops.

WESTCOMBE PARK RFC
Ground Address: Goddington Dene, Goddington Lane, Orpington, Kent BR6 9SH. Tel: 0689 834902.
Club Secretary: Robin Taylor, 24 Pinchbeck Road, Green Street Green, Orpington, Kent BR6 6DR. Tel: (H) 0689 855052 (W) 081 310 9868 (Car) 0374 212029.
Press Officer: John Ward Turner, Westerham Lodge, Westerham Road, Keston, Kent BR2 6DA. Tel: (H & W) 0689 854868 (Mobile) 0836 526959 (Fax) 0689 860246.
Club Colours: Navy & white hoops, navy shorts, navy & white hooped hose.

WORTHING RFC
Ground Address: The Rugby Park, Roundstone Lane, Angmering, West sussex. Tel: 0903 784706.
Club Secretary: Brian Vincent, 29 St Botolph's Road, Worthing, West Sussex. Tel: (H) 0903 206516 (W) 0903 236572.
Press Officer: Wally Stapleton, 18 Westlake Close, Worthing, West Sussex. Tel: (H) 0903 692019.
Club Colours: Blue, chocolate & gold hoops.

LONDON & SOUTH EAST DIVISION

LONDON THREE
SOUTH EAST
1993-94 FIXTURES

December 18 (Week 15)
Tunbridge Wells v Canterbury
Gillingham Anchorians v Old Beccehamians
Old Brockleians v Hove
Beckenham v Erith
Brighton v Haywards Heath
East Grinstead v Chichester

October 23 (Week 8)
Tunbridge Wells v Gillingham Anchorians
Chichester v Old Beccehamians
Haywards Heath v Hove
Gravesend v Erith
Brighton v Beckenham
East Grinstead v Old Brockleians

October 3O (Week X2)
Old Brockleians v Tunbridge Wells
Beckenham v East Grinstead
Erith v Brighton
Hove v Gravesend
Old Beccehamians v Haywards Heath
Canterbury v Chichester

November 13 (Week 1O)
Tunbridge Wells v Beckenham
Gillingham Anchorians v Old Brockleians
Haywards Heath v Canterbury
Gravesend v Old Beccehamians
Brighton v Hove
East Grinstead v Erith

November 2O (Week 11)
Beckenham v Gillingham Anchorians
Erith v Tunbridge Wells
Hove v East Grinstead
Old Beccehamians v Brighton
Canterbury v Gravesend
Chichester v Haywards Heath

December 4 (Week 13)
Tunbridge Wells v Hove
Gillingham Anchorians v Erith
Old Brockleians v Beckenham
Gravesend v Chichester
Brighton v Canterbury
East Grinstead v Old Beccehamians

December 11 (Week 14)
Erith v Old Brockleians
Hove v Gillingham Anchorians
Od Beccehamians v Tunbridge Wells
Canterbury v East Grinstead
Chichester v Brighton
Haywards Heath v Gravesend

January 8 (Week 18)
Hove v Beckenham
Old Beccehamians v Old Brockleians
Canterbury v Gillingham Anchorians
Chichester v Tunbridge Wells
Haywards Heath v East Grinstead
Gravesend v Brighton

January 29 (Week X5
Tunbridge Wells v Haywards Heath
Gillingham Anchorians v Chichester
Old Brockleians v Canterbury
Beckenham v Old Beccehamians
Erith v Hove
East Grintead v Gravesend

February 12 (Week 22)
Old Beccehamians v Erith
Canterbury v Beckenham
Chichester v Old Brockleians
Haywards Heath v Gillingham Anchorians
Gravesend v Tunbridge Wells
Brighton v East Grinstead

March 12 (Week 26)
Tunbridge Wells v Brighton
Gillingham Anchorians v Gravesend
Old Brockleians v Haywards Heath
Beckenham v Chichester
Erith v Canterbury
Hove v Old Beccehamians

March 26 (Week 28)
Canterbury v Hove
Chichester v Erith
Haywards Heath v Beckenham
Gravesend v Old Brockleians
Brighton v Gillingham Anchorians
East Grinstead v Tnbridge Wells

April 9 (Week 3O)
Gllingham Anchorians v East Grinstead
Old Brockleians v Brighton
Beckenham v Gravesend
Erith v Haywards Heath
Hove v Chichester
Old Beccehamians v Canterbury

440

LONDON THREE SOUTH EAST

BECKENHAM RFC
Ground Address: Balmoral Avenue, Elmers End, Beckenham, Kent, BR3 3RD. Tel: 081 650 7176.
Club Secretary: D B Davies, 6 Garden Court, Oaklands Road, Bromley, Kent, BR1 3SN. Tel: (H) 081 290 5403 (W) 081 741 1742.
Press Officer: John Snelders, 87 Meadowview Road, Catford, SE6 3NL. Tel: (H) 081 697 5563.
Club Colours: Royal blue & old gold hoops.

BRIGHTON RFC
Ground Address: Waterhall Playing Fields, Waterhall Road, Patcham, Brighton, Sussex, BN1 8YR. Tel: 0273 562729.
Club Secretary: S Bucklingham, 21 Victoria Street, Brighton, East Sussex, BN1 3FQ. Tel: (H) 0273 738234 (W) 0273 739211.
Press Officer: Frank Howard, 29 Benvan Road, Worthing, West Sussex, BN11 1HY.
Club Colours: Blue shirts, red socks.

BROCKLEIANS RFC
Ground Address: Eltham Palace Road, Eltham, SE9. Tel: 081 850 8650.
Club Secretary: R J C Ellery, 13 Peacock Gardens, Selsdon, Surrey, CR2 8TE. Tel: (H) 081 657 7973.
Club Colours: Chocolate, emerald and old gold.

CANTERBURY RFC
Ground Address: The Pavilion, Merton Lane, Canterbury, Kent. Tel: 0227 768958.
Club Secretary: Bill Davis, 62 Pier Avenue, Herne Bay, Kent, CT6 8PG. Tel: (H) 0227 741921 (W) 0622 750069.
Press Officer: David Haigh, Brambletye, Grove Road, Wickhambreaux, Littlebourne, Canterbury, Kent. Tel: (H) 0227 721411 (W) 0227 721411.
Club Colours: Black & amber.

CHICHESTER RFC
Ground Address: Oaklands Park, Chichester, West Sussex (entrance via Wellington Road). Tel: 0243 779820.
Club Secretary: Roger Harden, Beach Lodge, 186 Elmer Road, Middleton on Sea, West Sussex, PO20 6JA. Tel: (H) 0243 586379 (W) 0243 587306.
Press Officer: Roger Harcen, Beach Lodge, 186 Elmer Road, Middleton on Sea, West Sussex, PO20 6JA. Tel: (H) 0243 586379.
Club Colours: Darl & light blue hoops, dark blue shorts.

EAST GRINSTEAD RFC
Ground Address: Saint Hill Road, East Frinstead, West Sussex. Tel: 0342 322338.
Club Secretary: Philip Evans, 21 Hackenden Close, East Grinstead, West Sussex. Tel: (H) 0342 314413 (W) 0732 865023.
Press Officer: Steve Thompson, 6 Medway Drive, Forst Row, East Sussex, RH18 5WT. Tel: (H) 0342 822599/
Club Colours: Blue shirts with broad white hoop.

ERITH RFC
Ground Address: Northumberland Heath Playing Fields, Sussex Road, Erith, Kent. Tel: 03224 32295.
Club Secretary: J N McConville, 18 Buxton Road, Erith, Kent, DA8 3BS. Tel: (H) 0322 337064 (W) 081 303 5696.
Press Officer: E Reynolds, 5 Littleheath Road, Bexleyheath, Kent. Tel: 0322 440625.
Club Colours: Light & dark blue hoops.

GILLINGHAM ANCHORIANS RFC
Ground Address: Anchorians Club, Darland Avenue, Gillingham, Kent.
Club Secretary: J C R Jennings, 49 Marghall Road, rainham, Gillingham, Kent, ME8 0AW. Tel: (H) 0634 233431 (W) 0634 851182.

FINAL TABLE

	P	W	D	L	F	A	PD	Pts
Horsham	12	10	1	1	304	114	190	21
Brighton	12	9	1	2	202	121	81	19
Old Beccehamian	12	8	1	3	171	147	24	17
Hove	12	8	0	4	204	260	44	16
Beckenham	12	7	0	5	172	101	71	14
East Grinstead	12	6	0	6	171	148	23	12
Gillingham Anchor	12	5	0	7	156	153	3	10
Erith	12	5	0	7	94	142	-48	10
Tunbridge Wells	12	5	0	7	128	207	-73	10
Chichester	12	4	1	7	133	218	-85	9
Old Brockleians	12	4	0	8	198	137	61	8
Dartfordians	12	4	0	8	161	238	-77	8
Crawley	12	1	0	11	69	277	-208	2

Press Officer: M Cripps, 2 Derwent WKay, Rainham, Kent. Tel: (H) 0634 373156.
Club Colours: Purple, black & silver hoops, black shorts.

GRAVESEND RFC
Ground Address: Milton Road, Gravesend, Kent. Tel: 0474 534840.
Club Secretary: A C Panter, 21 Studley Crescent, L:ongfield, Dartford, Kent, DA3. Tel: (H) 0474 702202 (W) 071 962 1421.
Press Officer: R Bardell, 18 Parrock Avenue, Gravesend, Kent, DA12 1QQ. Tel: (H) 0474 320256 (W) 081 882 6121.
Club Colours: Black & white hoops.

HAYWARDS HEATH RFC
Ground Address: Whitemans Green, Cuckfield, Haywards Heath, West Sussex. Tel: 0444 413950.
Club Secretary: M K cook, 7 Wickham Close, Haywards Heath, West Sussex, RH16 1UH. Tel: (H) 0444 452327 (W) 071 753 1972.
Press Officer: I Beckett, 94 Sunnywood Drive, Haywards Heath, West Sussex. Tel: (H) 0444 412576 (W) 0737 224828.
Club Colours: Red & black.

HOVE RFC
Ground Address: Hove Park, Hove, East Sussex. Tel: 0273 505103.
Club Secretary: Mike Richardson, 6 Wayside, Westdene, Brighton, East Sussex, BN1 5HL. Tel: (H) 0273 500512 (W) 081 644 4388.
Club Colours: Maroon 7 sky blue hoops.

OLD BECCEHAMIAN RFC
Ground Address: Sparrows Den, Corkscrew Hill, West Wickham, Kent, BR4 9BB.
Club Secretary: F Ternent, 15 Tone Cross, Farm Cottages, Ashurst, Tunbridge Wells, Kent, TN3 9TA. Tel: (H) 0892 740057 (W) 081 663 0067.
Press Officer: F Ternent, 15 Tone Cross, Farm Cottages, Ashurst, Tunbridge Wells, Kent, TN3 9TA. Tel: (H) 0892 740057 (W) 081 663 0067.
Club Colours: Black, white & maroon hoops.

TUNBRIDGE WELLS RUFC
Ground Address: The Clubhouse, St Mark's Playing Fields, Frant Road, Tunbridge Wells, Kent. Tel: 0892 527448.
Club Secretary: Roger Clarke, 4 Wallace Close, Tunbridge Wells, Kent, TN2 5JW. Tel: (H) 0892 536748 (W) 0293 619998.
Press Officer: J R Bagwell, 4 Broom Park, Langton Green, Tunbridge Wells, Kent. Tel: (H) 0892 862488.
Club Colours: White & royal blue hoops, white shorts.

LONDON & SOUTH EAST DIVISION

KENT ONE
1993-94
FIXTURES

December 18 (Week 15)
Dartfordians v Sevenoaks
Bettershanger v Met. Police
Shepey v Park House
Bromley v Nat. West. Bank
New Ash Green v Medway
Thames Polytechnic v Old Dunstonians

October 23 (Week 8)
Dartfordians v Betteshanger
Old Dunstonians v Met. Police
Medway v Park House
Snowdown C.W. v Nat. West Bank
New Ash Green v Bromley
Thames Polytechnic v Sheppey

January 8 (Week 18)
Park House v Bromley
Met. Police v Hayes
Sevenoaks v Bettshanger
Old Dunstonians v Dartfordians
Medway v Thames Polytechnic
Snowdown C.W. v New Ash Green

October 3O (Week X2)
Sheppey v Dartfordians
Bromley v Thames Polytechnic
Nat. West. Bank v New Ash Green
Park House v Snowdown C.W.
Met.Police v Hayes
Sevenoaks v Old Dunstonians

January 29 (Week X5)
Dartfordians v Medway
Betteshanger v Old Dunstonians
Sheppey v Sevenoaks
Bromley v Met. Police
Nat. West. Bank v Park House
Thames Polytechnic v Snowdown C.W.

November 13 (Week 1O)
Dartfordians v Bromley
Bettershanger v Sheppey
Medway v Sevenoak
Snowdown C.W. v Met.Police
New Ash Green v Park House
Thames Polytechnic v Nat. West. Bank

February 12 (Week 22
Met. Police v Hayes
Sevenoaks v Bromley
Old Dunstonians v Sheppey
Medway v Betteshanger
Snowdown C.W. v Deartfordians
New Ash Green v Thames Polytechnic

November 2O (Week 11)
Bromley v Betteshanger
Nat. West. Bank v Dartfordians
Park House v Thames Polytechnic
Met. Police v Hayes
Sevenoaks v Snowdown C.W.
Old Dunstonians v Medway

March 12 (Week 26)
Dartfordians v New Ash Green
Betteshanger v Snowdown C.W.
Sheppey v Medway
Bromley v Old Dunstonians
Nat. West. Bank v Sevenoaks
Park House v Met. Police

December 4 (Week 13)
Dartfordians v Park House
Betteshanger v Nat.West.Bank
Sheppey v Bromley
Snowdown C.W. v Old Dunstonians
New Ash Green v Sevenoaks
Thames Polytechnic v Met. Police

March 26 (Week 28)
Sevenoaks v Park House
Old Dunstonians v Nat. West. Bank
Medway v Bromley
Snowdown C.W. v Bromley
New Ash Green v Betteshanger
Thames Plytechnic v Dartfordians

December 11 (Week 14)
Nat. West. Bank v Sheppey
Park House v Betteshanger
Met. Police v Hayes
Sevenoaks v Thames Polytechnic
Old Dunstonians v New Ash Green
Medway v Snowdown C.W.

April 9 (Week 3O)
Betteshanger v Thames Polytechnic
Sheppey v New Ash Green
Bromley v Snowdown C.W.
Nat. West. Bank v Old Dunstonians
Met. Police v Hayes

KENT ONE

BETTERSHANGER CW RFC
Ground Address: Welfare Ground, Cavell Square, Deal,
Kent. Tel: 0304 365090.
Club Secretary: Bob Pinnick, 65 Courtenay Road, Dunkirk,
Faversham, Kent, ME13 9LH. Tel: (H) 0227 750530.
Press Officer: Gerald Griffiths, 52 Thornbridge Road,
Deal, Kent. Tel: (H) 0304 374249.
Club Colours: Red & white hoops.

BROMLEY RFC
Ground Address: Barnet Wood Road, Hayes, Kent, BR2
7AA. Tel: 081 462 3430.
Club Secretary: J T A Bromage, 4 Sunningdale Road,
Bromley, Kent. Tel: (H) 081 467 4375 (W) 071 403 1171.
Press Officer: R S Pereira, 19 Blackbrook lane, Bromley,
Kent. Tel: (H) 081 467 8389 (W) 0737 226918.
Club Colours: Black & yellow hoops.

DARTFORDIANS RFC
Ground Address: Memorial Clubhouse, Bourne Road,
Bexley, Kent. Tel: 0322 524176.
Club Secretary: Jack Morris, 7 Irving Way, Swanley,
Kent, BR8 7EP. Tel: (H) 0322 669817.
Press Officer: T Kirk, 103 Avenue Road, Bexleyheath,
Kent. Tel: (H) 0322 340601.
Club Colours: Maroon & old gold shirt, navy shorts.

MEDWAY RFC
Ground Address: Priestfields, Rochester, Kent, ME1
3AD. Tel: 0634 817737.
Club Secretary: J Hillier, 9 Oxford Road, Gillingham,
Kent, ME7 4BP.
Press Officer: M Chaudrey, 38 St John's Way, Borstal,
Rochester, Kent. Tel: (H) 0634 401025.
Club Colours: Scarlet & gold hoops, navy blue shorts.

METROPOLITAN POLICE HAYES RFC
Ground Address: The Warren, Croydon Road, Hayes,
Kent. Tel: 081 462 1266.
Club Secretary: Mr Chris McHale, 37 West Avenue,
Wallington, Surrey SM6 8PH. Tel: (H) 081 462 1797 (W)
081 649 3035.
Club Colours: Blue & maroon quarters, black shorts.

NATIONAL WESTMINSTER BANK RFC
Ground Address: Copers Cope Road, Lower Sydenham,
Kent, BR3 1NZ. Tel: 081 650 9217/4559.
Club Secretary: Copers Cope Road, Lower Sydenham,
Kent, BR3 1NZ. Tel:081 650 9217/4559.
Press Officer: G W C Teale, 17 Queensway, Coney Hall,
West Wickham, Kent, BR4 9EP. Tel: (H) 081 462 9288
(W) 071 726 1702.
Club Colours: Light & dark blue regular hoops.

NEW ASH GREEN RFC
Ground Address: The Pavilion, New Ash Green, Kent.
Tel:0474 874660.
Club Secretary: K Milner, Ash House, Ash Road, New
Ash Green, Kent, DA3 9JD. Tel: (W) 0474 872746.
Press Officer: I Huston, Thorn Public Relations, Prospect
House, 11 Lonsdale Gardens, Tunbridge Wells, Kent, TN1
1NU. Tel: (H) 0474 87200 (W) 0892 511871.
Club Colours: Green & black quarters.

OLD DUNSTONIAN RFC
Ground Address: The Clubhouse, St Dunstans Lane,
Langley Park, Beckenham, Kent, BR3 3SS. Tel: 081 650 1779.
Club Secretary: M A Rogers, "Aboyne", Pickhurst Lane,
West Wickham, Kent, BR4 0HN. Tel: 081 462 3064
(W) 071 379 7383.
Press Officer: M A Rogers, "Aboyne", Pickhurst Lane,
West Wickham, Kent, BR4 0HN. Tel: (H) 081 462 3064
(W) 071 379 7383.
Club Colours: Navy blue & white circlet.

FINAL TABLE

	P	W	D	L	F	A	PD	Pts
Canterbury	12	11	0	1	289	79	210	22
Sevenoaks	12	10	1	1	339	104	235	21
Park House	12	10	0	2	254	117	137	20
Old Dunstonians	12	7	1	4	219	143	76	15
Snowdon CW	12	6	0	6	126	189	-63	12
Met Pol Hayes	12	5	2	5	120	203	-83	12
Bromley	12	5	1	6	214	136	18	11
Medway	12	5	1	6	177	217	-40	11
Betteshanger	12	5	0	7	136	153	-17	10
New Ash Green	12	5	0	7	194	214	-20	10
Sheppey	12	5	0	7	157	194	-37	10
Tonbridge	12	1	0	11	103	264	-161	2
Sittingbourne	12	0	0	12	82	337	-255	0

PARK HOUSE FC
Ground Address: Barnet Wood Road, Hayes, Bromley,
Kent. Tel: 081 462 7318.
Club Secretary: Jim Ferguson, "Amelanchier", Weavering
Street, Bearsted, Maidstone, Kent, ME14 7JF. Tel: (H)
0622 630377 (W) 0622 717341.
Press Officer: Patrick Solan, 23 Marion Crescent, St Mary
Cray, Orpington, Kent, BR5 2DE. Tel: (H) 0689 874658.
Club Colours: Black & red.

SEVENOAKS RFC
Ground Address: Knole Paddock, Plymouth Drive,
Sevenoaks, Kent. Tel: 0732 452027.
Club Secretary: Howard Pearl, 10 Barnfield Road,
Riverhead, Sevenoaks, Kent, TN13 2AY. Tel: (H) 0732
451641.
Press Officer: Richard Mais, 79 Seal hollow Road,
Sevenoaks, Kent, TN13 3RY. Tel: (W) 0732 454886 (W)
0895 846464.
Club Colours: Blue & yellow hoops.

SHEPPEY FC
Ground Address: The Ditch, Lower Road, Minster,
Sheerness, Kent, ME12. Tel: 0792 872082.
Club Secretary: Linda Neal, 16 New Road, Minster,
Sheerness, Kent, ME12 3PX. Tel: (H) 0795 873983 (W)
0622 832160 Ext 2511.
PRess Officer: Darren Yates, 120 High Street, Eastchurch,
Sheerness, Kent. Tel: (H) 0795 880219.
Club Colours: White with red hoop, black shorts.

SNOWDOWN COLLIERY WELFARE RFC
Ground Address: Welfare Ground, Aylesham, Canterbury,
Kent. Tel: 0304 840278.
Club Secretary: E J Sullivan, 4 Burgess Road, Aylesham,
Canterbury, Kent. Tel: (H) 0304 840052.
Club Colours: Red & blue hoops.

THAMES POLYTECHNIC RFC
Ground Address: Kidbrook Lane, Eltham, London, SE9
6TA. Tel: 081 850 1221.
Club Secretary: G O (Dusty) Miller, 85 Earlshall Road,
London, SE9 1PP. Tel: (H) 081 850 2794.
Press Officer: John Belfield, 117 Pickhurst Lane, Haynes,
Kent, BR2 7HU. Tel: (H) 081 462 1465.
Club Colours: Green with red, gold & red bands.

LONDON & SOUTH EAST DIVISION

<table>
<tr><td>

KENT TWO
1993-94
FIXTURES

</td></tr>
</table>

December 18 Week 15)
Deal v Bexley
Midland Bank v Ashford
Lloyds Bank v Old Shootershillians
Dover v Sittingbourne
Tonbridge v Vigo
Cranbrook v Old Elthamians

October 23 (Week 8)
Deal v Midland Bank
Old Elthamians v Ashford
Vigo v Old Shootershillians
Folkestone v Sittingbourne
Tonbridge v Dover
Cranbrook v Lloyds Bank

January 8 (Week 18)
Old Shootershillians v Dover
Ashford v Lloyds Bank
Bexley v Midland Bank
Old Elthamians v Deal
Vigo v Cranbrook
Folkestone v Tonbridge

October 3O (Week X2)
Lloyds Bank v Deal
Dover v Cranbrook
Sittingborne v Tonbridge
Old Shootershillians v Folkestone
Askford v Vigo
Bexley v Old Elthamians

January 29 (Week X5)
Deal v Vigo
Midland Bank v Old Elthamians
Lloyds Bank v Bexley
Dover v Ashford
Sittingbourne v Old Shootershillians
Cranbrook v Folkestone

November 13 (Week 1O)
Deal v Dover
Midland Bank v Lloyds Bank
Vigo v Bexley
Folkestone v Ashford
Tonbridge v Old Shootershillians
Cranbrook v Sittingbourne

February 12 (Week 22)
Ashford v Sittingborne
Bexley v Dover
Old Elthamians v Lloyds Bank
Vigo v Midland Bank
Folkestone v Deal
Tonbridge v Cranbrook

November 2O (Week 11)
Dover v Midland Bank
Sittingbourne v Deal
Old Shootershillians v Canbrook
Ashford v Tonbridge
Bexley v Folkestone
Old Elthamians v Vigo

March 12 (Week 26)
Deal v Tonbridge
Midland Bank v Folkestone
Lloyds Bank v Vigo
Dover v Old Elthamians
Sittingbourne v Bexley
Old Shootershillians v Ashford

December 4 (Week 13)
Deal v Old Shootershillians
Midland Bank v Sittingbourne
Lloyds Bank v Dover
Folkestone v Old Elthamians
Tonbridge v Bexley
Cranbrook v Ashford

March 26 (Week 28)
Bexley v Old Shootershillians
Old Elthamians v Sittingbourne
Vigo v Dover
Folkestone v Lloyds Bank
Tonbridge v Midland Bank
Cranbook v Deal

December 11 (Week 14)
Sittingborne v Lloyds Bank
Old Shootersillians v Midland Bank
Ashford v Deal
Bexley v Cranbrook
Old Elthamians v Tonbridge
Vigo v Folkeston

April 9 (Week 3O)
Midland Bank v Cranbrook
Lloyds Bank v Tonbridge
Dover v Folkestone
Sittingbourne v Vigo
Old Shootershillians v Old Elthamians
Ashford v Bexley

KENT TWO

ASHFORD (KENT) RFC
Ground Address: Kinneys Field, Bybrook Ground, Canterbury Road, Bybrook, Ashford, Kent. Tel: 0233 624693.
League Contact: Colin Yalden, 23 Weavers Way, Ashford, Kent, TN23 2DY. Tel: (H) 0233 640905 (W) 0622 673737.
Press Officer: Colin Yalden, 23 Weavers Way, Ashford, Kent, TN23 2DY. Tel: (H) 0233 640905 (W) 0622 673737.
Club Colours: Red, gold & black hoops.

BEXLEY RFC
Ground Address: Hall Place Park, Bourne Road, Bexley, Kent. Tel: 0322 556198.
League Contact: Mr J Butler, 39 Baldwyns Road, Bexley, Kent. Tel: (H) 0322 522693.
Press Officer: D Dalgliesh, 9 Albert Road, Bexley, Kent. Tel: (H) 0322 558010 (W) 071 936 3000.
Club Colours: Royal blue & white hoops, blue shorts.

CRANBROOK RFC
Ground Address: Tomlin Ground, Angley Road, Cranbrook, Kent, TN17 3LB. Tel: 0580 891448.
Club Secretary: David Davies, Beeches, Station Road, Staplehurst, Kent, TN12 0QG. Tel: (H) 0880 891448. (W) 081 686 9568.
Press Officer: Richard Thomas, 3 Boarden cottages, Hawkenbury, Staplehurst, Kent, TN12 0EB. Tel: (H) 0580 893381 (W) 0580 713250.
Club Colours: Magenta & white.

DEAL WANDERERS SPORTS CLUB RUFC
Ground Address: Western Road, Deal, Kent. Tel: 0304 365892.
Club Secretary: R Dorling, 13 Halstatt Road, Deal, Kent. Tel: (H) 0304 363629
Press Officer: Jane Dorling, 13 Halstatt Road, Deal, Kent. Tel: (H) 0304 363629.
Club Colours: Blue & yellow hoops.

DOVER RFC
Ground Address: Crabble Athletics Ground, Crabble Road, River, Dover, Kent. Tel: 0304 210296.
Club Secretary: J D Thomas, Karma, Minnis Lane, River, Dover, Kent, CT17 0PT. Tel: (H) 0304 822169.
Press Officer: J D Thomas, Karma, Minnis Lane, River, Dover, Kent, CT17 0PT. Tel: (H) 0304 822169.
Club Colours: Light & dark blue hoops.

FOLKESTONE RFC
Ground Address: New Burlington Field, Bargrove, Newington, Folkeston, Kent, CT18 8BH. Tel: 0303 266887.
Club Secretary: B Keating, Carbery, Church Hill, Hythe, Kent, CT21 5DW. Tel: (H) 0303 264604 (W) 0303 850206.
Press Officer: B Keating, Carbery, Church Hill, Hythe, Kent, CT21 5DW. Tel: (H) 0303 264604 (W) 0303 850206.
Club Colours: Green & white hoops.

LLOYDS BANK RFC
Ground Address: Lloyds Bank Sports Club, Copers Cope Road, Beckenham, Kent. Tel: 081 658 3818.
Club Secretary: Bob Brazier, 2 Crushes Close, Hutton, Brentwood, Essex. Tel: (H) 0277 213626 (W) 0277 227272.
Press Officer: Bob Brazier, 2 Crushes Close, Hutton, Brentwood, Essex, Tel: (H) 0277 213626 (W) 0277 227272.
Club Colours: White with magenta & black horizontal hoops.

MIDLAND BANK RFC
Ground Address: Lennard Road, New Beckenham, Kent. Tel: 081 778 7784.
Club Secretary: J D R Hayhow, Five Trees, 36 Holbrook Lane, Chislehurst, BR7 6PF. Tel: (H) 081 467 3314. (W) 071 623 9333.
Club Colours: Bottle Green shirts, navy shorts.

FINAL TABLE

	P	W	D	L	F	A	PD	Pts
Thames Polytech	12	10	1	1	218	94	124	21
Nat West Bank	12	9	2	1	213	114	99	20
Folkestone	12	9	1	2	220	129	91	19
O. Shootershillians	12	9	0	3	247	85	162	18
Ashford	12	7	0	5	145	138	7	14
Old Elthamians	12	6	0	6	181	119	62	12
Dover	12	5	1	6	143	194	-51	11
Deal	12	5	0	7	121	176	-55	10
Midland Bank	12	4	1	7	166	182	-16	9
Vogo	12	4	0	8	131	127	4	8
Bexley	12	4	0	8	74	164	-90	8
Linton	12	3	0	9	104	181	-77	6
O. Gravesendians	12	0	0	12	108	368	-260	0

OLD ELTHAMIANS RFC
Ground Address: Foxbury Avenue, Chislehurst, Kent, BR7 6HA. Tel: 081 467 14296.
Club Secretary: Gareth Evinson, 23 Woodmere, Court Road, Eltham, SE9 5NT. Tel: (H) 081 850 7400 (W) 071895 2643.
Press Officer: Ian McKinnon, 25 The Gardens, Beckenham, Kent, BR3 2PH. Tel: (H) 081 650 1936 (W) 0634 200844.
Club Colours: Amber & royal blue hoops.

OLD SHOOTERSHILLIANS RFC
Ground Address: Entrance between 123 & 125 Mayday Gardens, Kidbrook, London, SE3. Tel: 081 856 1511.
Club Secretary: Kevin Bailey, 13 Linden Avenue, Dartford, Kent, DA1 2RA. Tel: (H)0322 276192 (W) 0344 426826.
Press Officer: Neil Sharp, 17 Denver Road, Dartford, Kent. Tel (H) 0322 225643.
Club Colours: Red, blue, green & yellow.

SITTINGBOURNE RUFC
Ground Address: UK Paper Leisure Club, Gore Court Road, Sittingbourne, Kent. Tel: 0795 477047.
Club Secretary: J Chapman, 4 Morris Court Close, Bapchild, Sittingbourne, Kent, ME9 9PL. Tel: (H) 0795 475668 (W) 0634 271681.
Press Officer: Steve Smith, 34 Crouch Hill Court, Lower Halstow, Sittingbourne, Kent, ME9 7EJ. Tel: (H) 0795 843356 (W) 0753 672215.
Club Colours: Amber with single blue hoop.

TONBRIDGE RFC
Ground Address: The Clubhouse, Avebury Avenue, Tonbridge, Kent. Tel: 0732 350067.
Club Secretary: James Lark, 7 Newton Avenue, Tonbridge, Kent, TN10 4RP. Tel: (H) 0732 354581 (W) 0732 368326.
Press Officer: James Lark, 7 Newton Avenue, Tonbridge, Kent, TN10 4RP. Tel: (H) 0732 354581 (W) 0732 368326.
Club Colours: Chocolate & old gold hoops.

VIGO RFC
Ground Address: Swanswood Filed, Harvel Road. Tel: 0732 823830
Club Secretary: M Hughes, Rose Cottage, Ashbank, Leed, Maidstone, Kent, ME17 1RJ. Tel: (H) 0622 861115 (W) 0474 813783
Press Officer: D Pugh, 458 London Road, Ditton, Kent, ME20 6BZ. Tel: (H) 0732 841025 (W) 0622 883358.
Club Colours: Red jersey, black shorts.

LONDON & SOUTH EAST DIVISION

KENT THREE
1993-94
FIXTURES

October 23 (Week 8)
Linton v Old Gravesendians
Darenth Valley v Lordswood
Whitstable v STC Footscray
Citizens v Kent Police
Old Williamsonians v Orpington

October 3O (Week X2)
Kent Police v Linton
Orpington v Darenth Valley
Lordswood v Whitstable
STC Footscray v Citizens
Old Williamsonians v Old Gravesendians

November 13 (Week 1O)
Linton v STC Footscray
Old Gravesendians v Kent Police
Darenth Valley v Old Williamsonians
Citizens v Lordswood
Whitstable v Orpington

November 2O (Week 11)
STC Footscray v Old Gravesendians
Lordswood v Linton
Orpington v Citizens
Kent Police v Old Williamsonians
Darenth Valley v Whitstable

December 4 (Week 13)
Linton v Orpington
Old Gravesendians v Lordswood
Kent Police v STC Footscray
Old Williamsonians v Whitstable
Citizens v Darenth Valley

December 11 (Week 14)
Lordswood v Kent Police
Orpington v Old Gravesendians
Darenth Valley v Linton
Whitstable v Citizens
Old Williamsonians v STC Footcray

January 29 (Week X5)
Linton v Whitstable
Old Gravesendians v Darenth Valley
Kent Police v Orpington
STC Footscray v Lordswood
Citizens v Old Williamsonians

February 12 (Week 22)
Orpington v STC Footscray
Darenth Valley v Kent Police
Whitstable v Old Gravesendians
Citizens v Linton
Lordswood v Old Williamsonians

March 12 (Week 26)
Linton v Old Williamsonians
Old Gravesendians v Citizens
Kent Police v Whitstable
STC Footscray v Darenth Valley
Lordswood v Orpington

KENT THREE

CITIZENS RFC
Ground Address: UCL Athletic Ground, Perry Street, Chislehurst, Kent. Tel: 081 467 3859.
Club Secretary: C R Southgate, 122 The Ridgeway, Enfield, Middlesex, EN2 8JN. Tel: (H) 081 366 5791 (W) 081 367 5840.
Press Officer: C R Southgate, 122 The Ridgeway, Enfield, middlesex, EN2 8JN. Tel: (H) 081 366 5791 (W)081 367 5840.
Club Colours: Black with red & white hoops.

DARENTH VALLEY RFC
Ground Address: Leigh City Technology College, Green Street, Green Road, Dartford, Kent.
Club Secretary: Tony Fish, 4 Elm Cottages, Station Road, Eynsford, Kent, DA4 0ET. Tel: (H) 0322 862908 (W) 0322 224716.
Press Officer: Malcolm Elson, 3A Pilgrims Way, Dartford, Kent, DA1 1QZ. Tel: (H) 0322 287930.
Club Colours: Black shirts with white V, black shorts.

KENT POLICE RFC
Ground Address: Kent Poilice Headquarters, Sutton Road, Maidstone, Kent, ME15 9DZ. Tel: 0622 690690.
Club Secretary: Stephen Rose, 29 Sutton Road, Maidstone, Kent, ME15 9AE. Tel: (H) 0622 661979 (W) 0622 690055.
Press Officer: Carl Bramwell, 2 Greensands, Bearsted, Kent. Tel: (H) 0622 737465 (W) 0622 690055.
Club Colours: Red, white & blue bands.

LINTON RFC
Ground Address: Mote Park, Maidstone, Kent. Tel: 0622 754770.
Club Secretary: Kevin D Burbidge, 77 Holborough Road, Snodland, Kent, ME6 5PA. Tel: (H) 0634 242147 (W) 0474 337571.
Press Officer: Martin wells, 28 Charles Street, Maidstone, Kent, ME16 8ET. Tel: (H) 0622 683294 (W) 081 308 5629.
Club Colours: Red.

LORDSWOOD RFC
Ground Address: Marin Grove, North Dane Way, Lordswood, Chatham, Kent. Tel: 0634 669138.
Club Secretary: Andy Foley, 10 Bankside, Chatham, Kent. Tel: (H) 0634 404664 (W) 071 955 5000 Ext 2371.
Press Officer: Andy Foley, 10 Bankside, Chatham, Kent. Tel: (H) 0634 404664 (W) 071 955 5000 Ext 2371.
Club Colours: Black & amber irregular hoops, black shorts.

OLD GRAVESENDIANS RFC
Ground Address: Fleetway Sports Ground, Bronte View, Parrock Road, Gravesend, Kent. Tel: 0474 365503.
Club Secretary: Tim Mulholland, 9 Milton Court, Gravesend, Kent, DA12 1ND. Tel: (H) 0474 325895 (W) 071 601 5222.
Press Officer: Roger Ryan, 13 Christchurch Crescent, Gravesend, Kent. Tel: (H) 0474 365256 (W) 0474 365256.
Club Colours: Light & dark blue hoops.

OLD WILLIAMSONIAN RFC
Ground Address: Sir Joseph Williamson's Mathematical School, Maidstone Road, Rochester, Kent. Tel: 0634 842883.
Club Secretary: Simon Riddiford, 72 Castle Avenue, Rochester, Kent ME1 2SY. Tel: (H) 0634 408511.
Press Officer: Alan Brassell, 6 Stockleigh Court, St Leonards-on- Sea, East Sussex. Tel: (H) 0424 714910.
Club Colours: Navy blue with single gold hoop.

FINAL TABLE

	P	W	D	L	F	A	PD	Pts
Cranbrook	9	7	0	2	203	80	123	14
Lloyds Bank	9	6	0	3	128	105	23	12
STC Footscray	9	6	0	3	86	73	13	12
Old Williamsonians	9	5	0	4	111	80	31	10
Orpington	9	4	1	4	89	98	-9	9
Citizens	9	4	1	4	100	110	-10	9
Whitstable	9	4	0	5	125	122	3	8
Kent Polica	9	3	1	5	106	124	-18	7
Old Olavians	9	2	1	6	56	116	-60	5
Greenwich	9	2	0	7	88	184	-96	4

ORPINGTON RUFC
Ground Address: Hoblingwell Wood, Leesons Way, St Paul's Cray, Orpington, Kent, BR5. Tel: 0689 823913.
Club Secretary: Rachel Ridgeon, 4 Neville Close, Sidcup, Kent, DA15 7HF. Tel: (H) 081 300 5523.
Press Officer: Rachel Ridgeon, 4 Neville Close, Sidcup, Kent, DA15 7HF. Tel: (H) 081 300 5523.
Club Colours: Black & amber hoops.

STC FOOTSCRAY RUFC
Ground Address: Maidstone Road, Sidcup, Kent. Tel: 081 300 1504.
Club Secretary: Steve Roberts, 279 Burn Oak Lane, Sidcup, Kent, DA15 8LR. Tel: (H) 081 302 7141 (W) 0753 679253.
Club Colours: Blue & gold hoops.

WHITSTABLE RFC
Ground Address: Whitstable Waterfront Club, Beach Walk, Whitstable, Kent, CT5 1BU. Tel: 0227 265500.
Club Secretary: Dr R Petts, 9 Collingwood Road, Whitstable, Kent, CT5 2EJ. Tel: (H) 0227 277916.
Press Officer: Richard Davies, 72 Sydenham Street, Whitstable, Kent, CT5 1HL. Tel: (H) 0227 265245.
Club Colours: Blue & white hoops, white shorts.

LONDON & SOUTH EAST DIVISION

KENT FOUR
1993-94
FIXTURES

March 12 (Week 26)
Old Olavians v Faversham
Westerham v Edenbridge
Centurians v Greenwich

October 23 (Week 8)
Westerham v Old Olavians
Centurians v Edenbridge
Faversham v Greenwich

October 3O (Week X2)
Old Olavians v Centurians
Westerham v Faversham
Edenbridge v Greenwich

November 13 (Week 1O)
Centurians v Westerham
Greenwich v Old Olavians
Faversham v Edenbridge

November 2O (Week 11)
Old Olavians v Edenbridge
Westerham v Greenwich
Centurians v Faversham

December 4 (Week 13)
Greenwich v Centurians
Edenbridge v Westerham
Faversham v Old Olavians

December 11 (Week 14)
Old Olavians v Westerham
Edenbridge v Centurians
Greenwich v Faversham

January 8 (Week 18)
Greenwich v Edenbridge
Centurians v Old Olavians
Faversham v Westerham

January 29 (Week X5)
Edenbridge v Faversham
Westerham v Centurians
Old Olavians v Greenwich

February 12 (Week 22)
Greenwich v Westerham
Faversham v Centurians
Edenbridge v Old Olavians

KENT FOUR

CENTURIONS RFC
Ground Address: New Burlington Field, Barrgrove,
Newington. Tel: 0303 266887.
Club Secretary: Jack Godley, 3 Ferguson Close,
Sealbrook, Hythe, Kent. Tel: (H) 0303 267431 (W) 0233
625789.
Press Officer: Jack Godley, 3 Gerguson Close, Sealbrook,
Hythe, Kent. Tel: (W) 0233 625789.
Club Colours: Green & gold.

EDENBRIDGE RUFC
Ground Address: Recreation Ground, Lingfield Road,
Edenbridge. Tel: 0732 862435.
Club Secretary: R Peacock, 13 Hitchin Hatch Lane,
Sevenoaks, Kent, TN13 3AU. Tel: (H) 0732 461327 (W)
071 353 4881.
Press Officer: R Peacock, 13 Hitchin Hatch Lane,
Sevenoaks, Kent, TN13 3AU. Tel: (H) 0732 461327 (W)
071 353 4881.
Club Colours: Black & amber hoops.

FAVERSHAM RFC
Ground Address: Faversham Recreation Ground, Park
Road, Faversham, Kent.
Club Secretary: Pat Rowan, 14 Abbey Street, Faversham,
Kent, ME13 7BH. Tel: (H) 0795 590252.
Press Officer: Pat Rowan, 14 Abbey Street, Faversham,
Kent, ME13 7BH. Tel: (H) 0795 590252.
Club Colours: White & sky blue quarters, navy shorts.

GREENWICH RFC
Ground Address: The Pavilion, Old Mill Road,
Plumstead, London, SE18. Tel: 081 854 8637.
Club Secretary: A J Smith, 41 Ashen Drive, Dartford,
Kent, DA1 3L2. Tel: (H) 0322 222832.
Press Officer: A J Smith, 41 Ashen Drive, Dartford, Kent,
DA1 3L2. Tel: (H) 0322 222832.
Club Colours: Red & black quarters, black shorts.

OLD OLAVIANS RFC
Ground Address: St Olave's School, Gollington Lane,
Orpington, Kent. Tel: 0689 830744.
Club Secretary: S R Gill, 19 Forrwich Close, Orpington,
Kent, BR6 0TT. Tel: (H) 0689 836858.
Club Colours: Purple, black & white.

WESTERHAM RFC
Ground Address: King George Playing Fields,
Westerham, Kent.
Club Secretary: S Richardson, 44 Pennycroft, Off Pixton
Way, Forestdale, CR0 9LL. Tel: (H) 081 651 4302 (W) 081
654 3181.
Press Officer: S Richardson, 44 Pennycroft, Off Pixton
Way, Forestdale, CR0 9LL. Tel: (H) 081 651 4302 (W) 081
654 3181.
Club Colours: Black & white quarters.

FINAL TABLE

	P	W	D	L	F	A	PD	Pts
Lordswood	10	9	0	1	291	64	227	18
Darenth Valley	10	8	0	2	241	102	139	16
Edenbridge	10	6	0	4	98	74	24	12
Westerham	10	5	0	5	141	125	16	10
Centurians	10	2	0	8	103	236	-133	2
East Peckham	10	0	0	10	41	314	-273	0

LONDON & SOUTH EAST DIVISION

October 23 (Week 8)
Uckfield v Hastings & Bexhill
Ditchling v Eastbourne
Crowborough v Old Brightonians
Heathfield & Wald v Bognor
B. A. Wingspan v Burgess Hill
Crawley v Seaford

Ooctober 3O (Week X2)
Burgess Hill v Uckfield
Bognor v B.A. Wingspan
Old Brightonians v Heathfield & Wald
Eastbourne v Crowborough
Crawley v Ditchling
Seaford v Hastings & Bexhill

November 13 (Week 1O)
Uckfield v Bognor
Hastings & Bexhill v Burgess Hill
Crowborough v Crawley
Heathfield & Wald v Eastbourne
B. A. Wingspan v Old Brightonians
Ditchling v Seaford

November 2O (Week 11)
Bognor v Hastings & Bexhill
Old Brightonians v Uckfield
Eastbourne v B. A. Wingspan
Crawley v Heathfield & Wald
Ditchling v Crowborough
Seaford v Burgess Hill

December 4 (Week 13)
Uckfield v Eastbourne
Hastings & Bexhill v Old Brightonians
Burgess Hill v Bognor
Heathfield & Wald v Ditchling
B. A. Wingspan v Crawley
Crowborough v Seaford

December 11 (Week14)
Old Brightonians v Burgess Hill
Eastbourne v Hastings & Bexhill
Crawley v Uckfield
Ditchling v B. A. Wingspan
Crowborough v Heathfield & Wald
Seaford v Bogno

January 8 (Week 18)
Uckfield v Ditchling
Hastings & Bexhill v Crawley
Burgess Hill v Eastbourne
Bognor v Old Brightonians
B. A. Wingspan v Crowborough
Heathfield & Wald v Seaford

January 29 (Week X5)
Eastbourne v Bognor
Crawley v Burgess Hill
Ditchling v Hastings & Bexhill
Crowborough v Uckfield
Heathfield & Wald v B.A. Wingspan
Seaford v Old Brightonians

February 12 (Week 22)
Uckfield v Heathfield & Wald
Hastings & Bexhill v Crowborough
Burgess Hill v Ditchling
Bognor v Crawley
Old Brightonians v Eastbourne
B. A. Wingspan v Seaford

March 12 (Week 26)
Crawley v Old Brightonians
Ditchling v Bognor
Crowborough v Burgess Hill
Heathfield & Wald v Hastings & Bexhill
B. A. Wingspan v Uckfield
Seaford v Eastbourne

March 26 (Week 28)
Uckfield v Seaford
Hastings & Bexhill v B. A. Wingspan
Burgess Hill v Heathfield & Wald
Bognor v Crowborough
Old Brightonians v Ditchling
Eastbourne v Crawley

450

SUSSEX ONE

BRITISH AIRWAYS (WINGSPAN) RFC
Ground Address: Benbush Leisure Centre, Benbush, Breezehurt Drive, Crawley, West Sussex. Tel: 0293 546477.
Club Secretary: C Townsend, 6 Manor Road, East Grinstead, West Sussex, RH19 1LR. Tel: (H) 0342 322508.
Press Officer: H Townsend, 6 Manor Road, East Grinstead, West Sussex, RH19 1LR. Tel: (H) 0342 322508.
Club Colours: Blue with white band & red stripe.

BOGNOR RFC
Ground Address: Hawthorn Road, Bognor Regis, West Sussex. Tel: 0243 865462.
Club Secretary: Guy Tompkins, 11 Gilwynes, Aldwick Fields, Bognor Reigs, West Sussex, PO21 3SG. Tel: (H) 0243 868643 (W) 081 995 8465.
Press Officer: Purple, green & white hoops, black shorts.

BURGESS HILL RFC
Ground Address: Southway Playing Fields, Poveys Close, Burgess Hill, West Sussex. Tel: 0444 232221.
Club Secretary: Tim McDermott-Roe, Beavers, Norman Road, Burgess Hill, West Sussex, RH15 9TG. Tel: (H) 0444 243736 (W) 071 337 3151.
Press Officer: Mark Parsons, 16 Parkside, Burgess Hill, West Sussex. Tel: (H)0444 870429 (W) 071 438 4335.
Club Colours: All black.

CRAWLEY RFC
Ground Address: Willoughby Field, 1 Field Avenue, Crawley, Sussex. Tel: 0293 533995.
Club Secretary: Ray Lloyd, 105 Gales Drive, Three Bridges, Crawley, Sussex, RH10 1QD. Tel: (H) 0243 536664 (W) 071 865 5723.
Club Colours: Maroon & blue.

CROWBOROUGH RFC
Ground Address: Steel Cross, Crowborough, East Sussex. Tel: 0892 654832.
Club Secretary: Gavin Tyler, 109 Fermor Way, Crowborough, East Sussex, TN6 3BY. Tel: (H) 0892 665153 (W) 0892 515121.
Press Officer: Nick Mitchell, 109 Fermor Way, Crowborough, East Sussex, TN6 3BY. Tel: (H) 0892 665153 (W) 0892 515121.
Club Colours: Red & white hoops.

DITCHLING RFC
Ground Address: Ditchling Recreations Ground, Lewes Road, Ditchling, East Sussex. Tel: 0273 843423.
Club Secretary: Justin Walden, 10 Station Road, Burgess Hill, West Sussex, RH15 9DQ. Tel: (H) 0444 239347 (W) 1444 235664.
Press Officer: Steve Broth, 49 West Hill Street, Brighton, East Sussex, BN1 3RS. Tel: (H) 0273 321614 (W) 0737 770170.
Club Colours: Myrtle green.

EASTBOURNE RDC
Ground Address: Park Avenue, Hampden Park, Eastbourne, East Sussex. Tel: 0323 503076.
Club Secretary: Richard Platt, 289 Willingdon Road, Eastbourne, East Sussex, BN20 9AJ. Tel: (H) 0323 500286 (W) 071 4303163.
Press Officer: R Dunbavin, 33 Deane Drive, Eastbourne. Tel: (H) 0323 500709.
Club Colours: Blue & yellow hoops.

FINAL TABLE

	P	W	D	L	F	A	PD	Pts
Haywards Heath	11	11	0	0	365	82	283	22
Hastings & Bexhill	11	9	1	1	228	100	128	19
H'thf'ld & Waldren	11	8	0	3	215	107	108	16
Bognor	11	7	0	4	218	134	84	14
Uckfield	11	7	0	4	152	109	43	14
Seaford	11	6	0	5	156	131	25	12
Eastbourne	11	5	0	6	146	176	-30	10
Burgess Hill	11	4	1	6	170	196	-26	9
Crowborough	11	4	0	7	97	177	-80	8
Old Brightonians	11	3	0	8	133	204	-71	6
Hellingly	11	1	0	10	54	320	-266	2
St Francis	11	0	0	11	72	270	-198	0

HASTINGS & BEXHILL RFC
Ground Address: The Polegrove, Brockley Road, Bexhill-on-Sea. Tel: 0424 210224.
Club Secretary: R W Ellis, 24 Cranston Avenue, Bexhill-on-Sea, East Sussex, TN39 3QD. Tel: (H) 0424 731486 (W) 0424 439888.
Press Officer: Mr J Harris. Tel: (H) 0424 225632.
Club Colours: Blue & white hoops.

HEATHFIELD & WALDRON RFC
Ground Address: Hardy-Roberts Recreation Ground, Cross In Hand, Heathfield, East Sussex.
Club Secretary: P Mercer, Mapsedge, Cross in Hand, Heathfield, East Sussex. Tel: (H) 0435 863396 (W) 0424 433061.
Press Officer: B Burdett, 22 Bay Tree Close, Heathfield, East Sussex, TN21 8YG. Tel: (H) 0435 862825.
Club Colours: Grenn & white hoops.

OLD BRIGHTONIAN RFC
Ground Address: The Club House, c/o Brighton RFC, Waterhall Valley, Patcham, Brighton, Sussex. Tel: 0273 562729.
Club Secretary: F P Rumney, 17 Benett Drive, Hove, Sussex, BN3 6PL. Tel: (H) 0273 501981 (W) 0273 501981.
Press Officer: F P Rumney, 17 Benett Drive, Hove, Sussex, BN3 6PL. Tel: (H) 0273 501981 (W) 0273 501981.
Club Colours: Light blue, magenta & navy hoops.

SEAFORD RFC
Ground Address: Salts REcreation Ground, The Esplanade, Seaford, Sussex. Tel: 0323 392020.
Club Secretary: E A Pugh, "Shottery", 19 Chyngton Road, Seaford, Sussex, BN25 4HL. Tel: (H) 0323 892020.
Press Officer: G Shiret, 3 Downs Road, Seaford, Sussex. Tel: (H) 0323 895719.
Club Colours: Scarlet shirts, navy blue shorts.

UCKFIELD RFC
Ground Address: Hempstead Playing fields, Manor Park, Uckfield, Sussex. Tel: 0825 768956.
Club Secretary: Mr J Miller, 8 Streele View, Uckfield, Sussex, TN22 1UG. Tel: (H) 0825 767861 (W) 0892 503143.
Press Officer: Mr J Miller, 8 Streele View, Uckfield, Sussex, TN22 1UG. Tel: (H) 0825 767861 (W) 0892 503143.
Club Colours: Amber & purple.

LONDON & SOUTH EAST DIVISION

SUSSEX TWO
1993-94
FIXTURES

October 23 (Week 8)
Plumpton   v Newick
Midhurst   v St. Francis
Sunallon   v Hellingly
Pulborough v Sussex Police

October 3O (Week X2)
St. Francis   v Plumpton
Sussex Police v Newick
Pulborough   v Sunallon
Hellingly   v Midhurst

November 13 (Week 1O)
Plumpton   v Hellingly
Newick   v St. Francis
Midhurst   v Pulborough
Sussex Police v Sunallon

November 2O (Week 11)
Hellingly   v Newick
Pulborough   v Plumpton
Sunallon   v Midhurst
St. Francis v Sussex Police

December 4 (Week 13)
Plumpton   v Sunallon
Newick   v Pulborough
St. Francis v Hellingly
Midhurst   v Sussex Police

February 12 (Week 22)
Pulborough   v St. Francis
Sunallon   v Newick
Midhurst   v Plumpton
Sussex Police v Hellingly

March 12 (Week 26)
Plumpton   v Sussex Police
Newick   v Midhurst
St. Francis v Sunallon
Hellingly   v Pulborough

SUSSEX TWO

HELLINGLY RFC
Ground Address: Hellingly Sports Club, Lower Horsebridge, Hailsham, East Sussex.
Club Secretary: Ross Hollister, 17 Sycamore Drive, Hailsham, East Sussex, BN27 3TT. Tel: (H) 0323 840756.
Press Officer: Kev Saunders, 91 Stroma Gardens, Hailsham, East Sussex. Tel: (H) 0323 440564.
Club Colours: Amber & black.

MIDHURST RFC
Ground Address: The Ruins Ground, Cowdrey Park, Midhurst, West Sussex. Tel: 0730 816658.
Club Secretary: Simon Flint, Broadoak, Chichester Road, Midhurst, West Sussex, GU29 9PF. Tel: (H) 0730 816465 (W) 081 390 1144.
Press Officer: Simon Flint, Broadoak, Chichester Road, Midhurst, West Sussex, GU29 9PF. Tel: (H) 0730 816465 (W) 081 390 1144.
Club Colours: Yellow with blue hoop.

NEWICK RFC
Ground Address: Newick Recreational Ground, George V Recreation Ground, Allington Road, Newick, East Sussex. Tel: 0825 773293.
Club Secretary: Judy Whiteman, 29 Harmers Hill, Newick, East Sussex, BN8 4QU. Tel: (H) 0825 723615 (W) 0825 764829.
Press Officer: Mike Morton-George, Beechlands, Newick, East Sussex, BN8 4RX. Tel: (H) 0825 723161 (W) 0273 622777.
Club Colours: Maroon & white hoops.

PLUMPTON RFC
Ground Address: The Racecourse, Plumpton Lane, Plumpton, East Sussex.
Club Secretary: C Woodward, 55 Russell Row, Lenes, East Sussex, BN7 2EE. Tel: (H) 0273 476219 (W) 0273 526110.
Press Officer: Michael Johnstone, Nursery House, Plumpton Lane, Plumpton, East Sussex. Tel: (H) 0273 890202 (W) 0273 486244.
Club Colours: Maroon & gold.

PULBOROUGH RFC
Ground Address: Sports & Social Club, Rectory Lane, Pulborough, West Sussex. Tel: 0798 873020.
Club Secretary: Dr Chaz Trenham, 126 Flansham Lane, Feltham, Bognor Regis, West Sussex. Tel: 0243 584924 (W) 071 377 7000 Ext 2750.
Club Colours: Black & white hoops.

ST FRANCIS RFC
Ground Address: Broad Field Playing Field, Horsham Road, Horsham. Tel: 0293 533071.
League Contact: J W Wright, 220 Weald Drive, Furnace Green, Crawley, Sussex, RH10 6NJ. Tel: (H) 0293 529065 (W) 0293 656850.
Press Officer: Len Casselogan, 1 Early Commons, Three Bridges, Crawley, Sussex. Tel: (H) 0293 533117 (W) 0836 213356.
Club Colours: Black with a blue & white hoop.

SUNALLON RFC
Ground Address: North Heath Lane, Horsham, West Sussex. Tel: 0403 253814.
Club Secretary: B R Lewis, 2 Wain End, Wimblehurst Park, Horsham, West Sussex, RH12 5TQ. Tel: (H) 0403 266267.

FINAL TABLE

	P	W	D	L	F	A	PD	Pts
BA Wingspan	7	7	0	0	196	25	171	14
Ditchling	7	6	0	1	164	53	111	12
Pulborough	7	4	0	3	185	89	96	8
Newick	7	4	0	3	60	100	-40	8
Sunallon	7	3	0	4	46	85	-39	6
Sussex Police	7	2	0	5	45	115	-70	4
Plumpton	7	2	0	5	85	215	-130	4
Midhurst	7	0	0	7	52	151	-99	0

Press Officer: B R Lewis, 2 Wain End, Wimblehurst Park, Horsham, West Sussex, RH12 5TQ. Tel: (H) 0403 266267.
Club Colours: Yellow & blue.

SUSSEX POLICE RFC
Ground Address: Brighton RFC, Waterhall, Brighton, Sussex. Tel: 0273 562729.
Club Secretary: DC P Johnson, Police Station, Kingsham Road, Chichester, Sussex, PO19 2AD. Tel: (H) 0243 861982 (W) 0243 536733 Ext 20252.
Press Officer: DI B Sole, Police Station, Burgess Hill, Sussex. Tel: (W) 0444 232211.
Club Colours: Navy blue shirts or navy blue & gold quarters.

LONDON & SOUTH EAST DIVISION

LONDON THREE
SOUTH WEST
1993-94 FIXTURES

December 18 (Week 15)
Guy's Hospital v Southampton
Old Emanuel v Eastleigh
Cranleigh v Alton
Portsmouth v Old Walcountians
U.S. Portsmouth v Purley
Warlingham v Wincheste

Ooctober 23 (Week 8)
Guy's Hospital v Old Emanuel
Winchester v Eastleigh
Purley v Alton
Old Guildfordians v Old Walcountians
U.S. Portsmouth v Portsmouth
Warlingham v Cranleigh

January 8 (Week 18)
Alton v Portsmouth
Eastleigh v Cranleigh
Southampton v Old Emanuel
Winchester v Guy's Hospital
Purley v Warlingham
Old Guildfordians v U.S. Portsmouth

Ooctober 30 (Week X2)
Cranleigh v Guy's Hospital
Portsmouth v Warlingham
Old Walcountians v U.S. Portsmouth
Alton v Old Guildfordians
Eastleigh v Purley
Southampton v Winchester

January 29 (Week X5)
Guy's Hospital v Purley
Old Emanuel v Winchester
Cranleigh v Southampton
Portsmouth v Eastleigh
Old Walcountians v Alton
Warlingham v Old Guildfordians

November 13 (Week 1O)
Guy's Hospital v Portsmouth
Old Emanuel v Cranleigh
Purley v Southampton
Old Guildfordians v Eastleigh
U.S. Portsmouth v Alton
Warlingham v Old Walcountians

February 12 (Week 22)
Eastleigh v Old Walcountians
Southampton v Portsmouth
Winchester v Cranleigh
Purley v Old Emanuel
Old Guildfordians v Guy's Hospital
U.S.Portsmouth v Warlingham

November 2O (Week 11)
Portsmouth v Old Emanuel
Old Walcountians v Guy's Hospital
Alton v Warlingham
Eastleigh v U.S. Portsmouth
Southampton v Old Guildfordians
Winchester v Purle

March 12 (Week 26)
Guy's Hospital v U.S. Portsmouth
Old Emanuel v Old Guildfordians
Cranleigh v Purley
Portsmouth v Winchester
Old Walcountians v Southampton
Alton v Eastleigh

December 4 (Week 13)
Guy's Hospital v Alton
Old Emanuel v Old Walcountians
Cranleigh v Portsmouth
Old Guildfordians v Winchester
U.S. Portsmouth v Southampton
Warlingham v Eastleigh

March 26 (Week 28)
Southampton v Alton
Winchester v Old Walcountians
Purley v Portsmouth
Old Guildfordians v Cranleigh
U.S. Portsmouth v Old Emanuel
Warlingham v Guy's Hospital

December 11 (Week 14)
Old Walcountians v Cranleigh
Alton v Old Emanuel
Eastleigh v Guy's Hospital
Southampton v Warlingham
Winchester v U.S. Portsmouth
Purley v Old Guildfordians

April 9 (Week 3O)
Old Emanuel v Warlingham
Cranleigh v U.S. Portsmouth
Portsmouth v Old Guildfordians
Old Walcountians v Purley
Alton v Winchester
Eastleigh v Southampton

LONDON THREE SOUTH WEST

ACTON RFC
Ground Address: Anstey Park, Anstey Lane, Alton, Hants. Tel: 0420 82076.
Club Secretary: Jerry Pugh, 8 Silver Birch Close, Lise, Hants, GU33 7HP. Tel: (H) 0730 895248 (W) 0730 894638.
Press Officer: Ian Hogg, 15 Anstey Lane, Alton, Hants.
Club Colours: Red Shirts, black shorts.

CRANLEIGH RFC
Ground Address: Wildwood Lane, Cranleigh, Surrey. Tel: 0483 275843.
Club Secretary: J Spong, "Millook", New Park Road, Cranleigh, Surrey, GU6 7HJ. Tel: (H) 0483 272700.
Club Colours: Navy & red quarters.

EASTLEIGH RFC
Ground Address: Bishopstoke Road, Eastleigh, Hants. Tel: 0703 641312.
Club Secretary: H T Coulter, 16 Burnham Beeches, Chandlens Ford, Eastleigh, Hants. Tel: (H) 0703 252535 (W) 0703 823795.
Press Officer: H T Coulter, 16 Burnham Beeches, Chandlens Ford, Eastleigh, Hants. Tel: (H) 0703 252535 (W) 0703 823795.
Club Colours: Red, amber & black hoops.

GUY'S HOSPITAL
Ground Address: Honor Oak Park, London, SE23 1NW. Tel: 081 690 1612.
Club Secretary: R Dales, Rugby Pigeon Hole, Guy's Hospital, London SE1.
Press Officer: Pat Gush, Rugby Pigeon Hole, Guy's Hospital, London SE1.
Club Colours: Blue and gold wide hoops.

OLD EMANUEL RFC
Ground Address: Blagdon House, Blagdon Lane, New Malden, Surrey. Tel: 081 942 3857.
Club Secretary: Ian Blair, 28, Hunters Road, Chessington, Surrey, KT9 1RU. Tel: (H) 081 397 1272 (W) 071 873 2233.
Press Officer: Ken Lovegrove, 4 Melbury Close, West Byfleet, Surrey, KT14 6RG. Tel: (H) 0932 346657.
Club Colours: White.

OLD GUILDFORDIANS RFC
Ground Address: The Pavilion, Stoke Park, London Road, Guildford, Surrey. Tel: 0483 300752.
Club Secretary: Doug Pym, Flat 3, 4 Guildown Road, Guildford, Surrey, GU2 5EN. Tel: (H) 0483 69953 (W) 0483 403534.
Press Officer: K T Ash, 11 Boxgrove Lane, Boxgrove Park, Guildford, Surrey, GU1 2TE. Tel: (H) 0483 62327.
Club Colours: Green with narrow red & white hoops, green shorts.

OLD WALCOUNTIANS RFC
Ground Address: Clockhouse, Carsholton Road, Woodmansterne, Banstead, Surrey. Tel: 07373 54348.
Club Secretary: R Tait, Flat 3, 58 Mulgrave Road, Sutton, Surrey, SM2 6LX. Tel: (H) 081 661 6391 (W) 081 688 9243.
Press Officer: R Murphy, Flat 7, Brunswick Court, 27 Brunswick Road, Sutton, Surrey, SM1 4EH. Tel: (H) 081 643 6070.
Club Colours: Black, blue & gold hoops.

PORTSMOUTH RFC
Ground Address: Rugby Camp, Copnor Road, Hilsea, Portsmouth, PO3 5HJR. Tel: 0705 660610.
Club Secretary: I Henderson, Flat 1, 22 High Street, Portsmouth, Hants, PO1 2LR. Tel: (H) 0705 876185 (W) 0329 288644.

FINAL TABLE

	P	W	D	L	F	A	PD	Pts
O. Wimbledonians	12	12	0	0	353	67	286	24
Warlingham	12	8	1	3	203	111	92	17
Cranleigh	12	7	1	4	127	116	11	15
Old Walcountians	12	7	1	4	173	175	-2	15
Purley	12	6	2	4	199	154	45	14
Guy's Hospital	12	6	1	5	192	158	34	13
Eastleigh	12	5	1	6	156	175	-19	11
Winchester	12	4	2	6	138	203	-65	10
Old Emanual	12	5	0	7	144	210	-66	10
Alton	12	5	0	7	193	193	0	8
Portsmouth	12	3	0	9	125	188	-63	6
Millbrook	12	3	1	8	121	242	-121	7
Jersey	12	2	0	10	115	254	-139	4

Press Officer: Roger Hollis, 69 Blackbrook Road, Fareham, Hants, PO15 5DE. Tel: (H) 0329 236506.
Club Colours: Black, yellow & white.

PURLEY RFC
Ground Address: Parson's Dighlt, Coulsdon Road, Old Coulsdon, Surrey. Tel: 0737 553042.
Club Secretary: S F Hayes, 27A High Street, Caterham, Surrey, CR3 5UG. Tel: (H) 0883 343597 (W) 0883 343018.
Press Officer: C Davis, Pine Lodge, Tatsfield, Kent, TN16 2LE. Tel: (H) 0959 577616 (W) 0959 577616.
Club Colours: Black & white hoops, white shorts.

SOUTHAMPTON RFC
Ground Address: Lower Brownhill Road, Millbook, Southampton. Tel: 0703 4737777.
Club Secretary: George Matema, 29 Netley Firs Road, Hedge End, Southampton, SO3 9QA. Tel: (H) 0489 786704 (W) 0489 886611.
Press Officer: Andrew Carter, 175 Oakwood Drive, Southampton, SO1 8EL. Tel: (H) 0703 734944 (W) 0962 860411 Ext 212.
Club Colours: Red & white hoops.

UNITED SERVICES (PORTSMOUTH) RFC
Ground Address: Burnaby Road, Old Portsmouth, Hants.
Club Secretary: J C Dingle, Room 318, Semaphore Tower, Portsmouth, PO1 3LT. Tel: (H) 0705 504776 (W) 0705 822351 Ext 22918.
Press Officer: C Hookway, 5 Hamilton Road, Southsea, PO12 2LX. Tel: (H) 0705 817271 (W) 0705 822351 Ext 22918.
Club Colours: Red & blue hoops; blue hoops.

WARLINGHAM RFC
Ground Address: Limpsfield Road, Hamsey Green, Warlingham, Surrey. Tel: 0883 622825.
Club Secretary: Chris Cave, 57 Ridge Langely, Sanderstead, South Croydon, Surrey, CR2 0AP. Tel: (H) 081 651 0742 (W) 071 826 8789.
Press Officer: Peter Cotton, 12 Willow Way, Godstone, Surrey. Tel: (H) 0883 742486 (W)071 499 2008.
Club Colours: Light blue & white hoops, dark blue shorts.

WINCHESTER RFC
Ground Address: Nuns Road, Winchester, Hants. Tel: 0962 863405.
Club Secretary: I J Rewe, The Croft, Romsey Road, Kings Sombourne, Stockbridge, Hants, SO20 6PP. Tel: (H) 0794 388064 (W) 0264 364344.
Press Officer: A Perry-Smith, 16 Cranworth Road, Winchester, Hants.
Club Colours: Black & amber - change green.

LONDON & SOUTH EAST DIVISION

HAMPSHIRE ONE
1993-94
FIXTURES

December 18 (Week 15)
Millbrook v Petersfield
Andover v Trojans
Jersey v Fareham Heathens
Sandown & Shanklin v Farnborough
New Milton v Isle of Wight
Romsey v Tottonians

October 23 (Week 8)
Millbrook v Andover
Tottonians v Trojans
Isle of Wight v Fareham Heathens
Gosport v Farnborough
New Milton v Sandown & Shanklin
Romsey v Jersey

January 8 (Week 18)
Fareham Heathens v Sandown & Shanklin
Trojans v Jersey
Petersfield v Andover
Tottonians v Millbrook
Isle of Wight v Romsey
Gosport v New Milton

October 30 (Week X2)
Jersey v Millbrook
Sandown & Shanklin v Romsey
Farnborough v New Milton
Fareham Heathens v Gosport
Trojans v Isle of Wight
Petersfield v Tottonians

January 29 (Week X5)
Millbrook v Isle of Wight
Andover v Tottonians
Jersey v Petersfield
Sandown & Shanklin v Trojans
Farnborough v Fareham Heathens
Romsey v Gosport

November 13 (Week 10)
Millbrook v Sandown & Shanklin
Andover v Jersey
Isle of Wight v Petersfield
Gosport v Trojans
New Milton v Fareham Heathens
Romsey v Farnborough

February 12 (Week 22)
Trojans v Farnborough
Petersfield v Sandown & Shanklin
Tottonians v Jersey
Isle of Wight v Andover
Gosport v Millbrook
New Milton v Romsey

November 20 (Week 11)
Sandown & Shanklin v Andover
Farnborough v Millbrook
Fareham Heathens v Romsey
Trojans v New Milton
Petersfield v Gosport
Tottonians v Isle of Wight

March 12 (Week 26)
Millbrook v New Milton
Andover v Gosport
Jersey v Isle of Wight
Sandown & Shanklin v Tottonians
Farnborough v Petersfield
Fareham Heathens v Trojans

December 4 (Week 13)
Millbrook v Fareham Heathens
Andover v Farnborough
Jersey v Sandown & Shanklin
Gosport v Tottonians
New Milton v Petersfield
Romsey v Trojans

March 26 (Week 28)
Petersfield v Fareham Heathens
Tottonians v Farnborough
Isle of Wight v Sandown & Shanklin
Gosport v Jersey
New Milton v Andover
Romsey v Millbrook

December 11 (Week 14)
Farnborough v Jersey
Fareham Heathens v Andover
Trojans v Millbrook
Petersfield v Romsey
Tottonians v New Milton
Isle of Wight v Gosport

April 9 (Week 30)
Andover v Romsey
Jersey v New Milton
Sandown & Shanklin v Gosport
Farnborough v Isle of Wight
Fareham Heathens v Tottonians
Trojans v Petersfield

456

ANDOVER RFC
Ground Address: The Goodship Ground, Roxcotte Parke, Hatherden Road, Charlton, Andover, Hants, SP10 3EL. Tel: 0264 339518.
Club Secretary: W A J Kent, Croye Lodge, 3 The Avenue, Hants, SP10 3EL. Tel: (H) 0264 324963 (W) 0962 844755.
Press Officer: W A J Kent, Croye Lodge, 3 The Avenue, Hants, SP10 3EL. Tel: (H) 0264 324963 (W) 0962 844755.
Club Colours: Black.

FAREHAM HEATHENS RUFC
Ground Address: Cams Alders Sports Field, Highfield Avenue, Fareham, Hants. Tel: 0329 221793.
Club Secretary: Rob Townsend, 9 Daisy Lane, Locksheath, Southampton, SO3 6RA. Tel: (H) 0489 574945.
Press Officer: Cyril Turner, 4 Walberton Avenue, East Cosham, Portsmouth, Hants, PO6 2JH. Tel: (H) 0705 370139.
Club Colours: Red & black quarters.

FARNBOROUGH RFC
Ground Address: Tilebarn Close, Cove, Farnborough, Hants. Tel: 0252 542750.
Club Secretary: Adrian Hathaway, 2 Tees Close, Cove, Farnborough. Tel: 0252 522425.
Press Officer: Steve Draper, 15 Guildford Road West, Farnborough, Hants. Tel: (H) 0252 516543.
Club Colours: Light blue & dark blue hoops.

GOSPORT & FAREHAM RFC
Ground Address: The Clubhouse, Gosport Park, Dolphin Crescent, Gosport, PO12 2HQ. Tel: 0705 589852.
Club Secretary: J M Pazdzierski, 18 Palmerston Avenue, Fareham, Hants, PO16 7DP. Tel: (H)0329 232173 (W) 0329 224000.
Press Officer: B Lewis, 27 Galemoor Avenue, Gosport, PO12 2SG. Tel: (H) 0705 589604.
Club Colours: Royal blue & old gold.

ISLE OF WIGHT RFC
Ground Address: Wootton Recreation Ground, Off Foot Ways, Wootton, Isle of Wight. Tel: 0983 883240.
Club Secretary: Mr N W J Harris, 273 Arctic Road, Cowes, Isle of Wight, PO31 7PJ. Tel: (H) 0983 299358 (W) 0983 566011.
Press Officer: D Metcalfe, 2 Bristol Terrace, Clackbridge Road, Freshwater, Isle of Wight, PO40 9QW. Tel: (H) 0983 755339.
Club Colours: Navy blue with narrow gold hoops.

JERSEY RFC
Ground Address: La Rue des Lanes, St Peter, Jersey, JE3 7BG. Tel: 42255.
Club Secretary: R Lapidus, PO Box 141, St Peter, Jersey, C1. Tel: (H) 33483 (W) 33365.
Press Officer: J Taylor, PO Box 141, St Peter, Jersey, C1. Tel: (H) 863609 (W) 862137.
Club Colours: Red shirts, white shorts.

MILLBROOK RFC
Ground Address: WSSC, Redbridge Lane, Millbrook, Southampton. Tel: 0703 739759.
Club Secretary: J Neagle, 27 Gemini Close, Cordshill, Southampton, SO1 8BG. Tel: (H) 0703 736474 (W) 0703 636362.
Press Officer: Chris Rose, 125 Bellemore Road, Upper Shirley, Southampton, SO1 2QW. Tel: 0703 778262.
Club Colours: Green & red hoops.

NEW MILTON RFC
Ground Address: Ashley Sports Ground, Ashley, NewMilton, Hants. Tel: 0425 610401.

FINAL TABLE

	P	W	D	L	F	A	PD	Pts
Southampton	11	10	0	1	142	60	82	20
Gosport	11	9	0	2	216	76	140	18
Farnborough	11	8	0	3	161	103	58	16
Tottonians	11	6	1	4	110	92	18	13
New Milton	11	7	0	4	174	139	35	12
Andover	11	5	1	5	179	106	73	11
Sandown & Sh'klin	11	5	0	6	119	164	-45	10
F'ham Heathens	11	4	1	6	81	158	-77	9
Petersfield	11	4	0	7	113	153	-40	8
Isle of Wight	11	3	1	7	113	193	-80	7
Guernsey	11	3	0	8	106	172 .	-66	6
Esso	11	0	0	11	93	200	-107	0

Club Secretary: N Hanmer, Walsingham, Andrew Lane, Ashley, New Milton, BH25 5QD. Tel: (H) 0425 612613 (W) 0590 682495.
Press Officer: George Winch, 32 Litchford Road, Ashley, New Milton, Hants. Tel: (H) 0425 620863.
Club Colours: Green and white quarters.

PETERSFIELD RFC.
Ground Address: Penns Place, Peterfield, Hants, GU31 4EX. Tel: 0730 264588.
League Contact: Tim Dilks, 7 Stoneham Park, Petersfield, Hants, GU32. Tel: (H) 0730 267966 (W) 0730 263033.
Press Officer: Andy Millar, 31 Moggs Mead, Petersfield, Hants, GU31 4NX. Tel: (H) 0730 265488.
Club Colours: Red with a single white hoop.

ROMSEY RFC
Ground Address: Romsey Sports Centre, Romsey, Herts. Tel: 0794 515103.
Club Secretary: A Mott, 8 Herefield Court, Romsey, Herts. Tel: (H) 0794 512989.
Press Officer: B Walker, 9 Chapelside, Titchfield, Fareham. Tel: (H) 0329 45425 (W) 0705 827711.
Club Colours: Blue & gold hoops, blue shorts.

SANDOWN AND SHANKLIN RFC.
Ground Address: The Clubhouse, The Fairway Lake, Nr Sandown, Isle of Wight. Tel: 404707.
Club Secretary: J Routledge, 27 Atherley Road, Shanklin, Isle of Wight. Tel: (H) 0983 863994 (W) 0983 523611 x 281.
Press Officer: Dennis Hoyle, 13 Littlestairs Road, Shanklin, Isle of Wight. Tel: (H) 0983 862214 (W) 0983 406524.
Club Colours: Blue & white hoops.

TOTTONIANS RFC
Ground Address: Totton College, Water Lane, Totton, Hants.
Club Secretary: A D Hamilton, Wedgewood, Winsor Road, Southampton, Hants, SO4 2HN. Tel: (H) 0703 813217.
Press Officer: Julian Howell, 38 Lackspur Drive, Marchwood, Southampton. Tel: (H) 0703 660851.
Club Colours: Green, white & black hoops.

TROJANS FC
Ground Address: Stoneham Park, Stoneham Lane, Eastleigh, Hants, SO5 3HT. Tel: 0703 612400/613068.
Club Secretary: J W J Mist, Westbury House, 14 Bellevue Road, Southampton, SO1 2AY. Tel: (H) 0703 583450 (W) 0703 332844.
Press Officer: J Lawless, 36 Donnington Drive, Valley Park, Chandlers Ford, Hants, SO5 3PB. Tel: (H) 0703 268549 (W) 0703 635266.
Club Colours: Blue with red hoops.

HAMPSHIRE TWO
1993-94
FIXTURES

October 23 (Week 8)
A. C. Delco v Ellingham
Alresford v Overton
Esso v Nomads
Ventnor v Fordingbridge
Basingstoke Wombats v Waterlooville
Guernsey v Fleet

October 3O (Week X2)
Waterlooville v A.C. Delco
Fordingbridge v Basingstoke Wombats
Nomads v Ventnor
Overton v Esso
Guernsey v Alresford
Fleet v Ellingham

November 13 (Week 1O)
A. C. Delco v Fordingbridge
Ellingham v Waterlooville
Esso v Guernsey
Ventnor v Overton
Basingstoke Wombats v Nomads
Alresford v Fleet

November 2O (Week 11)
Fordingbridge v Ellingham
Nomads v A.C. Delco
Overton v Basingstoke Wombats
Guernsey v Ventnor
Alresford v Esso
Fleet v Waterlooville

December 4 (Week 13)
A.C. Delco v Overton
Ellingham v Nomads
Waterlooville v Fordingbridge
Ventnor v Alresford
Basingstoke Wombats v Guernsey
Esso v Fleet

December 11 (Week 14)
Nomads v Waterlooville
Overton v Ellingham
Guernsey v A.C. Delco
Alresford v Basingstoke Wombats
Esso v Ventnor
Fleet v Fordingbridge

January 8 (Week 18)
A.C. Delco v Alresford
Ellingham v Guernsey
Waterlooville v Overton
Fordingbridge v Nomads
Basingstoke Wombats v Esso
Ventnor v Fleet

January 29 (Week X5)
Overton v Fordingbridge
Guernsey v Waterlooville
Alresford v Ellingham
Esso v A.C. Delco
Ventnor v Basingstoke Wombats
Fleet v Nomads

February 12 (Week 22)
A. C. Delco v Ventnor
Ellingham v Esso
Waterlooville v Alresford
Fordingbridge v Guernsey
Nomads v Overton
Basingstoke Wombats v Fleet

March 12 (Week 26)
Guernsey v Nomads
Alresford v Fordingbridge
Esso v Waterlooville
Ventnor v Ellingham
Basingstoke Wombats v A.C. Delco
Fleet v Overton

March 26 (Week 28)
A.C. Delco v Fleet
Ellingham v Basingstoke Wombats
Waterlooville v Ventnor
Fordingbridge v Esso
Nomads v Alresford
Overton v Guernsey

HAMPSHIRE TWO

A C DELCO RUFC
Ground Address: A C Delco Sports & Social Club, Stoneham Lane, Eastleigh, Southampton. Tel: 0703 613334.
Club Secretary: S Fitzjohn, 104 Alma Road, Portswood, Southampton, SO2 1BW. Tel: (H) 0703 324061 (W) 0703 559651 Ext 29.
Press Officer: S Fitzjohn, 104 Alma Road, Portswood, Southampton, SO2 1BW. Tel: (H) 0703 324061 (W) 0703 559651 Ext 29.
Club Colours: Red & blue quarters.

ALRESFORD RFC
Ground Address: Perins School, Alresford, Hants.
Club Secretary: Stephen Carter, The Lodge, Arlebury Park, Arlesford, Hants, SO24 9ES. Tel: 0962 733413.
Club Colours: Green, gold & black hoops.

BASINGSTOKE WOMBATS RFC
Ground Address: Hockey Club, Down Grange, Pack Lane, Basingstoke.
Club Secretary: David Thurston, 3 Musket Copse, Chineham, Basingstoke, Hampshire. Tel: (H) 0256 462672 (W) 0256 817640.
Press Officer: David Thurston, 3 Musket Copse, Chineham, Basingstoke, Hampshire. Tel: (H) 0256 462672 (W) 0256 817640.
Club Colours: Red, green, yellow & blue quarters.

ELLINGHAM RFC
Ground Address: Picket Road, Ringwood, Hants.
Club Secretary: D Middleton, 56 Eastfield Lane, Ringwood, Hants. Tel: (H) 0425 475521.
Press Officer: D Middleton, 56 Easfield Lane, Ringwood, Hants. Tel: (H) 0425 475521.
Club Colours: Blue & amber quarters.

ESSO (FAWLEY) RFC
Ground Address: Esso Recreation Club, Long Lane, Holbury, Southampton. Tel: 0703 893750.
Club Secretary: Alan McElevey, 32 Butts Ash Avenue, Hythe, Southampton, SO4 6RE. Tel: (H) 0703 840201 (W) 0703 895400.
Club Colours: Red shirts, blue shorts, red socks.

FLEET RUFC
Ground Address: Wavell-Cody Communityh Campus, Lynchford Road, Farnborough, Hampshire, GU14 6BH. Tel: 0252 26092 Ext 150 or 26096.
Club Secretary: Berwyn Morgan, 7 Ryde Gardens, Yateley, Camberley, Surrey, GU17 7PX. Tel: (H) 0252 879976 (W) 0225 625373
Club Colours: Red & royal blue.

FORDINGBRIDGE RFC
Ground Address: Recreation Ground, Fordingbridge, Hampshire. Tel: 0425 652047.
Club Secretary: S Godden, 157 Station Road, Fordingbridge, Hampshire, SP6 1DF. Tel: (H) 0425 654069.
Club Colours: Sky blue.

GUERNSEY RUFC
Ground Address: Fottes Lane, St Peter Port, Guernsey. Tel: 0481 54590.
Club Secretary: B J Mildon, P O Box 181, St Peter Port, Guernsey. Tel: (H) 0481 65493 (W) 0481 715055.
Press Officer: R Pogier, P O Box 181, St Peter Port, Guernsey. Tel: (H) 0481 36548 (W) 0481 723191.

FINAL TABLE

	P	W	D	L	F	A	PD	Pts
Trojans	10	10	0	0	368	37	331	20
Romsey	10	8	0	2	262	108	154	14
Alresford	10	7	0	3	182	152	30	14
AC Delco	10	6	1	3	222	114	108	13
Overton	10	6	1	3	160	109	51	13
Fordingbridge	10	4	1	5	134	134	0	9
Ventnor	10	4	1	5	135	125	10	7
Ellingham	10	3	1	6	87	178	-91	7
Nomads	10	3	0	7	107	201	-94	6
Waterlooville	10	1	0	9	54	313	-259	2
Basingstoke Wom	10	0	1	9	59	304	-245	1

NOMADS RFC
Ground Address: Eastern Road, Portsmouth, Hants. Tel: 0705 643991.
Club Secretary: K Walker, 10 Colinton Avenue, Portchester, Fareham, Hants PO16 8LP. Tel: (H) 0705 611809 (W) 0705 665255.
Press Officer: Terry Williams, 3 Hadleigh Road, Wymering, PO6 3RD. Tel: (H) 0705 640263.
Club Colours: Red & black.

OVERTON RFC
Ground Address: Town Meadow, High Street, Overton, Hampshire.
League Contact: Alec Coles, 15 Rochford Road, Basingstoke, Hampshire. Tel: (H) 0256 462847.
Club Colours: Royal blue.

VENTNOR RUFC
Ground Address: Watcombe Bottom, Whitwell Road, Upper Ventnor, Isle of Wight. Tel: 0983 854155.
Club Secretary: J Adams, BI-IK, Avenue Road, Wroxall, Isle of Wight. Tel: (H) 0983 854201 (W) 0983 822833.
Press Officer: Warren Fresle, Appul Durcombe Farm, Wroxall, Ventnor, Isle of Wight. Tel: (H) 0983 840188.
Club Colours: Blue shirts with white hoop, blue shorts.

WATERLOOVILLE RFC
Ground Address: Rowlands Avenue Sports Club, Rowlands Avenue, Waterlooville, Hants.
Club Secretary: John Kingdon, 40 Jubilee Road, Waterlooville, Hants. Tel: (H) 0705 612739.
Press Officer: John Kingdon, 40 Jubliee Road, Waterlooville, Hants. Tel: (H) 0705 612739.
Club Colours: Sky blue, white & green.

LONDON & SOUTH EAST DIVISION

December 18 (Week 15)

Raynes Park	v	University Vandals
Shirley Wanderers	v	Chobham
Old Whitgiftians	v	Wimbledon
Old Rutlishians	v	Effingham
Kingston	v	Old Reedonians
Barnes	v	John Fisher Old Boys

October 23 (Week 8)

Raynes Park	v	Shirley Wanderers
John Fisher Old Boys	v	Chobham
Old Reedonians	v	Wimbledon
Mitcham	v	Effingham
Kingston	v	Old Rutlishians
Barnes	v	Old Whitgiftians

January 8 (Week 18)

Wimbledon	v	Old Rutlishians
Chobham	v	Old Whitgiftians
University Vandals	v	Shirley Wanderers
John Fisher Old Boys	v	Raynes Park
Old Reedonians	v	Barnes
Mitcham	v	Kingston

October 3O (Week X2)

Old Whitgiftians	v	Rayners Park
Old Rutlishians	v	Barnes
Effingham	v	Kingston
Wimbledon	v	Mitcham
Chobham	v	Old Reedonians
University Vandals	v	John Fisher Old Boys

January 29 (Week X5)

Raynes Park	v	Old Reedonians
Shirley Wanderers	v	John Fisher Old Boys
Old Whitgiftians	v	University Vandals
Old Rutlishians	v	Chobham
Effingham	v	Wimbledon
Barnes	v	Mitcham

November 13 (Week 1O)

Raynes Park	v	Old Rutlishians
Shirley Wanderers	v	Old Whitgiftians
Old Reedonians	v	University Vandals
Mitcham	v	Chobham
Kingston	v	Wimbledon
Barnes	v	Effingham

February 12 (Week 22)

Chobham	v	Effingham
University Vandals	v	Old Rutlishians
John Fisher Old Boys	v	Old Whitgiftians
Old Reedonians	v	Shirley Wanderers
Mitcham	v	Raynes Park
Kingston	v	Barnes

November 2O (Week 11)

Old Rutlishians	v	Shirley Wanderers
Effingham	v	Rayner Park
Wimbledon	v	Barnes
Chobham	v	Kingston
University Vandals	v	Mitcham
John Fisher Old Boys	v	Old Reedonians

March 12 (Week 26)

Raynes Park	v	Kingston
Shirley Wanderers	v	Mitcham
Old Whitgiftians	v	Old Reedonians
Old Rutlishians	v	John Fisher Old Boys
Effingham	v	University Vandals
Wimbledon	v	Chobham

December 4 (Week 13)

Rayner Park	v	Wimbledon
Shirley Wanderers	v	Effingham
Old Whitgiftians	v	Old Rutlishians
Mitcham	v	John Fisher Old Boys
Kingston	v	University Vandals
Barnes	v	Chobham

March 26 (Week 28)

University Vandals	v	Wimbledon
John Fisher Old Boys	v	Effingham
Old Reedonians	v	Old Rutlishians
Mitcham	v	Old Whitgiftians
Kingston	v	Shirley Wanderers
Barnes	v	Raynes Park

December 11 (Week 14)

Effingham	v	Old Whitgiftians
Wimbledon	v	Shirley Wanderers
Chobham	v	Rayner Park
University Vandals	v	Barnes
John Fisher Old Boys	v	Kingston
Old Reedonians	v	Mitcham

April 9 (Week 3O)

Shirley Wanderers	v	Barnes
Old Whitgiftians	v	Kingston
Old Rutlishians	v	Mitcham
Effingham	v	Old Reedonians
Wimbledon	v	John Fisher Old Boys
Chobham	v	University Vandals

SURREY ONE

BARNES RFC
Ground Address: Barn Elms, Queen Elizabeth Walk, Barnes, London, SW15 0DG.
Club Secretary: Paul Kirby, 53 Stanhope Gardens, London, SW7 5RF. Tel: (H) 071 373 0120 (W) 071 602 5678.
Press Officer: Rob Quick, IMP, 197 Knightsbridge, London, SW7 1RF. Tel: (H) 081 995 6880 (W) 071 581 7666.
Club Colours: Green & gold.

CHOBHAM RFC
Ground Address: Fowlers Wells, Windsor Road, Chobham, Surrey, GU24 8NA. Tel: 0276 858616.
Club Secretary: Wallace Hooper, Dunster, 8 Fowlers Mead, Chobham, Surrey, GU24 8LF. Tel: (H) 0276 858661.
Press Officer: Nigel Heslop, 98 Broad Street, Guildford, Surrey, GU3 3BE. Tel: (H) 0483 35840.
Club Colours: Scarlet & gold on dark blue, dark blue shorts.

EFFINGHAM RFC
Ground Address: King George V Playing Fields, Browns Lane, Effingham, Surrey. Tel: 0372 458845.
Club Secretary: Keith howieson, 3 Middle Farm Place, Effingham, Surrey, KT24 5LA. Tel: (H) 0372 456834.
Press Officer: Mike Wheeler, 34 Oakfields, Broadacres, Guildford, Surrey, GU3 3AU. Tel: (H) 0483 36022.
Club Colours: Green & gold hoops, black shorts.

JOHN FISHER OLD BOYS RFC
Ground Address: 198 Limpsfield Road, Hamsey Green, Warlingham, Surrey. Tel: 0883 625149.
Club Secretary: Tony Spong, 26 Glanfield Road, Beckenham, Kent, BR3 3JU. Tel: (H) 081 658 5189 (W) 071 437 4831.
Press Officer: Paul Edwards, 56 Brighton Road, Purley, Surrey. Tel: (H) 081 668 8566 (W) 081 660 9065.
Club Colours: Blue, white & gold hoops, blue shorts.

KINGSTON RFC
Ground Address: King Edward Sports Ground, Hook Road, Chessington, Surrey, KT9 1PL. Tel: 081 397 8385.
Club Secretary: I M Barnes, 4 Kenley Road, Kingston, Surrey, KT1 3RW. Tel: (H) 081 336 1481 (W) 071 380 2786.
Press Officer: I M Barnes, 4 Kenley Road, Kingston, Surrey, KT1 3RW. Tel: (H) 081 336 1481 (W) 071 3802786.
Club Colours: Maroon & white hoops.

MITCHAM RUFC
Ground Address: bishopsford Cottage, Poulter Park, Peterborough Road, Mitcham, Surrey.
Club Secretary: Steve Payne, 43 Prince of Wales Road, Carshalton, Surrey. Tel: (H) 081 715 4087 (W) 081 658 7626.
Press Officer: Mike Kelly, 47 Brookfield Avenue, Sutton, Surrey. Tel: (H) 081 770 0601 (W) 071 621 0066.
Club Colours: Green & purple hoops, white shorts.

OLD REEDONIANS RFC
Ground Address: Whiteley village, Off Burwood Road, Walton on Thames, Surrey. Tel: 0932 849616.
Club Secretary: Guy Bracewell, Flat 1, 18 Surbiton Road, Kingston upon Thames, Surrey KT1 2HX. Tel: (H) 081 549 6903 (W) 071 410 3104.
Club Colours: Red, white, light blue, dark blue hoops.

FINAL TABLE

	P	W	D	L	F	A	PD	Pts
Old Guildfordians	12	11	0	1	411	60	351	22
Wimbledon	12	11	0	1	267	64	203	22
University Vandals	12	9	0	3	152	74	78	18
Old Whitgiftians	1	9	0	3	194	125	69	18
Kingston	12	5	1	6	104	111	-7	11
John Fisher O. B.	12	5	1	6	153	192	-39	11
Raynes Park	12	5	0	7	138	172	-34	10
Shirley Wanderers	12	4	1	7	128	197	-69	9
Old Rutlishians	12	4	1	7	133	231	-98	9
Old Reedonians	12	3	2	7	140	187	-47	8
Mitcham	12	2	2	8	98	300	-202	6
Effingham	12	2	1	9	100	244	-144	5
Cobham	12	3	1	8	107	180	-73	3

OLD RUTLISHIANS RFC
Ground Address: The Clubhouse, Poplar Road, London, SW19 3JS. Tel: 081 542 3678.
Club Secretary: W H Griffin, 68 Love Lane, Morden, Surrey, SM4 6LP. Tel: (H) 081 395 1875.
Press Officer: W H Griffin, 68 Love Lane, Morden, Surrey, SM4 6LP. Tel: (H) 081 395 1875.
Club Colours: Gold, azure, silver & black.

OLD WHITGIFTIAN RFC
Ground Address: Croham Manor Road, South Croydon, Surrey, CR2 7BG. Tel: 081 688 3248.
Club Secretary: Geoff Austin, 97 Clifton Road, Kingston-upon- Thames, surrey, KT2 6PL. Tel: (H) 081 549 3757 (W) 071 926 6100.
Club Colours: Red, black & blue hoops, white shorts.

RAYNES PARK RFC
Ground Address: Taunton Avenue, Raynes Park, London, SW20.
Club Secretary: Russell Price, 101 Belmont Avenue, New Malden, Surrey, KT3 6QE. Tel: (H) 081 949 2448 (W) 071 396 6105.
Club Colours: Blue with gold circlet.

SHIRLEY WANDERERS RUFC
Ground Address: Kent Gate, Kent Gate Way, Addington Road, West Wickham, Kent. Tel: 081 777 5298.
League Contact: G Jeffcoat, 96 Woodland Way, West Wickham, Kent BR4 9LT. Tel: (H) 081 777 5174 (W) 071 703 0101.
Club Colours: All white.

UNIVERSITY VANDALS RFC
Ground Address: "Brown Acres", Towing Path, Walton-on-Thames, Surrey. Tel: 0932 227659.
Club Secretary: A G M Williams, 7 Clarence Close, Walton-on- Thames, Surrey, KT12 5JX. Tel: (H) 0932 229727 (W) 071 259 6633.
Press Officer: A Williams, 7 Clarence Close, Walton-on-Thames, Surrey, KT12 5JX. Tel: (H) 0932 229727 (W) 071 259 6633/
Club Colours: Black, purple & emerald green.

WIMBLEDON RFC
Ground Address: Beverley Meads, Barham Road, Copse Hill, Wimbledon, London, SW20 0ET. Tel: 081 946 3156.
Club Secretary: Dave Dixon-Smith, 42 Princes Road, Wimbledon, London, SW19 8RB. Tel: (W) 081 543 6244.
Press Officer: Scott Cordes, 44 South Park Road, Wimbledon, London, SW19. Tel: (H) 081 543 3198 (W) 081 687 4385.
Club Colours: Maroon & cambridge blue hoops, white shorts.

LONDON & SOUTH EAST DIVISION

SURREY TWO
1993-94
FIXTURES

December 18 (Week 15)
Old Haileyburians v Chipstead
Cobham v Charing X/Wes. Hosp.
Merton v Old Tiffinians
Law Society v Old Caterhamians
Wandworthians v BEC Old Boys
Reigate & Redhill v Farnham

October 23 (Week 8)
Old Haileyburians v Cobham
Farnham v Charing X/West. Hosp.
BEC Old Boys v Old Tiffinians
Old Cranleighans v Old Caterhamians
Wandsworthians v Law Society
Reigate & Redhill v v Merton

January 8 (Week 18)
Old Tiffinians v Law Society
Charing X/West. Hosp. v Merton
Chipstead v Cobham
Farnham v Old Haileyburians
BEC Old Boys v Reigate & Redhill
Old Cranleighans v Wandworthians

October 3O (Week X2)
Merton v Old Haileyburians
Law Society v Reigate & Redhill
Old Caterhamians v Wandsworthians
Old Tiffinians v Old Cranleighans
Charing X/West. Hosp. v BEC Old Boys
Chipstead v Farnham

January 29 (Week X5)
Old Haileyburians v BEC Old Boys
Cobham v Farnham
Merton v Chipstead
Law Society v Charing X/West. Hosp.
Old Caterhamians v Old Tiffinians
Reigate & Redhill v Old Cranleighans

November 13 (Week 1O)
Old Haileyburians v Law Society
Cobham v Merton
BEC Old Boys v Chipstead
Old Cranleighans v Charing X/West. Hosp.
Wandsworthians v Old Tiffinians
Reigate & Redhill v Old Caterhamians

February 12 (Week 22)
Charing X/West. Hosp. v Old Caterhamians
Chipstead v Law Society
Farnham v Merton
BEC Old Boys v Cobham
Old Cranleighans v Old Haileyburians
Wandsworthians v Reigate & Redhill

November 2O (Week 11)
Law Society v Cobham
Old Caterhamians v Old Haileyburians
Old Tiffinians v Reigate & Redhill
Charing X/West.Hosp. v Wandsworthians
Chipstead v Old Cranleighans
Farnham v BEC Old Boys

March 12 (Week 26)
Old Haileyburians v Wandsworthians
Cobham v Old Cranleighans
Merton v BEC Old Boys
Law Society v Farnham
Old Caterhamians v Chipstead
Old Tiffinians v Charing X/West. Hosp.

December 4 (Week 13)
Old Haileyburians v Old Tiffinians
Cobham v Old Caterhamians
Merton v Law Society
Old Cranleighans v Farnham
Wandsworthians v Chipstead
Reigate & Redhil v Charing X/West. Hosp

March 26 (Week 28)
Chipstead v Old Tiffinians
Farnham v Old Caterhamians
BEC Old Boys v Law Society
Old Cranleighans v Merton
Wandworthians v Cobham
Reigate & Redhill v Old Haileyburians

December 11 (Week 14)
Old Caterhamians v Merton
Old Tiffinians v Cobham
Charing X/West. Hosp. v Old Haileyburians
Chipstead v Reigate & Redhill
Farnham v Wandsworthians
BEC Old Boys v Old Cranleighans'

April 9 (Week 3O)
Cobham v Reigate & Redhill
Merton v Wandsworthians
Law Society v Old Cranleighans
Old Caterhamians v BBC Old Boys
Old Tiffinians v Farnham
Charing X/West. Hosp. v Chipstead

462

SURREY TWO

BEC OLD BOYS RFC
Ground Address: Northey Avenue, Cheam, Surrey. Tel: 081 642 3423.
Club Secretary: Carol Sanders, 58 Pollards Hill North, Norbury, London, SW16 4NL. Tel: (H) 081 764 0912.
Press Officer: E Sanders, Flat 3, Charlwood Mansions, Weir Road, Balham, London, SW12. Tel: (H) 081 673 5414.
Club Colours: Blue, old gold & white hoops.

CHARING CROSS & WESTMINSTER HOSPITALS RFC
Ground Address: CXW Athletics Union, Stoke D'Abernon, Cobham, Surrey. Tel: 0932 62013.
Club Secretary: F Banks, 43 Beryl Road, London W6. Tel: (H) 081 846 9941 (W) 081 846 7242.
Club Colours: Gold, sky blue and crimson hoops.

CHIPSTEAD RFC
Ground Address: The Meads, High Road, Chipstead, Surrey. Tel: 07375 53035.
Club Secretary: Alan Maylon, 4 Hillside Road, East Ewell, Surrey, KT17 3EH. Tel: (H) 081 393 3578.
Club Colours: Royal & amber.

COBHAM RFC
Ground Address: Old Surbitonians Memorial Ground, Fairmile Lane, Cobham, Surrey. Tel: 0932 863245.
Club Secretary: I J Johnson, 209 Portsmouth Road, Cobham, Surrey, KT11 1JR. Tel: (W) 081 942 1033.
Press Officer: Tony Maddocks, 18 Clayton Drive, Rydes Hill, Guildford, Surrey. Tel: 0483 576792.
Club Colours: Blue, maroon & gold quarters.

FARNHAM RUFC
Ground Address: Westfield Lane, Wrecclesham, Farnham, Surrey. Tel: 0252 721138.
Club Secretary: D R Wall, 22 Hope Lane, Farnham, Surrey GU9 0HZ. Tel: (H) 0252 710476.
Press Officer: John Fairley, Pine Edge, 4 Latchwood Lane, Lower Bourne, Farnham, Surrey. Tel: (H) 0252 793293 (W) 0252 21302.
Club Colours: Black & white 2" wide hoops, black shorts.

LAW SOCIETY RFC
Ground Address: c/o Old Wimbledonians Cricket Club, Clayton Road, Hook, Surrey. Tel: 081 397 1962.
Club Secretary: A Signy, 61 Ferntower Road, London, N5 2JE.
Press Officer: A Signy, 61 Ferntower Road, London, N5 2JE.
Club Colours: Maroon & black hoops.

MERTON RFC
Ground Address: Morden Recreation Ground, Faversham Road, Moredon, Surrey, SM4. Tel: 081 646 5192.
Club Secretary: Bob Smith, SCCS, Charrington Street, London NW1 1RG. Tel: (W) 071 387 0126.
Press Officer: Jack Canniff, 85 Arlington Drive, Carshalton, Surrey, SM5 2EU. Tel: (H) 081 669 4931.
Club Colours: Black, gold & white quartered shirts, black shorts.

OLD CATERHAMIAN RFC
Ground Address: Park Avenue, Caterham Surrey, CR3 6AH. Tel:0883 343488.
Club Secretary: Peter Smith, Three Chimneys, Gravelly Hill, Caterham, Surrey, CR3 6ES. Tel: (H) 0883 347919 (W) 0883 347919.

FINAL TABLE

	P	W	D	L	F	A	PD	Pts
Barnes Harrodians	12	12	0	0	268	95	173	22
Chobham	12	9	0	3	277	124	153	18
Merton	12	9	0	3	217	110	107	18
Old haileyburians	12	7	0	5	160	158	2	14
Charing X W Hosp	12	6	1	5	274	192	82	13
Old Cranleighians	12	5	1	6	158	142	16	11
Bec Old Boys	12	5	1	6	148	151	-3	11
Reigate & Redhill	12	5	1	6	153	182	-29	11
Law Sociaty	12	5	0	7	176	163	13	10
Farnham	12	4	1	7	159	209	-50	9
Old Tiffinians	12	3	1	8	135	223	-88	7
Wandsworthians	12	2	1	9	75	264	-189	5
Old Bevonians	12	2	1	9	97	297	-200	5

Press Officer: George Williams, 42 Woodhatch Spinney, Coulsdon, Surrey, CR5 2SU. Tel: (H) 081 668 4756 (W) 0344 484648.
Club Colours: Black, amber, silver & mauve, black shorts.

OLD CRANLEIGHAN RFC
Ground Address: Old Portsmouth Road, Thames Ditton, Surrey. Tel: 081 398 3092.
Club Secretary: T Price, 32 Beverley Road, New Malden, Surrey, KT3 4AW.
Press Officer: A Rodriguez, 11 Spring Gardens, East Molesey, Surrey, KT8 0JA. Tel: (H) 081 783 0114 (W) 071 262 0828.
Club Colours: Blue, orange & white.

OLD HAILEYBURIANS RFC
Ground Address: 27 Ruxley Lane, Kingston Road, Ewell. Tel: 081 393 3901.
Club Secretary: R Sheen, 29 Kenilworth Ave, Wimbledon SW19 7LN. Tel: (H) 081 879 7581 (W) 071 782 0990
Club Colours: Magenta and white.

OLD TIFFINIAN RFC
Ground Address: Grist Memorial Ground, Bummer Road, Off Hampton Court Way, East Molesey, Surrey. Tel: 081 398 1391.
Club Secretary: B A Bench, 12 Angas Court, Pine Grove, Weybridge, Surrey. Tel: (H) 0932 842533 (W) 081 549 9222.
Press Officer: Jon Dewey, Flat 3, 32 Montague Road, Richmond, Surrey. Tel: (H) 081 948 8494.
Club Colours: Violet, white & navy blue.

REIGATE & REDHILL RFC
Ground Address: Eric hodgkinson Memorial Ground, Colley Lane, Reigate, Surrey, RH2 9JL. Tel: 0737 221110.
Club Secretary: Norman Phillips, 19 Linnell Road, Redhill, Surrey, RH1 4DH. Tel: (H) 081 330 3135 (W) 081 741 6336.
Club Colours: Royal blue.

WANDSWORTHIANS RFC
Ground Address: Kings College Sports Ground, Windsor Avenue, New Malden, Surrey, KT3 5HA. Tel: 081 942 0495.
Club Secretary: Gary Kirkwood, 53 Leominster Road, Morden, Surrey, SM41 6HT. Tel: (H) 081 640 0263.
Press Officer: Dick Moody, 47 ARundel Road, Norbiton, Surrey. Tel: (H) 081 942 0263.
Club Colours: Maroon, gold & white hoops.

LONDON & SOUTH EAST DIVISION

SURREY THREE
1993-94
FIXTURES

December 18 (Week 15)
Woking v Battersea Ironsides
Lightwater v London Media
Old Suttonians v London Fire Brigade
Old Bevonians v Croydon
Old Pelhamians v Old Freemans
Haslemere v Kings Coll. Hospital

October 23 (Week 8)
Woking v Lightwater
Kings Coll. Hospital v London Media
Old Freemans v London Fire Brigade
Royal Holloway Coll. v Croydon
Old Pelhamians v Old Bevonians
Haslemere v Old Suttonians

January 8 (Week 18)
London Fire Brigade v Old Bevonians
London Media v Old Suttonians
Battersea Ironsides v Lightwater
Kings Coll. Hospital v Woking
Old Freemans v Haslemere
Royal Holloway Coll. v Old Pelhamians

October 3O (Week X2)
Old Suttonians v Woking
Old Bevonians v Haslemere
Croydon v Old Pelhamians
London Fire Brigade v Royal Holloway Coll.
London Media v Old Freemans
Battersea Ironsides v Kings Coll. Hospital

January 29 (Week X5)
Woking v Old Freema
Lightwater v Kings Coll. Hospital
Old Suttonians v Battersea Ironsides
Old Bevonians v London Media
Croydon v London Fire Brigade
Haslemere v Royal Holloway Coll.

November 13 (Week 1O)
Woking v Old Bevonians
Lightwater v Old Suttonians
Old Freemans v Battersea Ironsides
Royal Holloway Coll. v London Media
Old Pelhamians v London Fire Brigade
Haslemere v Croydon

February 12 (Week 22)
London Media v Croydon
Battersea Ironsides v Old Bevonians
Kings Coll. Hospital v Old Suttonians
Old Freemans v Lightwater
Royal Holloway Coll. v Woking
Old Pelhamians v Haslemere

November 2O (Week 11)
Old Bevonians v Lightwater
Croydon v Woking
London Fire Brigade v Haslemere
London Media v Old Pelhamians
Battersea Ironsides v Royal Holloway Coll.
Kings Coll. Hospital v Old Freemans

March 12 (Week 26)
Woking v Old Pelhamians
Lightwater v Royal Holloway Coll.
Old Suttonians v Old Freemans
Old Bevonians v Kings Coll. Hopital
Croydon v Battersea Ironsides
London Fire Brigade v London Media

December 4 (Week 13)
Woking v London Fire Brigade
Lightwater v Croydon
Old Suttonians v Old Bevonians
Royal Holloway Coll. v Kings Coll. Hospital
Old Pelhamians v Battersea Ironsides
Haslemere v London Media

March 26 (Week 28)
Battersea Ironsides v London Fire Brigade
Kings Coll. Hospital v Croydon
Old Freemans v Old Bevonians
Royal Holloway Coll. v Old Suttonians
Old Pelhamians v Lightwater
Haslemere v Woking

December 11 (Week 14)
Croydon v Old Suttonians
London Fire Brigade v Lightwater
London Media v Woking
Battersea Ironides v Haslemere
Kings Coll. Hospital v Old Pelhamians
Old Freemans v Royal Holloway Coll.

April 9 (Week 3O)
Lightwater v Haslemere
Old Suttonians v Old Pelhamians
Old Bevonians v Royal Holloway Coll.
Croydon v Old Freemans
London Free Brigade v Kings Coll. Hospital
London Media v Battersea Ironsides

SURREY THREE

BATTERSEA IRONSIDES RFC
Ground Address: Club House, Battersea Ironside SSC, Open View, London, SW17. Tel: 081 874 9913.
Club Secretary: P Tanner, 1 Woodland Way, Morden, Surrey, SM4 4DS. Tel: (H) 081 540 5784 (W) 0923 214123.
Press Officer: Charles Hardin, 77 Fernside Road, London, SW12 9LH. Tel: (H) 081 675 2446.
Club Colours: Green with white band.

CROYDON RFC
Ground Address: Layhams Road, Keston, Bromley, Kent (at Junction with King Henry's Drive). Tel: 0959 573409.
Club Secretary: Trevor Davies, 62 Coulsdon Road, Coulsdon, Surrey, CR5 2LB. Tel: (H) 081 668 4864 (W) 071 233 0288.
Press Officer: John Davies, 21 Waddon Court Road, Croydon, Surrey, CR0 4AN. Tel: (H) 081 686 2123 (W) 0737 776707.
Club Colours: Black, magenta & white hoops, dark shorts.

HASLEMERE RFC
Ground Address: Woolmer Hill Sports Ground, Woolmer Hill, Haslemere, Surrey. Tel: 0428 643072.
Club Secretary: Colin Andrews, Combedene, Portsmouth Road, Hindhead, Surrey, GU26 6TQ. Tel: (H) 0428 604511.
Press Officer: Mark Daly, Old Barn Farm Cottage, Hewshott Lane, Liphook, Hants GU27 75Y. Tel: (H) 0428 727185 (W) 0483 578060.
Club Colours: Medium blue & white hoops.

KINGS COLLEGE HOSPITAL RFC
Ground Address: The Griffin Sports Ground, 12 Dulwich Village, Dulwich. Tel: 081 693 6900/2330.
Club Secretary: S C Hughes, 21 Bettridge Road, Fulham, London, SW6 3QH. Tel: (H) 071 736 2605 (W) 071 274 6222 Ext 4051.
Press Officer: S C Hughes, 21 Bettridge Road, Fulham, London, SW6 3QH. Tel: (H) 071 736 2605 (W) 071 274 6222 Ext 4051.
Club Colours: Navy, sicy blue & claret hoops.

LIGHTWATER RUFC
Ground Address: The Sports Centre, The Avenue, Lightwater, Surrey, GU18 5RG. Tel: 0276 472664.
Club Secretary: A Sharpe, 66 Cedar Close, Bagshot, Surrey, GU19 5AB. Tel: (H) 0276 472994.
Press Officer: M W Keeley, 14 Gloucester Road, Bagshot, Surrey, GU19 5LR. Tel: (H) 0276 476732.
Club Colours: Green, & white quarters, black shorts.

LONDON FIRE BRIGADE RFC
Ground Address: LFCDA Welfare Fund Sports Ground, Banstead Road, Ewell, Surrey. Tel: 081 394 1946/393 0446.
Club Secretary: Stephen Foy, 24 Kent House, Hogarth Estate, Chiswick, London, W4 2JS. Tel: (H) 081 994 3819 (W) 071 587 4736.
Press Officer: Stephen Foy, 24 Kent House, Hogarth Estate, Chiswick, London, W4 2JS. Tel: (H) 081 994 3819 (W) 071 587 4736.
Club Colours: Red, old gold, black.

LONDON MEDIA RUFC
Ground Address: Battersea Park, Albert Bridge Road Entrance, Battersea, London.
:League Contact: Michael Jefferies, 64A Rosendale Road, West Dulwich, SE21 8DP. Tel: (H) 081 761 2346 (W) 071 831 2981.
Press Officer: Nick Field, 18 Walton Way, West Acton. Tel: (H) 081 993 5909 (W) 0895 239536.
Club Colours: Black & white quarters.

OLD BEVONIANS RFC
Ground Address: Ballard Coombe, Robin Hood Way, Kingston Vale, London, SW15 3QX. Tel: 081 942 2907.

FINAL TABLE

	P	W	D	L	F	A	PD	Pts
Old Caterhamians	10	9	0	1	375	65	310	18
Chipstead	10	8	0	2	148	95	53	16
Battersea Ironsides	10	7	0	3	213	133	80	14
Woking	10	5	1	4	183	117	66	11
Old Pelhamians	10	5	1	4	142	106	36	11
Old Suttonians	10	5	0	5	179	125	54	10
London Fire Brigade	10	5	0	5	160	120	40	10
Royal Holloway Coll	10	3	0	7	91	147	-56	6
Old Freemans	10	3	0	7	91	262	-171	6
Kings Coll Hospital	10	2	0	8	112	302	-190	4
Croydon	10	2	0	8	69	291	-222	4
Shene Old Gramm								0

Club Secretary: I P Sedgley, 363 Park Road, Kingston Upon Thames, Surrey, KT2 5LY. Tel: (H) 081 541 3610.
Press Officer: A Whitman, 133 Clarence Avenue, New Malden, Surrey, KT3 3TY. Tel: (H) 081 949 4751 (W) 081 390 9698.
Club Colours: Yellow, black & green hoops.

OLD FREEMEN'S RFC
Ground Address: City of London Freemen's School, Ashtead Park, Ashtead, Surrey. Tel: 0372 274158.
Club Secretary: J G Wild, "Beeches", Ermyn Way, Leatherhead, Surrey, KT22 8TW. Tel: (H) 0372 276085 (W) 071 887 2839.
Press Officer: T Innes, Heron Cottage, Betchworth, Surrey, RH3 7BP. Tel: (H) 0737 842385 (W) 0306 886661.
Club Colours: Dark blue with maroon & gold hoops, dark blue shorts.

OLD PELHAMIANS RFC
Ground Address: Poulter Park, Bishopsford Road, Mitcham, Surrey. Tel: 081 648 3755.
Club Secretary: Dave Turner, 49 Chelsham Road, Clapham, London, SW4 6NN. Tel: (H) 071 627 4778 (W) 071 926 9449.
Press Officer: Mike Nichols, 51 Gore Road, Raynes Park, London, SW20- 8JN. Tel: (H) 081 542 5026 (W) 071 236 0369.
Club Colours: All black.

OLD SUTTONIANS RFC
Ground Address: Walch Pavilion, Priest Hill Playing Fields, Banstead Road, Ewell, Surrey. Tel: 081 393 7427.
League Contact: Andrew Udall, 3 Netley Close, Cheam, Sutton, Surrey, SM3 8DN. Tel: (H) 081 644 7759 (W) 071 4092199.
Press Officer: Stuart Udall, 3 Netley Close, Cheam, Sutton, Surrey, SM3 8DN. Tel: (H) 081 644 7259 (W) 0279 411177.
Club Colours: Red, white & black hoops.

ROYAL HOLLLOWAY RFC
Ground Address: "Nobles", RHUL, Englefield Green, Egham, Surrey, TW20 0EX.
Club Secretary: K J Wheaton, Students Union, RHUL, Egham Hill, Egham, Surrey. Tel: (H) 0784 471178 (W) 0784 435035.
Club Colours: Purple & green.

WOKING RFC
Ground Address: Kings Head Lane, Off Chertsey Road, Byfleet, Surrey. Tel: 0932 343601.
League Contact: Ian Vousden, 142 Blackmore Crescent, Sheerwater, Woking, Surrey. Tel: (H) 0483 715715 (W) 0831 233962./
Club Colours: Blue & gold hoops.

LONDON & SOUTH EAST DIVISION

<table>
<tr><td>

SURREY FOUR
1993-94
FIXTURES

</td><td>

March 12 (Week 26)
Economicals v Sun Alliance
Shene Old Gramms v Egham
Oxted v Old Johnians
Old Epsomians v Surrey Police

</td></tr>
</table>

October 23 (Week 8)
Racal Decca v Economicals
Old Johnians v Old Epsomians
Egham v Oxted
Sun Alliance v Shene Old Gramms

October 3O (Week X2)
Shene Old Gramms v Racal Decca
Surrey Police v Old Johnians
Old Epsomians v Egham
Oxted v Sun Alliance

November 13 (Week 1O)
Racal Decca v Oxted
Economicals v Shene Old Gramms
Sun Alliance v Old Epsomians
Egham v Surrey Police

November 2O (Week 11)
Oxted v Economicals
Od Epsomians v Racal Decca
Surrey Police v Sun Alliance
Old Johnians v Egham

December 4 (Week 13)
Racal Decca v Surrey Police
Economicals v Old Epsomians
Shene Old Gramms v Oxted
Sun Alliance v Old Johnians

December 11 (Week 14)
Old Epsomians v Shene Old Gramms
Surrey Police v Economicals
Old Johnians v Racal Decca
Egham v Sun Alliance

January 29 (Week X5)
Racal Decca v Egham
Economicals v Old Johnians
Shene Old Gramms v Old Epsomians
Oxted v Old Epomians

February 12 (Week 22)
Surrey Police v Oxted
Old Johnians v Shene Old Gramms
Egham v Economicals
Sun Alliance v Racal Decca

466

SURREY FOUR

ECONOMICALS RUFC
Ground Address: LSE Sports Ground, Windsor Avenue, New Malden, Surrey. Tel: 081 942 1229.
Club Secretary: S Bowen, 97 Salehurst Road, Crofton Park, London, SE4 1AR. Tel: (H) 081 690 5393 (W) 071 486 1234.
Press Officer: S Bowen, 97 Salehurst Road, Crofton Park, London, SE4 1AR. Tel: (H) 081 690 5393 (W) 071 486 1234.
Club Colours: Green & white hoops.

EGHAM RFC
Ground Address: Strodes College, High Street, Egham, Surrey.
Club Secretary: A G Codwing, Brookside, 18 Vicarage Avenue, Egham, Surrey, TW20 8NW. Tel: (H) 0784 434139 (W) 0784 434139.
Press Officer: David Evans, 42 ARmstrong Road, Englefield Green, Egham, Surrey TW20. Tel: (H) 0784 432915.
Club Colours: Mid blue with gold hoop, gold cuffs & collar.

OLD EPSOMIAN RUFC
Club Secretary: T J Goodger, 53 Braithwaite Gardens, Stanmore, Middlesex, HA7 2QG. Tel: (H) 081 907 3886.
Press Officer: T J Goodger, 53 Braithwaite Gardens, Stanmore, Middlesex, HA7 2QG. Tel: (H) 081 907 3886.
Club Colours: Blue shirts, white shorts.

OLD JOHNIANS RFC
Ground Address: OJRFC, Oaken lane, Hinchley Wood, Surrey.
League Contact: Patrick Rogers, c/o I D K Media, 1 Wardour Street, London, W1V 3HE. Tel: (W) 071 734 8069.
Press Officer: Paul McIntyre, 62 Longfellow Road, Worcester Park, Surrey.
Club Colours: Green & white hoops, white shorts.

OXTED RFC
Ground Address: Holland Road, Hurst Green, Oxted, Surrey. Tel: 0883 717468.
Club Secretary: G A Metcalfe, Staffend, Icehouse Wood, Oxted, Surrey, RH8 9DN. Tel: (H) 0883 714609 (W) 081 668 0711.
Press Officer: N Kitchen, 39 High Street, Old Oxted, Surrey. Tel: (H) 0883 714050 (w) Westerham 63714.
Club Colours: White & blue.

RACAL-DECCA RFC
Ground Address: Racal-Decca Sports & Social Club, Kingston Road, Tolworth, KT5 9NU. Tel: 081 337 0519.
Club Secretary: William Tracey, 102 Clapham Common Northside, London, SW4 9SQ. Tel: (H) 071 228 2787 (W) 081 754 6456.
Press Officer: William Tracey, 102 Clapham Common Northside, London, SW4 9SQ. Tel: (H) 071 228 2787 (W) 081 754 6456.
Club Colours: Blue & white hoops.

SHENE OLD GRAMMARIANS RFC
Ground Address: Barn Elms Playing Fields, Queen Elizabeth Walk, Barnes, SW13. Tel: 081 876 2059.
Club Secretary: G PSmith, 175 Beresford Avenue, Surbiton, Surrey, KT5 9LR. Tel: (H) 081 399 0081 (W) 081 855 6664.
Press Officer: G Smith, 175 Beresford Avenue, Surbiton, Surrey, KT5 9LR. Tel: (H) 081 399 0081 (W) 081 855 6664.
Club Colours: Sky blue & black.

FINAL TABLE

	P	W	D	L	F	A	PD	Pts
Haslemere	9	9	0	0	338	63	275	18
Lightwater	9	7	0	2	188	48	140	14
London Media	9	7	0	2	206	92	114	14
Oxted	9	5	1	3	152	82	70	11
Old Johnians	9	5	0	4	163	74	89	10
Surrey Police	9	4	1	4	133	148	-15	9
Egham	9	4	0	5	110	115	-5	8
Racal-Decca	9	2	0	7	115	214	-99	4
Economicals	9	1	0	8	53	424	-371	2
Old Epsomoans	9	0	0	9	32	230	-198	0
Surrey University	9							0

SUN ALLIANCE RFC
Ground Address: North Heath Lane, Horsham, West Sussex, RH12 4PJ. Tel: 0403 253814.
Club Secretary: J B Williams, 121 Midfield Way, St Pauls Cray, Orpington, Kent. Tel: (H) 081 302 4630 (W) 071 734 7211 Ext 4353.
Press Officer: J B Williams, 121 Midfield Way, St Pauls Cray, Orpington, Kent. Tel: (H) 081 302 4630 (W) 071 734 7211 Ext 4353.
Club Colours: Red & blue.

SURREY POLICE RFC
Ground Address: Surrey Polic Headquarters, Mount Browne, Sandy Lane, Guildford, GU1 3HG. Tel: 0483 571212.
Club Secretary: S P Burrows, 4 Junewood Close, Woodham, Weybridge, Sussex, KT15 3PX. Tel: (H) 0932 344607 (W) 0483 571212 Ext 2540.
Press Officer: S P Burrows, 4 Junewood Close, Woodham, Weybridge, Sussex, KT15 3PX. Tel: (H) 0932 344607 (W) 0483 571212.
Club Colours: All black with red socks.

UNIVERSITY OF SURREY RFC
Ground Address: Manor Farm, Guildford, Surrey. Tel: 0483 509242.
Club Secretary: Gary Austin, C/O Student Union, University of Surrey, Guildford, Surrey, GU2 5XH.
Press Officer: Arther De-graft, Sports Office, Student's Union, University of Surrey, Guildford, Surrey, GU2 5XH. Tel: (W) 0483 509981.
Club Colours: Black with single amber, red & royal blue hoops.

THE BEST PACK IN THE CHAMPIONSHIP.

SOUTH WEST DIVISION

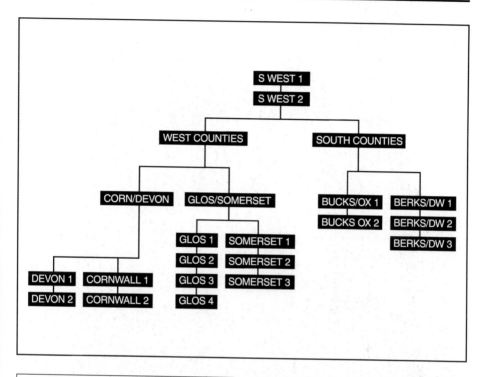

CHAIRMAN, League Sub-Committee
Dr. C.V. Phillips, "Barlowena", Alexandra Road, Illogan, Cornwall, TR16 4EN (H) 0209 842660
LEAGUES CO-ORDINATING SECRETARY
Jack D. Wooldridge, 16 Grange Drive, Durleigh, Bridgwater, Somerset, TA6 7LL (H) 0278 422009
LEAGUE SECRETARIES
South West One & South West Two Jack Wooldridge, 16 Grange Drive, Bridgwater, Somerset, TA6 7LL (H) 0278 422009.
Western Counties Mike Gee, Suhaila, 7 Hellesvane Close, St Ives, Cornwall, TR6 7HQ (H) 0736 797168.
Southern Counties Trevor Palm, 13 Dolesford Road, Aylesbury, Bucks (H) 0296 81847 (B) 0753 533223.
Cornwall/Devon Geoff Simpson, 108 Pattison Drive, Mainstone, Plymouth, Devon, PL6 8RU (H) 0752 707432.
Devon One & Devon Two Geoff Simpson, 108 Pattison Drive, Mainstone, Plymouth, Devon. (H) 0752 707432.

Cornwall One & Cornwall Two Beverley Davis, 8 Penrose Road, Helston, Cornwall, TR13 8TP (H) 0326 563744.
Glos/Somerset & Somerset One Bill Bishop, "Hellvellyn", 1 Wiltshire Place, Kingswood, Bristol, Avon BS15 4XA.(H) 0272 575729 (B) 0272 352017.
Somerset Two & Somerset Three Clive MacDonald, 8 Sycamore Drive, Crewkerne, Somerset, TA18 7BT (H) 0460 76136.
Glos One, Glos Two, Glos Three & Glos Four Allan Townsend, St Kelelm, 2 Kencourt Close, Kenilworth Avenue, Gloucester, GL2 0QL (H) 0452 522721.
Berk/Dorset & Wilts One, Berk/Dorset & Wilts Two & Berk/Dorset & Wilts Three Tony Bott, Kew House, Anchor Road, Calne, Wilts SN11 8DI (H) 0860 448328 (B)0249 821448.
Bucks/Oxon One & Bucks/Oxon Two Brian Flanders, Old Cross House, Coscote, Didcot, Oxon, OX11 0NP (H) 0235 816523.

THE BEST PACK IN THE CHAMPIONSHIP.

SOUTH WEST DIVISION

ADMINISTRATIVE RULES

1. MATCH RESULTS REPORTING INSTRUCTIONS

A. SOUTH WEST LEAGUE ONE AND LEAGUE TWO

I. Home Clubs will telephone the First Eleven Sports Agency on (0734) 861593 before 4.45pm on each League Saturday with the match result.

II. Both Clubs in each game will complete a Match Result Card listing the team and replacements and Match result and post it, first class, to the First Eleven Sports Agency by first post Monday.

B. WESTERN AND SOUTHERN COUNTIES LEAGUES

I. Home Clubs will telephone the First Eleven Sports Agency on (0734) 861593 before 4.45pm on each League Saturday with the match result.

II. Both Clubs in each game will complete a Match Result Card listing the team and replacements and Match result and post it, first class, to the First Eleven Sports Agency by first post Monday.

C. TWO-COUNTIES LEAGUES

I. Home Clubs will telephone the First Eleven Sports Agency on (0734) 861593 between 4.45pm and 5.00pm on each League Saturday with the match result.

II. Both Clubs in each game will complete a Match Result Card listing the team and replacements and Match result and post it, first class, to the First Eleven Sports Agency by first post Monday.

D. COUNTY LEAGUES

I. Home Clubs will telephone the First Eleven Sports Agency on (0734) 861593 between 5.00pm and 6.00pm on each League Saturday with the match result.

II. Both Clubs in each game will complete a Match Result Card listing the team and replacements and Match results and post it, first class, to the First Eleven Sports Agency by first post Monday.

E. NOTIFICATION OF RESULTS

Club Secretaries are responsible for their Club's compliance with the rules for notification of results. Failure to telephone and card-in the match result and team and replacements list, within the time limits laid down, will incur a fine for each offence of £10.00. Offending Clubs will be notified of fines imposed, failure to pay within 28 days will result in the offending Club being deducted two Competition points. Any outstanding fines at the end of the Season can result in points deduction in the following Season.

2. POSTPONED MATCHES

Club Secretaries of Clubs with Home matches must, in the event of a postponement of any League match, immediately inform the First Eleven Sports Agency on (0734) 861593 and their appropriate League Secretary. In addition, they must also notify the Agency and the League Secretary within SEVEN days, of the date of the re-arranged fixture.

In the absence of a notification of a mutually acceptable re-arranged date within the time specified, the League Secretary will direct the Clubs to play on a specified date.

3. PLAYER REGISTRATION FORMS

All Player Registration Forms must, on completion, be forwarded to: The Registrar, PO Box 11, Reading RG6 3DT.

SOUTH WEST DIVISION

SOUTH WEST ONE
1993-94
FIXTURES

December 18 (Week 15)
Brixham v Barnstaple
Cheltenham v Gordon lge
Cinderford v Salisbury
Henley v St Ives
Sherborne v Newbury
Stroud v Maidenhead.

October 23 (Week 8)
Henley v Brixham
Maidenhead v Salisbury
Newbury v Barnstaple
Sherborne v Cinderford
Stroud v Cheltenham
Torquay v Gordon Lge

January 8 (Week 18)
Barnstaple v Cinderford
Maidenhead v Sherborne
Newbury v Henley
Salisbury v Cheltenham
St Ives v Brixham
Torquay v Stroud

October 30 (Week X2)
Barnstaple v Maidenhead
Cheltenham v Sherborne
Cinderford v Henley
Gordon Lge v Stroud
Salisbury v Torquay
St Ives v Newbury

January 29 (Week X5)
Brixham v Newbury
Cheltenham v Barnstaple
Cinderford v St Ives
Gordon Lge v Salisbury
Henley v Maidenhead
Sherborne v Torquay

November 13 (Week 10)
Brixham v Cinderford
Henley v Cheltenham
Maidenhead v St Ives
Sherborne v Gordon Lge
Stroud v Salisbury
Torquay v Barnstaple

February 12 (Week 22)
Barnstaple v Gordon Lge
Maidenhead v Brixham
Newbury v Cinderford
St Ives v Cheltenham
Stroud v Sherborne
Torquay v Henley

November 20 (Week 11)
Barnstaple v Stroud
Cheltenham v Brixham
Gordon Lge v Henley
Newbury v Maidenhead
Salisbury v Sherborne
St Ives v Torquay

March 12 (Week 26)
Brixham v Torquay
Cheltenham v Newbury
Cinderford v Maidenhead
Gordon Lge v St ives
Henley v Stroud
Salisbury v Barnstaple

December 4 (Week 13)
Brixham v Gordon Lge
Cinderford v Cheltenham
Henley v Salisbury
Sherborne v Barnstaple
Stroud v St Ives
Torquay v Newbury

March 26 (Week 28)
Maidenhead v Cheltenham
Newbury v Gordon Lge
Sherborne v Henley
St Ives v Salisbury
Stroud v Brixham
Torquay v Cinderford

December 11 (Week 14)
Barnstaple v Henley
Gordon Lge v Cinderford
Maidenhead v Torquay
Newbury v Stroud
Salisbury v Brixham
St Ives v Sherborne

April 9 (Week 30)
Barnstaple v St Ives
Brixham v Sherborne
Cheltenham v Torquay
Cinderford v Stroud
Gordon Lge v Maidenhead
Salisbury v Newbury

472

SOUTH WEST ONE

BARNSTAPLE RFC
Ground Address: Pottington Road, Barnstaple, EX31
1DL. Tel: 0271 45627.
Club Secretary: P M Pettifer, Bailey's Cottage, Lake,
Barnstaple EX31 3HU. Tel: (H) 0271 73475 (W) 0271 46710.
Press Officer: B C Williams, The Mews, Whiddon Park,
Landkey Road, Barnstaple, EX32 9LA. Tel: 0271 79289.
Club Colours: Red

BRIXHAM RFC
Ground Address: Astley Park, Rea Barn Hill, Brixham.
Tel: 0803 882162.
Club Secretary: J D Irvine, 1 Great Rea Road, Brixham
TO5 9SW. Tel: 0803 882219.
Press Officer: R J Lovell, 4 Gillard Road, Brixham. Tel:
0803 855476 (W)0803 294753.
Club Colours: Black with wide white band.

CHELTENHAM RFC
Ground Address: Prince of Wales Stadium, Tommy
Taylor's Lane, Cheltenham GL50 4NJ. Tel: 0242 525393.
Club Secretary: T Parker, 39 Long Mynd Avenue,
Cheltenham GL51 5QT. Tel: 0242 521076.
Club Colours: Black & red hoops.

CINDERFORD RFC
Ground Address: Recreation Ground, Dockham Road,
Cinderford, Gloucester. Tel: 0594 822673.
Club Secretary: Mrs M Beavis, 5 Abbots Road,
Cinderford, Glos GL14 3BN. Tel: 0594 823779.
Press Officer: Mr R Allen, 14 Heywood Road, Cinderford,
Glos. Tel: 0594 826301.
Club Colours: Red, black & amber.

GORDON LEAGUE RFC
Ground Address: Hempsted Lane, Hempsted, Gloucester.
Tel: 0452 303434.
Club Secretary: W R King, 361 Innsworth Lane,
Churchdown, Gloucester GL3 1EY. Tel: (H) 0452 856787
(W) 0452 371371 x3131
Press Officer: Mr E Young, 273 Bodiham Avenue, Glos
GL4 0XW. Tel: (H) 0452 417777 (W) 0831 231614.
Club Colours: White with red sash.

HENLEY RFC
Ground Address: Dry Leas, Marlow Road,
Henley-on-Thames, Oxon. Tel: 0491 574499.
Club Secretary: Peter Allen, 8 St Katherines Road,
Henley-on- Thames, Oxon RG9 1PJ. Tel: (H) 0491 575154
(W) 081 788 7272.
Press Officer: Noel North, The Little House, Northfield
Avenue, Lower Shiplake, Henley-on-Thames. Tel: 0734
402297.
Club Colours: Navy, bottle green & amber hoops.

MAIDENHEAD RUFC
Ground Address: Braywick Road, Maidenhead. Tel: 0628
29663.
Club Secretary: J Hayden, 39 Oaken Grove, Maidenhead,
Berks SL6 6HN. Tel: (H)0628 31239 (W)0276 473363.
Press Officer: A G Cowen, 31 Furze Platt Road,
Maidenhead, Berks. Tel: (H) 0628 29237 (W) 0865 792336.
Club Colours: Magenta, violet & black hoops.

NEWBURY RFC
Ground Address: Pinchington Lane, Newbury, Berks
RG14 7HB. Tel: 0635 40103.
Club Secretary: T R Burwell, as above. Tel:
(H)0635255109 (W)0635 40103.
Club Colours: Navy & sky blue irregular hoops.

FINAL TABLE

	P	W	D	L	F	A	PD	Pts
Reading	12	11	0	1	267	99	168	22
Henley	12	9	0	3	312	143	169	18
Newbury	12	8	1	3	251	158	93	17
St Ives	12	7	0	5	167	147	20	14
Maidenhead	12	6	1	5	153	214	-61	13
Cheltenham	12	6	0	6	221	197	24	12
Salisbury	12	6	0	6	180	188	-8	12
Sherborne	12	5	1	6	182	171	11	11
Cinderford	12	5	0	7	170	269	-99	10
Brixham	12	4	0	8	207	217	-10	8
Torquay	12	4	0	8	117	263	-146	8
Gordon League	12	3	1	8	162	201	-39	7
Penryn	12	2	0	10	140	262	-122	4

SALISBURY RFC
Ground Address: Castle Road, Salisbury SP1 3SA. Tel:
0722 325317.
Club Secretary: C E Macey, 33 Montague Road, West
Harnham, Salisbury SP2 8NL. Tel: (H) 0722 322056 (W)
0722 327801.
Press Officer: R H Rowland, 1 Lode Hill, Downton,
Wiltshire. Tel: 0725 22064 (W) 01 734 8697.
Club Colours: Green & white.

SHERBORNE RFC
Ground Address: The Terrace Club, Terrace Playing
Fields, Sherborne, Dorset. Tel: 0935 812478.
Club Secretary: Michael Walker, 9 Morston, Thornford,
Sherborne, Dorset DT9 6RB. Tel: (H) 0935 873292 (W)
0935 703827.
Press Officer: Dale O'Loughlin, 36 McCreery Road,
Sherborne, Dorset DT9 4DZ. Tel: 0935 817396 (W)
816950.
Club Colours: Black.

ST IVES RFC
Ground Address: Alexandra Road, St Ives, Cornwall. Tel:
0736 795 346.
Club Secretary: J C Guppy, Cedar Court Bungalow,
Lelant, St Ives, Cornwall TR26 3JP. Tel: 0736 755127.
Club Colours: Navy & white.

STROUD RFC
Ground Address: Fromehall Park, Stroud, Gloucester GL5
3HS. Tel: 0453 763019.
Club Secretary: Norman Hall, 1 Elm Terrace, Foxmoor
Lane, Ebley, Stroud, Glos GL5 4QH. Tel: (H) 0453 824321
(W) 0453 763462.
Press Officer: David Red, Lower Green Farmhouse,
Haresfield, Stonehouse Glos GL10 3DS. Tel: (H) 0452
728264 (W) 0453 762251.
Club Colours: Blue & white hoops.

TORQUAY ATHLETIC RFC
Ground Address Recreation Ground, Sea Front, Torquay.
Tel: 0803 293842.
Club Secretary: Robin Foster, 110 Duchy Drive, Preston,
Paignton. Tel: (H) 0803 529508 (W) 0803 614567.
Club Colours: Black & white.

SOUTH WEST DIVISION

SOUTH WEST TWO 1993-94 FIXTURES

October 23 (Week 8)
Aylesbury v Gloucester OB
Oxford v Bridgwater
Penryn v Marlow
Swanage & W v Combe Down
Taunton v Banbury
Windsor v Matson

October 30 (Week X2)
Banbury v Swanage & W
Bridgwater v Penryn
Clevedon v Oxford
Combe Down v Windsor
Marlow v Taunton
Matson v Aylesbury

November 13 (Week 10)
Aylesbury v Combe Down
Gloucester OB v Matson
Penryn v Clevedon
Swanage & W v Marlow
Taunton v Bridgwater
Windsor v Banbury

November 20 (Week 11)
Banbury v Aylesbury
Bridgwater v Swanage & W
Clevedon v Taunton
Combe Down v Gloucester OB
Marlow v Windsor
Oxford v Penryn

December 4 (Week 13)
Aylesbury v Marlow
Gloucester OB v Banbury
Matson v Combe Down
Swanage & W v Clevedon
Taunton v Oxford
Windsor v Bridgwater

December 11 (Week 14)
Banbury v Matson
Bridgwater v Aylesbury
Clevedon v Windsor
Marlow v Gloucesster OB
Oxford v Swanage & W
Penryn v Taunton

December 18 (Week 15)
Aylesbury v Clevedon
Combe Down v Banbury
Gloucester OB v Bridgwater
Matson v Marlow
Swanage & W v Penryn
Windsor v Oxford

January 8 (Week 18)
Bridgwater v Matson
Clevedon v Gloucester OB
Marlow v Combe Down
Oxford v Aylesbury
Penryn v Windsor
Taunton v Swanage & W

January 29 (Week X5)
Aylesbury v Penryn
Banbury v Marlow
Combe Down v Bridgwater
Gloucester OB v Oxford
Matson v Clevedon
Windsor v Taunton

February 12 (Week 22)
Bridgwater v Banbury
Clevedon v Combe Down
Oxford v Matson
Penryn v Gloucester OB
Swanage & W v Windsor
Taunton v Aylesbury

March 12 (Week 26)
Aylesbury v Swanage & W
Banbury v Clevedon
Combe Down v Oxford
Gloucester OB v Taunton
Marlow v Bridgwater
Matson v Penryn

March 26 (Week 28)
Clevedon v Marlow
Oxford v Banbury
Penryn v Combe Down
Swanage & W v Gloucester OB
Taunton v Matson
Windsor v Aylesbury

April 9 (Week 30)
Banbury v Penryn
Bridgwater v Clevedon
Combe Down v Taunton
Gloucester OB v Windsor
Marlow v Oxford
Matson v Swanage & W

SOUTH WEST TWO

AYLESBURY RFC
Ground Address: Ostler's Field, Brook End, Western Turville, Aylesbury, Bucks. Tel: 0296 612556.
Club Secretary: B T Exell, The Hayloft, Church Lane, Wendover, Bucks, HP22 6NL. Tel: (H) 0296 625587 (W) 0296 622157.
Club Colours: Magenta & black.

BANBURY RUFC
Ground Address: Oxford Road, Banbury, Oxon. Tel: 0295 263862
Club Secretary: Malcolm Thomas, 24 Poplars Road, Chacombe, Banbury, Oxon, OX17 23Y. Tel: (H) 0295 711582.
Press Officer: Bryan A Davies, 34 Horton View, Banbury, Oxon, OX16 9HP. Tel: (H) 0295 262027 (W) 0865 276660.
Club Colours: Dark blue & white hoops.

BRIDGWATER & ALBION RFC
Ground Address: Broadway, Bridgwater, Somerset. Tel: 0278 423900.
Club Secretary: Anthony Pomeroy, "Hafod-Y-Gan", Newton Road, North Petherton, Somerset, TA6 6SN. Tel: (H) 0278 662181 (W) 0278 455631.
Press Officer: Chris Heal, 52b Chapel Road, Pawlett, Bridgwater. Tel: (H) 0278 683507.
Club Colours: Red, black & amber.

CLEVEDON RFC
Ground Address: Coleridge Vale Playing Fields, Clevedon, Avon, BS21 6PF. Tel: 0275 877772.
Club Secretary: R G Legge, 2 Kingston Avenue, Clevedon, Avon, BS21 6DS. Tel: (H) 0275 841624 (W) 0272 291031 Ext 2995.
Press Officer: M Thomas, 46 Treefield Road, Clevedon, Avon, BS21 6JB. Tel: (H) 0275 875497.
Club Colours: Royal blue & amber.

COMBE DOWN RFC
Ground Address: Holly's Corner, North Road, Combe Down, Bath. Tel: 0225 832075.
Club Secretary: John Heal, 3 Gladstone Place, Tyning Road, Combe Down, Bath. Tel: (H) 0225 837903.
Press Officer: Wyn Bailey, 3 Keels Hill, Peasdown, St John, Bath. Tel: (H) 0761 434845
Club Colours: Black & amber.

GLOUCESTER OLD BOYS RFC
Ground Address: Horton Road, Gloucester, GL1 3ZA. Tel: 0452 302390.
Club Secretary: Norman P Partridge, 17 Armscroft Place, Burnwood, Gloucester, CL2 0SW. Tel: (H) 0452 527658 (W) 0242 263300.
Press Officer: Gerald Artus, 62 Tuffley Avenue, Gloucester, GL1 5LX. Tel: (H) 0452 528465 (W) 0242 263300.
Club Colours: Claret, gold & navy hoops, navy shorts.

MARLOW RUFC
Ground Address: Riverwoods Drive, Marlow, Bucks. 062 84 483911.
Club Secretary: 6 Eastern Dene, Hazlemere, Bucks, HP15 7BT. Tel: (H) 0494 711391 (W) 0494 431717.
Press Officer: P Trunkfield, c/o Marlow RUFC, Riverwoods Drive, Marlow, Bucks. (H) 062 84 483911
Club Colours: Black & white hoops.

MATSON RFC
Ground Address: Redwell Road, Matson, Gloucester, GL4 9JG. Tel: 0452 528963.
Club Secretary: Gilbert Locke, 39 Oxmoor, Abbeydale, Gloucester, GL4 9XW. Tel: (H) 0452 419587 (W) 0452 712802.
Press Officer: Gilbert Locke, as above.
Club Colours: Black shirts, white shorts.

FINAL TABLE

	P	W	D	L	F	A	PD	Pts
Stroud	12	11	0	1	290	129	161	22
Barnstaple	12	9	1	2	201	123	788	19
Bridgwater & Albion	12	9	0	3	243	114	129	18
Matson	12	9	0	3	209	97	112	18
Banbury	12	7	0	5	199	172	27	14
Taunton	12	6	0	6	182	192	-10	12
Aylesbury	12	5	0	7	100	205	-105	10
Combe Down	12	4	1	7	191	201	-10	9
Oxford	12	4	1	7	200	298	-98	9
Clevedon	12	4	0	8	157	180	-23	8
Windsor	12	4	0	8	156	214	-58	8
Marlow	12	3	0	9	150	191	-41	6
O. Culverhaysians	12	1	1	10	88	250	-162	3

OXFORD RFC
Ground Address: Southern Bypass, North Kinksey, Oxford. Tel: 0865 243984.
Club Secretary: R L Martin, Pantiles, 22 Didcot Road, Long Wittenham, Oxon, OX14 4PZ. Tel: (H) 086730 7528.
Press Officer: R Tyrrell, 159 Banbury Road, Kidlington, Oxford. Tel: (H) 08675 77366.
Club Colours: Green, black & silver hoops.

PENRYN RFC
Ground Address: The Memorial Ground, Kernick Road, Penryn, Cornwall, TR10 8QP. Tel: 0326 372239.
Club Secretary: M O'Neill, 80 Bohelland Road, Penryn, TR10 8DY. Tel: (H) 0326 373283.
Press Officer: M O'Neill, 80 Bohelland Road, Penryn, TR10 8DY. Tel: (H) 0326 373283.
Club Colours: Red & black.

SWANAGE & WAREHAM RFC
Ground Address: Bestwall Road, Wareham, Dorset, BH20 4AY. Tel: 0929 552224.
Club Secretary: John Hopkins, "Sospan", Greenclose Lane, Wimborne, Dorset, BH21 2AL. Tel: (H) 0202 886804.
Press Officer: John Constable, "Grand View", Puddletown Road, Worgret, Wareham, Dorset, BH20 6AE. Tel: (H) 0929 551468 (W) 0202 292333 Ext 3548.
Club Colours: Maroon shirts, white shorts.

TAUNTON RDC
Ground Address: Priory Park, Bridge Road, Taunton, TA1 1QB. Tel: 0823 275670
Club Secretary: Jon Grace, 44 Th octagon, Middle Street, Taunton. Tel: (H) 0823 272748 (W) 0823 323221.
Press Officer: John Mackenry, 35 Bramley Road, Taunton, TA1 2XJ. Tel: (H) 0823 272533.
Club Colours: Crimson, white & black hoops.

WINDSOR RFC
Ground Address: Home Park, Datchet Road, Windsor, Berkshire, SL4 6HX. Tel: 0753 860807.
Club Secretary: Chris Blue, Salburton, Bedworth Road, Oakley Green, Windsor, LS4 4LN. Tel: (H) 0753 620229.
Press Officer: Ian Crawshaw, 2 Common Road, Eton Wick, Berkshire, SL3 8TE. Tel: (H) 0753 851297.
Club Colours: Black, gold, green & maroon quarters, black shorts.

SOUTH WEST DIVISION

WESTERN COUNTIES 1993-94 FIXTURES

December 18 (Week 15)
Avonmouth OB v Penzance-New
Bideford v Okehampton
Crediton v Old Culverhays
Drybrook v Devonport Ser
Old Patesians v Tiverton
Wiveliscombe v Launceston

October 23 (Week 8)
Avonmouth OB v Bideford
Launceston v Okehampton
Old Patesians v Drybrook
Spartans v Devonport Ser
Tiverton v Old Culverhays
Wiveliscombe v Crediton

January 8 (Week 18)
Launceston v Avonmouth OB
Okehampton v Crediton
Old Culverhays v Drybrook
Penzance-New v Bideford
Spartans v Old Patesians
Tiverton v Wiveliscombe

October 30 (Week X2)
Crediton v Avonmouth OB
Devonport Ser v Old Patesians
Drybrook v Wiveliscombe
Okehampton v Tiverton
Old Culverhays v Spartans
Penzance-New v Launceston

January 29 (Week X5)
Avonmouth OB v Tiverton
Bideford v Launceston
Crediton v Penzance-New
Devonport Ser v Old Culverhays
Drybrook v Okehampton
Wiveliscombe v Spartans

November 13 (Week 10)
Avonmouth OB v Drybrook
Bideford v Crediton
old Patesians v Old Culverhays
Spartans v Okehampton
Tiverton v Penzance-New
Wiveliscombe v Devonport Ser

February 12 (Week 22)
Launceston v Crediton
Okehampton v Devonport Ser
Old Patesians v Wivleiscombe
Penzance-New v Drybrook
Spartans v Avonmouth OB
Tiverton v Bideford

November 20 (Week 11)
Devonport Ser v Avonmouth OB
Drybrook v Bideford
Launceston v Tiverton
Okehampton v Old Patesians
Old Culverhays v Wiveliscombe
Penzance-New v Spartans

March 12 (Week 26)
Avonmouth OB v Old Patesians
Bideford v Spartans
Crediton v Tiverton
Devonport Ser v Penzance-New
Drybrook v Launceston
Old Culverhays v Okehampton

December 4 (Week 13)
Avonmouth v Old Culverhays
Bideford v Devonport Ser
Crediton v Drybook
Old Patesians v Penzance-New
Spartans v Launceston
Wiveliscombe v Okehampton

March 26 (Week 28)
Launceston v Devonport Ser
Old Patesians v Bideford
Penzance-New v Old Culverhays
Spartans v Crediton
Tiverton v Drybrook
Wiveliscombe v Avonmouth OB

December 11 (Week 14)
Devonport Ser v Crediton
Launceston v Old Patesians
Okehampton v Avonmouth OB
Old Culverhays v Bideford
Penzance-New v Wiveliscombe
Tiverton v Spartans

April 9 (Week 30)
Bideford v Wiveliscombe
Crediton v Old Patesians
Devonport Ser v Tiverton
Drybrook v Spartans
Okehampton v Penzance-New
Old Culverhays v Launceston

476

WESTERN COUNTIES

AVONMOUTH OLD BOYS RFC
Ground Address: Barracks Lane, Shirehampton, Bristol BS11. Tel: 0272 829093.
Club Secretary: I McNab, 48 Nibley Road, Shirehampton, Bristol, BS11 9XR. Tel: (H) 0272 823870.
Press Officer: Pat Chilcott, 448 Portway, Shirehampton, Bristol, BS11. Tel: (H) 0272 829753.
Club Colours: Black with single red hoop.

BIDEFORD RFC
Ground Address: King George's Field, Bank End, Bideford. Tel: 0237 474049.
Club Secretary: Bernie Ridd, Higher Benton, Stoke Rivers, Devon. Tel: (H) 0598 710298 (W) 0271 75561.
Press Officer: S Braddick, Braddicks Furnishing Centre, Mill Street, Bideford, Devon. Tel: (H) 0237 472564 (W) 0237 472564.
Club Colours: Red & white hoops.

CREDITON RFC
Ground Address: Exhibition Road, Crediton, Devon, EX17 3BY. Tel: 0363 772784.
Club Secretary: P M Gibbins, South Coombe, Cheriton Fitzpaine, Nr Crediton, EX17 4HP. Tel: (H) 0363 866413 (W) 0363 866413.
Press Officer: J C Hayes, 13 Brookside Crescent, Exeter, Devon, EX4 8NF. Tel: (H) 0392 466534.
Club Colours: Black & amber.

DEVONPORT SERVICES RFC
Ground Address: The Rectory, Second Avenue, Devonport, Plymouth, PL1 5QE. Tel: 0752 501559.
Club Secretary: Lt Cdr J L Large, Office of Captain Fleet Maintenance, HM Naval Base, Devonport, Plymouth. Tel: (H) 0753 793463 (W) 0753 553740 Ext 65556.
Press Officer: Lpt K Bowen, The Rectory, Second Avenue, Devonport, Plymouth, PL1 5QE. Tel: 0752 501559.
Club Colours: Navy blue shirts & short, red stockings.

DRYBROOK RFC
Ground Address: Mannings Ground, High Street, Drybrook, Glos. Tel: 0594 542595.
Club Secretary: Glyn Tingue, Southview, Hazel Hill, Drybrook, Glos. Tel: (H) 0594 543294 (W) 0594 542769.
Press Officer: Paul Mason, 29 Caris Brook Road, Mitcheldean, Glos. Tel: (H) 0594 543948 (W) 0594 542461.
Club Colours: Green with black on white band.

LAUNCESTON RFC
Ground Address: The New Clubhouse, Polson, Launceston, Cornwall. Tel: 0566 773406.
Club Secretary: Middle Bamham, Launceston, Cornwall, PL15 9QJ. Tel: (H) 0566 772071.
Club Colours: Black & white.

OKEHAMPTON RFC
Ground Address: Oaklands Park, Hatherleigh Road, Okehampton, Devon. Tel: 0837 52508.
Club Secretary: Ted Cann, 11 Exeter Road, Okehampton, Devon, EX20 1NN. Tel: (H) 0837 52759 (W) 0837 63170.
Press Officer: Eddie Williamson, Ashbury House, Northlew, Nr Okehampton, Devon. Tel: (H) 0837 87351.
Club Colours: Maroon & amber.

OLD CULVERHAYSIANS RFC
Ground Address: Glasshouse Ground, Bradford Road, Combe Down, Bath, Avon. Tel: 0225 832081.
Club Secretary: Dick Stevens, 43 Inverness Road, Twerton, Bath, Avon, BA2 3RX. Tel: (H) 0225 422433 (W) 0225 312791.
Press Officer: Dick Stevens, 43 Inverness Road, Twerton, Bath, Avon, BA2 3RX. Tel: (H) 0225 422433 (W) 0225 312791.
Club Colours: Black.

FINAL TABLE

	P	W	D	L	F	A	PD	Pts
Gloucester O B	12	12	0	0	321	86	235	24
Launceston	12	11	0	1	317	75	242	22
Okehampton	12	9	0	3	223	172	51	18
Penzance-Newlyn	12	8	0	4	314	129	185	16
Spartans	12	7	0	5	208	141	67	14
Wiveliscombe	12	6	0	6	183	200	-17	12
Bideford	12	5	0	7	167	175	-8	10
Drybrook	12	5	0	7	169	198	-29	10
Tiverton	12	5	0	7	170	208	-38	10
Avonmouth	12	5	0	7	137	187	-50	10
Crediton	12	3	0	9	163	232	-69	6
Plymouth C S	12	2	0	10	117	349	-232	4
Devon & C'wall Pol	12	0	0	12	95	432	-337	0

OLD PATESIANS RFC
Ground Address: Everest Road, Leckhampton, Cheltenham, Gloucestershire. Tel: 0242 524633.
Club Secretary: PJ McMurray, Avon, Victoria Terrace, Cheltenham, Gloucestershire, GL52 6BN. Tel: (H) 0242 570947 (W) 0242 515881.
Press Officer: C Smith, 7 Oxford Street, Cheltenham, Gloucestershire. Tel: (H) 0242 526379 (W) 0905 23444.
Club Colours: Magenta, blue & white hoops.

PENZANCE-NEWLYN RFC
Ground Address: Alexandra Road, Penzance. Tel: 0736 64227.
Club Secretary: P P Harvey, "Chy Kerensa", 27 Gurnick Road, Newlyn, Penzance, Cornwall, TR18 5DG. Tel: (H) 0736 65797 (W) 0736 65797.
Press Officer: P P Harvey, "Chy Kerensa", 27 Gurnick Road, Newlyn, Penzance, Cornwall, TR18 5DG. Tel: (H) 0736 65797 (W) 0736 65797.
Club Colours: Red, white & black hoops, black shorts.

SPARTANS RFC
Ground Address: Archdeacon Meadow, Cattle Market, Gloucester. Tel: 0452 910552.
Club Secretary: S Stroud, 1 Swallow Crescent, Innsworth, Gloucester, GL3 1BL. Tel: (H) 0452 731913 (W) 0452 423497.
Press Officer: S Stoud, 1 Swallow Crescent, Innsworth, Gloucester, GL3 1BL. Tel: (H) 0452 731913 (W) 0452 423497.
Club Colours: Red.

TIVERTON RFC
Ground Address: Coronation Field, Bolham Road, Tiverton, EX16 6SG. Tel: 0884 252271.
Club Secretary: Kathy Morgan, "Station House", 26 Luke Street, Bampton, Nr Tiverton, EX16 9NF. Tel: (H) 0398 331589.
Press Officer: Geoff Bulley, 2 Besley Close, Tiverton, Devon, EX16 4JF. Tel: (H) 0884 259316 (W) 0392 382207.
Club Colours: Light & dark blue.

WIVELISCOMBE RFC
Ground Address: Recreation Ground, West Road, Wiveliscombe, Taunton, Somerset, TA4. Tel: 0984 23897.
Club Secretary: A Weaver, 21 Mount Street, Bishops Lyudeard, Taunton, Somerset, TA4 3AN. Tel: (H) 0823 433632.
Press Officer: C Mann, "Lockyers", Fore Street, Milverton, Taunton, Somerset, TA4 1JV. Tel: (H) 0823 400673.
Club Colours: Blue with red sash.

SOUTH WEST DIVISION

CORNWALL/DEVON 1993-94 FIXTURES

October 23 (Week 8)
D & C Police v Paignton
Exmouth v Ivybridge
Liskeard-Looe v Veor
Newquay H v Plymouth CS
Sidmouth v Truro
Teignmouth v South Molton

October 30 (Week X2)
Hayle v Exmouth
Ivybridge v Sidmouth
Plymouth CS v D & C Police
South Molton v Liskeard-Looe
Truro v Teignmouth
Veor v Newquay H

November 13 (Week 10)
D & C Police v Veor
Liskeard-Looe v Truro
Newquay H v South Molton
Paignton v Plymouth CS
Sidmouth v Hayle
Teignmouth v Ivybridge

November 20 (Week 11)
Exmouth v Sidmouth
Hayle v Teignmouth
Ivybridge v Liskeard-Looe
South Molton v D & C Police
Truro v Newquay H
Veor v Paignton

December 4 (Week 13)
D & C Police v Truro
Liskeard-Looe v Hayle
Newquay H v Ivybridge
Paignton v South Molton
Plymouth CS v Veor
Teignmouth v Exmouth

December 11 (Week 14)
Exmouth v Liskeard-Looe
Hayle v Newquay H
Ivybridge v D & C Police
Sidmouth v Teignmouth
South Molton v Plymouth CS
Truro v Paignton

December 18 (Week 15)
D & C Police v Hayle
Liskeard-Looe v Sidmouth
Newquay H v Exmouth
Paignton v Ivybridge
Plymouth CS v Truro
Veor v South Molton

January 8 (Week 18)
Exmouth v D & C Police
Hayle v Paignton
Ivybridge v Plymouth CS
Sidmouth v Newquay H
Teignmouth v Liskeard-Looe
Truro v Veor

January 29 (Week X5)
D & C Police v Sidmouth
Newquay H v Teignmouth
Paignton v Exmouth
Plymouth CS v Hayle
South Molton v Truro
Veor v Ivybridge

February 12 (Week 22)
Exmouth v Plymouth CS
Hayle v Veor
Ivybridge v South Molton
Liskeard-Looe v Newquay H
Sidmouth v Paignton
Teignmouth v D & C Police

March 12 (Week 26)
D & C Police v Liskeard-Looe
Paignton v Teignmouth
Plymouth CS v Sidmouth
South Molton v Hayle
Truro v Ivybridge
Veor v Exmouth

March 26 (Week 28)
Exmouth v South Molton
Hayle v Truro
Liskeard-Looe v Paignton
Newquay H v D & C Police
Sidmouth v Veor
Teignmouth v Plymouth CS

April 9 (Week 30)
Ivybridge v Hayle
Paignton v Newquay H
Plymouth CS v Liskeard-Looe
South Molton v Sidmouth
Truro v Exmouth
Veor v Teignmouth

478

CORNWALL & DEVON

DEVON & CORNWALL CONSTABULARY RFC
Ground Address: Police Headquarters, Middlemoor,
Exeter. Tel: 0392 68485.
Club Secretary: Simon Bassett, Tavistock Police Station,
Tavistock, Devon. Tel: (H) 0822 854510 (W) 0822 612217.
Club Colours: White with black hoops.

EXMOUTH RFC
Ground Address: Imperial Recreation Ground, Royal
Avenue, Exmouth, Devon. Tel: 0395 263665.
Club Secretary: Stuart Kesteven (Kes), 56 Marpool Hill,
Exmouth, Devon. Tel: (H) 0395 263351.
Club Colours: Heliotrope and white (change strip, gold).

HAYLE RFC
Ground Address: Memorial Park, Marsh Lane, Hayle. Tel:
0736 753320.
Club Secretary: Clive Rowe, Lonskyber, 3 Churchtown
Gwinear, Hayle, Cornwall TR27 5JZ. Tel: (H) 0736 850
389 (W) 0736 850 389.
Club Colours: Green, black & white.

IVYBRIDGE RFC
Ground Address: Cross-in-Hand, Exeter Road, Ivybridge,
Devon. Tel: 0752 894392.
Club Secretary: P G Smith, 1 Croft Cottages, Galpin St,
Modbury, Devon PL21 0QA. Tel: (H) 0548 830009 (W)
0752 264810.
Club Colours: Green, black, white.

LISKEARD-LOOE RFC
Ground Address: Lux Park, Liskeard. Tel: 0579 342665.
Club Secretary: Geff Collings, Little Polsloe, Lostwithiel,
Cornwall PL22 0HS. Tel: (H) 0208 873201.
Club Colours: Red & black 4" hoops.

NEWQUAY HORNETS RFC
Ground Address: Newquay Sports Centre, Tretherras,
Newquay, Cornwall. Tel: 0637 875533
Club Secretary: Russell Edwards, 17 St Thomas Road,
Newquay, Cornwall TR7 1RS. Tel: (H) 0637 871479 (W)
0637 871479.
Press Officer: T Delbridge, Thurso, Cubert, Nr Newquay,
Cornwall. Tel: (H) 0637 830441.
Club Colours: Green & white.

PAIGNTON RFC
Ground Address: Queens Park, Queens Road, Paignton.
Tel: 0803 557715.
Club Secretary: Ray Squires, 67 Brantwood Drive,
Paignton TQ4 5HY. Tel: (H) 0803 554360.
Press Officer: Alan Vanstone, 38 Pillar Avenue, Brixham
TQ5 8LB. Tel: (H) 0803 854889.
Club Colours: Red & white hoops.

PLYMOUTH CIVIL SERVICE RFC
Ground Address: Civil Service Sports Club, Beacon
Down, Recreation Road, Plymouth PL2 3WA. Tel: 0752
702303.
Club Secretary: Danny R Avery, 25 Weston Mill Hill,
Weston Mill, Plymouth PL5 2AR. Tel: (H) 0752 365890
(W) 0752 552182.
Press Officer: Roger Jewell, CSSA Club, Beacon Down,
Recreation Road, Plymouth PL2 3WA. Tel: (H) 0752.
705579.
Club Colours: Red & white shirts, black shorts, red socks.

FINAL TABLE

	P	W	D	L	F	A	PD	Pts
Devonport Services	12	12	0	0	301	98	203	24
Exmouth	12	8	0	4	226	174	52	16
Teignmouth	12	7	1	4	205	137	68	15
Truro	12	7	1	4	186	146	40	15
South Molton	12	6	2	4	215	215	0	14
Sidmouth	12	6	1	5	175	169	6	13
Liskeard-Looe	12	6	1	5	174	173	1	13
Newquay Hornets	12	5	1	6	152	148	4	11
Ivybridge	12	5	0	7	214	217	-3	10
Hayle	12	4	1	7	137	175	-38	9
Bude	12	3	2	7	117	150	-33	8
Exeter Saracens	12	1	2	9	98	228	-130	4
Saltash	12	2	0	10	143	313	-170	4

SIDMOUTH RFC
Ground Address: Blackmore Field, Heydon's Lane,
Sidmouth, Devon. Tel: 0395 51816.
Club Secretary: Brian Showell, 3 Connaught Close,
Sidmouth, Devon EX10 8TU. Tel: (H) 0395 512055.
Club Colours: Green shirts, white shorts.

SOUTH MOLTON RFC
Ground Address: Unicorn Park, Station Road, South
Molton, Devon EX36 3LH. Tel: 0769 572024.
Club Secretary: Mrs Annie White, 8 Duke St, South
Molton, Devon EX36 3AL. Tel: (H) 0769 573741 (W)
573204 (FAX) 0769 573200.
Press Officer: Peter Snow, 4 Gwythers, South Molton,
Devon. Tel: (H) 0769 573027 (W) 573204.
Club Colours: All black.

TEIGNMOUTH RFC
Ground Address: Bitton Sports Ground, Bitton Park Road,
Teignmouth, Devon TQ14 9DR. Tel: 0626 774714.
Club Secretary: Robert Loveridge, 59 Second Avenue,
Teignmouth TQ14 9DN. Tel: (H) 0626 775891 (W) 0626
774556.
Press Officer: John Ware, Minden Lodge, Landscore
Road, Teignmouth TQ14 9HW. Tel: (H) 0626 773972.
Club Colours: Red, white & black hoops.

TRURO RFC
Ground Address: St Clements Hill, Truro. Tel: 0872
74750.
Club Secretary: Gregg Oldrieve, Chydavas, Idless, Truro
TR4 9QS. Tel: (H) 0872 42091 (W) 0872 71033.
Club Colours: Blue & amber quarters.

VEOR RFC
Ground Address: Wheal Gerry, Cliff View Road,
Camborne, Cornwall.
Club Secretary: N J Barber JP, 86 Dolcoats Road,
Camborne, Cornwall TR14 8RP. Tel: (H) 0209 710593 (W)
0752 665951.
Club Colours: Amber with black collars, cuffs & shorts.

SOUTH WEST DIVISION

DEVON ONE
1993-94
FIXTURES

October 23 (Week 8)
Dartmouth v Exeter Sara
Honiton v Old Technicians
Newton Abbot v Old Plymothian
Old Public Oaks v Jesters
Tavistock v Ilfracombe
Withycombe v Kingsbridge

October 30 (Week X2)
Ilfracombe v Dartmouth
Jesters v Withycombe
Kingsbridge v Tavistock
Old Plymothian v Honiton
Old Technicians v Old Public Oaks
Topsham v Newton Abbot

November 13 (Week 10)
Dartmouth v Kingsbridge
Exeter Sara v Ilfracombe
Honiton v Topsham
Old Public Oaks v Old Plymothian
Tavistock v Jesters
Withycombe v Old Technicians

November 20 (Week 11)
Jesters v Dartmouth
Kingsbridge v Exeter Sara
Newton Abbot v Honiton
Old Plymothian v Withycombe
Old Technicians v Tavistock
Topsham v Old Public Oaks

December 4 (Week 13)
Dartmouth v Old Technicians
Exeter Sara v Jesters
Ilfracombe v Kingsbridge
Old Public Oaks v Newton Abbot
Tavistock v Old Plymothian
Withycombe v Topsham

December 11 (Week 14)
Honiton v Old Public Oaks
Jesters v Ilfracombe
Newton Abbot v Withycombe
Old Plymothian v Dartmouth
Old Technicians v Exeter Sara
Topsham v Tavistock

December 18 (Week 15)
Dartmouth v Topsham
Exeter Sara v Old Plymothian
Ilfracombe v Old Technicians
Kingsbridge v Jesters
Tavistock v Newton Abbot
Withycombe v Honiton

January 8 (Week 18)
Honiton v Tavistock
Newton Abbot v Dartmouth
Old Plymothian v Ilfracombe
Old Public Oaks v Withycombe
Old Technicians v Kingsbridge
Topsham v Exeter Sara

January 29 (Week X5)
Dartmouth v Honiton
Exeter Sara v Newton Abbot
Ilfracombe v Topsham
Jesters v Old Technicians
Kingsbridge v Old Plymothian
Tavistock v Old Public Oaks

February 12 (Week 22)
Honiton v Exeter Sara
Newton Abbot v Ilfracombe
Old Plymothian v Jesters
Old Public Oaks v Dartmouth
Topsham v Kingsbridge
Withycombe v Tavistock

March 12 (Week 26)
Dartmouth v Withycombe
Exeter Sara v Old Public Oak
Ilfracombe v Honiton
Jesters v Topsham
Kingsbridge v Newton Abbot
Old Technicians v Old Plymothian

March 26 (Week 28)
Honiton v Kingsbridge
Newton Abbot v Jesters
Old Public Oaks v Ilfracombe
Tavistock v Dartmouth
Topsham v Old Technicians
Withycombe v Exeter Sara

April 9 (Week 30)
Exeter Sara v Tavistock
Ilfracombe v Withycombe
Jesters v Honiton
Kingsbridge v Old Public Oaks
Old Plymothian v Topsham
Old Technicians v Newton Abbot

DEVON ONE

DARTMOUTH RFC
Ground Address: The Clubhouse, Roseville Street, Dartmouth, South Devon. Tel: 0803 833994.
Club Secretary: Ms A Reaburn, 7 Crowthers Hill, Dartmouth, Devon TQ6 9QX. Tel: 0803 832957.
Press Officer: S Atkins, 125 Victoria Road, Dartmouth, Devon TQ6 9DY. Tel: (H) 0803 832381 (W) 0803 833829.
Club Colours: Emerald & scarlet.

EXETER SARACENS
Ground Address: Exhibition Fields, Summer Lane, Whipton, Exeter. Tel: 0392 462651.
Club Secretary: R W Buchanan, 72 Sylvan Road, Pennsylvania, Exeter EX4 6HA. Te: (H) 0392 430804 (W) 0395 263795.
Press Officer: M Heddon, 2 Wessex Close, Topsham, Exeter. Tel: (H) 0392 877888.
Club Colours: Red shirts, black shorts.

HONITON RFC
Ground Address: Allhallows Playing Fields, Honiton, Devon. Tel: 0404 41239.
Club Secretary: D Todd, "Omega", Sidmouth Road, Honiton. Tel: 0404 41608.
Press Officer: Ken Clark, Millhouse, Nillhayes, Storkland. Tel: (H) 0404 88249 (W) 0404 41866.
Club Colours: Red, amber & black.

ILFRACOMBE RFC
Ground Address: Brimlands, Hillsborough Road, Ilfracombe. Tel: 0271 864249.
Club Secretary: Andrew Burke, 14 South Borrow Road, Ilfracombe. Tel: (H) 0271 862879 (W) 0271 72128.
Press Officer: Robert Fairchild, 14 St James Place, Ilfracombe. Tel: 0271 862147.
Club Colours: Blue & white hoops.

JESTERS RFC
Ground Address: Marsh Meadows, Lower Leigham, Plymouth, Devon.
Club Secretary: J M Smith, 31 Erle Gardens, Plympton, St Morris, Plymouth PL7 3NZ. Tel: (H) 0752 344233 (W) 0752 730311.
Club Colours: Red, white, black & gold quarters.

KINGSBRIDGE RFC
Ground Address: High House, Kingsbridge, Devon TQ7 1JL. Tel: 0548 852051.
Club Secretary: Martin Newman, "Fourwinds", 46 Saffron Park, Kingsbridge, Devon TQ7 1RL. Tel: (H) 0548 853976 (W) 0548 853101.
Club Colours: Blue & white hoops.

NEWTON ABBOT RFC
Ground Address: Rackerhayes, Kingsteignton Road, Newton Abbot, Devon. Te: 0626 54150.
Club Secretary: Mrs Sherrill Lock, 38 Mile End Road, Newton Abbot, Devon TQ12 1RW. Tel: 0626 54835.
Press Officer: Keith Maclean, 121 Exeter Road, Kingsteignton, Newton Abbot, Devon TQ12 3NA. Tel: 0626 51493.
Club Colours: All white.

OLD PLYMOTHIAN & MANNAMEADIANS RFC
Ground Address: Brickleigh Down Lane, Roborough, Plymouth.
Club Secretary: E J Bolster, 22 Carlton Close, Lower Compton, Plymouth PL3 6JS. Tel: (H) 0752 223908 (W) 0752 385630.
Club Colours: Claret & blue squares.

FINAL TABLE

	P	W	D	L	F	A	PD	Pts
Paignton	12	10	1	1	239	74	165	21
Honiton	12	9	0	3	296	128	168	18
Kingsbridge	12	8	2	2	264	119	145	18
Newton Abbot	12	9	0	3	172	81	91	18
Tavistock	12	7	0	5	218	136	82	14
Old Plymothian	12	7	0	5	207	179	28	14
Topsham	12	6	0	6	297	184	113	12
Ilfracombe	12	6	0	6	151	195	-44	12
Old Technicians	12	5	0	7	133	118	15	10
Old Public Oaks	12	4	2	6	151	143	8	10
Jesters	12	1	1	10	74	269	-195	3
Cullompton	12	1	1	10	82	299	-217	3
Plymouth Argaum	12	1	1	10	80	439	-359	3

OLD PUBLIC OAKS RFC
Ground Address: King George V Playing Fields, Elburton, Plymouth.
Club Secretary: G H Matthews, 25 Colwill Road, Mainstone, Plymouth PL6 8RP. Tel: (H) 0752 707363 (W) 0752 663231.
Club Colours: Green & gold hoops.

OLD TECHNICIANS RFC
Ground Address: Weston Mill Oak Villa, Ferndale Road, lymouth, Devon. Tel: 0752 363352.
. **Club Secretary:** T Carney, 2 Tedburn Crescent, Ham, Plymouth PL2 2MY. Tel: 0752 364884.
Press Officer: Trevor Williams, 29 Beaumont Street, Pymouth, Devon. Tel: 0752 660599.
Club Colours: Black with white circlet.

TAVISTOCK RFC
Ground Address: Sandy Park, Trelawney Road, Tavistock, Devon. PL19 0JL. Tel: 0822 618275.
Club Secretary: Trevor Masters, 10 Uplands, Tavistock, Devon PL19 8ET. el: 0822 14323.
Press Officer: G Lavis, 10 Pinder Court, King Street, Tavistock. Tel: 0822 615020.
Club Colours: Red shirts, black shorts, red socks, red eyes!

TOPSHAM RFC
Ground Address: The Bonfire Field, Exeter Road, Topsham, Exeter, Devon. Tel: 0392 873651.
Club Secretary: Keith Smith, 63 High Street, Topsham, Exeter EX3 0DY. Tel: (H) 0392 875675.
Press Officer: Geoff Hog, 431 Topsham Road, Countess Wear, Exeter EX2 7AB. Tel: (H) 0392 874129 (W) 0392 383934.
Club Colours: Dark & light blue hoops.

WITHYCOMBE RFC
Ground Address: Rayleih Park, Hulham Road, Withycobe, Exmouth, Devon. Tel: 0395 266762.
Club Secretary: M J Norman, 2 Claremont Lane, Exmouth EX8 2LE. Tel: 0395 290644.
Press Officer: A Hirst. Tel 0395 268316.
Club Colours: Green & black hoops.

SOUTH WEST DIVISION

DEVON TWO
1993-94 FIXTURES

October 23 (Week 8)
Cullompton v DHSOB
Plymouth Argaum v St Columba
Salcombe v Prince Rock
Tamar Saracens v Plymstock
Torrington v Plympton
Totnes v Plymouth YMCA
Victoria v North Tawton

October 30 (Week X2)
DHSOB v Plymouth Argaum
North Tawton v Cullompton
Plymouth YMCS v Victoria
Plympton v Totnes
Plymstock v Torrington
Prince Rock v Tamar Saracens
St Columba v Salcombe

November 13 (Week 10)
Cullompton v Plymouth YMCA
DHSOB v North Tawton
Plymouth Argaum v Salcombe
Tamar Saracens v St Columba
Torrington v Prince Rock
Totnes v Plymstock
Victoria v Plympton

November 20 (Week 11)
North Tawton v Plymouth Argaum
Plymouth YMCA v DHSOB
Plympton v Cullompton
Plymstock v Victoria
Prince Rock v Totnes
Salcombe v Tamar Saracens
St Columba v Torrington

December 4 (Week 13)
Cullompton v Plymstock
DHSOB v Plympton
North Tawton v Plymouth YMCA
Plymouth Argaum v Tamar Saracens
Torrington v Salcombe
Totnes v St Columba
Victoria v Prince Rock

December 11 (Week 14)
Plymouth YMCA v Plymouth Argaum
Plympton v North Tawton
Plymstock v DHSOB
Prince Rock v Cullompton
Salcombe v Totnes
St Columba v Victoria
Tamar Saracens v Torrington

December 18 (Week 15)
Cullompton v St Columba

DHSOB v Prince Rock
North Tawton v Plymstock
Plymouth Argaum v Torrington
Plymouth YMCA v Plympton
Totnes v Tamar Saracens
Victoria v Salcombe

January 8 (Week 18)
Plympton v Plymouth Argaum
Plymstock v Plymouth YMCA
Prince Rock v North Tawton
Salcombe v Cullompton
St Columba v DHSOB
Tamar Saracens v Victoria
Torrington v Totnes

January 29 (Week X5)
Cullompton v Tamar Saracens
DHSOB v Salcombe
North Tawton v St Columba
Plymouth Argaum v Totnes
Plymouth YMCA v Prince Rock
Plympton v Plymstock
Victoria v Torrington

February 12 (Week 22)
Plymstock v Plymouth Argaum
Prince Rock v Plympton
Salcombe v North Tawton
St Columba v Plymouth YMCA
Tamar Saracens v DHSOB
Torrington v Cullompton
Totnes v Victoria

March 12 (Week 26)
Cullompton v Totnes
DHSOB v Torrington
North Tawton v Tamar Saracens
Plymouth Argaum v Victoria
Plymouth YMCA v Salcombe
Plympton v St Columba
Plymstock v Prince Rock

March 26 (Week 28)
Prince Rock v Plymouth Argaum
Salcombe v Plympton
St Columba v Plymstock
Tamar Saracens v Plymouth YMCA
Torrington v North Tawton
Totnes v DHSOB
Victoria v Cullompton

April 9 (Week 30)
DHSOB v Victoria
North Tawton v Totnes
Plymouth Argaum v Cullompton
Plymouth YMCA v Torrington
Plympton v Tamar Saracens
Plymstock v Salcombe
Prince Rock v St Columba

DEVON TWO

CULLOMPTON RFC
Ground Address: Stafford Parke, Knowle Lane, Cullompton, Devon. Tel: 0884 32480.
Club Secretary: Nigel Nichols, 91 Bilbie Close, Cullompton, Devon, EX15 1LG. Tel: (H) 0884 38365 (W) 0884 840458. **Press Officer:** Rivers Barry, 27 Bovet Street, Wellington, Somerset, TA21 8JJ. Tel: (H) 0823 666845.
Club Colours: Scarlet & black hoops.

DEVONPORT HIGH SCHOOL OLD BOYS RFC
Ground Address: DHS for Boys, Millbridge, Devonport, Plymouth, PL1 5OP.
Club Secretary: Ian Robertson, 69 Merrivale Road, Beacon Park, Plymouth, PL2 2RW. Tel: (H) 0752 559377. **Press Officer:** Ian Robertson, 69 Merrivale Road, Beacon Park, Plymouth, PL2 2RW. Tel: (H) 0752 559377.
Club Colours: Green, black & white irregular hoops, black shorts.

NORTH TAWTON RFC
Ground Address: The butts, Barton Street, North Tawton, Devon.
Club Secretary: G M Hoggins, The Old Forge, North Street, North Tawton, Devon, EX20 2DE. Tel: (H) 0837 82516. **Press Officer:** R P Stoddart, 43 Fore Street, North Tawton, Devon, EX20 2DT. Tel: (H) 0837 82693.
Club Colours: Black & amber.

PLYMOUTH ARGAUM RFC
Ground Address: The Clubhouse, Bickleigh Down Road, Roborough, Plymouth. Tel: 0752 772156.
Club Secretary: P A Evans, 34A Park View, Knighton Road, St Judes, Plymouth, PL4 9BY. Tel: (H) 0752 672030 (W) 0752 385402. **Press Officer:** P Cartwright, 11 Debden Close, Ernesettle, Plymouth. Tel: (H) 0752 364322.
Club Colours: Green, black & white.

PLYMOUTH YM RFC
Ground Address: Suttons Field, John Kitto Community College, Burrington Way, Honicknowle, Plymouth. Tel: 0752 702492 (8334434 Post Game).
Club Secretary: John Michael Lee, 40 Sparke Close, Chaddlewood, Plymouth, PL7 3YA. Tel: (H) 0752 341013 (W) 0752 668000 Ext 4592. **Press Officer:** John Michael Lee, 40 Sparke Close, Chaddlewood, Plymouth, PL7 3YA. Tel: (H) 0752 341013 (W) 0752 668000 Ext 4592.
Club Colours: Black, red, white quarters.

PLYMPTON RFC
Ground Address: King George V Playing Field, Elburton, Plymstock, Plymouth, Devon.
Club Secretary: J E Northcott, 31 Dunetone Road, Plymstock, lymouth PL9 8RF. Tel: (H) 0752 408348.
Press Officer: J E Northcott, 31 Dunetone Road, Plymstock, Plymouth PL9 8RF. Tel: (H) 0752 408348.
Club Colours: White with red hoop.

PLYMSTOCK RFC
Ground Address: Plymstock RFC
Ground Address: King George V Playing Fields, Elburton, Plymouth.
Club Secretary: Bill Pinhey, 269 Crownhill Road, Crownhill, Plymouth. Tel: (H) 0752 708569.
Club Colours: Blue Shirts & socks & black shorts.

PRINCE ROCK RFC
Ground Address: Seaton Barracks, Crownhill, Plymouth.
Club Secretary: Dave Bishop, 19 Grafton Road, Mutley, Plymouth, PL4 6QR. Tel: (H) 0752 220031. **Press Officer:** Matt Jacques, 352 St Peters Road, Manadon, Plymouth. Tel: (H) 0752 783151.
Club Colours: Amber shirts, white shorts.

ST COLUMBA TORPOINT RFC

FINAL TABLE

	P	W	D	L	F	A	PD	Pts
Dartmouth	13	12	0	1	467	50	417	24
Withycombe	13	12	0	1	378	41	337	24
Totnes	13	11	0	2	375	164	211	22
Torrington	13	9	0	4	293	276	17	18
Prince Rock	13	8	1	4	191	143	48	17
North Tawton	13	8	0	5	247	234	13	16
St Columba	13	8	0	5	153	156	-3	16
Plymstock	13	6	0	7	144	185	-41	12
Tamar Saracens	13	4	1	8	124	260	-136	9
Salcombe	13	4	0	9	195	244	-49	8
Plymouth YMCA	13	2	1	10	131	356	-225	5
Plympton	13	2	1	10	100	331	-231	5
Devonport HSOB	13	2	0	11	107	259	-152	4
Victoria	13	1	0	12	108	314	-206	2

Ground Address: Defiance Field, Torpoint, Cornwall.
Club Secretary: P C Summers, 112 Rochford Crescent, Ernesettle, Plymouth, PL5 2QD. Tel: (H) 0752 362785 (W) 0752 552115. **Press Officer:** D Franklin, 22 Langdon Down Way, Torpoint, Cornwall, PL11 2HH. Tel: (H) 0752 813203.
Club Colours: Scarlet & royal blue quarters or hoops.

SALCOMBE RFC
Ground Address: Campderdown Road, Salcombe, South Devon, TQ8. Tel: 054 884 2639.
Club Secretary: Darren Hind, 67 Cumber Close, Malborough, Nr Kings Bridge, TQ7 3DF. Tel: (H) 0548 560944 (W) 0548 825853. **Press Officer:** Adriand Masters, 9 Northville Park, Kings Bridge, TQ7 1AR.
Club Colours: Red & white and black & white.

TAMAR SARACENS RFC
Ground Address: Parkway Sports Club, Ernesettle Lane, Ernesettle, Plymouth. Tel: 0752 363080.
Club Secretary: Kevin Midermottroe, 8 Pinewood Close, Plympton, Plymouth, PL7 3DW. Tel: (H) 0752 344633 m(W) 0752 364341. **Press Officer:** Ray Hancock, 42 Ron Lane, St Budeaux, Plymouth. Tel: (H) 0734 362171.
Club Colours: Black shirts, red hoops and black shorts.

TORRINGTON RUFC
Ground Address: Downacroft, Torrington, Devon. Tel: 0805 22202.
Club Secretary: James Loud, Norwood Farm, Torrington, Devon. **Press Officer:** Stuart Smithson, Wyvern House, Torrington, Devon.
Club Colours: Green, black & white hoops.

TOTNES RFC
Ground Address: Borough Park, Totnes, Devon. Tel: 0803 867796.
Club Secretary: J V Pantry, 50 Punchards Down, Follaton, Totnes, Devon, TQ9 5FC. Tel: (H) 0803 866560. **Press Officer:** R D Cooper, 1 Cromwell Park, Dark Lane, Modbury, Kingsbridge, Devon. Tel: (H) 0548 830045.
Club Colours: Royal blue & white.

VICTORIA RFC
Ground Address: King George V Playing Fields, Elburton, Plymouth, Devon
Club Secretary: C Humphreys, 17 Wasford Close, Staddiscombe, Plymouth PL9 9UW. Tel: (H) 0752 482736.
Club Colours: Black

SOUTH WEST DIVISION

CORNWALL ONE
1993-94
FIXTURES

October 23 (Week 8)
Bodmin v Bude
Helston v St Austell
Saltash v Falmouth
Stithians v Illogan Park
Wadebridge v St Just

November 13 (Week 10)
Falmouth v Wadebridge
Illogan Park v Saltash
Redruth Albany v Helston
St Austell v Stithians
St Just v Bodmin

November 20 (Week 11)
Bodmin v Falmouth
Bude v St Just
Saltash v St Austell
Stithians v Redruth Albany
Wadebridge v Illogan Park

December 4 (Week 13)
Falmouth v Bude
Helston v Stithians
Illogan Park v Bodmin
Redruth Albany v Saltash
St Austell v Wadebridge

December 18 (Week 15)
Bodmin v St Austell
Bude v Illogan Park
Saltash v Helston
St Just v Falmouth
Wadebridge v Redruth Albany

January 8 (Week 18)
Helston v Wadebridge
Illogan Park v St Just
Redruth Albany v Bodmin
St Austell v Bude
Stithians v Saltash

January 29 (Week X5)
Bodmin v Helston
Bude v Redruth Albany
Falmouth v Illogan Park
St Just v St Austell
Wadebridge v Stithians

February 12 (Week 22)
Helston v Bude
Redruth Albany v St Just
Saltash v Wadebridge
St Austell v Falmouth
Stithians v Bodmin

March 12 (Week 26)
Bodmin v Saltash
Bude v Stithians
Falmouth v Redruth Albany
Illogan Park v St Austell
St Just v Helston

March 26 (Week 28)
Helston v Falmouth
Redruth Albany v Illogan Park
Saltash v Bude
Stithians v St Just
Wadebridge v Bodmin

April 9 (Week 30)
Bude v Wadebridge
Falmouth v Stithians
Illogan Park v Helston
St Austell v Redruth Albany
St Just v Saltash

CORNWALL ONE

BODMIN RFC
Ground Address: Cliffden Park, Bodmin, Cornwall. Tel: 0208 74629.
Club Secretary: Geoff Wood, 20 Alexandra Road, Bodmin, Cornwall PL31 2PS. Tel: 0208 73894.
Press Officer: D Saunter, "Kingsley", Cardinham, Nr Bodmin, Cornwall. Tel: 0208 82217.
Club Colours: Light blue with navy band.

BUDE RFC
Ground Address: Bencoolen Meadow, off Kings Hill, Bude, Cornwall. Tel: 0288 354795.
Club Secretary: Miss M Cockbill, 2 Lee Cottages, Morwenstow, Bude, Cornwall EX23 9HT. Tel: (H) 0288 83690 (W) 0409 253013.
Press Officer: P J Cottle, Knapps Farm, Holsworth, Devon EX22 6JN. Tel: (H) 0409 254411 (W) 0409 253262.
Club Colours: Maroon & sky blue hoops.

FALMOUTH RFC
Ground Address: Recreation Ground, Dracarena Avenue, Falmouth, Cornwall. Tel: 03261 311304.
Club Secretary: J K Dryden, 15 Penbarth Road, Falmouth, Cornwall TR11 2TY. Tel: 0326 316644.
Press Officer: W H Williams, 18 Grove Hill Crescent, Falmouth, Cornwall. Tel: 0326 313453.
Club Colours: Black & white.

HELSTON RFC
Ground Address: King George V Memorial Playing Fields, Clodgey Lane, Helston. Tel: 0326 573423.
Club Secretary: Beverly Davis, 8 Penrose Road, Helston, Cornwall TR13 8TP. Tel: (H) 0326 563744 (W) 0209 215620.
Club Colours: Navy, blue & white hoops.

ILLOGAN PARK RFC
Ground Address: Payton Lane, Illogan, Redruth, Cornwall.
Club Secretary: A G Nicholls, "Seaton", 2 Spernon Terrace, Redruth, Cornwall. Tel: 0209 214824.
Club Colours: Yellow with black hoops.

REDRUTH ALBANY RFC
Ground Address: Trewergie, Redruth, Cornwall. Tel: 0209 216945.
Club Secretary: C A Weeks, 63 Windy Ridge, Mt Ambrose, Redruth, Cornwall TR15 1NX. Tel: (H) 0209 213687 (W) 0872 223939.
Club Colours: Navy blue shirts & socks; white shorts.

ST AUSTELL RFC
Ground Address: Tregorrick Lane, St Austell, Cornwall PL26 7AG. Tel: 0726 76300.
Club Secretary: Peter Bishop, as above. Tel: (H) 0726 852145 (W) 0726 822485.
Press Officer: Peter Denham, 11 St Sulien, Luxulyan, Cornwall. Tel: 0726 851197.
Club Colours: Red & white hoops.

ST JUST RFC
Ground Address: Tregeseal Valley, St Just, Penzance, Cornwall TR19 7PF. Tel: 0736 788593.
Club Secretary: A Luscombe, Carne House, Market Square, St Just, Penzance, Cornwall TR19 7HX. Trl: (H) 0736 787587 (W) 0850 720407.
Club Colours: Black.

FINAL TABLE

	P	W	D	L	F	A	PD	Pts
Veor	8	7	0	1	164	63	101	14
Falmouth	8	6	0	2	175	80	95	12
St Austell	8	6	0	2	190	98	92	12
Bodmin	8	5	0	3	101	71	30	10
Illogan Park	8	3	1	4	65	67	-2	7
Stithians	8	3	0	5	89	137	-48	6
St Just	8	2	1	5	98	152	-54	5
Redruth Albany	8	2	0	6	119	249	-130	4
Camborne S o M	8	1	0	7	94	178	-84	2

SALTASH RFC
Ground Address: Moorlands Lane, Burraton, Saltash, Cornwall. Tel: 0752 847227.
Club Secretary: David Jenkins, "Windward", St Anns Chapel, Gunnislake, Cornwall PL18 9HQ. Tel: 0822 832785.
Press Officer: D Lawrencw, "Fraville", Quethiock, Liskeard, Cornwall. Tel: 0579 347309.
Club Colours: Red, black & gold hoops.

STITHIANS RFC
Ground Address: Playing Fields, Stithians, Cornwall.
Club Secretary: T J Knight, 6 Chainwalk Drive, Truro, Cornwall. Tel: (H) 0872 70849 (W) 0872 76116.
Club Colours: Maroon.

WADEBRIDGE CAMELS RFC
Ground Address: Molesworth Ground, Egloshayle, Wadebridge, Cornwall.
Club Secretary: Mark Richards, Perlees Farm, St Breock, Wadebridge, Cornwall. Tel: (H) 0208 812848 (W) 0726 860308.
Club Colours: Gold with chocolate band.

SOUTH WEST DIVISION

CORNWALL TWO 1993-94 FIXTURES

April 9 (Week 30)
Camborne SoM v Perranporth
Lankelly v St Agnes
St Day v Roseland

October 23 (Week 8)
Camborne SoM v Lankelly
Roseland v St Agnes
St Day v Perranporth

November 13 (Week 10)
Lankelly v Perranporth
Roseland v Camborne SoM
St Agnes v St Day

November 20 (Week 11)
Camborne SoM v St Agnes
Perranporth v Roseland
St Day v Lankelly

December 11 (Week 14)
Lankelly v Roseland
St Agnes v Perranporth
St Day v Camborne SoM

January 8 (Week 18)
Perranporth v Camborne SoM
Roseland v St Day
St Agnes v Lankelly

January 29 (Week X5)
Lankelly v Camborne SoM
Perranporth v St Day
St Agnes v Roseland

February 12 (Week 22)
Camborne SoM v Roseland
Perranporth v Lankelly
St Day v St Agnes

March 12 (Week 26)
Lankelly v St Day
Roseland v Perranporth
St Agnes v Camborne SoM

March 26 (Week 28)
Camborne SoM v St Day
Perranporth v St Agnes
Roseland v Lankelly

CORNWALL TWO

CAMBORNE SCHOOL OF MINES RFC
Ground Address: The Memorial Grounds, Boundevean Lane, Penponds, Camborne, Cornwall. Tel: 0209 612959.
Club Secretary: Dr C V Phillips, "Barlowena", Alexandra Road, Illogan, Redruth, Cornwall TR16 4EN. Tel: (H) 0209 842660 (W) 0209 914866.
Club Colours: Navy, gold & white hoops.

LANKELLY - FOWEY RFC
Ground Address: Lankelly Farm, Fowey, Cornwall.
Club Secretary: D Sainsbury, 2 Safron Close, Fowey, Cornwall PL23 1EU. Tel: 0726 832342.
Press Officer: J Lewis, 62 Esplanade, Fowey. Tel: 0726 833464.
Club Colours: Black & white hoops.

PERRANPORTH RFC
Ground Address: Perranporth S & S Club, Ponsmere Valley, Perranporth, Cornwall.
Club Secretary: Nick Lewis, Cornerways, Goonhaven, Nr Perranporth, Cornwall. Tel: 0872 572888.
Club Colours: Green & gold.

ROSELAND RFC
Ground Address: Philleigh, Truro, Cornwall. Tel: 0872 580254.
Club Secretary: C R Thomas, Parton Vrane, Gerrans, Portscatho, Truro, Cornwall TR2 5ES. Tel: 0872 580475.
Club Colours: Navy & scarlet.

ST AGNES RFC
Ground Address: Enys Park, Trevanance Road, St Agnes, Cornwall. Tel: 0872 553673.
Club Secretary: Tim Barnes, T & JB Produce, Stanley Way, Cardrew Ind Est, Redruth, Cornwall TR15 1SP. Tel: (H) 0209 890218 (W) 0209 314477.
Club Colours: Red & black hoops.

ST DAY RFC
Ground Address: The Playing Fields, St Day, Redruth, Cornwall.
Club Secretary: P C Newcombe, 21 Martinvale Parc, Mount Ambrose, Redruth, Cornwall TR15 1SD. Tel: (H) 0209 212834 (W) 0872 76477.
Club Colours: White with red hoop.

FINAL TABLE

	P	W	D	L	F	A	PD	Pts
Helston	10	9	0	1	312	101	211	18
Wadebridge Cams	10	7	0	3	190	75	115	14
St Agnes	10	7	0	3	201	175	26	14
St Day	10	4	0	6	177	201	-24	8
Lankelly Fowey	10	2	1	7	100	215	-115	5
Roseland	10	0	1	9	69	282	-213	1

SOUTH WEST DIVISION

GLOUCESTER/SOMERSET 1993-94 FIXTURES

October 23 (Week 8)
Cirencester v Bristol Harl
O. Redcliffians v Hornets
Oldfield OB v Keynsham
St Mary's OB v Coney Hill
Thornbury v Dings Crusaders
Whitehall v North Bristol

October 30 (Week X2)
Coney Hill v Thornbury
Dings Crusaders v Cirencester
Frome v O. Redcliffians
Hornets v Oldfield OB
Keynsham v Whitehall
North Bristol v St Mary's OB

November 13 (Week 10)
Bristol Harl v Dings Crusaders
Cirencester v Coney Hill
Oldfield OB v Frome
St Mary's OB v Keynsham
Thornbury v North Bristol
Whitehall v Hornets

November 20 (Week 11)
Coney Hill v Bristol Harl
Frome v Whitehall
Hornets v St Mary's OB
Keynsham v Thornbury
North Bristol v Cirencester
O. Redcliffians v Oldfield OB

December 4 (Week 13)
Bristol Harl v North Bristol
Cirencester v Keynsham
Dings Crusaders v Coney Hill
St Mary's OB v Frome
Thornbury v Hornets
Whitehall v O. Redcliffians

December 11 (Week 14)
Frome v Thornbury
Hornets v Cirencester
Keynsham v Bristol Harl
North Bristol v Dings Crusaders
O. Redcliffians v St Mary's OB
Oldfield OB v Whitehall

December 18 (Week 15)
Bristol Harl v Hornets
Cirencester v Frome
Coney Hill v North Bristol
Dings Crusaders v Keynsham
St Mary's OB v Oldfield OB
Thornbury v O. Redcliffians

January 8 (Week 18)
Frome v Bristol Harl
Hornets v Dings Crusaders
Keynsham v Coney Hill
O. Redcliffians v Cirencester
Oldfield OB v Thornbury
Whitehall v St Mary's OB

January 29 (Week X5)
Bristol Harl v O. Redcliffians
Cirencester v Oldfield OB
Coney Hill v Hornets
Dings Crusaders v Frome
North Bristol v Keynsham
Thornbury v Whitehall

February 12 (Week.22)
Frome v Coney hill
Hornets v North Bristol
O. Recliffians v Dings Crusaders
Oldfield v Bristol Harl
St Mary's OB v Thornbury
Whitehall v Cirencester

March 12 (Week 26)
Bristol Harl v Whitehall
Cirencester v St Mary's OB
Coney Hill v O. Redcliffians
Dings Crusaders v Oldfield OB
Keynsham v Hornets
North Bristol v Frome

March 26 (Week 28)
Frome v Keynsham
O. Redcliffians v North Bristol
Oldfield OB v Coney Hill
St Mary's OB v Bristol Harl
Thornbury v Cirencester
Whitehall v Dings Crusaders

April 9 (Week 30)
Bristol Harl v Thornbury
Coney Hill v Whitehall
Dings Crusaders v St Mary's OB
Hornets v Frome
Keynsham v O. Redcliffians
North Bristol v Oldfield OB

GLOUCESTERSHIRE & SOMERSET

BRISTOL HARLEQUINS RFC
Ground Address: "Valhalla", Broomhill Road, Brislington, Bristol BS4. Tel: 0272 721650.
Club Secretary: C Croot, 29 Calcott Road, Knowle, Bristol. Tel: 0272 777445.
Press Officer: R Hobbs, 4 Cowling Drive, Stockwood, Bristol. Tel: 0275 834520.
Club Colours: Blue, black & white.

CIRENCESTER RFC
Ground Address: CRFC Whiteway, Cirencester, Gloucestershire. Tel: 0285 654434.
Club Secretary: R H Evans, 66 Rose Way, Cirencester, Gloucestershire GL7 1PS. Tel: (H) 0285 640954 (W) 0285 720400.
Press Officer: P Singleton, "Lough Rigg", Somerford Keynes, Cirencester, Glos GL7 6EN. Tel: 0285 861517.
Club Colours: Red & black hoops.

CONEY HILL RFC
Ground Address: Metz Way, Coney Hill, Glos. Tel: 0452 306239.
Club Secretary: Rick Poole, 4 Sycamore Close, Poosmead, Glos GL1 5TY. Tel: 0452 524963.
Club Colours: Gold, white & black hoops; black shorts.

DINGS CRUSADERS RFC
Ground Address: Landseer Avenue, Lockleaze, Bristol. Tel: 0272 691367.
Club Secretary: Gerry Williams, 22 Crowther Road, Horfield, Bristol BS7 9NS. Tel: (H) 0272 516059 (W) 0272 436205.
Press Officer: R Stevens, 4 Fonthill Way, Cherry Gardens, Bitton, Nr Bristol BS15 6JY. Tel: 0272 329128.
Club Colours: Royal blue & black.

FROME RFC
Ground Address: The Pavillion, Gypsy Lane, Frome, Somerset. Tel: 0373 462506.
Club Secretary: D J Rose, 140 High Street, Chapmanslade, Westbury, Wilts BA13 4AP. Tel: 0373 832647.
Press Officer: T Doyle, The Coach House, Leaze House Mews, Vallis Road, Frome. Tel: 0373 431794.
Club Colours: Red, white & black.

HORNETS RFC
Ground Address: Hutton Moor Road, Weston-Super-Mare, Avon BS22 8LY. Tel: 0934 621433.
Club Secretary: Richard Farrelly, Flat 1, 44 Walliscote Road, Weston-Super-Mare, Avon BS23 1XF Tel: (W) 0272 273710.
Press Officer: Lester Gaulton, "St Johns" 83 Spring Hill, Worle, W-S-M, Avon. Tel: 0934 412404.
Club Colours: Black & amber.

KEYNSHAM RFC
Ground Address: The Crown Fields, Bristol Road, Keynsham, Bristol BS18 2BE. Tel: 0272 867879.
Club Secretary: W R Harwood, 3 Windrush Road, Keynsham, Bristol BS18 1QL. Tel: 0272 862323.
Press Officer: A Harrison, 12 Medway Drive, Keynsham, Bristol. Tel: 0272 863125.
Club Colours: Amber & black.

NORTH BRISTOL RFC
Ground Address: Oaklands, Almondsbury, Bristol BS12. Tel: 0454 612740.
Club Secretary: C H Hill, 7 Keinton Walk, Henbury, Bristol BS10 7EE. Tel: 0272 508123.

FINAL TABLE

	P	W	D	L	F	A	PD	Pts
Old Patesians	12	11	0	1	307	94	213	22
Keynsham	12	10	1	1	276	89	187	21
Dings Crusaders	12	6	3	3	194	128	66	15
Whitehall	12	7	1	4	207	152	55	15
North Bristol	12	7	1	4	179	130	49	15
Oldfield Old Boys	12	7	0	5	180	177	3	14
Frome	12	7	0	5	183	182	1	14
Old Redcliffians	12	6	0	6	183	156	27	12
Thornbury	12	4	1	7	135	273	-138	9
Bristol Harlequins	12	3	1	8	127	194	-67	7
Coney Hill	12	3	1	8	153	221	-68	7
Cirencester	12	1	1	10	104	331	-227	3
Old Sulians	12	1	0	11	160	261	-101	2

Press Officer: S Bold, 17 Redfield Road, Patchway, Bristol BS12. Tel 0272 698200.
Club Colours: Royal blue & scarlet hoops.

OLDFIELD OLD BOYS RFC
Ground Address: Shaft Road, Combe Down, Bath, Avon. Tel: 0225 834135.
Club Secretary: Steve Godwin, 12 Lime Grove Gardens, Bath, Avon. Tel: (H) 0225 318612 (W) 0258 451441.
Press Officer: Barry Quintin, 10 Gordon Road, Peasdown St John, Radstock, Bath. Tel: 0761 433308.
Club Colours: Maroon & gold hoops.

OLD REDCLIFFIANS RFC
Ground Address: Stockwood Lane, Brislington, Bristol. Tel: 0272 778501.
Club Secretary: Richard Yandell, 11 Imperial Walk, Knowle, Bristol BS14 9AD. Tel: (H) 0272 777657 (W) 0272 823382.
Press Officer: Richard Fisher, 20 Rookery Road, Knowle, Bristol. Tel: 715543.
Club Colours: Red & black hoops.

ST MARY'S OLD BOYS RFC
Ground Address: Northwood Park, Trench Lane, Winterbourne, Bristol.
Club Secretary: Mrs L Collins, 18 Belmont Road, St Andrews, Bristol BS6 5AS. Tel: 0272 49879.
Press Officer: P Dowager, 18 Clarence Road, Downend, Bristol. Tel: 0272 575214.
Club Colours: Emerald green & black.

THORNBURY RFC
Ground Address: Cooper's Farm, Rockhampton Road, Newton Thornbury. Tel: 0454 412096.
Club Secretary: Howard Bowker, 2 Brunksea Road, Filton Park, Bristol BS7 0SE. Tel: 0272 698744 (W) 0272 299511.
Press Officer: P Dack, 13 Pitville Close, Thornbury, Bristol. Tel: 0454 416068.
Club Colours: Black & amber hoops; black shorts.

WHITEHALL RFC
Ground Address: Foundry Lane, Speedwell, Bristol. Tel: 0272 659636.
Club Secretary: P J Rainsworth-Evans, 4 Elstree Road, Whitehall, Bristol BS5 7DX. Tel: (H) 0272 516756 (W) 0272 733322.
Club Colours: Myrtle & gold.

SOUTH WEST DIVISION

GLOUCESTERSHIRE ONE 1993-94 FIXTURES

October 23 (Week 8)
Bream v Ashley Down OB
Brockworth v Longlevens
Old Cryptians v Frampton Cott
Old Richians v Saintbridge
Stow-on-the-Wold v Painswick
Widden OB v Cheltenham Nth

October 30 (Week X2)
Cheltenham Nth v Old Cryptians
Cleve v Stow-on-the-Wold
Frampton Cott v Old Richians
Longlevens v Widden OB
Painswick v Brockworth
Saintbridge v Bream

November 13 (Week 10)
Ashley Down OB v Saintbridge
Bream v Frampton Cott
Brockworth v Cleve
Old Cryptians v Longlevens
Old Richians v Cheltenham Nth
Widden OB v Painswick

November 20 (Week 11)
Cheltenham Nth v Bream
Cleve v Widden OB
Frampton Cott v Ashley Down OB
Longlevens v Old Richians
Painswick v Old Cryptians
Stow-on-the-Wold v Brockworth

December 4 (Week 13)
Ashley Down OB v Cheltenham Nth
Bream v Longlevens
Old Cryptians v Cleve
Old Richians v Painswick
Saintbridge v Frampton Cott
Widden OB v Stow-on-the-Wold

December 11 (Week 14)
Brockworth v Widden OB
Cheltenham Nth v Saintbridge
Cleve v Old Richians
Longlevens v Ashley Down OB
Painswick v Bream
Stow-on-the-Wold v Old Cryptians

December 18 (Week 15)
Ashley Down OB v Painswick
Bream v Cleve
Frampton Cott v Cheltenham Nth
Old Cryptians v Brockworth
Old Richians v Stow-on-the-Wold
Saintbridge v Longlevens

January 8 (Week 18)
Brockworth v Old Richians
Cleve v Ashley Down OB
Longlevens v Frampton Cott
Painswick v Saintbridge
Stow-on-the-Wold v Bream
Widden OB v Old Cryptians

January 29 (Week X5)
Ashley Down OB v Stow-on-the-Wold
Bream v Brockworth
Cheltenham Nth v Longlevens
Frampton Cott v Painswick
Old Richians v Widden OB
Saintbridge v Cleve

February 12 (Week 22)
Brockworth v Ashley Down OB
Cleve v Frampton Cott
Old Cryptians v Old Richians
Painswick v Cheltenham Nth
Stow-on-the-Wold v Saintbridge
Widden OB v Bream

March 12 (Week 26)
Ashley Down OB v Widden OB
Bream v Old Cryptians
Cheltenham Nth v Cleve
Frampton Cott v Stow-on-the-Wold
Longlevens v Painswick
Saintbridge v Brockworth

March 26 (Week 28)
Brockworth v Frampton Cott
Cleve v Longlevens
Old Cryptians v Ashley Down OB
Old Richians v Bream
Stow-on-the-Wold v Cheltenham Nth
Widden OB v Sainthbridge

April 4 (Week 30)
Ashley Down OB v Old Richians
Cheltenham Nth v Brockworth
Frampton Cott v Widden OB
Longlevens v Stow-on-the-Wold
Painswick v Cleve
Saintbridge v Old Cryptians

GLOUCESTERSHIRE ONE

ASHLEY DOWN OLD BOYS RFC
Ground Address: Lockleaze Combination Ground, Bonnington Walk, Lockleaze, Bristol. Tel: 0272 312642.
Club Secretary: Dennis N Williams, 8 Headford Avenue, St George, Bristol BS5 8PF. Tel: (H) 0272 678002.
Club Colours: White with purple band.

BREAM RFC
Ground Address: High Street, Bream, Nr Lydney, Glos. GL15 6JG. Tel: 0594 562320.
Club Secretary: John Grail, 31 Highbury Road, Bream, Nr Lydney, Glos. GL15 6EF. Tel: (H) 0594 562737 (W) 0594 562320.
Club Colours: Red & black.

BROCKWORTH RFC
Ground Address: Mill Lane, Brockworth. Tel: 0452 862556.
Club Secretary: R J Cassidy, 90 Boverton Drive, Brockworth, Glos. Tel: (H) 0452 862621 (W) 0452 413531.
Club Colours: Black & white.

CHELTENHAM NORTH RFC
Ground Address: Stoke Orchard Road, Bishops Cleeve, Nr Cheltenham. Tel: 0242 675968.
Club Secretary: A D Page, Baytrees, 3 Chargrove Lane, Uphatherley, Cheltenham GL51 5IP. Tel: (H) 0242 510932.
Press Officer: M K Edward, 35 Courtiers Drive, Bishops Cleeve, Nr Cheltenham. Tel: (H) 0242 675424 (W) 0242 238866.
Club Colours: Black & red.

CLEVE RFC
Ground Address: Bromley Heath Road, Downend. Tel: 0272 560323.
Club Secretary: Mr R Pocock, 44 Spring Hill, Kingswood, Bristol BS15 1XT. Tel: (H) 0272 611079.
Club Colours: Maroon.

FRAMPTON COTTERELL RFC
Ground Address: School Road, Frampton Cotterell, Bristol. Tel: 0454 772947.
Club Secretary: Steve Buckley, 44 Meadow View, Frampton Cotterell, Bristol BS17 2NG. Tel: (H) 0454 776809 (W) 0272 791234 x93798.
Press Officer: Mike Weaver, 77 Friary Grange Park, Winterbourne, Bristol BS17 1NB. Tel: (H) 0454 775070.
Club Colours: Green, black & gold shirts, black shorts.

LONGLEVENS RFC
Ground Address: Longford Lane, Longlevens, Gloucester. Tel: 0452 306880.
Club Secretary: Colin F Dunford, 66 Estover Road, Gloucester GL1 3LG. Tel: (H) 0452 522795 (W) 0452 411666.
Club Colours: Red.

OLD CRYPTIANS RFC
Ground Address: Memorial Ground, Tuffley Avenue, Gloucester GL1 5NS. Tel: 0452 520052.
Club Secretary: Kevin Bendall, 391 Stroud Road, Gloucester GL4 0DB. Tel: (H) 0452 501484 (W) 0452 740607.
Club Colours: Shirts: maroon, yellow & blue stripes, black shorts, maroon socks.

OLD RICHIANS RFC
Ground Address: Sandyleaze, Longlevens, Gloucester. Tel: 0452 524649.

FINAL TABLE

	P	W	D	L	F	A	PD	Pts
St Mary's Old Boys	12	10	0	2	229	88	141	20
Bream	12	9	0	3	295	99	196	18
Cleve	12	9	0	3	246	117	129	18
Frampton Cotterell	12	7	1	4	139	135	4	15
Longlevens	12	7	0	5	197	134	63	14
Cheltenham North	12	6	1	5	262	151	111	13
Ashley Down O B	12	6	0	6	161	192	-31	12
Old Richians	12	6	0	6	134	168	-34	12
Saintbridge	12	5	1	6	184	177	7	11
Old Cryptians	12	4	1	7	167	224	-57	9
Brockworth	12	3	2	7	132	161	-29	8
Widden Old Boys	12	1	2	9	77	290	-213	4
Bristol Saracens	12	1	0	11	104	391	-287	2

Club Secretary: Paukl Toleman, 4 Upper Rea, Hempsted, Gloucester GL2 6LR. Tel: (H) 0452 422274.
Press Officer: Rob Fletcher, 130 Paygrove Lane, Longlevens, Gloucester. Tel: (H) 0452 410070.
Club Colours: Royal blue & gold.

PAINSWICK RFC
Ground Address: Broadham Sports Field, Stroud Road, Painswick. Tel: 0452 813861.
Club Secretary: Mr D Patrick, Rose Cottage, Tibbiwell Lane, Painswick Stroud, Glos. Tel: (H) 0452 814104.
Press Officer: M Hayward, 12 White Horse Lane, Vicarage Street, Painswick, Stroud, Glos. Tel: (H) 0452 812592.
Club Colours: Cherry & white.

SAINTBRIDGE FORMER PUPILS RFC
Ground Address: Saintbridge Sports Centre, Painswick Road, Gloucester. Tel: Glos 303768.
League Contact: Mr S Fritchley, 7 Saintbridge Close, Gloucester. Tel: Glos 522690.
Club Secretary: Mr P K Fritchley, 195 Seymour Road, Gloucester. Tel: (H) Glos 418425.
Press Officer: Mr Phil Buck, c/o Saintbridge Sports Centre, Painswick Road, Gloucester. Tel: Glos 303768.
Club Colours: Navy blue, royal blue, gold ringed shirts, black shorts.

STOW-OM-THE-WOLD & DISTRICT RFC
Ground Address: Oddington Road, Stow-on-the-Wold, Glos. Tel: 0451 830887.
Club Secretary: N P Drury, Aston House, Broadwell, Moreton-in- Marsh, Glos GL56 0TJ. Tel: (H) 0451 830961 (W) 0608 50428.
Press Officer: Ian Roberts, 2 The Piece, Lower Swell, Cheltenham, Glos GL54 1LG. Tel: (H) 0451 830024 (W) 0451 832334.
Club Colours: Black & white hoops.

WIDDEN OLD BOYS RFC
Ground Address: Memorial Ground, Tuffley Avenue, Gloucester. Tel: 0452 413480.
League Contact: Mike Taylor, 285 Tuffley Lane, Tuffley, Gloucester GL4 0RP. Tel: (H) 0452 413480.
Club Secretary: Chris Hinde, 32 Millfields, Hucclecote, Gloucester. Tel: (H) 617010.
Press Officer: Mike Taylor, 285 Tuffley Lane, Tuffley, Gloucester GL4 0RP. Tel: (H) 0452 413480.
Club Colours: Myrtle green, red & white.

SOUTH WEST DIVISION

GLOUCESTERSHIRE TWO 1993-94 FIXTURES

December 18 (Week 15)
Barton Hill   v   Cotham Park
Bristol Saracens   v   Cheltenham CS
Chipping Sodbury   v   Bristol Tel
Dursley   v   O Bristolians
Hucclecote   v   Cheltenham Saracens
Tetbury   v   Chosen Hill

October 23 (Week 8)
Chipping Sodbury   v   Barton Hill
Chosen Hill   v   Cotham Park
Dursley   v   Bristol Saracens
O Bristolians   v   Cheltenham Saracens
Tetbury   v   Hucclecote
Tredworth   v   Cheltenam CS

January 8 (Week 18)
Bristol Tel   v   Barton Hill
Cheltenham Saracens   v   Bristol Saracens
Chosen Hill   v   Chipping Sodbury
Cotham Park   v   Hucclecote
O Bristolians   v   Tetbury
Tredworth   v   Dursley

October 30 (Week X2)
Bristol Saracens   v   Tetbury
Bristol Tel   v   Chosen Hill
Cheltenham CS   v   Dursley
Cheltenham Saracens   v   Tredworth
Cotham Park   v   O Bristolians
Hucclecote   v   Chipping Sodbury

January 29 (Week X5)
Barton Hill   v   Chosen Hill
Bristol Saracens   v   Cotham Park
Cheltenham CS   v   Cheltenham Saracens
Chipping Sodbury   v   O Bristolians
Hucclecote   v   Bristol Tel
Tetbury   v   Tredworth

November 13 (Week 10)
Barton Hill   v   Hucclecote
Chipping Sodbury   v   Bristol Saracens
Dursley   v   Cheltenham Saracens
O Bristolians   v   Bristol Tel
Tetbury   v   Cheltenham CS
Tredworth   v   Cotham Park

February 12 (Week 22)
Bristol Tel   v   Bristol Saracens
Chosen Hill   v   Hucclecote
Cotham Park   v   Cheltenham CS
Dursley   v   Tetbury
O Bristolians   v   Barton Hill
Tredworth   v   Chipping Sodbury

November 20 (Week 11)
Bristol Saracens   v   Barton Hill
Bristol Tel   v   Tredworth
Cheltenham CS   v   Chipping Sodbury
Cheltenham Saracens   v   Tetbury
Chosen Hill   v   O Bristolians
Cotham Park   v   Dursley

March 12 (Week 26)
Barton Hill   v   Tredworth
Bristol Saracens   v   Chosen Hill
Cheltenham CS   v   Bristol Tel
Cheltenham Saracens   v   Cotham Park
Chipping Sodbury   v   Dursley
Hucclecote   v   O Bristolians

December 4 (Week 13)
Barton Hill   v   Cheltenham CS
Chipping Sodbury   v   Cheltenham Saracens
Dursley   v   Bristol Tel
Hucclecote   v   Bristol Sara
Tetbury   v   Cotham Park
Tredworth   v   Chosen Hill

March 26 (Week 28)
Bristol Tel   v   Cheltenham Saracens
Chosen Hill   v   Cheltenham CS
Dursley   v   Barton Hill
O Bristolians   v   Bristol Saracens
Tetbury   v   Chipping Sodbury
Tredworth   v   Hucclecote

December 11 (week 14)
Bristol Tel   v   Tetbury
Cheltenham CS   v   Hucclecote
Cheltenham Saracens   v   Barton Hill
Chosen Hill   v   Dursley
Cotham Park   v   Chipping Sodbury
O Bristolians   v   Tredworth

April 9 (Week 30)
Barton Hill   v   Tetbury
Bristol Saracens   v   Tredworth
Cheltenham CS   v   O Bristolians
Cheltenham Saracens   v   Chosen Hill
Cotham Park   v   Bristol Tel
Hucclecote   v   Dursley

492

GLOUCESTERSHIRE TWO

BARTON HILL OLD BOYS RFC
Ground Address: Duncombe Lane, Speedwell, Bristol.
Tel: 0272 583541.
Club Secretary: M G Watts, 22 Coberley, Hanham, Bristol
BS15 2ES. Tel: 0272 614524.
Press Officer: D Mulcahy, 18 Elmtree Way, Kingswood,
Bristol. Tel: 406307.
Club Colours: White with red hoop; black shorts.

BRISTOL SARACENS RFC
Ground Address: Station Road, Cribbs Causeway,
Henbury, Bristol. Tel: 0272 500037.
Club Secretary: A E Swash, 6 Downs Road,
Westbury-on-Trym, Bristol BS9 3TX. Tel: (H) 0272
629047 (W) 0626 832283.
Press Officer: J Preen, 20 Southdown Road,
Westbury-on-Trym, Bristol BS8 3NL. Tel: (H) 0272
590643 (W) 0272 795972.
Club Colours: Myrtle green & white hoop shirts; black
shorts.

BRISTOL TELEPHONE AREA RFC
Ground Address: British Telecom Sports Ground,
Stockwood Lane, Stockwood, Bristol BS14. Tel: 0275
891776.
Club Secretary: Shaun Partridge, 22 Colthrst Drive,
Hanham, Bristol BS15 3SF. Tel: (H) 0272 601096 (W)
0272 205462.
Club Colours: Blue, red & white.

CHELTENHAM CIVIL SERVICE RFC
Ground Address: Civil Service Sports Ground,
Tewkesbury Road, Cheltenham, Glos. Tel: 0242 680424.
Club Secretary: Brian Didlick, 66a Clarence Street,
Cheltenham, Glos. GL50 3LE.
Press Officer: Terry Cann, 102 Leckhampton Road,
Cheltenham, Glos. Tel: (H) 0242 518766 (W) 0242 221491
x2275.
Club Colours: Navy blue.

CHELTENHAM SARACENS RFC
Ground Address: King George V Playing Fields,
Brooklyn Road, Cheltenham, Glos.
Club Secretary: Colin Wheeler, Bredon School, Pull
Court, Bushley, Nr Tewkesbury, Glos GL20 6AH. Tel: (H)
0684 294119 (W) 0684 293156.
Club Colours: Blue with gold circlet.

CHIPPING SODBURY RFC
Ground Address: The Ridings, Wickwar Road, Chipping
Sodbury. Tel: 0454 312852.
Club Secretary: Mark Kirkham, 27 Suterland Avenue,
Yate, Bristol BS17. Tel: 0454 324496.
Press Officer: Richad Wade, 32 Whitcombe, Yate, Bristol
BS17. Tel: 0454 321794.
Club Colours: Black.

CHOSEN HILL FORMER PUPILS RFC
Ground Address: Brookfield Road, Churchdown,
Gloucester. Tel: 0452 712384.
Club Secretary: Mr MC Reid, 212 Cheltenham Road East,
Churchdown, Glos. Tel: 0452 856312.
Press Officer: Mr I Yeates, 20 Westover Court,
Churchdown Glos. Tel: 0452 713502.
Club Colours: Myrtle green & white.

FINAL TABLE

	P	W	D	L	F	A	PD	Pts
Stow-on-the-Wold	12	11	0	1	339	115	224	22
Painswick	12	8	2	2	204	93	111	18
Old Bristolians	12	8	1	3	219	118	101	17
Cheltenham Sara	12	7	0	5	151	136	15	14
Chosen Hill F P	12	6	1	5	179	148	31	13
Tredworth	12	6	0	6	201	157	44	12
Hucclecote	12	6	0	6	144	152	-8	12
Chipping Sodbury	12	5	1	6	120	163	-43	11
Bristol Telephones	12	5	1	6	83	137	-54	11
Cheltenham C S	12	5	0	7	135	216	-81	10
Cotham Park	12	4	1	7	158	202	-44	9
Barton Hill	12	1	2	9	86	262	-176	4
Cainscross	12	1	1	10	151	271	-120	3

COTHAM RFC
Ground Address: Beggar Bush Lane, Failand, Bristol. Tel:
0275 392501.
Club Secretary: John Crocker, Grove House, Tennessee
Grove, Bristol BS6 7XH. Tel: (H) 424885 (W) 292227.
Press Officer: B Cochlan, 12 Sherborne Street, St George,
Bristol.
Club Colours: Black & white.

DURSLEY RFC
Ground Address: Stinchcombe Stragglers, Hounds Green,
Stinchcombe, Dursley, Glos. Tel: 0453 543693.
Club Secretary: John Darlston, Windrush, Field Lane,
Dursley, Glos GL11 6JF. Tel: (H) 0453 543135 (W) 0453
812026.
Press Officer: David Weeks, 3 Yew Tree Close, Cam,
Dursley, Glos. GL11 6JF.
Club Colours: Maroon with amber hoop.

HUCCLECOTE OLD BOYS RFC
Ground Address: King George V Playing Fields, Old
Upton Lane, Hucclecote.
Club Secretary: John Ring, 9 Conway Road, Hucclecote,
Glos GL3 3PD. Tel: 0452 618920.
Club Colours: Amber & black.

OLD BRISTOLIANS RFC
Ground Address: Memorial Playing Field, Failand,
Bristol. Tel: 0275 392137.
Club Secretary: S Williams, 7 Old Sneed Avenue, Stoke
Bishop, Bristol. Tel: (H) 0272 685136 (W) 0272 25077.
Press Officer: Richard Berry, 57 Thornleigh Road,
Horfield, Bristol BS7 8PZ. Tel: 0272 243182.
Club Colours: Maroon, amber & green.

TETBURY RFC
Ground Address: Recreational Ground, New Church
Street, Tetbury, Glos.
Club Secretary: Mrs S P Dyer, "Prince of Wales Inn",
West Street, Tetbury, Glos. GL8 8DR. Tel: 0666 502318.
Press Officer: Helen Drew, 12 Nymphsfield Road, Forest
Green, Nailsworth, Glos. GL6 0EE. Tel: 0453 835295.
Club Colours: Black with amber hoops.

TREDWORTH RFC
Ground Address: The Lannet, King Edward Avenue,
Glos. Tel: 0452 308939.
Club Secretary: L M Thomas, 110 Longford Lane, Glos
GL2 9EU. Tel: 0452 524739.
Club Colours: Green with black hoops.

SOUTH WEST DIVISION

GLOUCESTERSHIRE THREE 1993-94 FIXTURES

October 23 (Week 8)
Bishopston v O Colstonians
Cainscross v Glos All Blues
O Elizabethans v Kingwood
Smiths Ind v Bristol Aero
Southmead v Aretians
Westbury-on-Sev v Broad Plain

October 30 (week X2)
Aretians v Cainscross
Bristol Aero v Bishopston
Broad Plain v Smiths Ind
Glos All Blues v Westbury-on-Sev
Glos Civil Ser v O Elizabethans
Kingswood v Southmead

November 13 (week 10)
Bishopston v Broad Plain
Cainscross v Kingwood
O Colstonians v Bristol Aero
Smiths Ind v Glos All Blues
Southmead v Glos Civil Ser
Westbury-on-Sev v Aretians

November 20 (Week 11)
Aretians v Smiths Ind
Broad Plain v O Colstonians
Glos All Blues v Bishopston
Glos Civil Ser v Cainscross
Kingswood v Westbury-on-Sev
O Elizabethans v Southmead

December 4 (Week 13)
Bishopston v Aretians
Bristol Aero v Broad Plain
Cainscross v O Elizabethans
O Colstonians v Glos All Blues
Smiths Ind v Kingswood
Westbury-on-Seven v Glos Civil Ser

December 11 (Week 14)
Aretians v O Colstonians
Glos All Blues v Bristol Aero
Glos Civil Ser v Smiths Ind
Kingswood v Bishopston
O Elizabethans v Westbury-on-Sev
Southmead v Cainscross

December 18 (Week 15)
Bishopston v Glos Civil Ser
Bristol Aero v Aretians
Broad Plain v Glos All Blues
O Colstonians v Kingswood
Smith Ind v Old Elizabethans
Westbury-on-Sev v Southmed

January 8 (Week 18)
Aretians v Broad Plain
Cainscross v Westbury-on-Sev
Glos Civil Ser v O Colstonians
Kingswood v Bristol Aero
O Elizabethans v Bishopston
Southmead v Smiths Ind

January 29 (week X5)
Bishopston v Southmead
Bristol Aero v Glos Civil Ser
Broad Plain v Kingswood
Glos All Blues v Aretians
O Colstonians v O Elizabethans
Smiths Ind v Cainscross

February 12 (Week 22)
Cainscross v Bishopston
Glos Civil Ser v Broad Plain
Kingswood v Glos All Blues
O. Elizabethans v Bristol Aero
Southmead v O Colstonians
Westbury-on-Sev v Smiths Ind

March 12 (Week 26)
Aretians v Kingswood
Bishopston v Westbury-on-Sev
Bristol Aero v Southmead
Broad Plain v O Elizabethans
Glos All Blues v Glos Civil Ser
O Colstonians v Cainscross

March 26 (Week 28)
Cainscross v Bristol Aero
Glos Civil Ser v Aretians
O Elizabethans v Glos All Blues
Smiths Ind v Bishopston
Southmead v Broad Plain
Westbury-on-Sev v O Colstonians

April 9 (Week 30)
Aretians v O Elizabethans
Bristol Aero v Westbury-on-Sev
Broad Plain v Cainscross
Glos All Blues v Southmead
Kingswood v Glos Civil Ser
O Colstonians v Smiths Ind

GLOUCESTERSHIRE THREE

ARETIANS RFC
Ground Address: Station Road, Little Stoke, Bristol BS12 6HW.
Club Secretary: Paul Pritchard, 25 Kewstoke Road, Moke Bishop. Bristol BS9 1HA. Tel: (H) 0272 683595 (W) 0275 373497.
Press Officer: Bob Williams, 88 Bush Avenue, Little Stoke, Bristol. Tel: 0454 409367.
Club Colours: Black.

BISHOPSTON RFC
Ground Address: Bonnington Walk Playing Fields, Loskleaze, Bristol. Tel: 0272 691916.
Club Secretary: D G J Hockley, 21 Pinewood Close, Westbury-on- Trym, Bristol BS9 4AJ. Tel: (H) 0272 623509 (W) 0272 291031.
Press Officer: Andrew Mellor, 4 Charlton Gardens, Westbury-on- Trym, Bristol BS10 6LX. Tel: 0272 508301.
Club Colours: Red with black hoop.

BRISTOL AEROPLANE COMPANY RFC
Ground Address: BAWA 589 Southmead Road, Filton, Bristol BS12 7RG. Tel: 0272 768064.
Club Secretary: I M Gibson, 11 Hurstwood Road, Downend, Bristol BS16 5EG. Tel: (H) 0272 565626 (W) 0272 368224.
Press Officer: C E Prewett, Gable End, The Common, Patchway, BristolBS12 6AL. Tel: 0454 613670.
Club Colours: Red, white & blue hoops.

BROAD PLAIN RFC
Ground Address: Hatcliffe School, Bishport Avenue, Hatcliffe, Bristol, Avon. Tel: 0272 649757.
Club Secretary: I Gregory, 7 Luxton street, Easton, Bristol BS5 0HT. Tel: (H) 0272 540706 (W) 0272 552866.
Press Officer: J White, c/o Club.
Club Colours: Blue, maroon & gold hoops.

CAINSCROSS RFC
Ground Address: Victory Park, Cainscross, Nr Stroud, Glos. Tel: 0453 766707.
Club Secretary: W R Tocknell, Pendaleon House, Sesley Road, Woodchester, Stroud, Glos. GL5 5PH. Tel: (H) 0453 872333 (W) 0453 762773.
Club Colours: Amber & blue.

GLOUCESTER ALL BLUES RFC
Ground Address: The Oxleaze, Westgate Street, Glos. Tel: 0452 306984.
Club Secretary: Guy Selwyn, "Millbank", Chessgrove Lane, Longthorpe, Glos GL17 0LE. Tel: (H) 831215 (W) 529553.
Press Officer: Robert McTaggart, 23 India Road, Glos. GL1 4DR.
Club Colours: Navy blue.

GLOUCESTER CIVIL SERVICE TIGERS RFC
Ground Address: Civil Service Sports Ground, Estcourt Road, Glos. Tel: 0452 28317.
Cub Secretary: D M Oliver, 60 Larkhay Road, Glos GL3 3NB. Tel: 0452 613418.
Club Colours: Red & blue hoops.

KINGSWOOD RFC
Ground Address: Church Avenue Playing Fields, London Road, Warmley, Nr Bristol. Tel: 0272 675001.
Club Secretary: R Clease, 166 Mounthill Road, Kingswood, Bristol BS15 2SX. Tel: (H) 0272 750890 (W) 0272 701549.

FINAL TABLE

	P	W	D	L	F	A	PD	Pts
Dursley	12	10	0	2	329	129	200	20
Tetbury	12	9	1	2	344	132	202	19
Old Elizabethans	12	8	1	3	223	121	102	17
Bishopston	12	7	2	3	268	114	154	16
Kingswood	12	8	0	4	210	132	78	16
Broad Plain	12	8	0	4	218	166	52	16
Gloucester C S	12	6	1	5	213	130	101	13
Westbury on Severn	12	6	0	6	149	128	21	12
Bristol Aeroplanes	12	4	0	8	136	250	-114	8
Old Colstonians	12	3	1	8	132	201	-69	7
Gloucester All Blues	12	3	0	9	79	218	-139	6
Southmead	12	2	0	10	83	267	-184	4
Tewkesbury	12	1	0	11	68	472	-404	2

Press Officer: Chris Hussey, 71 Magpie Bottom Lane, Hanham, Nr Bristol. Tel: 0272 671515.
Club Colours: Sky blue & brown.

OLD COLSTONIANS RFC
Ground Address: New Road, Stoke Gifford, Bristol. Tel: 0272 690009.
Club Secretary: David Parker, 37 Ratcliffe Drive, Stoke Gifford, Bristol BS12 6TX. Tel: (H) 0272 697438 (W) 0275 555434.
Press Officer: John Griffiths, 34 Frampton End Road, Frampton Cotterell, Bristol BS17 2JZ. Tel: 0454 773544.
Club Colours: Black, blue & gold hoops.

OLD ELIZABETHANS RFC
Ground Address: Severn Road, Hallen, Bristol. Te: 0272 591072.
Club Secretary: David Langdon, 13 Gloucester Street, Wooton- under-Edge. Tel: (H) 0453 845349 (W) 0272 668431.
Press Officer: Phil Crispin-Cheek, 39 Grange Court Road, Westbury-on-Trym, Bristol. Tel: (H) 0272 623849 (W) 0272 827237.
Club Colours: White, orange & blue.

SMITHS INDUSTRIES RFC
Ground Address: The Newlands, Oversham Road, Bishops Cleave, Cheltenham, Glos. Tel: 0242 672752.
Club Secretary: Gerald Owen, 79, Station Road, Bishops Cleeve, Cheltenham, Glos. Tel: (H) 0242 676345 (W) 0242 673333.
Club Colours: White with royal blue hoop.

SOUTHMEAD RFC
Ground Address: Greenway Center, Doncaster Road, Southmead, Bristol. Tel: 0272 593060.
Club Secretary: John Cockwell, 7 Dean Lane, Bedinster, Bristol BS3 1DB. Tel: 0272 632979.
Press Officer: Brian Thomas, 67 Peache Road, Downend, Bristol. Tel: 566793.
Club Colours: Blue with emerald green hoop.

WESTBURY-ON-SEVERN RFC
Ground Address Parish Grounds, Westbury-on-Severmn, Glos. Tel: 0452 760359.
Club Secretary: Phil Bleathman, The Hollies, Elton, Westbury-on- Severn, Glos GL14 1JJ. Tel: 0452 760751.
Club Colours: Royal blue & white hoops.

SOUTH WEST DIVISION

GLOUCESTERSHIRE FOUR 1993-94 FIXTURES

October 23 (Week 8)
Glos Police v Dowty
Minchinhampton v Pilning
Wotton-u-Edge v Newent

October 30 (week X2)
Dowty v Tewkesbury
Minchinhampton v Glos Police
Pilning v Newent

November 13 (Week 10)
Glos Police v Newent
Pilning v Wotton-u-Edge
Tewkesbury v Minchinhampton

November 20 (Week 11)
Newent v Dowty
Pilning v Glos Police
Wotton-u-Edge v Tewkesbury

December 4 (Week 13)
Dowty v Pilning
Glos Police v Tewkesbury
Minchinhampton v Newent

December 11 (Week 14)
Pilning v Minchinhampton
Tewkesbury v Dowty
Wotton-u-Edge v Glos Police

December 18 (Week 15)
Dowty v Wotton-u-Edge
Minchinhampton v Tewkesbury
Newent v Pilning

January 8 (Week 18)
Glos Police v Pilning
Newent v Minchinhampton
Wotton-u-Edge v Dowty

January 15 (Week 19)
Dowty v Glos Police
Tewkesbury v Newent
Wotton-u-Edge v Minchinhampton

January 29 (Week X5)
Glos Police v Minchinhampton
Newent v Wotton-u-Edge
Pilning v Tewkesbury

February 12 (Week 22)
Minchinhampton v Dowty
Tewkesbury v Glos Police
Wotton-u-Edge v Pilning

March 12 (Week 26)
Newent v Glos Police
Pilning v Dowty
Tewkesbury v Wotton-u-Edge

March 26 (Week 26)
Dowty v Minchinhampton
Glos Police v Wotton-u-Edge
Newent v Tewkesbury

April 9 (Week 30)
Dowty v Newent
Minchinhampton v Wotton-u-Edge
Tewkesbury v Pilning

GLOUCESTERSHIRE FOUR

DOWTY RFC
Ground Address: Dowty Sports and Social Society, Staverton Division, Down Hatherly Lane, Glos. GL2 9QD. Tel: 0452 714567.
Club Secretary: A D Green, Willows, Reddings Road, Cheltenham, Glos. Tel: (H) 0425 856937 (W) 0242 533068.
Press Officer: C Roberts, 57 Springfield Close, The Reddings, Cheltenham, Glos. Tel: 0452 71326.
Club Colours: Blue & white hoops.

GLOUCESTER CONSTABULARY RFC
Ground Address: Dowty Rotol RFC, Down Hatherley Lane, Glos. GL2 9QD. Tel: 0452 714567.
Club Secretary: G R Brooks, 59 Bondend Road, Opton St Leonards, Glos. Tel: (H) 0452 619071 W) 0242 528282.
Club Colours: All black.

MINCHINHAMPTON RFC
Ground Address: Windmill Road, Minchinhampton, Glos.
Club Secretary: Rob Edwards, Woodlands Cottage, 205 Slad Road, Stroud, Glos. Tel: (H) 0453 766662 (W) 0452 308989 x139.
Press Officer: Martin Saunders, 13 Frithwood, Brownshill, Nr Stroud, Glos. Tel: 0453 882217.
Club Colours: Green, white & black hoops; black shorts.

NEWENT RFC
Ground Address: Recreation Ground, Watery Lane, Newent, Glos. Tel: 0531 821517.
Club Secretary: Keri Evans, 303 Foley Raod, Newent, Glos. Tel: 0531 822328.
Club Colours: Green with gold "V".

PILNING RFC
Ground Address: The Pitch, Beach Road, Severn Beach, Bristol. Tel: 0454 633549.
Club Secreatry: Alison Long, 38 Wainbridge Crescent, Pilning, Bristol. Tel 633204.
Press Officer: A Lewis, Cartref, 17 Christchurch Avenue, Downend, Bristol. Tel: 570882.
Club Colours: Blue & white hoops.

TEWKESBURY RFC
Ground Address: Vineyards, Tewkesbury.
Club Secretary: D Bailey, 14 King JOhn Court, Tewkesbury, Glos. GL20 6EB. Tel: (H) 293197 (W) 274945.
Press Officer: M Bruckshaw, 9 Manor Park, Tewkesbury. Tel: 292356.
Club Colours: Black & amber hoops.

WOTTON-UNDER-EDGE RFC
Club Secretary: J C Atkin, 30 Water Lane, Wotton-under-Edge, Glos GL12 7LG. Tel: (H) 053 521581 (W) 0272 701517.
Club Colours: Black & amber hoops.

FINAL TABLE

	P	W	D	L	F	A	PD	Pts
Smiths (Industries)	12	10	1	1	323	83	240	21
Aretians	12	10	0	2	370	102	268	20
Newent	12	7	0	5	202	175	27	14
Pilning	12	6	1	5	155	146	9	13
Dowty	12	3	1	8	138	176	-38	7
Minchinhampton	12	3	0	9	95	201	-106	6
Wotton-under-Edge	12	1	1	10	57	457	-400	3

SOUTH WEST DIVISION

SOMERSET ONE
1993-94
FIXTURES

December 18 (Week 15)
Chard v St Bernadette
Imperial v Stothert & Pitt
Midsomer Ntn v Wells
N Petherton v Minehead
Old Sulians v Wellington
Yeovil v Walcot OB

October 23 (Week 8)
Midsomer Ntn v Chard
Old Sulians v N Petherton
Walcot OB v St Bernadette
Wellington v Stothert & Pitt
Yatton v Minehead
Yeovil v Imperial

January 8 (Week 18)
St Bernadette v Imperial
Stothert & Pitt v N Petherton
Walcot OB v Midsomer Ntn
Wellington v Yeovil
Wells v Chard
Yatton v Old Sulians

October 30 (Week X2)
Imperial v Midsomer Ntn
Minehead v Old Sulians
N Petherton v Yeovil
St Bernadette v Wellington
Stothert & Pitt v Yatton
Wells v Walcot OB

January 29 (Week X5)
Chard v Walcot OB
Imperial v Wells
Midsomer Ntn v Wellington
Minehead v Stothert & Pitt
N Petherton v St Bernadette
Yeovil v Yatton

November 13 (Week 10)
Chard v Imperial
Midsomer Ntn v N Petherton
Old Sulians v Stothert & Pitt
Wellington v Wells
Yatton v St Bernadette
Yeovil v Minehead

February 12 (Week 22)
Old Sulians v Yeovil
St Bernadette v Minehead
Walcot OB v Imperial
Wellington v Chard
Wells v N Petherton
Yatton v Midsomer Ntn

November 20 (week 11)
Minehead v Midsomer Ntn
N Petherton v Chard
St Bernadette v Old Sulians
Stothert & Pitt v Yeovil
Walcot OB v Wellington
Wells v Yatton

March 12 (Week 26)
Chard v Yatton
Imperial v Wellington
Midsomer Ntn v Old Sulians
Minehead v Wells
N Petherton v Walcot OB
Stothert & Pitt v St Bernadette

December 4 (Week 13)
Chard v Minehead
Imperial v N Petherton
Midsomer Ntn v Stothert & Pitt
Old Sulians v Wells
Yatton v Walcot OB
Yeovil v St Bernadette

March 26 (Week 28)
Old Sulians v Chard
Walcot OB v Minehead
Wellington v N Petherton
Wells v Stothert & Pitt
Yatton v Imperial
Yeovil v Midsomer Ntn

December 11 (Week 14)
Minehead v Imperial
St Bernadette v Midsomer Ntn
Stothert & Pitt v Chard
Walcot OB v Old Sulians
Wellington v Yatton
Wells v Yeovil

April 9 (Week 30)
Chard v Yeovil
Imperial v Old Sulians
Minehead v Wellington
N Petherton v Yatton
St Bernadette v Wells
Stothert & Pitt v Walcot OB

SOMERSET ONE

CHARD RFC
Ground Address: The Park Essex Close, Chard, Somerset. Tel: 0460 62495.
Club Secretary: N J Urch, 2 South View, Listers Hill, Ilminster, Somerset TA19 0EJ. Tel: (H) 0460 57864 (W) 0935 702913.
Press Officer: T Bradford, First Floor Flat, 74 Holyrood Street, Chard, Somerset. Tel: (W) 0460 67474.
Club Colours: Black, red & gold.

IMPERIAL (BRISTOL) RFC
Ground Address: West Town Lane, Knowle, Bristol. Tel: 0272 777210.
Club Secretary: P Francomb, 151 Wick Road, Brslington, Bristol BS4 4HH. Tel: (W) 0272 779188.
Press Officer: Roy Leitch, 19 Wellsford Road, Stapleton, Bristol.
Club Colours: Myrtle green & amber.

MIDSOMER NORTON RFC
Ground Address: Norton Down Palying Fields, Stratton on the Fosse, Somerset BA3 4RW. Tel: 0761 412827.
Club Secretary: John Presley, 73 Welton Grove, Midsomer Norton, Bath, Avon BA3 2TT. Tel: 0761 416089.
Club Colours: Red shirts & socks; black shorts.

MINEHEAD BARBARIANS RFC
Ground Address: Ellicombe Lane, Ellicombe, Minehead TA24 6TR. Tel: 0643 707155.
Club Secretary: Malcom Parslow, Ladbrook, The Holloway, Minehead TA24 5BB. Tel: 0643 702101.
Club Colours: Black & white hoops.

NORTH PETHERTON RFC
Ground Address: Beggars Brook, North Petherton, Somerset. Tel: 0278 663023.
Club Secretary: P Ham, 12 Fir Tree Close, Bridgwater, Somerset TA6 4EH. Tel: 0278 445834.
Club Colours: Black & white hoops.

OLD SULIANS RFC
Ground Address: Lansdown Road, Bath, Avon. Tel: 0225 310201.
Club Seretary: T Haines, 24 Rockcliffe Avenue, Bathwick, Bath, Avon. Tel: 0225 465107.
Press Officer: A Suee, 8 Heathfield Close, Weston, Bath, Avon. Tel: 0225 317256.
Club Colours: Red band on blue.

ST BERNADETTES OLD BOYS RFC
Ground Address: Hengrove Park, Bamfield, Whitchurch, Bristol. Tel: 0275 891500.
Club Secretary: Barry Taylor, 39 Woodleigh Gardens, Whitchurch, Bristol BS14 9JA. Tel: 0275 831880.
Press Officer: Mark Hanson, 37 Ponsford Road, Knowle, Bristol BS4 2UJ. Tel: 0272 712848.
Club Colours: Blue & green hoops.

STOTHERT & PITT RFC
Ground Address: Newton Field, Lower Bristol Road, Bath. Tel: 0225 425569.
Club Secretary: R V Garraway, 2 Westfield Park South, Lower Weston, Bath BA1 3HT. Tel: (H) 0225 316863 (W) 0225 428321.
Press Officer: R Saunders, 8 Dartmouth Avenue, Oldfield Park, Bath. Tel: 0225 337028.
Club Colours: Blue, black & amber.

FINAL TABLE

	P	W	D	L	F	A	PD	Pts
Hornets	12	12	0	0	428	53	375	24
Walcot Old Boys	12	10	0	2	164	85	179	20
Midsomer Norton	12	10	0	2	241	101	140	20
Wellington	12	8	1	3	195	162	33	17
Wells	12	7	0	5	228	195	33	14
Imperial	12	7	0	5	161	160	1	14
St Bernadettes O B	12	6	0	6	203	158	45	12
Yeovil	12	5	0	7	136	160	-24	10
Minehead Barbs	12	4	0	8	126	188	-62	8
Yatton	12	3	1	8	150	249	-99	7
Stothert & Pitt	12	3	0	9	143	283	-140	6
Gordano	12	2	0	10	120	249	-129	4
Westland	12	0	0	12	66	418	-352	0

WELLINGTON RFC
Ground Address: The Athletic Ground, Corams Lane, Wellington, Somerset. Tel: 0823 663758.
Club Secretary: R K Colman, Meadowside, Mantle Street, Wellington, Somerset TA21 8BG. Tel: (H) 0823 663307 (W) 0823 33451 x5121.
Club Colours: Red & back.

WALCOT OLD BOYS RFC
Ground Address: Albert Field, Lansdown, Bath. Tel: 0225·330199.
Club Secretary: K Jones, 14 Canterbury Road, Oldfield Park, Bath BA2 3LG. Tel: (H) 0225 427045 (W) 0249 712051.
Club Colours: Black & white hoops.

WELLS RFC
Ground Address: Charter Way, Wells, Somerset BA5 2FB.
Club Secretary: A C Cox, 10 Mount Pleasant Avenue, Wells, Somerset BA5 2JZ. Tel: 0749 673407.
Press Officer: M F P Dennis, 2 Bilbury Lane, Glastonbury, Somerset. Tel: (Glast) 834625.
Club Colours: Black & white hoops.

YATTON RFC
Ground Address: The Park, North End, Yatton, Avon. Tel: 0934 832085.
Club Secretary: J G Crabtree, 22 Cadbury Farm, Yatton, Avon BS19 4HW. Tel: (H) 0934 833721 (W) 0272 432399.
Press Officer: Paul Friend, 19 Stonewell Prk Road, Congresbury, Bristol. Tel: 0934 838185.
Club Colours: Amber & black.

YEOVIL RFC
Ground Address: Johnson Park, Yeovil, Somerset BA21 3NY. Tel: 0935 74433.
Club Secretary: William Harding, 43 Ivel Court, Yeovil, Somerset BA21 4HX. Tel: (H) 0935 78084 (W) 0935 703794.
Press Officer: Andrew Jarvis, 1 Wayside, Vagg Hill, Chilthorpe Domer, Yeovil, Somerset BA21 3PT. Tel: (H) 0935 26615 (W) 0935 21812.
Club Golours: Blue & yellow hoops.

SOUTH WEST DIVISION

SOMERSET TWO
1993-94
FIXTURES

Decmeber 18 (Week 15)
Avon v Crewkerne
Avonvale v Tor
Backwell v Bath Saracens
Blagdon v Old Ashtonians
Chew Valley v Gordano
Westlands v Bath Old Eds

October 23 (Week 8)
Avonvale v Backwell
Bath Old Eds v Bath Saracens
Blagdon v Chew Valley
Old Ashtonians v Crewkerne
Westlands v Avon
Winscombe v Gordano

January 8 (Week 18)
Bath Old Eds v Avonvale
Bath Saracens v Avon
Crewkerne v Chew Valley
Old Ashtonians v Westlands
Tor v Backwell
Winscombe v Blagdon

October 30 (Week X2)
Avon v Avonvale
Bath Saracens v Old Ashtonians
Chew Valley v Westlands
Crewkerne v Winscombe
Gordano v Blagdon
Tor v Bath Old Eds

January 29 (Week X5)
Avon v Tor
Avonvale v Old Ashtonians
Backwell v Bath old Eds
Chew Valley v Bath Saracens
Gordano v Crewkerne
Westlands v Winscombe

November 13 (Week 10)
Avonvale v Chew Valley
Backwell v Avon
Blagdon v Crekerne
Old Ashtonians v Tor
Westlands v Gordano
Winscombe v Bath Saracens

February 12 (Week 22)
Bath Old Eds v Avon
Bath Saracens v Gordano
Blagdon v Westlands
Old Ashtonians v Backwell
Tor v Chew Valley
Winscombe v Avonvale

November 20 (Week 11)
Bath Old Eds v Old Ashtonians
Bath Saracens v Blagdon
Chew Valley v Backwell
Crewkerne v Westlands
Gordano v Avonvale
Tor v Winscome

March 12 (Week 26)
Avon v Old Ashtonians
Avondale v Blagdon
Backwell v Winscombe
Chew Valley v Bath Old Eds
Crewkerne v Bath Saracens
Gordano v Tor

December 4 (Week 13)
Avon v Chew Valley
Avonvale v Crewkerne
Backwell v Gordano
Blagdon v Tor
Westlands v Bath Saracens
Winscombe v Bath Old Eds

March 26 (Week 28)
Bath Old Eds v Gordano
Blagdon v Backwell
Old Ashtonians v Chew Valley
Tor v Crewkerne
Westlands v Avonvale
Winscombe v Avon

December 11 (Week 14)
Bath Old Eds v Blagdon
Bath Saracens v Avonvale
Crewkerne v Backwell
Gordano v Avon
Old Ashtonians v Winscombe
Tor v Westlands

April 9 (Week 30)
Avon v Blagdon
Backwell v Westlands
Bath Saracens v Tor
Chew Valley v Winscombe
Crewkerne v Bath Old Eds
Gordano v Old Ashtonians

SOMERSET TWO

AVON
Ground Address: Hicks Field, London Road, Batheaston, Bath. Tel: 0225 852446
Club Secretary/Press Officer: Kevin Newton, 2 Dene Villas, Tunley, Bath BA3 1EB. Tel: (H) 0761 471149
Club Colours: Black and amber hoops.

AVONVALE RFC
Ground Address: Bathford Playing Field, Bathford, Bath, Avon. Tel: 0225 858295.
Club Secretary: P J Kilmister, 33 West Park Road, Corsham Wiltshire, SN13 9LW. Tel: (H) 0249 712906 (W) 0249 443322.
Press Officer: P J Kilmister, 33 WSest Park Road, Corsham, Wiltshire, SN13 9LW. Tel: (H) 0249 712906 (W) 0249 443322.
Club Colours: Navy blue & white - alternative: Red.

BACKWELL RFC
Ground Address: Rodney Road, Backwell.
Club Secretary: A P Nelson, 51 Westway, Nailsea, Bristol, BS19 1CF. Tel: (H) 0275 851340.
Press Officer: A P Nelson, 51 Westway, Naisea, Bristol, BS19 1CF. Tel: (H) 0275 851340.
Club Colours: Black with a white band.

BATH SARACENS RFC
Ground Address: Civil Service Sports Club, Claverton Down, Bath. Tel: 0225 837259.
Club Secretary: N D Pirie, 34 Poolemead Road, Twerton, Bath, Avon. Tel: (H) 0225 314521 (W) 0225 884577.
Press Officer: H Evans, 120 Queens Drive, Foxhill, Bath BA2 5PE Tel: (H) 0225 840722 (W) 0225 883011.
Club Colours: Navy blue, red & gold.

BATH OLD EDWARDIANS RFC
Ground Address: King Edwards School Playing Fields, Bathampton, Bath. Tel: 0225 462354.
Club Secretary: Philip C Stuart-Harris, 8 Beaufort East, London Road, Bath, BA1 6QD. Tel: (H) 0225 338215 (W) 0225 448944.
Press Officer: Richard M Caudle, 6 Chapel Row, Queen Square, Bath, BA1 1HN. Tel: (H) 0225 318844 (W) 0225 425361.
Club Colours: Maroon, gold & blue hoops.

BLAGDON RFC
Ground Address: The Mead, Blagdon, Bristol. Tel: 0761 463196.
Club Secretary: Nigel Williams, 1 Clive Road, Hengrove, Bristol. Tel: (H) 0275 833796 (W) 0272 701732.
Press Officer: Tony Brown, 16 Harrington Avenue, Stocklwood, Bristol. Tel: 0275 839332.
Club Colours: Green.

CREWKERNE RFC
Ground Address: Henhayes, Crewkerne, Somerset. Tel: 0460 76422.
Club Secretary: Bob Physick, 4 Henley View, Crewkerne, Somerset, TA18 8JD. Tel: (H) 0460 75482.
Press Officer: Bob Physick, 4 Henley View, Crewkerne, Somerset, TA18 8JD. Tel: (H) 0460 75182.
Club Colours: Scarlet & black hoops.

CHEW VALLEY OLD BOYS RFC
Ground Address: Lobbingtons, Chew Lane, Chew Stoke, BS18.
Club Secretary: Tim Weatherley, 10 Malayo Walk, The Ridings, Bioshpsworth, Bristol, BS13 8NZ. Tel: (H) 0272 783216.
Press Officer: Duncan Soiper, 3 Bendak Bridge, Clutton, Bristol. Tel: (H) 0761 453525.
Club Colours: Green & white hoops.

FINAL TABLE

	P	W	D	L	F	A	PD	Pts
North Petherton	12	11	0	1	339	66	273	22
Chard	12	10	0	2	271	82	189	20
Tor	12	8	2	2	345	139	206	18
Winscombe	12	7	0	5	206	144	62	14
Blagdon	12	6	1	5	206	132	74	13
Bath Saracens	12	6	0	6	164	204	-40	12
Avonvale	12	6	0	6	143	201	-58	12
Crewkerne	12	5	1	6	221	136	85	11
Bath O Edwards	12	5	1	6	146	147	-1	11
Backwell	12	5	1	6	185	227	-42	11
Avon	12	4	2	6	185	197	-12	10
Castle Cary	12	1	0	11	72	385	-313	2
Burnham on Sea	12	0	0	12	58	481	-423	0

GORDANO RFC
Ground Address: Caswell Lane, Portbury, Nr Bristol, BS20 9UF. Tel: 0275 373486.
Club Secretary: C H Howard, 10 Priory Road, Portbury, Nr Bristol, BS20 9TH. Tel: (H) 0275 373551 (W) 0272 225421.
Press Officer: C H Howard, 10 Priory Road, Portbury, Nr Bristol, BS20 9TH. Tel: (H) 0275 373551 (W) 0272 225421.
Club Colours: Red & black hoops, black shorts.

OLD ASHTONIANS RFC
Ground Address: Ashton Park School, Blackmoors Lane, Bower Ashton, Bristol.
Ground Address: Ian Reed, The Bear Inn, 261/3 Hotwells Road, Hotwells, Bristol, BS8 4SF. Tel: (H) 0272 268385 (W) 0272 268385.
Press Officer: Craig Pocock, 12 Raynes Road, Ashton, Bristol. Tel: (H) 0272 666388.
Club Colours: Light blue with yellow, green & white band.

THE TOR RFC
Ground Address: Lowerside Park, Lowerside Lane, Glastonbury, Somerset, BA6 9AE. Tel: 0458 832236.
Club Secretary: The Lovells, Lubborn Lane, Baltonsborough, Glastonbury, Somerset. Tel: (H) 0458 50498.
Press Officer: Rachel Barker, 69 Bere Lane, Glastonbury, Somerset. Tel: (H) 0458 835470.
Club Colours: Maroon shirts, blue shorts.

WESTLAND RFC
Ground Address: Bunford Lane, Yeovil, Somerset. Tel: 0935 74297.
Club Secretary: Ian Prestwood, 11 Hillingdon Court, Abbey Manor Park, Yeovil, Somerset, BA21 3TA. Tel: (H) 0935 72878 (W) 0935 22298.
Press Officer: Alan Young, Wicketts Beer Farm, East Coker, Yeovil, Somerset. Tel: (H) 0935 863401 (W) 0935 79164.
Club Colours: Maroon & sky blue quarters.

WINSCOMBE RFC
Ground Address: Longfield Recreation Ground, Winscombe, Avon. Tel: 0934 842720.
Club Secretary: Alan George, 9 Gooset Lane, St Georges, Weston- Super-Mare, Avon, BS22 0XA. Tel: (H) 0934 515397.
Press Officer: Roger Calcraft, Broadway house, The Broadway, Shipham, Somerset. Tel: (H) 0934 843997.
Club Colours: Black with white band.

SOUTH WEST DIVISION

SOMERSET THREE
1993-94
FIXTURES

September 18 (Week 3)
Aller v Burnham-on-Sea
Castle Cary v Wincanton
Morganians v SW Gas
St Brendans OB v Martock

September 25 (Week 4)
Burnham-on-Sea v Cheddar Valley
Martock v Morganians
SW Gas v Aller
Wincanton v St Brendans OB

October 2 (Week 5)
Aller v Martock
Cheddar Valley v SW Gas
Morganians v Wincanton
St Brendans OB v Castle Cary

October 9 (Week 6)
Castle Cary v Morganians
Martock v Cheddar Valley
SW Gas v Burnham-on-Sea
Wincanton v Aller

October 23 (Week 8)
Aller v Castle Cary
Burnham-on-Sea v Martock
Cheddar Valley v Wincanton
Morganians v St Brendans OB

October 30 (Week X2)
Castle Cary v Cheddar Valley
Martock v SW Gas
St Brendans OB v Aller
Wincanton v Burnham-on-Sea

November 13 (Week 10)
Aller v Morganians
Burnham-on-Sea v Castle Cary
Cheddar Valley v St Brendans OB
SW Gas v Wincanton

November 20 (Week 11)
Castle Cary v SW Gas
Morganians v Cheddar Valley
St Brendans Ob v Burnham-on-Sea
Wincanton v Martock

December 4 (Week 13)
Burnham-on-Sea v Morganians
Cheddar Valley v Aller
Martock v Castle Cary
SW Gas v St Brendans OB

December 11 (Week 14)
Burnham-on-Sea v Aller
Martock v St Brendans OB
SW Gas v Morganians
Wincanton v Castle Cary

December 18 (Week 15)
Aller v SW Gas
Cheddar Valley v Burnham-on-Sea
Morganians v Martock
St Brendans OB v Wincanton

January 8 (Week 18)
Castle Cary v St Brendans OB
Martock v Aller
SW Gas v Cheddar Valley
Wincanton v Morganians

January 15 (Week 19)
Aller v Wincanton
Burnham-on-Sea v SW Gas
Cheddar Valley v Martock
Morganians v Castle Cary

January 29 (week X5)
Castle Cary v Aller
Martock v Burnham-on-Sea
St Brendans OB v Morganians
Wincanton v Cheddar Valley

February 12 (Week 22)
Aller v St Brendans OB
Burnham-on-Sea v Wincanton
Cheddar Valley v Castle Cary
SW Gas v Martock

March 12 (Week 26)
Castle Cary v Burnham-on-Sea
Morganians v Aller
St Brendans OB v Cheddar Valley
Wincanton v SW Gas

March 26 (Week 28)
Burnham-on-Sea v St Brendans OB
Cheddar Valley v Morganians
Martock v Wincanton
SW Gas v Castle Cary

April 9 (Week 30)
Aller v Cheddar Valley
Castle Cary v Matock
Morganians v Burnham-on-Sea
St Brendans OB v SW Gas

502

SOMERSET THREE

ALLER RFC
Ground Address: Playing Fields, Westfield, Curry Rivel, Somerset. Tel: 0458 252687.
Club Secretary: Mark Roddie, 5 Camden Road, Somerton, Somerset, TA11 6RN. Tel: (H) 0458 72675 (W) 0458 73740.
Press Officer: Patrick Robinson, 30 Ashbourne Crescent, Taunton, TA10 2RB. Tel: (H) 0823 284490 (W) 0823 331657.
Club Colours: Green & red hoops.

BRITISH GAS (BRISTOL) RFC
Ground Address: Beeches Gas Club, Brislington, Bristol. Tel: 0272 777148.
Club Secretary: Andrew Hibbitt, 4 Hope Court, Canada Way, Bristol, BS1 6XU. Tel: (H) 0272 276061 (W) 0272 354405.
Press Officer: Andrew Hibbitt, 4 Hope Court, Canada Way, Bristol, BS1 6XU. Tel: (H) 0272 276061 (W) 0272 354405.
Club Colours: Blue & white hoops.

BURNHAM ON SEA RFC
Ground Address: Base Ground, Stoddens Road, Burnham on Sea, Somerset. Tel: 0278 788355.
Club Secretary: J Clist, Sherwood House, 42 Berrow Road, Burnham on Sea, Somerset, TA8 2EX. Tel: (H) 0228 785751.
Press Officer: J Clist, Sherwood House, 42 Berrow Road, Burnham on Sea, Somerset, TA8 2EX. Tel: (H) 0228 785751.
Club Colours: Blue & white hoops.

CASTLE CARY RFC
Ground Address: Brook House Field, Alhampton, Castle Cary, Somerset.
Club Secretary: A Bailey, 2 Enfield Terrace, Weymouth Road, Evercreech, Somerset, BA4 6JE. Tel: (H) 0749 830268.
Press Officer: Peter Hardy, Brooklands, North Cadbury, Yeovil, Somerset, BA2 1DB. Tel: (H) 0963 40620.
Club Colours: Red & black.

CHEDDAR VALLEY RFC
Ground Address: Sharpham Road, Cheddar, Somerset. t0934 743623.
Club Secretary: Ceri Davies, 16 Round Oak Grove, Cheddar, Somerset, BS27 3BW. Tel: (H) 0934 744167.
Press Officer: Mark Hemmings, 16 Round Oak Grove, Cheddar, Somerset, BS27 3BW. Tel: (H) 0934 743540.
Club Colours: Scarlet & sky blue hoops.

MARTOCK RFC
Ground Address: The Nags Head, East Street, Martock, Somerset, TA12 6JQ.
Club Secretary: D F Pates, The South Grange, Water Street, Martock, Somerset, TA12 6JN. Tel: (H) 0935 825268 (W) 0935 825268.
Press Officer: Paul Cregan, 23 Cedar Court, Stapleton Road, Martock, TA12 6HH. Tel: (H) 0935 826270.
Club Colours: Green & black quarters.

MORGANIANS RFC
Ground Address: The Clubhouse, Chedzoy Lane, Bridgwater, Somerset. Tel: 0278 423434.
Club Secretary: D G Presdee, 66 Woodbury Road, Bridgwater, Somerset, TA6 7LJ. Tel: (H) 0278 451366.
Press Officer: D G Presdee, 66 Woodbury Road, Bridgwater, Somerset, TA6 7LJ. Tel: (H) 0278 451366.
Club Colours: Navy blue with red & yellow bands.

FINAL TABLE

	P	W	D	L	F	A	PD	Pts
Chew Valley	12	11	1	0	370	42	328	23
Old Ashtonians	12	9	1	2	295	63	232	19
Cheddar Valley	12	9	0	3	223	101	122	18
St Brendans O B	12	4	1	7	133	286	-153	9
Aller	12	4	0	8	107	218	-111	8
Morganians	12	2	0	10	56	240	-184	4
South West Gas	12	1	1	10	54	288	-234	3

ST BRENDANS OLD BOYS RFC
Ground Address: Combination Ground, Northway, Filton, Bristol. Tel: 0272 692793.
Club Secretary: Richard Kolanko, 91 Church Road, Horfield, Bristol Tel: (H) 0272 241390.
Press Officer: Dominic Shield, 2 Shoplands, Rylestone Park, Stoke Bishop, Bristol. Tel: (H) 0272 688181.
Club Colours: Maroon & Old Gold horizontal hoops.

WINCANTON RFC
Ground Address: Lattiford Park, Lattiford, Nr Wincanton, Somerset.
Club Secretary: T J Kitts, 1 Quarry Cottage, Nr Cheriton, Templecombe, Somerset, BA8 0AD. Tel: (H) 0963 33020 (W) 0963 33234.
Press Officer: T J Kitts, 1 Quarry Cottage, Nr Cheriton, Templecombe, Somerset, BA8 0AD. Tel: (H) 0963 33020 (W) 0963 33234.
Club Colours: Black & amber.

THE BEST PACK IN THE CHAMPIONSHIP.

THE BEST PACK IN THE CHAMPIONSHIP.

SOUTH WEST DIVISION

SOUTHERN COUNTIES
1993-94
FIXTURES

December 18 (Week 15)
Abbey v Wootton Bass
Bicester v Dorchester
Bletchley v Bournemouth
Chippenham v Wimborne
Olney v Oxford Mara
Slough v Redingensians

October 23 (Week 8)
Abbey v Bicester
Bracknell v Oxford Mara
Chippenham v Olney
Redingensians v Dorchester
Slough v Bletchley
Wimborne v Bournemouth

January 8 (Week 18)
Bournemouth v Olney
Bracknell v Chippenham
Dorchester v Bletchley
Redingensians v Abbey
Wimborne v Slough
Wootton Bass v Bicester

October 30 (Week X2)
Bletchley v Abbey
Bournemouth v Bracknell
Dorchester v Wimborne
Olney v Slough
Oxford Mara v Chippenham
Wootton Bass v Redingensians

January 29 (Week X5)
Abbey v Wimborne
Bicester v Redingensians
Bletchley v Wootton Bass
Olney v Dorchester
Oxford Mara v Bournemouth
Slough v Bracknell

November 13 (Week 10)
Abbey v Olney
Bicester v Bletchley
Bracknell v Dorchester
Chippenham v Bournemouth
Slough v Oxford Mara
Wimborne v Wootton Bass

February 12 (Week 22)
Bracknell v Abbey
Chippenham v Slough
Dorchester v Oxford Mara
Redingensians v Bletchley
Wimborne v Bicester
Wootton Bass v Olney

November 20 (Week 11)
Bournemouth v Slough
Dorchester v Chippenham
Olney v Bicester
Oxford Mara v Abbey
Redingensians v Wimborne
Wootton Bass v Bracknell

March 12 (Week 26)
Abbey v Chippenham
Bicester v Bracknell
Bletchley v Wimborne
Bournemouth v Dorchester
Olney v Redingensians
Oxford Mara v Wootton Bass

December 4 (Week 13)
Abbey v Bournemouth
Bicester v Oxford Mara
Bletchley v Olney
Bracknell v Redingensians
Chippenham v Wootton Bass
Slough v Dorchester

March 26 (Week 28)
Bracknell v Bletchley
Chippenham v Bicester
Redingensians v Oxford Mara
Slough v Abbey
Wimborne v Olney
Wootton Bass v Bournemouth

December 11 (Week 14)
Bournemouth v Bicester
Dorchester v Abbey
Oxford Mara v Bletchley
Redingensians v Chippenham
Wimborne v Bracknell
Wootton Bass v Slough

April 9 (Week 30)
Bicester v Slough
Bletchley v Chippenham
Bournemouth v Redingensians
Dorchester v Wootton Bass
Olney v Bracknell
Oxford Mara v Wimborne

SOUTHERN COUNTIES

ABBEY RFC
Ground Address: Rosehill, Emmer Green, Reading Berks. Tel: 0734 722881.
Club Secretary: Mike Mellor, 46 Grosvenor Road, Caversham, Reading. RG4 0EN. Tel: (H) 0734 477939 (W) 0895 826066.
Club Colours: Navy blue with green & white hoops.

BICESTER RFC
Ground Address: Bicester Sport Club, Oxford Road, BIcester, Oxon. Tel: 0869 241000.
Club Secretary: Bernard Hutt, 7 Kennet Close, Bicester, Oxon OX6 8AS. Tel: 0869 241918.
Press Officer: Andy Suter, 12 Keble Road, Bicester, Oxon. Tel: 0869 253040.
Club Colours: Red, amber & brown.

BLETCHLEY RUFC
Ground Address: Manor Fields, Bletchley, Milton Keynes. Tel: 0908 372298.
Club Secretary: Robin Bowen-Williams, 130 Water Eaton Road, Bletchley, Milton Keynes MK2 3AJ. Tel: (H) 0908 378120 (W) 0908 376614.
Club Colours: Bergundy & white.

BOURNEMOUTH RFC
Ground Address: Chapel Gate, Parley Lane, West Parley, Christchurch, Dorset. Tel: 0202 581933.
Club Secretary: M Wilkes, 581 Christchurch Road, Dorset BH1 1BU. Tel: (H) 0202 395168 (W) 0202 302345.
Club Colours: Sable & ore.

BRACKNELL RFC
Ground Address: Lily Hill Park, Lily Hill Road, Bracknell, Berks RG12 2UG. Tel: 0344 424013.
Club Secretary: D R Rutherford, 30 Knoll Road, Fleet, Hants GU13 8PU. Tel: 0252 622381.
Press Officer: C Vaal, 76 Northcott, Bracknell. Tel: 0344 424409.
Club Colours: Green, gold & black shirts; black shorts.

CHIPPENHAM RFC
Ground Address: Allington Field, Frogwell, Chippenham, Wilts SN14 0YZ. Tel: 0249 446997.
Club Secretary: John Wilding, 8 Foscote Cottages, Grittleton, Chippenham, Wilts SN14 6AQ. Tel: (H) 0249 782611 (W) 0793 812588.
Press Officer: Brian Reid, 46 Oaklands, Chippenham, Wilts. Tel: 0249 655777.
Club Colours: Black & white hoops.

DORCHESTER RFC
Ground Address: Coburg Road, Dorchester. Tel: 0305 265692.
Club Secretary: G Aspley, 5 Nappers Court, Charles Street, Dorchester, Dorset DT1 1EE. Tel: (H) 0305 814802 (W) 0305 269944.
Press Officer: M Andrews, 53 Stanstead Road, Maiden Newton, Dorchester, Dorset. Tel: 0300 21205.
Club Colours: Green & white hoops.

OLNEY RFC
Ground Address: Recreation Ground, East Street, Olney, Bucks. Tel: 0234 712880.
Club Secretary: Stuart Parkin, West View Farm, Olney, Bucks. Tel: (H) 0234 713165 (W) 0234 711992.
Press Officer: Rosary Cottage, Tapp Yard, Stoke Yoldington, Bucks. Tel: 0905 55455.
Club Colours: Cerise & French grey.

FINAL TABLE

	P	W	D	L	F	A	PD	Pts
Swanage & W'ham	12	9	2	1	251	96	155	20
Dorchester	12	9	2	1	198	115	83	20
Bournemouth	12	9	0	3	235	95	140	18
Bracknell	12	8	1	3	198	95	103	17
Olney	12	8	1	3	218	129	89	17
Wimborne	12	8	0	4	172	95	77	16
Bicester	12	7	0	5	166	131	35	14
Abbey	12	5	0	7	121	187	-66	10
Chippenham	12	4	0	8	164	144	20	8
Slough	12	3	0	9	128	234	-106	6
Bletchley	12	3	0	9	119	244	-125	6
Redingensians	12	1	0	11	82	229	-147	2
Grove	12	1	0	11	59	317	-258	2

OXFORD MARATHON RFC
Ground Address: Horspath Road Sports Ground, Oxford. Tel: 0805 775705.
Club Secretary A Barsin, "Springfield", 97 Oxford Road, Garsington, Oxford OX44 9AD. Tel: 0867 36540.
Press Officer: Roger King, 13 Walton Crescent, Oxford.
Club Colours: Navy & amber hoops.

REDINGENSIANS RUFC
Ground Address: Old Bath Road, Sonning, Berks. Tel: 0734 695259.
Club Secretary: J H Cook, 95 Century Court, Grove End Road, Lendon NW8 9LD. Tel: (H) 071 289 1887 (W) 071 814 8700.
Press Officer: K G Davis, 16 Penwood Heights, Burghclere, Newbury, Berks. Tel: 0635 253827.
Club Colours: White, dark & light blue hoops.

SLOUGH RFC
Ground Address: Tamblyn Fields, Upton Court Park, Slough, Berks SL3 7LT. Tel: 0753 522107.
Club Secretary: Malcom Carter, 15 Wavell Road, Maidenhead, Berks SL6 5AB. Tel: (H) 0628 25640 (W) 081 848 6436.
Press Officer: Colin Prococil, 63 Kenda Drive, Slough, Berkshire SL3 7DG. Tel: 0753 823855.
Club Colours: Bottle green with white hoop; navy shorts.

WIMBORNE RFC
Ground Address: Leigh Park, Wimborne, Dorset. Tel: 0202 882602.
Club Secretary: Graham Reeves, 37 Leigh Gardens, Wimborne, Dorset. Tel: (H) 0202 889526 (W) 0202 881000.
Press Officer: Roger Whyle, 393 Sopwith Crescent, Merley, Wimborne. Tel: 0202 889637.
Club Colours: All black.

WOOTTON BASSETT RFC
Ground Address: Rylands Field, Stoneover Lane, Wootton Bassett SN4 8QX. Tel: 0793 851425.
Club Secretary: C Applegate, 8 Arran Close, Wootton Bassett, Swindon, Wilts SN4 8LS. Tel: (H) 0793 854377 (W) 0793 496464 x151.
Press Officer: G Loughlin, 51 Copse Avenue, Swindon, Avon. Tel: 0793 610400.
Club Colours: Black.

SOUTH WEST DIVISION

BUCKS/OXON ONE
1993-94
FIXTURES

December 18 (Week 15)
Abingdon v Grove
Beaconsfield v Milton Keynes
Chesham v Littlemore
Chinnor v Chipping Norton
Drifters v Witney
Ox Old Boys v Amersham & Chiltern

October 23 (Week 8)
Beaconsfield v Abingdon
Chesham v Ox Old Boys
Drifters v Chinnor
Littlemore v Chipping Norton
Pennanians v Amersham & Chiltern
Witney v Grove

January 8 (Week 18)
Chipping Norton v Ox Old Boys
Grove v Chinnor
Littlemore v Drifters
Milton Keynes v Abingdon
Pennanians v Chesham
Witney v Beaconsfield

October 30 (Week X2)
Amersham & Chiltern v Chesham
Chinnor v Beaconsfield
Chipping Norton v Pennanians
Grove v Littlemore
Milton Keynes v Witney
Ox Old Boys v Drifters

January 29 (Week X5)
Abingdon v Witney
Amersham & Chiltern v Chipping Norton
Beaconsfield v Littlemore
Chinnor v Milton Keynes
Drifters v Pennanaians
Ox Old Boys v Grove

November 13 (Week 10)
Abingdon v Chinnor
Beaconsfield v Ox Old Boys
Chesham v Chipping Norton
Driftrers v Amersham & Chiltern
Littlemore v Milton Keynes
Pennanians v Grove

February 12 (Week 22)
Chesham v Drifters
Grove v Amersham & Chiltern
Littlemore v Abingdon
Milton Keynes v Ox Old Boys
Pennanians v Beaconsfield
Witney v Chinnor

November 20 (week 11)
Amersham & Chiltern v Beaconsfield
Chipping Norton v Drifters
Grove v Chesham
Milton Keynes v Pennanians
Ox Old Boys v Abingdon
Witney v Littlemore

March 12 (Week 26)
Abingdon v Pennanians
Amersham & Chiltern v Milton Keynes
Beaconsfield v Chesham
Chinnor v Littlemore
Chipping Norton v Grove
Ox Old Boys v Witney

December 4 (Week 13)
Abingdon v Amersham & Chiltern
Beaconsfield v Chipping Norton
Chesham v Milton Keynes
Chinnor v Ox Old Boys
Drifters v Grove
Pennanians v Witney

March 26 (Week 28)
Chesham v Abingdon
Drifters v Beaconsfield
littlemore v Ox Old Boys
Milton Keynes v Chipping Norton
Pennanians v Chinnor
Witney v Amersham & Chiltern

December 11 (Week 14)
Amersham & Chiltern v Chinnor
Chipping Norton v Abingdon
Grove v Beaconsfield
Littlemore v Pennanians
Milton Keynes v Drifters
Witney v Chesham

April 9 (Week 30)
Abingdon v Drifters
Amersham & Chiltern v Littlemore
Chinnor v Chesham
Chipping Norton v Witney
Grove v Milton Keynes
Ox Old Boys v Pennanians

508

BUCKINGHAM & OXFORDSHIRE ONE

ABINGDON RFC
Ground AddressSOUTHERN Sports Park, Lambrick Way, Abingdon, Oxon, Ox14 5TJ. Tel No: O235 55381O.
Club Secretary;Kelvin Syres, c/o S Akid, 39 Ladycroft Park, Blewbury, Oxon, OX11 9QW. O235 85O145 (W) O81 748 61OO.
Press Officer: Mark Hover, c/o Abingdon RFC Ground, Lambrick Way, OX14 5TJ.
Club Colours;Emerald/amber hooped shirts, black shorts, emerald socks.

AMERSHAM AND CHILTERN RFC
Ground AddressAshgrove, Weddon Lane, Amersham, Bucks, Tel No: O494 725161.
Club SecretaryColin G Maloney, Shorthills, Doggetts Wood Lane, Chalfont St Giles, Bucks. (H) O494 763388 (W) O71 831 9561
Club Colours:Claret and White

BEACONSFIELD RFC
Ground Address: Oak Lodge Meadow, Windsor End, Beaconsfield, Buckinhamshire, Tel No:O494 673783
Club Secretary:Jason Forsythe, 4 Rosebery Avenue, High Wycombe, Bucks HP13 7AH, Tel No: (H) O494 524169 (W) O71 725 9416.
Press Officer: Rik Accastello, 2O Windmill Lane, Widmer End, High Wycombe, Bucks. Tel No:O494 713653 (W) O7O7 323434 x 3411.
Club Colours:Shirts - green and gold hoops, shorts -white, stockings as shirts.

CHESHAM RUFC
Ground Address:The Pavillion, Chesham Cricket Club, The Meadow, Amy Lane, Chesham, Bucks. Tel No; O494 783635.
Club Secretary:Morris Hogg, 37 Lye Green Road, Chesham, Bucks HP5 3LR, Tel No: (H) O494 77156 (W) O494 791656
Press Officer:Jonathan Smith, 396 Chartridge Lane, Chesham, Bucks,
Tel No: (H) O494 78525O (W) O494 423557.
Club Colours:Claret & blue hoops.

CHINNOR RFC
Ground Address: Kingsey Road,Thame, Oxon. Tel No: O844 213735
Club Secretary:Jon Durrant, 17A Worminghall Road, Oakley, Aylesbury, Bucks, HP18 9QU. Tel No: (H) O844 238O3O.
Press Officer: Kevin Robinson, 1O Craft Close, Thame, Oxon, Tel No: O844 213822.
Club Colours: Black & white hoops, white shorts.

CHIPPING NORTON RUFC
Ground Address: Greystones, Burford Road, Chipping Norton, Tel No: O6O8 64398.
Club Secretary: Mrs Val Smith, Four Winds Wards Road, Chipping Norton, OX7 5BU, Tel No: O6O8 64312O.
Press Officer:T. Busby, 3O Walter Bush Road, Chipping Norton, OX7 5DN. Tel No: (H) O6O8 64217O.
Club Colours: Red/Black 4" hoops.

DRIFTERS RFC
Ground Address:Farnham Common Sports Club, One Pin Lane, Farnham Common, Bucks. Tel No: O753 64419O.
Club Secretary:Patrick Spellman, 44 Iverdale Close, Iver, Bucks, SLO 9RL. Tel No: (H) O753 654153.
Press Officer:Chris Pritchard, Tel No: O753 64669O (W) O753 647277.
Club Colours: Black and Magenta - Red 9Spare strip).

GROVE RFC
Ground Address:Grove Rrecreation Ground, Cain Lane, Grove, Oxon, Tel No: O2357 275O

FINAL TABLE

	P	W	D	L	F	A	PD	Pts
Oxford Marathon	12	11	0	1	402	77	325	22
Chiltern	12	11	0	1	262	86	176	22
Oxford Old Boys	12	9	0	3	300	133	167	18
Chinnor	12	8	0	4	215	141	74	16
Witney	12	8	0	4	159	87	72	16
Drifters	12	6	1	5	140	120	20	13
Pennanians	12	5	1	6	168	190	-22	11
Beaconsfield	12	5	0	7	166	232	-66	10
Abingdon	12	3	2	7	143	266	-123	8
Chesham	12	3	0	9	139	231	-92	6
Milton Keynes	12	2	2	8	76	204	-128	6
Buckingham	12	2	0	10	176	351	-175	4
Wheatley	12	1	2	9	62	290	-228	4

Club Secretary:Robert Teasdale, 111 Stockham Park, Wantage, Oxon, OX12 9HH.
Club Colours:Red, white and blue hooped jerseys, white shorts and red socks.

LITTLEMORE RFC
Ground Address:Peers School, Sandy Lane, Littlemore, Oxford. Tel No: O865 715776.
Club Secretary: C D Bowler, 4O South Avenue, Kidlington, Oxford, OX51DQ, (H) O8625 3715279 (W) O865 376427.
Press Officer:T Stevens, 47 Eaton Ave, Littlemore, Oxford, Oxon.
Club Colours: White.

MILTON KEYNES RUFC
Ground Address:Field Lane, Greenleys, Wolverton, Milton Keynes, Bucks. Tel No: O9O8 313858.
Club Secretary:Mr Peter Hemingway, 6 Malvern Drive, Hilltop, Stony Stratford, Milton keynes, MK11 2AE. Tel No: O9O8 564931 (W) O81 863 5611 X2474.
Press Officer: Paul Baker, 2 Hale Avenue, Stony Stratford, Milton Keynes. Tel No:(H) O9O8 56193O (W) O9O8 68273O3.
Club Colours: Black with single wide white chest band.

OXFORD OLD BOYS
Ground Address:Marston Ferry Road, Oxford. Tel No: O865 52813.
Club Secretary:Mr Richard Wardle, 4 St Leonards Road, Headington, Oxford OX3 8AA.Tel No: (H) O865 69442 (W) O235 826254.
Press Officer:Mr John Cope, 3 Browns Close, Batley, Oxford. Tel No: O865 862234.
Club Colours:Maroon & white hoops, navy shorts, red socks.

PENNANIANS RUFC
Ground Address:Farnham Park, Beaconsfield Road, Farnham Common, Bucks. Tel No: O753 646252.
Club Secretary:Eleanor James, 47 Pearl Gardens, Cippenham, Slough. Tel No: (H) O753 516886 (W) O753 5O7524.
Press Officer:Martin James, 47 Pearl Gardens, Cippenham, Slough Tel No: O753 5168656 (W) O628 7OO21.
Club Colours:Black + 2 white hoops, black shorts, red socks.

WITNEY RFC
Ground Address: The Clubhouse, Witney Road. Hailey, Oxon, OX8 5XX. Tel No: O993 771043.
Club Secretary:Chris Birks, 112 Colwell Drive, Witney, OX8 7NH, Tel No:(H) O993 777834.
Press Officer: Dave 'Scotty' Gardner, Flat D, Burwell Court, Witney, Oxon. Tel No: (H) 779222 (W) O635 563573.
Club Colours:Black hoops on sky blue.

SOUTH WEST DIVISION

BUCKS/OXON TWO
1993-94
FIXTURES

September 18 (Week 3)
Buckingham v Didcot
Gosford v Phoenix
Harwell v Winslow
Wheatley v T. Valley Pol

September 25 (Week 4)
Didcot v Cholsey
Phoenix v Buckingham
T. Valley Pol v Gosford
Winslow v Wheatley

October 2 (Week 5)
Buckingham v T. Valley Pol
Cholsey v Phoenix
Gosford v Winslow
Wheatley v Harwell

October 9 (Week 6)
Harwell v Gosford
Phoenix v Didcot
T. Valley Pol v Cholsey
Winslow v Buckingham

October 23 (Week 8)
Buckingham v Harwell
Cholsey v Winslow
Didcot v T. Valley Pol
Gosford v Wheatley

October 30 (Week X2)
Harwell v Cholsey
T. Valley Pol v Phoenix
Wheatley v Buckingham
Winslow v Didcot

November 13 (Week 10)
Buckingham v Gosford
Cholsey v Wheatley
Didcot v Harwell
Phoenix v Winslow

November 20 (Week 11)
Gosford v Cholsey
Harwell v Phoenix
Wheatley v Didcot
Winslow v T. Valley Pol

December 4 (Week 13)
Cholsey v Buckingham
Didcot v Gosford
Phoenix v Wheatley
T. Valley Pol v Harwell

December 11 (Week 14)
Didcot v Buckingham
Phoenix v Gosford
T. Valley Pol v Wheatley
Winslow v Harwell

December 18 (Week 15)
Buckingham v Phoenix
Cholsey v Didcot
Gosford v T. Valley Pol
Wheatley v Winslow

January 8 (Week 18)
Harwell v Wheatley
Phoenix v Cholsey
T. Valley Pol v Buckingham
Winslow v Gosford

January 15 (Week 19)
Buckingham v Winslow
Cholsey v T. Valley Pol
Didcot v Phoenix
Gosford v Harwell

January 29 (Week X5)
Harwell v Buckingham
T. Valley Pol v Didcot
Wheatley v Gosford
Winslow v Cholsey

February 12 (Week 22)
Buckingham v Wheatley
Cholsey v Harwell
Didcot v Winslow
Phoenix v T. Valley Pol

March 12 (Week 26)
Gosford v Buckingham
Harwell v Didcot
Wheatley v Cholsey
Winslow v Phoenix

March 26 (Week 28)
Cholsey v Gosford
Didcot v Wheatley
Phoenix v Harwell
T. Valley Pol v Winslow

April 9 (Week 30)
Buckingham v Cholsey
Gosford v Didcot
Harwell v T. Valley Pol
Wheatley v Phoenix

510

BUCKINGHAM & OXFORDSHIRE TWO

BUCKINGHAM RUFC
Ground Address: Floyd Field, Moreton Road, Maid Moreton, Buckingham MK18 1RF. Tel: 0280 815474.
Club Secretary: Finlay Gemmel, 2 Elmfield Gate, Winslow, Bucks MK18 3JG. Tel: (H) 0296 714640 (W) 0628 893772.
Press Officer: Anthony Smith, 10 Mare Leys, Buckingham MK18 7AX. Tel: 0280 815634.
Club Colours: Green & white hoop shirts; blue shorts.

CHOLSEY RFC
Ground Address: Hithercroft Road, Wallingford, Oxon. Tel: 0491 835044.
Club Secretary: G A Thompson, 13 The Murren, Wallingford OX10 9DZ. Tel: (H) 0491 836910 (W) 071 245 6262.
Press Officer: R Payne, 9 Poplar Farm Road, Chalgrove, Oxon OX44 7QZ. Tel: (H) 0865 891795 (W) 0734 323123.
Club Colours: Black & amber hoops.

DIDCOT RUFC
Ground Address: Edmonds Park, Park Road, Didcot.
Club Secretary: Mrs Jane Lllewellyn, 54 Loyd Road, Didcot, Oxon OX11 8JT. Tel: 0235 813634.
Club Colours: Red & white hoops; white shorts.

GOSFORD ALL BLACKS RFC
Ground Addrss: Langford Lane, Kidlington, Oxfordshire. Tel: 0865 373994.
Club Secretary: Dr S Butcher, as above. Tel: (H) 0865 373106 (W) 0865 841921.
Press Officer: Martin Cook, as above.
Club Colours: Black.

HARWELL RUFC
Ground Address: The Central Sports Field, Harwell Laboratory, Didcot, Oxon.
Club Secretary: C F Bartlett, 66 Upthorpe Drive, Wantage, Oxon OX12 7DG. Tel: 02357 67596.
Club Colours: Light & navy blue & white hoops.

PHEONIX RFC
Ground Address: The Sports Ground, Institute Road, Taplow, Bucks. Tel: 0628 664319.
Club Secretary: Steve Lucas, 4 Chiltern Road, Burnham, Bucks SL1 7NQ. Tel: (H) 0628 605557 (W) 0628 70969.
Press Officer: Steve Rafferty, 86 Chalklands, Bourne End SL8 5TJ. Tel: (H) 0628 523364 (W) 0628 540346.
Club Colours: Red with black hoops; black shorts.

THAMES VALLEY POLICE RFC
Ground Address: c/o Oxford RFC, Southern Bypass, Oxford. Tel: 0865 243984.
Club Secretary: David McWhirter, c/o Thames Valley Police HQ, Kidlington, Oxon OX5 2NX. Tel: (H) 0805 820508 (W) 0865 846607.
Press Officer: Richard Tyrell, c/o Operations Dept. Thames Valley Police HQ, Kidlington, Oxon. Tel: (H) 08675 72366 (W) 0805 846514.
Club Colours: Old gold; dark blue shorts.

WHEATLEY RFC
Ground Address: Holton Playing Fields, Holton, Oxford. Tel: 0865 873476.
Club Secretary: Mrs Elaine Murray, The Mead, 56 Clifden Road, Worminghall, Bucks. Tel: 0844 338940.
Press Officer: John Wilkins, 3 Lobb Hill, Milton Common OX9 2NT. Tel: 0844 238407.
Club Colours: Purple with white band.

FINAL TABLE

	P	W	D	L	F	A	PD	Pts
Littlemore	14	12	0	2	436	98	338	24
Chipping Norton	14	12	0	2	312	128	184	24
Thames Val Police	14	9	1	4	220	150	70	19
Gosford All Blacks	14	9	0	5	224	121	103	18
Harwell	14	5	0	9	117	343	-226	10
Cholsey	14	4	1	9	169	280	-111	9
Phoenix	14	4	0	10	178	250	-72	8
Didcot	14	0	0	14	100	386	-286	0

WINSLOW RUFC
Ground Address: The Bell Hotel, Winslow, Bucks.
Club Secretary: N R Stapells, 40 Magpie Way, Winslow, Bucks MK18 3OT. Tel: (H) 0296 713815 (W) 0296 314000.
Press Officer: I Barnham, Two Ways Cottage, Back Fleet, Gawcott, Bucks. Tel: 0280 815384.
Club Colours: Blue & gold.

SOUTH WEST DIVISION

BERKS, DORSET & WILTS ONE 1993-94 FIXTURES

December 18 (Week 15)
Aldermaston v Bradford
Devizes v Swindon
Lytchett Min v Weymouth
Marlborough v Melksham
North Dorset v Swindon College OB
Puddletown v Corsham

October 23 (Week 8)
Corsham v Swindon
Lytchett Min v North Dorset
Marlborough v Devizes
Puddletown v Aldermaston
Supermarine v Swindon College OB
Weymouth v Bradford

January 8 (Week 18)
Bradford v North Dorset
Corsham v Marlborough
Melksham v Devizes
Supermarine v Lytchett Min
Swindon v Aldermaston
Weymouth v Puddletown

October 30 (Week X2)
Aldermaston v Marlborough
Bradford v Supermarine
Melksham v Corsham
North Dorset v Puddletown
Swindon College OB v Lytchett Min
Swindon v Weymouth

January 29 (Week X5)
Aldermaston v Melksham
Devizes v Corsham
Marlborough v Weymouth
North Dorset v Swindon
Puddletown v Supermarine
Swindon College OB v Bradford

November 13 (Week 10)
Devizes v Aldermaston
Lytchett Min v Bradford
Marlborough v North Dorset
Puddletown v Swindon College OB
Supermarine v Swindon
Wymouth v Melksham

February 12 (Week 22)
Corsham v Aldermaston
Lytchett Min v Puddletown
Melksham v North Dorset
Supermarine v Marlborough
Swindon v Swindon College OB
Weymouth v Devizes

November 20 (Week 11)
Bradford v Puddletown
Corsham v Weymouth
Melksham v Supermarine
North Dorset v Devizes
Swindon College OB v Marlborough
Swindon v Lytchett Min

March 12 (Week 26)
Aldermaston v Weymouth
Bradford v Swindon
Devizes v Supermarine
Marlborough v Lytchett Min
North Dorset v Corsham
Swindon College OB v Melksham

December 4 (Week 13)
Aldermaston v North Dorset
Devizes v Swindon College OB
Lytchett Min v Melksham
Marlborough v Bradford
Puddletown v Swindon
Supermarine v Corsham

March 26 (Week 28)
Corsham v Swindon College OB
Lytchett Min v Devizes
Melksham v Bradford
Puddletown v Marlborough
Supermarine v Aldermaston
Weymouth v North Dorset

December 11 (Week 14)
Bradford v Devizes
Corsham v Lytchett Min
Melksham v Puddletown
Swindon College OB v Aldermaston
Swindon v Marlborough
Weymouth v Supermarine.

April 4 (Week 30)
Aldermaston v Lytchett Min
Bradford v Corsha
Devizes v Puddletown
North Dorset v Supermarine
Swindon College OB v Weymouth
Swindon v Melksham

512

BERKSHIRE, DORSET & WILTSHIRE ONE

ALDERMASTON RUFC
Ground Address: AWE Recreational Society SPorts Ground, Tadley RG7 4PR. Tel: 0734 817603.
Club Secretary: K Jones, 13 Stratfield Road, Basingstoke, Hants RG21 2RG. Tel: (H) 0256 811175 (W) 0734 814111 x6751.
Press Officer: Ms Eira Warner, 72 Whitedown Road, Tadley, Hants. Tel: 0734 816904.
Club Colours: Scarlet.

BRADFORD ON AVON RFC
Ground Addrss: Dog and Fox Public House, Ashley Road, Bradford on Avon, Wilts.
Club Secretary: Chris Awdry, Ashton Hill Farm, West Ahton, Trowbridge, Wilts BA14 6AR. Tel: 0225 760359.
Club Colours: Black & red.

CORSHAM RFC
Ground Address: Lacock Road, Corsham. Tel: 0249 701064.
Club Secretary: J G Wiltshire, 84 Springfield Close, Rudloe, Corsham, Wilts SN13 0JR. Tel: 0225 81080.
Press Officer: P Kaljusko, 7 Penleigh Close, Corsham, Wilts. Tel: 0249 712344.
Club Colours: Red & white hoops.

DEVIZES RFC
Ground Address: Chivers Ground, London Road, Devizes. Tel: 0380 723763.
Club Secretary: M J Moundrell, Manor Farm House,Calstone, Calne, Wilts SN11 8P. Tel: 0249 812373.
Press Officer: Richard Evans, Hunters Rest, Church Lane, Beechingstoke,pewsey,Wilts. Tel: 0672 851520.
Club Colours: Black with white hoops.

LYTCHETT MINSTER RUFC
Ground Address: South Manor Drive, Lytchett Minster, Poole, Dorset.
Club Secretary: D H Smurthwaite, 23 Lynn Road, Canford Heath, Poole, Dorset. Tel: (H) 0202 678961 (W) 0202 622413.
Club Colours: Red & blue hoops.

MARLBOROUGH RFC
Ground Address: Willingham Road, Market Raven. Tel: 0637 843162.
Club Secretary: R Nocton, 2 West End, Woodborough, Pewsey, Wilts SN9 5PL. Tel: (H) 0672 851404 (W) 0672 513471.
Club Colours: Black & amber hoops.

MELKSHAM (AVON) RFC
Ground Address: Melksham Sports and Social Club, Melksham HOuse, Market Place, Melksham, Wilts. Tel: 0225 704982.
Club Secretary: A C Butcher, 37 Locking Close, Bowerhill, Melksham, Wilts SN12 6XR. Tel: (H) 0225 707426 (W) 0225 703325.
Press Officer: P Spooner, 29 Barnwell Road, Melksham, Wilts SN12. Tel: 0225 706125.
Club Colours: Blue & sky blue hoops.

NORTH DORSET RFC
Ground Address: Slaughtergate, Gillingham, Dorset. Tel: 0747 822748.
Club Secretary: Paul Phillips, 10 Black Lawn, Gillingham, Dorset SP8 4SD. Tel: (H) 0747 825271 (W) 0373 831800.
Press Officer: Aubrey Aviss, 33 Beaufoy Close, Shaftesbury, Dorset SP7 8PT. Tel: 0831 317959.
Club Colours: Green shirts & socks; navy shorts.

FINAL TABLE

	P	W	D	L	F	A	PD	Pts
Wootton Bassett	12	11	0	1	324	112	212	22
Swindon	12	10	2	0	286	78	208	22
Swindon College	12	8	0	4	241	129	112	16
Devizes	12	6	2	4	196	116	80	14
Melksham	12	6	1	5	147	192	-45	13
Aldermaston	12	6	0	6	119	173	-54	12
Lytchett Minster	12	5	1	6	158	145	13	11
Corsham	12	5	1	6	132	139	-7	11
Bradford on Avon	12	5	1	6	159	207	-48	11
Weymouth	12	5	0	7	143	149	-6	10
North Dorset	12	4	1	7	142	207	-65	9
Puddletown	12	1	1	10	110	308	-198	3
Bournemouth Uni	12	1	0	11	83	285	-202	2

PUDDLETOWN RUFC
Ground Address: Greenfields. Piddlehinton, Nr Dorchester, Dorset Dt2 7VA. Tel: 0305 848808.
Club Secreatry: Philip Barnard, 21 Harveys Terace, Dorchester, Dorset DT1 1LE. Tel: (H) 0305 254087 (W) 0305 267411.
Club Colours: Red shirts, black shorts.

SUPERMARINE RFC
Ground Address: Supermarine Sports and Social CLub, Highworth Road, South Marston, Swindon. Tel: 0793 824828.
Club Secreatry: R J Medland, 12 Chedworth Gate, Broome Manor, Swindon SN3 1NE. Tel: (H) 0793 642958 (W) 0793 514514 x2842.
Press Officer: Sarah Davies, Ynsyball, Station road, Shrivenham, SN6 8ED. Tel: 0793 782531.
Club Colours: ight & dark blue hoops.

SWINDON RUFC
Ground Address: Greenbridge Road, Swindon. Tel: 0793 521148.
Club Secretary: Mark Bates, as above. Tel: (H) 0793 497134 (W) 0793 514514 x4836.
Press Officer: Graham Howes, as above. Tel: (H) 624003 (W) 0753 690599/0860 575602.
Club Colours: Navy blue & amber; white shorts.

SWINDON COLLEGE OLD BOYS RFC
Ground Address: New College, Helston Road, Swindon, Wiltshire. Tel: 0793 611470.
Club Secretary: Bob Harriss, 9 Hallam Moor, Liden, Swindon Witshire SN3 6LS. Tel: (H) 0793 496958 (W) 0793 547200.
Press Officer: Tim Waters, 80 Mulberry Grove, Swindon SN2 1HY. Tel: (H) 0793 520337 (W) 0860 400576.
Club Colours: Red & black quarters.

WEYMOUTH RFC
Ground Address: Monmouth Avenue, Weymouth. Tel: 0305 778889.
Club Secretary: Mrs G Llewellwym, 2 Goulds Hill Close, Upway, Weymouth DT3 4LG. Tel: 0305 812415.
Press Officer: Mike Richardson, 266a Dorchenston, Weymouth DT3 5AX. Tel: 772961.
Club Colours: Light blue with dark blue hoop.

SOUTH WEST DIVISION

BERKS, DORSET & WILTS TWO 1993-94 FIXTURES

December 18 (Week 15)
Blandford v Oakmedians
Bournemouth v Warminster
Hungerford v Bridport
Poole v Minety
Thatcham v Calne
Trowbridge v Westbury

October 23 (Week 8)
Bournemouth Univ v Hungerford
Calne v Oakmedians
Tadley v Minety
Thatcham v Poole
Trowbridge v Blandford
Westbury v Bridport

January 8 (Week 18)
Bridport v Blandford
Calne v Trowbridge
Oakmedians v Poole
Tadley v Thatcham
Warminster v Hungerford
Westbury v Bournemouth Univ

October 30 (Week X2)
Blandford v Bournemouth Univ
Bridport v Calne
Minety v Thatcham
Oakmedians v Tadley
Poole v Trowbridge
Warminster v Westbury

January 29 (Week X5)
Blandford v Warminster
Bournemouth Univ v Calne
Hungerford v Westbury
Minety v Oakmedians
Poole v Bridport
Trowbridge v Tadley

November 13 (Week 10)
Bournemouth Univ v Poole
Calne v Warminster
Hungerford v Blandford
Tadley v Bridport
Thatcham v Oakmedians
Trowbridge v Minety

February 12 (Week 22)
Bridport v Minety
Calne v Hungerford
Tadley v Bournemouth Univ
Thatcham v Trowbridge
Warminster v Poole
Westbury v Blandford

November 20 (Week 11)
Bridport v Thatcham
Minety v Bournemouth Univ
Oakmedians v Trowbridge
Poole v Hungerford
Warminster v Tadley
Westbury v Calne

March 12 (Week 26)
Blandford v Calne
Bournemouth Univ v Thatcham
Hungerford v Tadley
Minety v Warminster
Oakmedians v Bridport
Poole v Westbury

December 4 (Week 13)
Blandford v Poole
Bournemouth Univ v Oakmedians
Hungerford v Minety
Tadley v Westbury
Thatcham v Warminster
Trowbridge v Bridport

March 26 (Week 28)
Calne v Poole
Tadley v Blandford
Thatcham v Hungerford
Trowbridge v Bournemouth Univ
Warminster v Oakmedians
Westbury v Minety

December 11 (Week 14)
Bridgport v Bournemouth Univ
Calne v Tadley
Minety v Blandford
Oakmdedians v Hungerford
Warminster v Trowbridge
Westbury v Thatcham

April 9 (Week 30)
Blandford v Thatcham
Bridport v Warminster
Hungerford v Trowbridge
Minety v Calne
Oakmedians v Westbury
Poole v Tadley

BERKSHIRE, DORSET & WILTSHIRE TWO

BLANDFORD RFC
Ground Address: Larksmead Rec, Blandford, Club House, 53a Esat Street, Blandford. Tel 0258 450665.
Club Secretary: Dave Stringer, 21 Damory Street, Blandford, Dorset DT11 7EU. Tel: (H) 0258 450954 (W) 0258 453698.
Press Officer: Simon Mitchell, 8 Bryanston, Blandford, Dorset. Tel: (H) 0258 450210 (W) 0202 678731.
Club Colours: Gold, red & white.

BOURNEMOUTH UNIVERSUTY RFC
Ground Address: White Farm, Slades Farm, Ensbury Park, Bournemouth.
Club SEcretary: Dai Dower. Bournemouth University, Poole House, Talbot Campus, Fern Barrow, Poole, Dorset BH12 5BB. Tel: (H) 751814 (W) 595012.
Club Colours: Navy with white hoops.

BRIDPORT RFC
Ground Address: Bridport Leisure Centre, Skilling Hill Road, Bridport, Dorset DT6 5LN. Tel: 0308 27464.
Club SEcretary: Richard Salt, 21 South Street, Bridport, Dorset DT6 3NR. Tel: (H) 0297 89237 (W) 0308 22236.
Press Officer: Malcom Heaver, "Heavers", Old Laundry Estate, Bridport, Dorset DT6 4RR. Tel: (H) 0308 68519 (W) 0308 22963.
Club Colours: Dark blue.

CALNE RFC
Ground Address: Calne Recreation Club, Anchor Road, Calne, Wiltshire SN11 8JX. Tel: (H) 0249 821178 (W) 0761 414471.
Club Secretary: SEan Lambourne, 195 Quemerford, Calne, Wilts SN11 8JX. Tel: (H) 0249 821178 (W) 0761 414471.
Press Officer: Sean Riches, 1 Wessington Avenue, Calne, Wiltshire SN11 0AL. Tel: (H) 0249 812382 (W) 0249 814700.
Club Colours: Blue & white hoop, bordered in red.

HUNGERFORD RFC
Club Secretary: Jeremy Smeddle, 5 Hawthorne Way, Great Sheffield, Nr Newbury, Berks RG16 7BT. Tel: (H) 0488 648231 (W) 0895 862432.
Club Colours: Claret & porter.

MINETY RFC
Ground Address: The Playing Fields, Silver Street, Minety, Wilts. Tel: 0666 860802.
Club Secretary: Stuart Read, "Springwell House", Brinkworth, Wilts SN15 5DR. Tel: 0666 510658 (W) 0932 567677.
Press Officer: Tony Kemp, "The Paddock", Watts Lane, Hullavington, Chippenham, Wilts. Tel: (H) 0666 837675 (W) 0793 496789.
Club Colours: Purple & green.

OAKMEADIANS RFC
Ground Address: The Pavilion, Meyrick Park, Bournemouth BH2 6LH. Tel: 0202 789497.
Club Secretary: Alison Cope, 3 Comber Road, Bournemouth BH9 2XG. Tel: 0202 520170.
Club Colours: Royal blue & white hoop.

FINAL TABLE

	P	W	D	L	F	A	PD	Pts
Supermarine	12	11	0	1	290	83	207	22
Marlborough	12	10	1	1	325	95	230	21
Thatcham	12	10	0	2	226	87	139	20
Blandford	12	7	1	4	208	165	43	15
Calne	12	6	2	4	182	132	50	14
Tadley	12	6	1	5	184	176	8	13
Bridport	12	6	0	6	178	204	-26	12
Trowbridge	12	5	1	6	191	175	17	11
Oakmedians	12	5	0	7	114	191	-77	10
Warminster	12	4	1	7	189	229	-40	9
Hungerford	12	3	1	8	75	154	-79	7
Minety	12	1	0	11	77	311	-234	2
Berkshire Shire Hall	12	0	0	12	101	339	-238	0

POOLE RFC
Ground Address: Poole RFC, Club House and Ground, Turlin Moor, Hamworthy, Poole, Dorset. 0202 687170.
Club Secretary: Phil Morgan, 17 Halstock Crescent, Poole, Dorset BH17 9BD. Tel: (H) 0202 697987.
Press Officer: Mal Warriner, Flat 14, Napier Court, 3 Durley Gardens, Bournemouth. Te: (H) 0202 319325 (W) 0202 552099.
Club Colours: Blue & amber.

TADLEY RFC
Ground Address: Red Lane, Aldermaston, Reading, Berks.
Club Secretary: Roy Mears, 18 Tewkesbury Close, Basingstoke, Hants RG24 9DU. Tel: (H) 0256 461612.
Press Officer: Frank Jose, 2 Mount Pleasant, Tadley, Hants. Tel: 0734 814642.
Club Colours: Black with amber hoop.

THATCHAM RFC
Ground Address: Kennet School, Stoney Lane, Thatcham, Berks. Tel: School 0635 862121 Sports Centre 0635 871112.
Club Seretary: Roger Rance, 21 Ilkley Way, Thatcham, Berks RG13 4LG. Tel: (H) 0635 866739 (W) 0635 33636.
Club Colours: Red & blue quarters.

TROWBRIDGE RFC
Ground Address: Green Lane, Ashton Park, Trowbridge, Wilts. BA14 7DH. Tel: 0225 761389.
Club Secretary: B Parfitt, 60 Paxcroft, Trowbridge, Wilts BA14 7DJ. Tel: 0225 764953.
Press Officer: N Fleming, 9 Avondale Road, Trowbridge, Wilts BA14 8QS. Tel: 0225 761760.
Club Colours: Light blue, dark blue & gold.

WARMINSTER RFC
Ground Address: The Cricket Club, Sambourne Road, Warminster, Wiltshire. Tel: 0985 219039.
Club Secretary: R A Hone, 1 Bradford Close, Warminster, Wilts BA12 9JT. Tel: (H) 0985 218824 (W) 0249 812351.
Club Colours: Royal blue & gold.

WESTBURY RFC
Ground Address: Leighton Sports Ground, Wellhead Lane, Westbury, Wilts. Te: 0373 826438.
Club Secretary: Mark Knott, 14 Studland Park, Westbury, Wilts BA13 3HL. Tel: 0373 823479.
Press Officer: Janes Maslin, 144 Eden Vale, Westbury, Wilts. Tel: 0373 826364.
Club Colours: Green & black.

SOUTH WEST DIVISION

BERKS, DORSET & WILTS THREE 1993-94 FIXTURES

October 23 (Week 8)
Amesbury   v   Colerne
Pioneers   v   Christchurch
Portcastrians   v   Berks Shire H

October 30 (Week X2)
Berks Shire H   v   Christchurch
Colerne   v   Pewsey Vale
Portcastrians   v   Amesbury

November 13 (Week 10)
Amesbury   v   Christchurch
Berks Shire H   v   Pioneers
Pewsey Vale   v   Portcastrians

November 20 (Week 11)
Berks Shire H   v   Amesbury
Christchurch   v   Colerne
Pioneers   v   Pewsey Vale

December 4 (Week 13)
Amesbury   v   Pewsey Vale
Colerne   v   Berks Shire H
Portcastrians   v   Christchurch

Decmeber 11 (Week 14)
Berks Shire H   v   Portcastrians
Pewsey Vale   v   Colerne
Pioneers   v   Amesbury

December 18 (Week 15)
Christchurch   v   Berks Shire H
Colerne   v   Pioneers
Portcastrians   v   Pewsey Vale

January 8 (week 18)
Amesbury   v   Berks Shire H
Christchurch   v   Portcastrians
Pioneers   v   Colerne

January 15 (Week 19)
Colerne   v   Amesbury
Pewsey Vale   v   Christchurch
Pioneers   v   Portcastrians

January 29 (week X5)
Amesbury   v   Portcastrians
Berks Shire H   v   Pewsey Vale
Christchurch   v   Pioneers

February 12 (Week 22)
Pewsey Vale   v   Amesbury
Pioneers   v   Berks Shire H
Portcastrians   v   Colerne

March 12 (Week 26)
Berks Shire H   v   Colerne
Christchurch   v   Amesbury
Pewsey Vale   v   Pioneers

March 26 (Week 28)
Amesbury   v   Pioneers
Christchurch   v   Pewsey Vale
Colerne   v   Portcastrians

April 9 (week 30)
Colerne   v   Christchurch
Pewsey Vale   v   Berks Shire H
Portcastrians   v   Pioneers

516

BERKSHIRE, DORSET & WILTSHIRE 3

AMESBURY TOWN RFC
Ground Address: Holders Road, Amesbury, Wilts. Tel: 622173.
Club Secretary: B Price, 3 School Lane, Amesbury, Wilts. SP4 7DT. Tel: 625113.
Club Colours: Black & white hoops.

BERKSHIRE SHIRE HALL RUFC
Ground Address: Berkshire Sports Club, Sonning Lane, Sonning, Nr Redaing, Berks. Tel: 0734 691340.
Club Secretary: D Norris, 74 Coldbeck Drive, Reading, Berks. Tel: (H) 0734 696439 (W) 0344 713061.
Club Colours: Blue & gold hoops.

CHRISTCHURCH RFC
Ground Address Grange Road, Somerford, Christchurch, Dorset Tel NO; O2O2 4O4279
Club Secretary; Mr I J Pacey 18 Vicarage Way, Burton, Christchurch, Dorset, BH23 7NE Tel No. (H) O2O2 475716 (W) O2O3 4O81O3
Press Officer's Name As Secreary
Club Colours; Royal Blue & White Hoops

COLERNE RFC
Ground Address Higgins Field, Bath Road, Colerne, Wiltshire
Tel; O225 742835
Club Secretary Karen Kerkin
25 Cleaves Avenue, Colerne, Chippenham, Wiltshire, SN14 8BX
Tel No (H) O225 744165 (W) O272 6O38O4
Press Officer: Karen Kerkin
25 Cleaves Avenue, Colerne, Chippenham, Wiltshire SN14 8BX Tel No: (H) O225 744165 (W) O272 6O38O4
Club Colours: Black

PEWSEY VALE RFC
Ground Address: Pewsey Vale School, Wilcot Road, Pewsey, Wilts
Club Secretary; D S Aroskin, 2OA Rawlins Road, Ramsey, Wilts 5GB (H)O672 62218 (W) O672 62218
Press Officer Mike Brekspear, Slater Road, Pewsey, Wilts. Tel No: O672 6444O.
Club Colours: Red, Royal Blue & White & Black Quarters.

PIONEERS (BOVINGTON) RFC
Ground Address: Bovington Middle School, Bovington, Dorset BH2O 6NU
Club Secretary: G Somerset, 39 Victoria Close, Bovington, Dorset BH2O 6HY Tel NO: O929 463176
Club Colours: Amber & Royal Blue

PORTCASTRIANS RFC
Ground Address: Iford Playing fields, Iford, Lane, Bournemouth, **Club Secretary:** Leadbittor, 127 Stourvale Road, Bournemouth, BH6 5HE. (H) O2O2 421463 (W) O7O3 644599
Press Officer M Leadbittor
Club Colours: Red, Yellow and Blue Hoops.

FINAL TABLE

	P	W	D	L	F	A	PD	Pts
Poole	10	9	0	1	210	62	148	18
Westbury	10	8	0	2	285	82	203	16
Portcastrians	10	6	0	4	357	112	145	12
Colerne	10	4	0	6	134	151	-17	8
Amesbury	10	2	0	8	132	271	-139	4
Christchurch	10	1	0	9	50	390	-340	2

THE BEST PACK IN THE CHAMPIONSHIP.

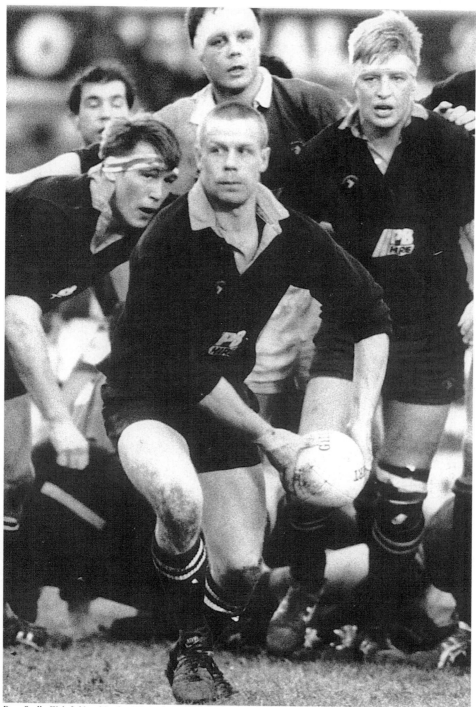

Dave Scully, Wakefield and England Under 21 and Sevens scrum half

Photo: Joe McCabe

BRITISH ISLES TOUR TO NEW ZEALAND

MAY, JUNE & JULY 1993

22nd May 1993	v North Auckland	Whangarei	W 30-17
26th May 1993	v North Harbour	Auckland	W 29-13
29th May 1993	v New Zealand Maoris	Wellington	W 24-20
2nd June 1993	v Canterbury	Christchurch	W 28-10
5th June 1993	v Otago	Dunedin	L 24-37
8th June 1993	v Southland	Invercargill	W 34-16
12th June 1993	v **New Zealand** (1st Test)	Christchurch	L 18-20
16th June 1993	v Taranaki	New Plymouth	W 49-25
19th June 1993	v Auckland	Eden Park Auckland	L 18-23
22nd June 1993	v Hawke's Bay	Napier	L 17-29
26th June 1993	v **New Zealand** (2nd Test)	Wellington	W 20-7
29th June 1993	v Waikato	Hamilton	L 10-38
3rd July 1993	v **New Zealand** (3rd Test)	Eden Park Auckland	L 13-30

Summary: Played 13, won 7, lost 6, points for 314, against 285.

SCORERS (Test Matches):

G Hastings 12 pens 1 con 38 pts, R Underwood 1 try 5 pts, S Gibbs 1 try 5 pts, R Andrew 1 DG 3 pts.

APPEARANCES

NB   1. (+) Denotes replacement appearance.
2. Figures in brackets denote test appearances
3. *Denotes tour replacement after commencement.
4. Figures are in order of first appearance.

BACKS: (England caps unless stated)

A.Cement (Swansea/Wales) 6+1; I.Hunter (Northampton) l; S. Hastings (Watsonians/Scotland) 2+1; J.Guscott (Bath) 7+2(3); R. Uunderwood (Leicester/RAF) 7(3); S. Barnes (Bath) 6+2; R Jones (Swansea/Wales) 6; G.Hastings (Watsonians/Scotland) 8+1 (3); I. Evans (Llanelli/Wales) 7(3); W.Carling (Harleqins) 6+1 (1); S.Gibbs (Swansea/Wales) 7(2); T.Underwood (Leicester) 6; R.Andrew (Wasps) 7(3); D Morris (Orrell) 7+1(3); *R.Wallace (Garryowen/Ireland) 5; *V.Cunningham (St.Mary's College/Ireland) 3; A Nicol (Dundee High School FP/Scotland) 0+1.

FORWARDS; (England caps unless stated)

J.Leonard (Harlequins) 7+1(2); B. Moore (Harlequins) 7(2); P.Wright (Boroughmuir/Scotland) 6; M.Galwey (Shannon/Ieland) 6+1; D.Cronin (London Scottish/Scotland) 6; A.Reed (Bath/Scotland) 6(1); R.Webster (Swansea/Wales) 6+1; B.Clarke (Bath) 7+1(3); N.Popplewell (Greystones/Ireland) 7(3); K.Milne (Heriot's FP/Scotland) 6+1(1); P.Burnell (London Scottish/Scotland) 6(1); M.Teague (Moseley) 7; M.Bayfield (North-ampton) 7(3); W.Dooley (Preston Grasshoppers) 3; P. Winterbottom (Harlequins) 7(3); D.Richards (Leicester) 6(3); *M.Johnson (Leicester) 4(2).

SCORERS (All matches):

G.Hastings (1 try, 24 pens., 12 cons.) 101 pts., S. Barnes (7 pens., 6 cons.) 33 pts.; R.Andrew (2 tries, 2 d.g., 2 pens., 1 con.) 24 pts.; I.Evans (4 tries) 20 pts.; R Underwood (3 tries) 15 pts.; A. Clement (2 Tries, 1 d.g.) 13 pts.; J.Guscott (2 tries) 10 pts.; T. Underwood (2 tries) 10 pts.; R. Webster (2 tries) 10 pts.; V.Cunning-ham (2 tries) 10 pts.; S.Gibbs (2 tries) 10 pts.; 2 penalty tries - 10 pts.; W.Carling (1 try, 1 d.g.) 8 pts.; S.Hastings(1 try) 5 pts.; M.Galwey (1 try) 5 pts.; D.Richards (1 try) 5 pts.; A. Reed (1 try) 5 pts.; D. Cronin (1 try) 5 pts.; M.Teague (1 try) 5 pts.; R Jones (1 try) 5 pts.; R. Wallace (1 try) 5 pts.;

1st Match, Saturday 22nd May 1993 At Whangarei

NORTH AUCKLAND 17   BRITISH ISLES 30

Te Puni 1 Try, Seymour 1 Try, T Going 1 Try,   Guscott 1 Try, S Hastings 1 Try, Clement 1 Try, R
Johnston 1 Con   Underwood 1 Try, Barnes 1 PG, 1 Con, Hastings 1 PG
1 Con.
Half Time 12-15.

2nd Match, Wednesday 26th May 1993 at Mount Smart Stadium, Auckland

NORTH HARBOUR 13   BRITISH ISLES 29

Perelini 1 Try, Carter 2 PG, 1 Con   Andrew 1 Try, T Underwood 1 Try, Evans 1 Try,
Webster 1 Try, G Hastings 1 PG, 3 Con.

3rd Match, Saturday 29th May 1993 in Wellington

NEW ZEALAND MAORIS 20   BRITISH ISLES 24

Prince 1 Try, Hirini 1 Try, 2 PG, 2 Cons,   Evans 1 Try, R Underwood 1 Try, G Hastings 1 Try,
1 PG, 3 Cons.
Half Time 20.0.

4th Match, Wednesday 2nd June 1993 in Christchurch

CANTERBURY 10   BRITISH ISLES 28

Smith 1 Try, Goffey 1 PG, 1 Con   Guscott 1 Try, Galwey 1 Try, T Underwood 1 Try,
Andrew 1 Try, 1 DG, 1 PG, 1 Con.
Half Time 7-8.

5th Match, Saturday 5th June 1993 in Dunedin

OTAGO 37   BRITISH ISLES 24

Cooke 2 Tries, Leslie 1 Try, Latta 1 Try, Timu 1 Try,   Richards 1 Try, Evans 1 Try, G Hastings 4 PG, 1 Con.
Bachop 1 DG, Bell 1 PG, 3 Cons
Half Time 13-18

6th Match, Tuesday 8th June in Invercargill

SOUTHLAND 16   BRITISH ISLES 34

Cormack 1 Try, Johnston 1 Try, Culhane 2 PG   Reed 1 Try, Clement 1 Try, Clement 1 DG, G Hastings
4 PG, 2 Con.
Half Time 0-24

7th Match (1st Test) Saturday 12th June 1993 in Christchurch

NEW ZEALAND 20   BRITISH ISLES 18

Bunce 1 Try, Fox 5 PG   G Hastings 6 PG.
Half Time 11-9.

8th Match, Wednesday 16th June 1993 in New Plymouth

TARANAKI 25   BRITISH ISLES 49

O'Sullivan 1 Try, A Slater 1 Try, McDonald 1 Try,   Cunningham 2 Tries, Cronin 1 Try, Teague 1 Try,
Crowley 2 PG, 2 Cons   Jones 1 Try, Wallace 1 Try, Gibbs 1 Try. Barnes 2 PG,
4 Con.
Half Time 13-20.

9th Match, Saturday 19th June 1993 at Eden Park, Auckland

AUCKLAND 23   BRITISH ISLES 18

Kirwan 1 Try, Fox 6 PG   Evans 1 Try, G Hastings 1 PG, 1 Con. Andrew 1 PG.

Half Time 11-18.

10th Match, Tuesday 22nd June 1993 in Napier

HAWKE'S BAY 29   BRITISH ISLES 17

Hewitt 1 Try, Weber 1 Try, Tremain 1 Try, Kerr 1 DG,   Webster 1 Try, Carling 1 DG, Barnes 3 PG.
1 PG, 1 Con, Cunningham 2 PG

Half Time 5-17.

11th Match (2nd Test) Saturday 26th June 1993 in Wellington

NEW ZEALAND 7   BRITISH ISLES 20

Clarke 1 Try, Fox 1 Con   R Underwood 1 Try, Andrew 1 DG, G Hastings 4 PG.

Half Time 7-9.

12th Match, Tuesday 29th June 1993 in Hamilton

WAIKATO 38   BRITISH ISLES 10

Monkley 2 Tries, Wilson 1 Try, Collins 1 Try, Gatland   Carling 1 Try, Barnes 1 PG, 1 Con.
1 Try, Cooper 3 PG, 2 Con

Half Time 26-3

Final Match (3rd Test) Saturday 3rd July 1993 in Auckland

NEW ZEALAND 30   BRITISH ISLES 13

Bunce 1 Try, Fitzpatrick 1 Try, Preston 1 Try, Fox 3   Gibbs 1 Try, G Hastings 2 PG, 1 Con.
PG, 3 Cons

Half Time 14-10.

INTERNATIONAL TOURS

FRANCE TOUR TO ARGENTINA

June & July 1992

v Corboda	Corboda	W62-20
v Buenos Aires XV	Buenos Aires	W28-12
v Tucuman	San Miguel	L23-25
v Argentina 'B'	San Juan	W32-18
v Cuyo	Mendoza	l3032
v ARGENTINA (1st Test)	Buenos Aires	W27-12
v Rosario	Rosario	Ab 6-8*
v ARGENTINA (2nd Test)	Buenos Aires	W33-9

* Power cut at half-time

Summary of Results

P	W	D	L	F	A
8	5	-	2	241	136

NEW ZEALAND TOUR TO SOUTH AFRICA

August 1992

v Natal	Durban	W43-25
v Orange Free State	Bloemfontein	W33-14
v Junior Springboks	Pretoria	W25-10
v Central Unions	Witbank	W39-6
v SOUTH AFRICA	Johnnesburg	W27-24

Summary of Results

P	W	D	L	F	A
5	5	-	-	167	79

AUSTRALIA TOUR TO SOUTH AFRICA

August 1992

v Western Tranvaal	Potchefstroom	W46-13
v Northern Transvaal	Pretoria	W24-17
v Eastern Province	Port Elizabeth	W34-8
v SOUTH AFRICA	Cape Town	W26-3

Summary of Results

P	W	D	L	F	A
4	4	-	-	130	41

AUSTRALIA TOUR TO IRELAND

October 1992

v Leinster	Dublin	W38-11
v Munster	Cork	L19-22
v Ulster	Belfast	W35-11
v Connacht	Galway	W14-6
v IRELAND	Dublin	W42-17

Summary of Results

P	W	D	L	F	A
5	4	-	1	148	67

AUSTALIA TOUR OF IRELAND, WALES AND ENGLAND

Wales & England

November 1992

v Swansea	Swansea	L6-21
v Wales 'B'	Cardiff Arms Park	W24-11
v Neath	Neath	W 16-8
v Llanelli	Llanelli	L9-13
v Monmouthshire	Ebbw Vale	W19-9
v WALES	Cardiff Arms Park	W23-6
v Welsh Students	Bridgend	W37-6
v Barbarians	Twickenham	W30-20

Summary of Results

P	W	D	L	F	A
8	6	-	2	164	94

Overall Record

P	W	D	L	F	A
13	10	-	3	312	161

SOUTH AFRICA TOUR TO FRANCE & ENGLAND
South Africa in France
October 1992

v France Espoirs	Bordeaux	L17-24
v Aquitaine XV	Pau	W29-22
v Midi-Pyrenees XV	Toulouse	W18-15
v Provence-Cote-D'Azure XV	Marseille	W41-12
v FRANCE	Lyon	W20-5
v Languedoc-Rousillon	Beziers	W36-15
v FRANCE	Paris	L16-29
v French Universities	Tours	L13-18
v French Barbarians	Lille	L20-25

Summary of Results

P	W	D	L	F	A
9	5	-	4	210	175

ENGLAND 'A' TOUR TO CANADA
May & June 1993

v British Columbia	Victoria	W26-10
v British Columbia President's XV	Vancouver	W26-11
v CANADA	Vancouver	L12-15
v Ontario	Toronto	W40-7
v CANADA	Ottawa	W19-14

Summary of Results

P	W	D	L	F	A
5	4	-	1	123	57

SCOTLAND TOUR TO FIJI, TONGA & WESTERN SAMOA
May & June 1993

v Fiji 'B'	Nadi	W14-7
v Fiji Juniors	Suva	W51-3
v FIJI	Suva	W21-10
v Tongan President's XV	Nuku'alofa	W23-5
v TONGA	Nuku'alofa	W23-5
v Western Samoa President's XV	Apia	W33-8
v WESTERN SAMOA	Apia	L11-28

Summary of results

P	W	D	L	F	A
7	6	-	1	174	66

WALES TOUR TO AFRICA
May & June 1993

v ZIMBABWE	Bulawayo	W35-14
v Zimbabwe 'B'	Harare	W64-13
v ZIMBABWE	Harare	W42-13
v Nambia 'B'	Windhoek	W47-10
v NAMIBIA	Windhoek	W38-23
v South African Barbarians	Windhoek	W56-17

Summary of results

P	W	D	L	F	A
6	6	-	-	282	90

FRANCE TOUR TO SOUTH AFRICA
June & July 1993

v Eastern Province	Port Elizabeth	W18-8
v Western Province	Capt Town	W12-6
v South Africa 'B'	East London	L22-35
v Orange Free State	Bloemfontein	D22-22
v Northern Transvaal	Pretoria	L19-38
v SOUTH AFRICA (1st Test)	Durban	D20-20
v South Africa Development XV	Welkom	W38-13
v SOUTH AFRICA (2nd Test)	Johannesburg	W18-17

Summary of Results

P	W	D	L	F	A
8	4	2	2	169	159

SCORERS (TEST MATCHES): T Lacroix (1DG 7P) 24 pts, A Penaud (2DG) 6 pts, P Saint-Andre (1T) 5 pts, A Hueber (1DG) 3pts.

FIVE NATIONS CHAMPIONSHIP 1993

Saturday 16th January 1993   At Twickenham

ENGLAND 16   FRANCE 15

Hunter 1 Try, Webb 1 Con 1 PG   Saint-Andre 2 Tries, Camberabero 1 Con 1 PG

England: J.M. Webb (Bath), I.G. Hunter (Northampton), W.D.C. Carling (Harlequins, captain), J.C. Guscott (Bath), R. Underwood (Leicester & RAF), C.R. Andrew (Wasps), C.D. Morris (Orrell), J. Leonard (Harlequins), B.C. Moore (Harlequins), J.A. Probyn (Wasps), M.C. Bayfield (Northampton), M. Johnson (Leicester), M.C. Teague (Moseley), P.J. Winterbottom (Harlequins), B.B. Clarke (Bath).

France: J-B. Lafond (Begles), P. Saint-Andre (Montferrand), P. Sella (Agen), T. Lacroix (Dax), P. Hontas (Biarritz), D. Camberabero (Beziers), A. Hueber (Toulon), L. Armary (Lourdes), J-F. Tordo (Nice, captain), L. Seigne (Merignac), A. Benazzi (Agen), O. Roumat (Dax), P. Benetton (Agen), L. Cabannes (Racing), M. Cecillon (Bourgoin). Replacements: S. Ougier (Toulouse) for Lacroix, F. Mesnal (Racing) for Sella.

Saturday 16th January 1993   At Murrayfield

SCOTLAND 15   IRELAND 3

Stark 1 Try, Stanger 1 Try, G. Hastings 1 Con 1 PG   Malone 1 PG

Scotland: G. Hastings (Watsonians, captain), A. Stanger (Hawick), S. Hastings (Watsonians), G. Shiel (Melrose), D. Stark (Boroughmuir), C. Chalmers (Melrose), G. Armstrong (Jed-Forest), A. Watt (Glasgow H/K), K. Milne (Heriot's), P. Burnell (London Scottish), A. Reed (Bath), D. Cronin (London Scottish), D. Turnbull (Hawick), I. Morrison (London Scottish), G. Weir (Melrose)

Ireland: C. Wilkinson (Malone), S. Geoghegan (London Irish), V. Cunningham (St. Mary's Coll), P. Danaher, R. Wallace (Garryowen), N. Malone (Oxford Univ), M. Bradley (Cork Const, captain), N. Popplewell (Greystones), S. Smith (Ballymena), P. McCarthy (Cork Const.), P. Johns (Dungannon), R. Costello (Garryowen), P. Lawlor (Bective Rangers), W. McBride (Malone), N. Mannion (Lansdowne).

Saturday February 6th 1993   At Cardiff

WALES 10   ENGLAND 9

I.C. Evans 1 Try, Jenkins 1 Con 1 PG   Guscott 1 DG, Webb 2 PG

Wales: M.A. Rayer (Cardiff), I.C. Evans (Llanelli, captain), M.R. Hall (Cardiff), I.S. Gibbs (Swansea), W.T. Procter (Llanelli), N.R. Jenkins (Pontypridd), R.N. Jones (Swansea), R.L. Evans (Llanelli), N. Meek (Pontypridd), H. Williams-Jones (South Wales Police), G.O. Llewellen (Neath), A.H. Copsey, E.W. Lewis (Llanelli), R.E. Webster, S. Davies (Swansea)

England: J.M. Webb (Bath), I. Hunter (Northampton), J.C. Guscott (Bath), W.D.C. CArling (Harlequins, captain), R. Underwood (RAF & Leicester), C.R. Andrew (Wasps), C.D. Morris (Orrell), J. Leonard, B.C. Moore (Harlequins), J.A. Probyn (Wasps), M.C. Bayfield (Northampton), W.A. Dooley (Preston Grasshoppers) M.C. Teague (Moseley), P.J. Winterbottom (Harlequins), B.B. Clarke (Bath) Replacement: P.R. de Glanville (Bath) for Hunter.

FRANCE 11 SCOTLAND 3

Lacroix 1 Try, Camberabero 2 PG Hastings 1 PG

France: J-B. Lafond (Begles), P. Saint-Andre (Montferrand), P. Sella (Agen), T. Lacroix (Dax), P. Hontas (Biarritz), D. Camberabero (Beziers), A. Hueber (Toulon), L. Armary (Lourdes), J-F. Tordo (Nice, captain), L. Seigne (Merignac), A. Benazzi (Agen), O. Roumat (Dax), P. Benetton (Agen), L. Cabannes (Racing), M. Cecillon (Bourgoin).
Scotland: G. Hastings (Watsonians, captain), A. Stanger (Hawick), S. Hastings (Watsonians), G. Shiel (Melrose), D. Stark (Boroughmuir), C. Chalmers (Melrose), G. Armstrong (Jed-Forest), P. Wright (Boroughmuir), K. Milne (Heriot's), P. Burnell (London Scottish), A. Reed (Bath), D. Cronin (London Scottish), D. Turnbull (Hawick), I. Morrison (London Scottish), G. Weir (Melrose)

Saturday 20th February 1993 At Murrayfield

SCOTLAND 20 WALES 0

Turnbull 1 Try, A.G. Hastings 5 PG

Scotland: G. Hastings (Watsonians, captain), A. Stanger (Hawick), S. Hastings (Watsonians), G. Shiel (Melrose), D. Stark (Boroughmuir), C. Chalmers (Melrose), G. Armstrong (Jed-Forest), P. Wright (Boroughmuir), K. Milne (Heriot's), P. Burnell (London Scottish), A. Reed (Bath), D. Cronin (London Scottish), D. Turnbull (Hawick), I. Morrison (London Scottish), G. Weir (Melrose)
Wales: M.A. Rayer (Cardiff), I.C. Evans (Llanelli, captain), M.R. Hall (Cardiff), I.S. Gibbs (Swansea), W.T. Procter (Llanelli), N.R. Jenkins (Pontypridd), R.N. Jones (Swansea), R.L. Evans (Llanelli), N. Meek (Pontypridd), H. Williams-Jones (South Wales Police), G.O. Llewellen (Neath), A.H. Copsey, E.W. Lewis (Llanelli), R.E. Webster, S. Davies (Swansea)

Saturday 20th February 1993 At Lansdowne Road

IRELAND 6 FRANCE 21

Malone 2 PG Saint-Andre 1 Try, Sella 1 Try, Camberabero 1 Con 1 PG

Ireland: C. Clarke (Terenure), S. Geoghegan (London Irish), V. Cunningham (St. Mary's Coll), P. Danaher, R. Wallace (Garryowen), N. Malone (Oxford Univ), M. Bradley (Cork Const, captain), N. Popplewell (Greystones), T. Kingston (Dolphin), P. Clohessy (Young Munstar), P. Johns (Dungannon), N. Francis (Blackrock), P. O'Hara (Cork Const.), D. McBride (Malone), M Galwey (Shannon). Replacement: B. Glennon (Landsowne) for Danaher.
France: J-B. Lafond (Begles), P. Saint-Andre (Montferrand), P. Sella (Agen), T. Lacroix (Dax), P. Hontas (Biarritz), D. Camberabero (Beziers), A. Hueber (Toulon), L. Armary (Lourdes), J-F. Tordo (Nice, captain), L. Seigne (Merignac), A. Benazzi (Agen), O. Roumat (Dax), P. Benetton (Agen), L. Cabannes (Racing), M. Cecillon (Bourgoin).

Saturday 6th March 1993 At Twickenham

ENGLAND 26 SCOTLAND 12

Guscott 1 Try, R. Underwood 1 Try, T. Underwood 1 A.G. Hastings 3 PG, Chalmers 1 DG
Try, Webb 1 Con 3 PG

England: J.M. Webb (Bath), T. Underwood (Leicester), J.C. Guscott (Bath), W.D.C. Carling (Harlequins, captain), R. Underwood (RAF & Leicester), S. Barnes (Bath), C.D. Morris (Orrell), J. Leonard, B.C. Moore (Harlequins), J.A. Probyn (Wasps), M.C. Bayfield (Northampton), W.A. Dooley (Preston Grasshoppers) M.C. Teague (Moseley), P.J. Winterbottom (Harlequins), B.B. Clarke (Bath)
Scotland: A.G. Hastings (Watsonians, captain), A. Stanger (Hawick), S. Hastings (Watsonians), G. Shiel (Melrose), D. Stark (Boroughmuir), C. Chalmers (Melrose), G. Armstrong (Jed-Forest), P. Wright (Boroughmuir), K. Milne (Heriot's), P. Burnell (London Scottish), A. Reed (Bath), D. Cronin (London Scottish), D. Turnbull (Hawick), I. Morrison (London Scottish), G. Weir (Melrose). Replacements: G.P.J. Townsend (Gala) for Chalmers, K.M. Logan (Stirling Co) for S Hastings.

WALES 14   IRELAND 19

Evans 1 Try, Jenkins 3 PG   Elwood 1 Try 3 PG, Robinson 1 Try, Clarke 1 DG

Wales: M.A. Rayer (Cardiff), I.C. Evans (Llanelli, captain), M.R. Hall (Cardiff), I.S. Gibbs (Swansea), N. Walker (Cardiff), N.R. Jenkins (Pontypridd), R.N. Jones (Swansea), R.L. Evans (Llanelli), N. Meek (Pontypool), H. Williams-Jones (South Wales Police), G.O. Llewellen (Neath), A.H. Copsey, E.W. Lewis (Llanelli), R.E. Webster, S. Davies (Swansea). Replacement: A. Clement (Swansea) for I.C. Evans.
Ireland: C. Clarke (Terenure), R. Wallace (Garryowen), V. Cunningham (St. Mary's Coll), P. Danaher, S.P. Geoghegan (London Irish), E. Ellwood (Lansdowne), M. Bradley (Cork Const, captain), N. Popplewell (Greystones), T. Kingston (Dolphin), P. Clohessy (Young Munstar), P. Johns (Dungannon), M.J. Galwey (Shannon), P. O'Hara (Cork Const.), D. McBride (Malone), B. Robinson (London Irish)

IRELAND 17   ENGLAND 3

Galwey 1 Try, Elwood 2 DG 2 PG   Webb 1 PG

Ireland: C. Clarke (Terenure), R. Wallace (Garryowen), V. Cunningham (St. Mary's Coll), P. Danaher, S.P. Geoghegan (London Irish), E. Ellwood (Lansdowne), M. Bradley (Cork Const, captain), N. Popplewell (Greystones), T. Kingston (Dolphin), P. Clohessy (Young Munstar), P. Johns (Dungannon), M.J. Galwey (Shannon), P. O'Hara (Cork Const.), D. McBride (Malone), B. Robinson (London Irish)
England: J.M. Webb (Bath), T. Underwood (Leicester), J.C. Guscott (Bath), W.D.C. Carling (Harlequins, captain), R. Underwood (RAF & Leicester), S. Barnes (Bath), C.D. Morris (Orrell), J. Leonard, B.C. Moore (Harlequins), J.A. Probyn (Wasps), M.C. Bayfield (Northampton), W.A. Dooley (Preston Grasshoppers) M.C. Teague (Moseley), P.J. Winterbottom (Harlequins), B.B. Clarke (Bath)

FRANCE 26   WALES 10

Benetton 2 Tries, Lafond 1 Try 1 Con, Lacroix 3 PG   Walker 1 Try, Jenkins 1 Con 1 PG

France: J-B. Lafond (Begles), P. Saint-Andre (Montferrand), P. Sella (Agen), T. Lacroix (Dax), P. Hontas (Biarritz), F. Mesnel (Racing), A. Hueber (Toulon), L. Seigne (Merignac), J-F. Tordo (Nice, captain), L. Armary (Lourdes), O. Roumat (Dax), A. Benazzi (Agen), P. Benetton (Agen), L. Cabannes (Racing), M. Cecillon (Bourgoin).
Wales: A. Clement (Swansea), I.C. Evans (Llanelli, captain), N.G. Davies (Llanelli), I.S. Gibbs (Swansea), N. Walker (Cardiff), N.R. Jenkins (Pontypridd), R.H. St.J.B. Moon, R.L. Evans, A. Lamerton (Llanelli), H. Williams-Jones (South Wales Police), P.T. Davies (Llanelli), G.O. Llewellen (Neath), M.A. Perago (Llanelli), R.E. Webster, E.W. Lewis (Llanelli). Replacements: J.D. Davies (Neath) for R.L. Evans, P. Arnold (Swansea) for Perego.

FINAL CHAMPIONSHIP TABLE

	P	W	D	L	F	A	Pts
France	4	3	1	0	73	35	6 +38
Scotland	4	2	2	0	50	40	4 +10
England	4	2	2	0	50	54	4 -
Ireland	4	2	2	0	45	53	4 -7
Wales	4	1	3	0	34	74	2 -40

'A' INTERNATIONALS 1992-93

Sunday 13th September 1992   In Madrid

SPAIN 'A' 14   SCOTLAND 'A' 35

Guttierrez 1 Try, Azkargorta 1 Try, Puertas 2 Cons   Moncrieff 1 Try, Roxburgh 1 Try, Wyllie 1 Try, Logan 1 Try, Townsend 3 Cons 3 Pens

Saturday 19th December 1992   At Melrose

SCOTLAND 'A' 22   ITALY 'B' 17

(Half-time 9-9) Attendance 6000

S Hastings 1 Try, G Townsend 1 Try, Chalmers 4 Pens   Checcinato 1 Try, Dominguex 3 Pens 1 DG

Monday 28th December 1992   At Lansdowne Road, Dublin

IRELAND 'A' 13   SCOTLAND 'A' 22

Cronin 1 Try, Malone 1 Pen 1 Con   Stanger 2 Tries, Nicol 1 Try, Logan 1 Try, Townsend 1 Con

Friday 15th January 1993   At Leicester

ENGLAND 'A' 29   FRANCE 'B' 17

T Underwood 1 Try, Hopley 1 Try, Thorneycroft 1 Try, Challinor 1 Con 4 Pens   Berty 1 Try, Campan 1 Try 2 Cons 1 Pen

Wednesday 3rd February 1993   At Bath

ENGLAND 'A' 59   ITALY 'B' 0

Potter 2 Tries, Thorneycroft 1 Try, Underwood 2 Tries, Buzza 1 Try 2 Cons, Back 2 Tries, Challinor 2 Cons 2 Pens

Friday 5th March 1993   At Richmond

ENGLAND 'A' 66   SPAIN 5

Dunn 1 Try, Johnson 1 Try, Hull 2 Tries 4 Cons 1 Pen, Hackney 4 Tries, Thorneycroft 1 Try, Richards 1 Try, Challinor 1 Try   Hernandez-Gil 1 Try

Friday 5th March   At Rodney Parade, Newport

WALES 'A' 28   IRELAND 'A' 29

Bidgood 2 Tries, Jones 1 Try, Proctor 1 Try, A Davies 2 Pens 1 Con   Humphreys 1 Try 2 DG, 2 Pens 1 Con, Staples 1 Try, Walsh 1 Try

Friday 20th March 1993   At Donnybrook

IRELAND 'A' 18   ENGLAND 'A' 22

Walsh 1 Try, Carey 1 Try, Humphries 1 Con 1 Pen 1 DG   Dawson 2 Tries, Hall 1 Try, Hull 2 Cons, 1 PG

Saturday 20th March 1993   In Aberdeen

SCOTLAND 'A' 19   FRANCE 'A' 29

Logan 1 Try Donaldson 4 Pens 1 Con   Bertranck 2 Tries, Arbo 1 Try, Galthie 1 Try Larran 1 Try, Bellot 1 Con, Labit 1 Con

'B' INTERNATIONALS 1992-93

Saturday 6th February 1993   At Den Bosch

HOLLAND 12   WALES 'B' 57

Koenen 2 Tries, Bos 1 Con   Bigwood 1 Try, Howley 1 Try, Williams 1 Try, Walker 3 Tries, Davies 1 Try, Ford 2 Tries, Williams 6 Cons

Saturday 7th November 1992   At Bristol RFC

ENGLAND 'B' 16   SOUTH AFRICA 20
(Half-time 5-8) Attendance 14000

Hunter 1 Try, T Underwood 1 Try, Barnes 2 Pens   Hattingh 1 Try, Oliver 1 Try, Richter 1 Try, Botha 1 Con 1 DG

Saturday 7th November 1992   In Cardiff

WALES 'B' 11   AUSTRALIA 24
(Half-time 3-3) Attendance 17295

N Davies 1 Try, Stephens 2 Pens   Smith 1 Try, Morgan 1 Try, Roebuck 1 Con 4 Pens

UNDER 21 INTERNATIONALS 1992-93

Saturday 5th September 1992   At Leicester

ENGLAND 37   ITALY 12

Mapletoft 2 Tries 1 Pen 3 Conversions, O'Leary 1 Try, Bramley 1 Try, Sleightholme 1 Try, Grayson 1 Pen   Re 1 Try, Caione 1 Try, Visentin 1 Con

Wednesday 9th September 1992   At Kelso

SCOTLAND 18   ITALY 29

Thomson 6 Pens   Babbo 3 Tries 4 Pens 1 Con

Wednesday 14th October 1992   At Gosforth

ENGLAND 39   IRELAND 28

O'Leary 2 Tries, Rennell 1 Try, Mapletoft 1 Try 1 Con, Burke 1 Try 1 Pen 2 Cons   Toland 1 Try, Wallace 1 Try McGowan 2 Pens 2 Cons. 1 Penalty Try

Friday 15th January 1993   At Murrayfield (rear pitch)

SCOTLAND 3   IRELAND 18

Thomson 1 Pen   Toland 1 Try, Longwell 1 Try, Carolan 1 Pen 1 Con

Friday 19th February 1993   At Myreside, Edinburgh

SCOTLAND 8   WALES 16

Rudkin 1 Try, Thomson 1 Pen   Appleyard 1 Try, Quinnell 1 Try Williams 2 Pens

Saturday 1st May 1993   Curtain raiser to Pilkington Cup Final at Twickenham

ENGLAND 31   FRENCH ARMED FORCES 3

Hill 1 Try, Stimpson 1 Try, Catt 1 Try 1 Pen 1 Con   S Bertranck 1 DG

OTHER INTERNATIONALS 1992-93

Wednesday 7th October 1992   At Cardiff Arms Park

WALES 43   ITALY 12

Clement 1 Try, Evans 1 Try, Stephens 1 Try 4 Cons,   Francescato 1 Try, Marcello Cuttita 1 Try, Bonomi 1
Gibbs 1 Try, Davies 1 Try, Webster 1 Try, Rayer 1   Con
Try

Saturday 17th October 1992   At Wembley

ENGLAND 26   CANADA 13
(Half time 16-13) Attendance 39737

Hunter 2 Tries, Winterbottom 1 Try, Guscott 1 Try,   Graff 1 Try, Rees 1 Con 2 Pens
Webb 2 Pens

Saturday 17th October 1992   First Test

FRANCE 15   SOUTH AFRICA 20
(Half time 0-13)

Pernaud 2 Tries, Viars 1 Con 1 Pen
Gerber 1 Try, Small 1 Try, Botha 2 Cons 1 Pen 1 DG

Saturday 24th October 1992   Second Test. Paris

FRANCE 29   SOUTH AFRICA 16
(Half-time 6-6)

Roumac 1 Try, Penaud 1 Try, Lacroix 2 Cons 5 Pens
Gerber 1 Try, Botha 1 Con 2 Pen 1 DG

Saturday 31st October 1992   At Lansdowne Road

IRELAND 17   AUSTRALIA 42
(Half-time 6-19) Attendance 46500

Wallace 1 Try, Russell 4 Pens   Campese 1 Try, McKenzie 1 Try, Little 1 Try, Kelaher
       1 Try, Horan 1 Try, Roebuck 4 Cons 3 Pens

Saturday 31st October 1992   Bucharest

ROMANIA 18   ARGENTINA 21

Saturday 14th October 1992   At Twickenham

ENGLAND 33   SOUTH AFRICA 16

T Underwood 1 Try, Guscott 1 Try, Morris 1 Try,   Strauss 1 Try, Botha 2 Pens 1 DG
Carling 1 Try, Webb 3 Cons 3 Pens

Saturday 21st November 1992   At Cardiff Arms Park

WALES 6   AUSTRALIA 23
(Half-time 3-5) Attendance 51000

Stephens 2 Pens   Wilson 1 Try, McCall 1 Try, Campese 1 Try, Roebuck
       1 Con 2 Pens

ADDITIONAL REPRESENTATIVE MATCHES 1992-93

Friday 15th January 1993   At Cambridge

ENGLAND STUDENTS 20   FRANCE STUDENTS 9

Bracken 1 Try, Sleightholme 1 Try, Stimpson 2 Cons   Mazas 3 Pens
2 Pens

Friday 5th March 1993

ENGLAND STUDENTS 71   SCOTLAND STUDENTS 20

O'Leary 1 Try, Diprose 3 Tries, Adams 2 Tries,   Burns 1 Try, Jackson 1 Try, Laurie 2 Cons 2 Pens
Johnson 1 Try, Savermotto 1 Try, Sleightholme 1 Try,
Greenwood 2 Tries, Stimpson 8 Cons

Saturday 6th March 1993

ENGLISH UNIVERSITIES 52   SCOTTISH UNIVERSITIES 13

Nolan 1 Try, Dallwood 1 Try, Drury 1 Try, Williams   Hall 1 Try, Mardon 1 Con 2 Pens
2 Tries, Dickinson 1 Try, Fennell 1 Try, Brennand
1 Try, Cathcart 3 Cons 3 Pens

FIRA CHAMPIONSHIP

Thursday 20th May 1993   In Bucharest

ROMANIA 20   FRANCE 37

Neaga 1 Try, Leonte 1 Try, Nichitean 2 Pens 2 Cons   Bernat-Salles 3 Tries, Cecillon 1 Try, Viars 3 Pens 4
Cons

SPECIAL MATCH

Saturday 5th September   At Leicester

LEICESTER 11   ENGLAND 18

Hackney 1 Try, Liley 2 Pens   Heslop 2 Tries, Andrew 1 DG, Webb 1 Pen 1 Con

REPRESENTATIVE MATCH

Sunday 11th April 1993   At Hartlepool

R.F. OAKES XV 23   ENGLAND 30

Cassidy 1 Try, Clayton-Hibbott 1 Try, Wellens 1 Pen,   Redman 1 Try, Linnett 1 Try, Hackney 1 Try, Grayson
Old 1 Pen 1 Con   1 Pen

ADT DIVISIONAL CHAMPIONSHIP

Saturday 5th December 1992   At Wasps, Sudbury

LONDON 26   MIDLANDS 16

Ryan 1 Try, Andrew 1 Try 1 Con 3 Pens, O'Leary   Johnson 1 Try, Liley 1 Con 3 Pens
1 Try

London: A. Buzza, S. Pilgrim (Wasps), M. Evans (Harlequins), J. Buckton, D. O'Leary (Saracens), R. Andrew (captain), S. Bates (Wasps), J. Leonard, B. Moore (Harlequins), J. Probyn (Wasps), M. Russell, R. Langhorn (Harlequins), M. Skinner (Blackheath), J. Cassell (Saracens), D. Ryan (Wasps).

Midlands: J. Liley, S. Hackney, S. Potter (Leicester), F Packman, H. Thorneycroft, J. Steele (Northampton), A. Kardooni (Leicester), M. Linnett (Moseley), J. Olver (Northampton), P. Shillingford (Moseley), N. Back, D. Richards (captain) (Leicester). Replacement: M. Dawson (Northampton) for Kardooni.

Saturday 5th September 1992   At Headingley

NORTH 9   SOUTH WEST 29

Grayson 3 Pens   Morris 3 Tries, Beal 2 Tries, Webb 2 Cons

North: I. Hunter (Northampton), N. Heslop (Orrell), B. Barley (Wakefield), K. Simms (captain) (Liverpool St Helens), R. Underwood (Leicester), P. Grayson (Waterloo), D. Morris, M. Hynes (Orrell), S. Mitchell (West Hartlepool), M. Whitcombe (Sale), T. Rodber (Northampton), W. Dooley (Preston Grasshoppers), P. Walton (Northampton), M. Greenwood (Wasps), M. Pepper (Nottingham). Replacements: D. Sculley (Wakefield) for Morris, M. Jackson (Fylde) for Heslop.

South West: (Bath unless stated) J. Webb, N. Beal (Northampton), P. de Glanville, J Guscott, S. Morris (Gloucester), S. Barnes (captain), R. Hill, C. Clark (Swansea), K. Dunn (Wasps), J. Mallet, N. Redman, A. Blackmore (Bristol), B. Clark, J. Hall, A. Robinson.

Saturday 12th December 1992   At Blundell Sands

NORTH 13   MIDLANDS 16

T. Underwood 1 Try, Grayson 1 Con 2 PG   Potter 1 Try, Johnson 1 Try, Steele 2 PG

North: I. Hunter (Northampton), T. Underwood (Leicester), B. Barley (Wakefield), K. Simms (captain) (Liverpool St Helens), R. Underwood (Leicester), P. Grayson (Waterloo), D. Scully (Wakefield), M. Hynes (Orrell), S. Mitchell (West Hartlepool), M. Whitcombe (Sale), K. Westgarth (West Hartlepool), D. Baldwin (Sale), T. Rodber (Northampton), M. Greenwood (Wasps), M. Pepper (Nottingham).

Midlands: J. Liley, S. Hackney, S. Potter (Leicester), F Packman, H. Thorneycroft (Northampton), R. Angel (Coventry), M. Dawson (Northampton), M. Linnett (Moseley), J. Olver (Northampton), M. Johnson (Leicester), M. Bayfield (Northampton), P. Shillingford (Moseley), D. Richards (captain) (Leicester). N. Back (Leicester). Replacements: J. Stele (Northampton) for Hackney.

532

At Kingsholm

SOUTH WEST 26 LONDON 24

Robinson 1 Try, Beal 1 Try, Guscott 1 Try, Webb 1 Con 3 PG   Snow 1 Try, Andrew 1 Try 1 Con, 4 PG

South West: J. Webb (Bath), N. Beal (Northampton), J. Guscott, P. de Glanville (Bath), S. Morris (Gloucester), S. Barnes (captain), R. Hill (Bath), C. Clark (Swansea), K. Dunn (Wasps), J. Mallett, N Redman (Bath), A. Blackmore (Bristol), J. Hall, A. Robinson, B. Clarke (Bath)

London: A. Buzza, S. Pilgrim, F Clough (Wasps), D. Hopley (Cambridge Univ.), D. O'Leary (Saracens), R. Andrew (captain), S. Bates (Wasps), J. Leonard, B. Moore (Harlequins), J. Probyn (Wasps), A. Snow, R. Langhorn (Harlequins), M. Skinner (Blackheath), J. Cassell (Saracens), D. Ryan (Wasps).

Saturday 19th September 1992   At Twickenham

LONDON 20 NORTH 24

Skinner 1 Try, Hopley 1 Try, Pilgrim 1 Con, Andrew 1 Con, 1 PG   Brown 1 Try, R. Underwood 1 Try, Grayson 1 Con 4 PG

London: (Wasps unless stated) A. Buzza, S. Pilgrim, F. Clough, D. Hopley, D. O'Leary (Saracens), R. Andrew (captain), S. Bates, J. Leonard (Harlequins), B. Moore (Harlequins), J. Probyn, A. Snow (Harlequins), R. Langhorn (Harlequins), M. Skinner (Blackheath), J Cassell (Saracens), D. Ryan.

North: I. Hunter (Northampton), T. Underwood (Leicester), J. Fletcher (Tynedale), K. Simms (captain) (Liverpool St. Helens), R. Underwood (Leicester), P Grayson (Waterloo), D. Morris (Orrell, M. Hynes (Orrell), S. Mitchell (West Hartlepool), M. Whitcombe (Sale), K. Westgarth (West Hartlepool), D. Baldwin (Sale), M. Greenwood (Wasps), A. Brown (West Hartlepool), T. Rodber (Northampton). Replacements: P. Hackett (Waterloo) for Mitchell, J. Mallender (Sale) for Fletcher..

Saturday 19th September 1992

MIDLANDS 18 SOUTH WEST 18

Richards 1 Try, Potter 1 Try, Liley 1 Con, 2 PG   Callard 1 Try 1 Con 1 PG, Blackmore 1 Try, Barnes 1 PG

Midlands: J. Liley, F. Packman (Northampton), I. Bates, S. Potter (Leicester), H. Thorneycroft (Northampton), R. Angell (Coventry), M. Linnett (Moseley), J. Olver (Northampton), D. Garforth, M. Johnson (Leicester), S. Lloyd, P. Shillingford (Moseley), N. Back, D. Richards (captain) (Leicester). Replacement: R. Cockerill (Leicester) for Olver.

South West: J. Callard (Bath), N. Beal (Northampton), J. Guscott, P. de Glanville (Bath), S. Morris (Gloucester), S. Barnes (captain), R. Hill (Bath), C. Clark (Swansea), K. Dunn (Wasps), D. Crompton, N. Redman (Bath), A. Blackmore (Bristol), J. Hall, A. Robinson, B. Clarke (Bath).

FINAL TABLE

	P	W	D	L	F	A	Pts
SOUTH WEST	3	2	1	0	73	51	5
MIDLANDS	3	1	1	1	50	57	3
LONDON	3	1	0	2	70	66	2
NORTH	3	1	0	2	46	65	2

ADT COUNTY CHAMPIONSHIP

DIVISION 1 NORTH

Cumbria 5	Yorkshire 31
Lancashire 29	Northumberland 11
Northumberland 29	Cumbria 3
Yorkshire 16	Lancashire 23
Lancashire 20	Cumbria 0
Northumberland 11	Yorkshire 27

DIVISION 1 SOUTH

Cornwall 15	Middlesex 14
Hampshire 18	Surrey 6
Middlesex 29	Hampshire 10
Surrey 8	Cornwall 9
Hampshire 9	Cornwall 12
Surrey 8	Middlesex 54

DIVISION 2 NORTH

North Midlands 3	Durham 10
Warwickshire 16	Leicestershire 12
Durham 20	Wawickshire 3
Leicestershire 11	North Midlands 6
Durham 17	Leicestershire 10
North Midlands 12	Warwickshire 44

DIVISION 2 SOUTH

Devon 19	Gloucestershire 21
Hertfordshire 6	Kent 29
Gloucestershire 36	Hertfordshire 5
Kent 22	Devon 5
Devon 15	Hertfordshire 13
Gloucestershire 19	Kent 17

DIVISION 3 NORTH

Cheshire 60	East Midlands 3
Notts Lincs & Derby 11	Staffs 8
East Midlands 8	Notts Lincs & Derby 40
Cheshire 18	Notts Lincs & Derby 3
East Midlands 26	Staffs 22

DIVISION 3 SOUTH

Dorset & Wilts 23	Buckinghamshire 8
Sussex 38	Berkshire 5
Berkshire 14	Dorset & Wilts 27
Buckinghamshire 19	Sussex 12
Buckinghamshire 22	Berkshire 6
Dorset & Wilts 15	Sussex 6

DIVISION 4 SOUTH

Oxfordshire 24	Eastern Counties 21
Eastern Counties 13	Somerset 11
Somerset 35	Oxfordshire 11

FINAL TABLES

DIVISION 1 NORTH	P	W	D	L	F	A	Pts
Lancashire	3	3	0	0	72	27	6
Yorkshire	3	2	0	1	74	39	4
Northumberland	3	1	0	2	51	59	2
Cumbria	3	0	0	3	8	80	0

DIVISION 1 SOUTH	P	W	D	L	F	A	Pts
Cornwall	3	3	0	0	36	31	6
Middlesex	3	2	0	1	97	33	4
Hampshire	3	1	0	2	37	47	2
Surrey	3	0	0	3	22	81	0

DIVISION 2 NORTH	P	W	D	L	F	A	Pts
Durham	3	3	0	0	47	16	6
Warwickshire	3	2	0	1	63	44	4
Leicestershire	3	1	0	2	33	39	2
North Midlands	3	0	0	3	21	65	0

DIVISION 2 SOUTH	P	W	D	L	F	A	Pts
Gloucestershire	3	3	0	0	76	41	6
Kent	3	2	0	1	68	30	4
Devon	3	1	0	2	39	56	2
Hertfordshire	3	0	0	3	24	80	0

DIVISION 3 NORTH	P	W	D	L	F	A	Pts
Cheshire	3	3	0	0	101	15	6
Notts Lincs & Derby	3	2	0	1	54	34	4
East Midlands	3	1	0	2	37	122	2
Staffs	3	0	0	3	39	60	0

DIVISION 3 SOUTH	P	W	D	L	F	A	Pts
Dorset/Wilts	3	3	0	0	65	28	6
Bucks	3	2	0	1	49	41	4
Sussex	3	1	0	2	56	39	2
Berkshire	3	0	0	3	25	87	0

DIVISION 4 SOUTH	P	W	D	L	F	A	Pts
Somerset	2	1	0	1	46	24	2
E. Counties	2	1	0	1	34	35	2
Oxfordshire	2	1	0	1	35	56	2

ADT COUNTY CHAMPIONSHIP — SEMI-FINALS

Saturday 20th February 1993

LANCASHIRE 17   MIDDLESEX 11
Hamer 1 Try, Ainscough 4 PG   Tarbuck 1 Try, Challinor 2 PG

Saturday 20th February 1993

CORNWALL 3   YORKSHIRE 20
Chapman 1PG   Tipping 1 Try, Crowley 1 Try, Liley 2 Cons 2PG

ADT COUNTY CHAMPIONSHIP — FINAL

Saturday 17th April 1993   At Twickenham

LANCASHIRE 9   YORKSHIRE 6
Ainscough 3 PG   Liley 2 PG

ADT UNDER 21 CHAMPIONSHIP

Saturday 17th April   At Twickenham

BUCKINGHAMSHIRE 22   WARWICKSHIRE 0
Harvey 1 Try, Shaw 1 Try, Robertson 1 Try, Braithwaite 1 Con 1 PG

INTER SERVICES CHAMPIONSHIP

Willis Group Trophy

Saturday 13th March 1993

At Twickenham

ROYAL NAVY 15   THE ARMY 37

Palmer 1 Try, Sibson 1 Try, Bethwaite 1 Con 1 PG   Atkins 1 Try, Brammer 1 Try, Deans 1 Try 1 DG, Watson 2 Tries, Graham 1 Con, Spowart 2 Cons 1 DG

Royal Navy: K. Bethwaite, E. Gibbs, D. Sibson, R. Bigland, L. Oman, J. Kaye, C. Read, M. Dunhan, M. Clay, N. Bartlett, C. Palmer, S. Trench, R. Armstrong, S. Jones, C. Dixon (captain)

Army: H. Graham, J. Simon, A. Glasgow, C. Spowart, E. Atkins, A. Deans (captain), D. Williams, S. Stewart, J. Brammer, J. Fowers, D. Dahinten, T. Swan, T. Rodber, G. James, M. Watson. Replacement: D. Coghlan for Stewart.

Windsor Life Challenge Cup

Wednesday 24th March 1993

At Twickenham

THE ARMY 17   ROYAL AIR FORCE 20

Glasgow 1 Try, Rodber 1 Try, Spowart 2 Cons 1 PG   Watkins 1 Try, Underwood 1 Try, Hull 1 Con 1 PG

Army: H. Graham, P. Simon, A. Glasgow, C. Spowart, E. Atkins, A. Deans (captain), D. Williams, D. Coghlan, J. Brammer, J. Fowers, D. Dahinten, T. Swan, T. Rodber, G. James, M. Watson.

Royal Air Force: S. Lazenby, S. Crossland, G. Sharp, S. Roke, R. Underwood, P. Hull, S. Worrall (captain), D. Robson, S, Collins, A. Billett, B. Richardson, R. Burn, C. Morgan, C. Moore

Windsor Life Trophy

Wednesday 31st March 1993

At Twickenham

ROYAL NAVY 7   ROYAL AIR FORCE 23

Palmer 1 Try, Oman 1 Con   Worrall 1 Penalty Try, Hull 2 Cons 1 PG

Royal Navy: K. Bethwaite, E. Gibbs, D. Sibson, R. Bigland, L. Oman, J. Kaye, I. Torpey, W. Dunhan, M. Clay, N. Bartlett, I. Russell, S. Trench, R. Armstrong, I. Dixon (captain), C. Palmer. Replacement: S. Burns for N. Bartlett.

Royal Air Force: S. Lazenby, S. Crossland, G. Sharp, S. Roke, R. Underwood, P. Hull, S. Worrall (captain), D. Robson, S, Collins, A. Billett, B. Richardson, R. Burn, C. Morgan, C. Moore. Replacement: M. Cooke for S. Lazenby

FINAL TABLE

	P	W	D	L	F	A	Pts
Royal Air Force	2	2	0	0	43	24	4
Army	2	1	0	1	54	35	2
Royal Navy	2	0	0	2	22	60	0

THE BEST PACK IN THE CHAMPIONSHIP.

THE PILKINGTON CUP

FIRST ROUND — Saturday 19th September 1992

Amber Valley 3	Hereford 6
Askeans 24	Ruislip 0
Berry Hill 24	Salisbury 10
Bradford & Bingley 23	Aspatria 9
Bridgwater Albion 20	Old Alleynians 17
Brixham 16	Tabard 18
Camborne 11	Redruth 24
Chesterfield 8	Worcester 13
Clifton 43	Horsham 10
Exeter 30	Newbury 6
Harrogate 25	Leamington 15
High Wycombe 27	Old Colfeans 0
Lichfield 52	Penrith 3
London Welsh 31	Havant 8
Lydney 13	Basingstoke 6
Sedgley Park 6	Leeds 20
Sheffield 17	Liverpool St Helens 14
Sudbury 19	North Walsham 12
Tiverton 21	Henley 30
Towcestrians 15	Macclesfield 10
Tynedale 39	Hartlepool Rovers 16
Vale of Lune 3	Otley 46
Vipers 5	Broughton Park 15
Westcombe Park 7	Old Blues 18

SECOND ROUND — Saturday 7th November 1992

Bedford 21	Askeans 12
Bridgwater Albion 3	Redruth 7
Coventry 34	Hereford 15
Exeter 15	Berry Hill 13
Fylde 21	Leeds 6
Henley 18	London Welsh 40
Lichfield 8	Waterloo 39
Lydney 6	Clifton 9
Morley 39	Broughton Park 17
Moleley 16	Harrogate 12
Old Blues 3	Blackheath 27
Otley 8	Sale 14
Richmond 37	Sudbury 15
Rosslyn Park 49	Plymouth 3
Tabard 14	High Wycombe 9
Towcestrians 8	Newcastle Gosforth 36
Tynedale 21	Sheffield 14
Wakefield 31	Bradford & Bingley 9
Worcester 15	Nottingham 39

THIRD ROUND — Saturday 28th November 1992

Clifton 3	Exeter 14
Coventry 14	Nottingham 28
Morley 10	Tynedale 6
Moseley 19	Fylde 6
Newcastle Gosforth 13	Gloucester 10
Orrell 20	Sale 3
Redruth 16	London Welsh 7
Richmond 22	Wakefield 25
Rosslyn Park 10	Wasps 37
Rugby 27	Bedford 14
Saracens 20	Bristol 15
Tabard 13	Northampton 50
Waterloo 9	Bath 8
West Hartlepool 13	London Irish 8
Harlequins 72	Blackheath 3
London Scottish 11	Leicester 20

FOURTH ROUND — Saturday 23rd January 1993

Harlequins 47	Wakefield 18
Northampton 33	Newcastle Gosforth 3
Nottingham 3	Leicester 28
Redruth 3	Exeter 8
Rugby 5	Moseley 11
Wasps 18	Saracens 17
Waterloo 8	Orrell 3
West Hartlepool 21	Morley 3

QUARTER FINAL
Saturday 27th February 1993

Leicester 76	Exeter 0
Northampton 37	Moseley 15
Waterloo 14	Harlequins 21
West Hartlepool 9	Wasps 15

SEMI FINAL
Saturday 10th April 1993

WASPS 13   HARLEQUINS 14

Oti 1 Try, Andrew 1 Con, 2 PG   Thompson 1 Try, Challinor 1 PG 1 DG, Glenister 1 DG

LEICESTER 28   NORTHAMPTON 6

Richards 1 Try, Back 1 Try, Boyle 1 Try, Liley 2 Cons   Beal 2 PG
2 PG, Harris 1 DG

FINAL
Saturday 1st May 1993 At Twickenham

HARLEQUINS 16   LEICESTER 23

Glenister 1 Try, Challinor 1 Con 1 PG   Potter 1 Try, Johnson 1 Try, Liley 1 Con 2 PG, Harris
1 DG

Harlequins: K. Bray, C. Madderson, W. Carling, G. Thompson, J. Alexander, P. Challinor, R. Glenister, J. Leonard, N. Killick, A. Mullins, A. Snow, R. Langhorn, M. Russell, P. Winterbottom (captain), C. Sheasby
Leicester: J. Liley, T. Underwood, S. Potter, I. Bates, R. Underwood, J. Harris, A. Kardooni, G. Rowntree, R. Cockerill, D. Garforth, M. Johnson, M. Poole, J. Wells (captain), N. Back, D. Richards

539

THE BEST PACK IN THE CHAMPIONSHIP.

PROVINCIAL INSURANCE CUP

QUARTER FINAL

Saturday, 23rd January 1993

NORTH
Old Anselmians 9   Kidderminster Carolians 15

Old Northamptonians 12   Fleetwood* 17

SOUTH
Hitchin 8   Datchworth 0

Tredworth 5   Stow-on-the-Wold 0

* Played Saturday, 30th January 1993

SEMI FINAL

Saturday, 27th February 1993   At Moseley

Fleetwood 24   Tredworth 5

At Nuneaton

Hitchin 19   Kidderminster Carolians 10

FINAL

Saturday, 3rd April 1993   At Twickenham

Fleetwood 13   Hitchin 7

Wilkinson 1 Try, Berry 1 Try, Burnage 1 DG   Marshall 1 Try, Jeffries 1 Con

Fleetwood: M Hill, P Seed, A Crowther, S Fearn, M Wilkinson, S Burnage, J Wright, B Gawne, B Baxter (Capt.), M Pilkington, A Burman, P Hanley, S Merrick, D Berry, I Cameron

Hitchen: C Lee, V Donnelly, L Jeffries, A Smith, R Simon, A Forrest, R Owen, P Joyce, I Callicott (A Nicol 40), P Tasko, D Marshall (Capt.), R Coley, p Broadhurst, D Thompson, B James

Referee: R Quittenton (Sussex Society)

SCOTLAND

McEWAN'S SCOTTISH INTER-DISTRICT CHAMPIONSHIP

SATURDAY 21st NOVEMBER
Edinburgh 13   Glasgow 13
North & Midlands 3   South 26

SATURDAY 28TH NOVEMBER
Glasgow 9   South 7
North & Midlands 18   Edinburgh 45

WEDNESDAY 2ND DECEMBER
Exiles 17   Glasgow 7

SATURDAY 5TH DECEMBER
Glasgow 15   North & Midlands 22
South 8   Exiles 6

WEDNESDAY 9TH DECEMBER
Edinburgh 20   Exiles 19

SATURDAY 12 DECEMBER
Exiles 15   North & Midlands 17
South 19   Edinburgh 15

FINAL TABLE

	P	W	D	L	F	A	Pts
South	4	3	0	1	60	33	6
Edinburgh	4	2	1	1	93	69	5
North & Midlands	4	2	0	2	60	101	4
Glasgow	4	1	1	2	44	59	3
Exiles	4	1	0	3	57	52	2

LEAGUE TABLE - DIVISION 1

	P	W	D	L	F	A	Pts
Melrose	13	12	0	1	326	134	24
Edinburgh Acads	13	9	1	3	265	155	19
Gala	13	9	1	3	275	171	19
Currie	13	9	1	3	275	171	19
Jed-Forest	13	7	0	6	206	185	14
Borouhmuir	11	6	0	5	208	162	12
Hawick	12	5	1	6	197	199	11
Heriot's FP	13	5	0	8	295	285	10
Stirling County	13	5	0	8	179	208	10
Watsonians	13	5	0	8	196	277	10
Kelso	13	5	0	8	211	345	10
Selkirk	13	4	1	8	194	316	9
Glasgow High/Kelv	13	4	0	9	291	255	8
Dundee HS FP	12	3	0	9	142	269	6

LEAGUE TABLE - DIVISION 2

	P	W	D	L	F	A	Pts
West of Scotland	13	11	0	1	377	156	22
Stew/Melv FP	13	11	0	2	354	156	22
Musselburgh	13	11	0	2	283	124	22
Glasgow Acads	13	8	1	4	331	208	17
Clarkston	13	7	1	5	267	173	15
Ayr	13	7	0	6	165	210	14
Peebles	13	6	1	6	150	178	13
Preston Lodge FP	13	5	2	6	204	205	12
Kirkcaldy	13	5	1	7	233	234	11
Grangemouth	13	4	0	9	189	261	8
Edinburgh Wands	13	4	0	9	176	253	8
Wigtownshire	13	3	2	8	160	294	8
Dunfermline	13	2	2	9	141	322	6
Kilmarnock	13	2	0	11	120	376	4

LEAGUE TABLE - DIVISION 3

	P	W	D	L	F	A	Pts
Haddington	13	10	0	3	346	94	20
Biggar	12	9	0	3	278	117	18
Hutch/Aloy	12	9	0	3	226	133	18
Hill/Jord	13	7	0	6	199	194	14
Howe	13	6	2	5	190	188	14
Langholm	13	7	0	6	144	190	14
Potobello	13	6	0	7	221	177	12
Dumfries	13	6	0	7	242	241	12
Royal H	12	5	1	6	165	197	11
Corstorphine	12	5	1	6	160	201	11
Morgan	12	5	0	7	169	202	10
Perthshire	12	4	0	8	138	181	8
Gordonians	12	4	0	8	193	242	8
St Boswells	12	2	0	10	118	432	4

LEAGUE TABLE - DIVISION 4

	P	W	D	L	F	A	Pts
Stewartry	13	13	0	0	295	96	26
East Kilbride	12	11	0	1	281	120	22
Dalziel	13	9	0	4	182	143	18
Trinity	11	8	0	3	255	116	16
Aber GS	12	7	0	5	331	165	14
Leith	13	7	0	6	218	276	14
Cambus	11	5	0	6	151	182	10
Highland	12	5	0	7	145	179	10
Edinburgh Uni	13	5	0	8	174	211	10
CQP	12	4	0	8	116	153	8
Linlithgow	12	4	0	8	119	208	8
Livinston	12	3	0	9	128	209	6
Alloa	12	3	0	9	133	222	6
Lismore	12	1	0	11	131	379	2

LEAGUE TABLE - DIVISION 5

	P	W	D	L	F	A	Pts
Ardrossan	12	11	0	1	255	97	22
N Berwick	13	10	0	3	277	125	20
Clydebank	13	8	0	5	240	172	16
Falkirk	12	8	0	4	176	126	16
Irvine	13	7	1	5	214	115	15
Glenrothes	12	6	1	5	177	153	13
Hillfoots	13	6	0	7	164	169	12
Aberdeenshire	12	6	0	6	189	199	12
Penicuik	12	5	0	7	155	193	10
Madras	13	5	0	8	152	224	10
Paisley	13	5	0	8	174	255	10
Lenzie	13	4	1	8	182	218	9
Waysiders	12	3	1	8	146	195	7
Moray	13	2	0	11	138	396	4

LEAGUE TABLE - DIVISION 6

	P	W	D	L	F	A	Pts
Duns	13	13	0	0	585	111	26
Berwick	13	10	0	3	312	96	20
Marr	13	8	0	5	245	107	16
Harris	13	8	0	5	207	158	16
Forrester	13	7	1	6	218	217	14
Greenock	13	6	0	7	267	197	12
Lasswade	13	6	0	7	170	186	12
Earlston	12	6	0	6	177	237	12
Dunbar	13	6	0	7	126	263	12
Murrayfield	13	6	0	7	151	309	12
St Andrews	13	5	0	8	216	236	10
Cumbernauld	12	5	0	7	126	219	10
Broughton	13	3	0	10	112	286	6
Drumpellier	13	1	0	12	116	406	2

WALES

WELSH RUGBY UNION CHALLENGE CUP

5TH ROUND

23rd January 1993

Cardiff 14	v	St Peters 16
Kenfihill 6	v	Llanelli 17
Trimsaren 10	v	Bonymaen 20
Pyle 10	v	Neath 20
Cwmwrach 14	v	Crosskeys 23
Cardiff Quins 20	v	Butler Wells 13
Tredegar 0	v	South Wales Police 21
Fleur de Lys 0	v	Bridend 12
Pontypool United 0	v	Newport 10
Colwyn Bay 0	v	Pontypool 18
Tonyrefail 6	v	Dunvant 12
Tenby United 6	v	Swansea 22
Llandovery 15	v	Tondu 12
Abercarn 3	v	Tallywain 18
Tumble 3	v	Newbridge 11

30th January 1993

Pontypridd 62	v	Pencoed 0

6TH ROUND

27th February 1993

Bridgend 41	v	Llandovery 0
Dunvant 10	v	Cross Keys 10
Llanelli 67	v	Newbridge 3
Neath 30	v	Talywaun 7
Pontypool 18	v	Pontypridd 21
St Peters 13	v	Bonymaen 18
South Wales Police 11	v	Swansea 27

QUARTER FINALS

Saturday 3rd April 1993

Bonymaen 0   Swansea 13
Bridgend 18   Newport 16
Llanelli 24   Pontypridd 6
Neath 24   Cross Keys 24

SEMI FINALS

Bridgend 15   Neath 33
Llanelli 29   Swansea 18

FINAL

Saturday 8th May 1993

Llanelli 2   Neath 18
Half Time: 12-3

I Evans (2T), Lewis (1DG), Stephens (2P 1C)

Bowling (1T), Varney (1T0, Thorburn (2P 1C)

Llanelli: I Jones, I Evans, N Boobyer, N Davies, W Proctor, C Stephens, R Moon (Capt), R Evans, A Lamerton, D Joseph, M Perego, P Davies, A Copsey, L Jones, E Lewis

Neath: P Thorburn, J Reynolds, H Woodland, A Donovan, S Bowling, M McCarthy, R Jones, B Williams, A Thomas, J Davies, M Morris, G Llewellyn, G Llewellyn (Capt), A Varney, S Williams.

Referee: G Simmonds, WRU

IRELAND

IRELAND INTER PROVINCIAL CHAMPIONSHIP

Saturday 28th November

Connacht 29   Leinster 9

Munster 11   Ulster 12

Saturday 5th December

Leinster 21   Munster 20

Ulster 19   Connacht 6

Saturday 19th December

Ulster 12   Leinster 8

Connacht 17   Exiles 17

FINAL TABLE

	P	W	D	L	F	A	Pts
Ulster	4	4	0	0	59	40	8
Connacht	4	1	2	1	62	65	3
Munster	3	1	2	0	51	43	2
Leinster	3	1	2	0	38	61	2
Exiles	2	0	1	1	32	33	1

PROVINCIAL CUPS

Connacht
Corinthians 1   Ballina 5

Leinster
St Mary's College 12   Old Wesley 6

Munster
Garryowen 12   Young Munster 5

Ulster
Dungannon 20   Ballymena 18

LEAGUE TABLE - DIVISION 1

Young Munster	8	6	1	1	114	44	70	13	6	3	6	20
Cork Constitution	8	5	0	2	166	128	38	12	15	5	2	20
St Mary's	8	5	1	2	170	94	75	11	15	10	2	23
Greystones	8	4	1	3	132	132	0	9	11	10	3	16
Old Wesley	8	4	0	4	107	151	-44	8	7	6	3	17
Dungannon	3	3	0	5	144	172	-28	8	11	4	5	22
Shannon	8	2	1	5	86	75	11	5	8	2	2	12
Garryowen	8	2	0	6	132	117	15	4	8	4	4	24
Ballymena	8	2	0	6	107	148	-41	4	4	3	4	23

LEAGUE TABLE - DIVISION 2

Lansdowne	9	9	0	0	209	118	91	18	22	15	6	17
Wanderers	9	7	0	2	168	121	47	14	17	7	1	22
Blackrock	9	6	1	2	148	95	54	13	12	4	2	25
Dolphin	9	5	0	4	133	124	9	10	14	6	3	15
Terenure	9	5	0	4	123	121	2	10	13	5	1	15
Instonians	9	5	0	4	124	126	-2	10	11	6	3	16
Old Crescent	9	3	0	6	130	166	-36	6	7	4	2	23
Galwegians	9	1	2	6	97	143	-46	4	11	6	0	10
Bangor	9	1	1	7	112	174	-62	3	8	6	5	15
Clontarf	9	1	0	8	86	133	-47	2	11	5	0	7

UNIVERSITY MATCH

Tuesday 8th December 1992   At Twickenham

OXFORD 11   CAMBRIDGE 17

Spence 1 Try, Malone 1 Penalty Goal & 1
Dropped Goal

Blastone 1 Try, Davies 1 Conversion & 2
Penalty Goals, Davies 2 Dropped Goals,
Flood 2 Dropped Goals

OXFORD: M Joy, A Lumsden, *K Street, D O'Mahoney, D Spence, N Malon, *S du Toit, I Buckett, *M Patton, *A Williams, *D Evans, J Daniell, B Nasser, C Lion-Catchet, B O'Mahony, Replacement: D Currie

CAMBRIDGE: *L Davies, S Burns,J Flood, D Hopley, G Batston, *K Price, *M de Maid, D Perrett, A Read, P Callow, D Bicke, *D Dix, M Duthie, R Jenkins, *E Peters

Referee: E F Morrison (Bristol)

*Denotes Old Blue

BARBARIANS 1992-93

Tuesday 3rd November 1992	v Newport	Newport	W48-23
Saturday 28th November 1992	v AUSTRALIA	Twickenham	L20-30
Monday 28th December 1992	v Leicester	Leicester	L23-41
Wednesday 10th March 1993	v East Midlands	Northampton	W77-59
Saturday 10th April 1993	v Cardiff	Cardiff	W36-34
Monday 12th April	v Swansea	Swansea	W36-26

	P	W	D	L	F	A
SUMMARY	6	4	-	2	240	213

UNIVERSITIES ATHLETIC UNION
U.A.U. Championship

Loughborough 24   West London Institution 11
Bristol University 20   Durham University 13

Wednesday, 17th March 1993   At Twickenham

FINAL

Bristol University 18   Loughborough 25

Tomlinson 1 Try, Metcalfe 1 Try, Diprose 1 Try,   Nolan 1 Try, Bracken 1 Try, John 1 Con 2 PG.
Tomlinson 2 Cons 2 PG

Loughborough:N Stork, M Nicholson, P Bingham, R Tomlinson, M Dawson, G Williams, R Stone, G Reynolds, C Johson, D Lockyer, M Wright, D Jones, A Metcalf, N Richardson (Capt), A Diprose

Bristol University: M Singer, A Dalwood, M Nolan, M Jones, A Robertson, C John, K Braken, T Murray, J Binks (Capt), A Reuben, O Johnson, J Nakhorn, G Bulstrode, A Maynard, K Seecharan.

Referee: D Matthews (Liverpool).

COUNTY CUP FINALS

NORTH

Cheshire	New Brighton 11	Winnington Park 38
Cumbria	Aspatria 17	Wigton 8
Durham	Stockton 24	Hartlepool Rovers 13
Lancashire	Waterloo 13	Liverpool St Helens 11
Northumberland	Newcastle Gosforth 6	Tynedale 6 (Shared)
Yorkshire	Otley 22	Rotherham 5

MIDLANDS

East Midlands	Kettering 24	Peterborough 10
Leicestershire	Syston 9	Westleigh 3
North Midlands	Birmingham & Solihull 35	Hereford 0
Notts/Lincs/Derbys	Scunthorpe 5	Derby 3
Staffordshire	Stoke-on-Trent 8	Walsall 5
Warwickshire	Broadstreet 19	Barker's Butts 10
Nottinghamshire	Mansfield 20	Newark 15

SOUTH WEST

Berkshire	Reading 35	Windsor 10
Buckinghamshire	High Wycombe 21	Amersham-Chiltern 18
Cornwall	Redruth 28	St Ives 6
Devon	Exeter 31	Brixham 14
Dorset & Wilts	Wimborne 10	Salisbury 3
Gloucestershire	Stroud 16	Matson 14
Oxfordshire	Henley 13	Oxford 3
Somerset	Bridgwater & Albion 21	Old Redcliffians 5

LONDON & SOUTH EAST

Eastern Counties	Sudbury 9	North Walsham 8
Hampshire	Basingstoke 37	Alton 3
Hertfordshire	Tabard 26	Cheshunt 12
Kent	Westcombe Park 18	Askeans 11
Middlesex	Ruislip 18	Grasshoppers 3
Surrey	Old Midwhitgiftians 20	Dorking 6
Sussex	Worthing 3	Lewes 0

HOSPITALS CUP

1st ROUND

St Bartholomew's 10   Royal Free 3
Chislehurst

Kings College 15   St George's 3
Dulwich

2nd ROUND

St Bartholomew's 0   St Mary's 27
Chislehurst

Guy's 6   Charing Cross-Westminster 10
Cobham

St Thomas's 0   The London 18
Cobham

King's College 26   University College-Middlesex 3
Dulwich

SEMI-FINAL

St Mary's 23   The London 0
Old Deer Park

Charing Cross-Westminster 48   King's College 0

Wednesday, 10th March 1993   **At Old Deer Bark, Richmond**

FINAL

Charing Cross-Westminster 16   St Mary's 9

Sinclair 1 Try, Swartz 1 Try, Clift 2 Penalty Goals   Morgan 1 Dropped Goal, Berry 2 Penalty Goals

Charing Cross-Westminster: A Redman, A Sinclair, G O'Driscoll, M Hutton, C Swartz, D Clift (Capt), E Rowe, I Josephs, A Dalrymple, A Norrish, M Jeffrey, H Lewis, B Whitehouse, J Hickley, R Walker.

St Mary's: D Abrams, R Wintle, A Morgan, J Waters, C Boos, S Berry, C Wright (Capt), N Hunt, L O'Hara, J Reid, J Torkington, P Tooze-Hobson, M Tremelling, C Langrish, M Crowther.

WORLD CUP SEVENS

POOL A: Fiji 42 v Latvia 0; S Africa 28 v Japan 5; Wales 33 v Romania 7; Fiji 28 v Japan 17; Latvia 5 v Romania 22; S Africa 26 v Wales 14; Fiji 40 v Romania 0; Japan 7 v Wales 35; Latvia 5 v S Africa 47.

POOL B: New Zealand 49 v Holland 7; France 22 v US 7; Ireland 21 v S Korea 12; New Zealand 19 v US 5; Holland 12 v S Korea 28; France 9 v Ireland 17.

POOL C: Australia 28 v Taiwan 0; Scotland 15 v Tonga 7; Argentina 17 v Italy 7; Australia 7 v Tonga 10; Taiwan 14 v Italy 15; Scotland 10 v Argentina 14; Australia 40 v Italy 0; Tonga 17 v Argentina 5; Taiwan 5 v Scotland 26.

POOL D: England 40 v Hong Kong 5; W Samoa 47 v Spain 0; Canada 21 v Namibia 7; England 31 v Spain 0; Hong Kong 19 v Namibia 17; W Samoa 28 v Canada 14.

QUARTER FINALS

POOL E: Ireland 17 v W Samoa 0; Fiji 21 v Tonga 7; Fiji 13 v W Samoa 12; Ireland 14 v Tonga 12; W Samoa 42 v Tonga 7; Fiji 31 v Ireland 7

POOL F: Australia 7 v S Africa 5; England 21 v New Zealand 12; England 14 v S Africa 7; New Zealand 42 v Australia 0; S Africa 31 v New Zeland 12; Australia 21 v England 12

SEMI FINALS

England 21   Fiji 7
Australia 21   Ireland 19

FINAL
England 21   Australia 17

Harriman 1 Try, Dallaglio 1 Try, Rodber 1 Try, Beal 3 Cons.   Lynagh 1 Try, Campese 1 Try, Taupeaafe 1 Try, Lynagh 1 Con.

England: A Harriman, A Adebayo, N Beal, D Scully, C Sheasby, T Rodber (J Cassell 15), L Dallaglio.

Australia: D Campese, R Constable, M Lynagh, S Taupeaafe, J Fenwicke, M Burke, W Ofahengaue.

Referee: P Robin (France).

PLATE
(For teams finishing 3rd in qualifying pools):

SEMI FINAL
Argentina 24   Korea 0
Spain 10   Wales 7

FINAL
Argentina 19   Spain 12

BOWL
(For teams finishing fourth in qualifying pools):

SEMI FINAL
Scotland 14   France 7
Japan 14   Canada 0

FINAL
Japan 33   Scotland 19

HONG KONG SEVENS

Saturday 27th March 1993

GROUP A: Fiji 49 v Malaysia 0; Namibia 38 v Malaysia 7; Fiji 40 v Namibia 7.
GROUP B: Canada 28 v Papua New Guinea 12; Welsh President's VII 40 v Canada 0.
GROUP C: Ireland 7 v Italy 5; Italy 19 v Hong Kong 14; Ireland 24 v Hong Kong 0.
GROUP D: Australia 47 v Singapore 5; American Eagles 42 v Singapore 0; Australia 45 v American Eagles 42.
GROUP E: W Samoa 35 v Thailand 0; Japan 40 v Thailand 0; W Samoa 40 v Japan 7.
GROUP F: Scotland 28 v Romania 5; Tonga 31 v Romania 14; Scotland 10 v Tonga 7.
GROUP G: S Africa 49, v, Sri Lanka 0; Argentina 19 v Sri Lanka 7; S Africa 28 v Argentina 0.
GROUP H: New Zealand 28 v Taiwan 5; Taiwan 14 v S Korea 7; New Zealand 34 v S Korea 0.

QUARTER FINAL
Fiji 33 v Welsh President's VII 7; Australia 17 v Ireland 12; W Samoa 28 v Scotland 14; New Zealand 20 v South Africa 12.

SEMI FINAL
Fiji 17   Australia 14
W Samoa 24   New Zealand 14.

FINAL
W SAMOA 24   V FIJI 12

553

LONDON FLOODLIT SEVENS

Wednesday, 28th April 1993, At Rosslyn Park RFC, Roehampton.
POOL A: London Scottish 7 v Wasps 26; London Scottish 21 v London Welsh 21; Wasps 22 v London Welsh 14, Wasps qualify for semi-final.
POOL B: fiji 24 v Cambridge University 5; Fiji 21 v Harlequins 1O; Cambridge University 12 v Harlequins 19; Fiji qualify for semi-finals.
POOL C: Western Samoa 21 v Blackheath 7; Western Samoa 14 v Richmond 7; Blackheath 7 v Richmond 14; Western Samoa qualify for the semi-finals.
POOL D: London Irish 21 v Rosslyn Park 17; London Irish 29 v Saracens 14; Rosslyn Park 7 v Saracens 35. London Irish qualify for semi-finals.
Semi-Finals: Wasps 7 v Fiji 26; Western Samoa 12 v London Irish O.

FINAL
Fiji 19   Western Samoa 12
N.B. Fiji were represented by Fiji Spartans.

MIDDLESEX SEVENS

Final Rounds Saturday 8th May 1993 at Twickenham
SIXTH ROUND: London Scottish 19 v Blackheath 15 (aet); Richmond 12 v Northampton 1; Glocester 5 v Saracens 27; Reading O v Harlequins 48; Wellington (NZ) v Rosslyn Park 12; Wasps 31 v Basingstoke O; Orrell 5 v London Irish 33; Old Gaytonians 5 v Western Samoa 38.
QUARTER-FINAL: London Scottish 12 v Northampton 26; Saracens 14 v Harlequins 21; Well (NZ) 1O v Wasps 35; London Irish 14 v Western Samoa 17.
SEMI-FINALS: Northampton 26 v Harlequins 5; Wasps 17 v Western Samoa 12 (aet).

FINAL
NORTHAMPTON 24   WASPS 26
PLATE
1ST ROUND: Blackheath 7 v Richmond 14; Gloucester 14 v Reading 28; Rosslyn Park 15 v Basingstoke 26; Orrell 31 v Old Gaytonians 7.
SEMI-FINALS: Richmond 26 v Reading 14: Basingstoke 31 v Orrell 14.

FINAL
Richmond 36   Basingstoke 7

HARLEQUINS SEVENS

Sunday 7th September 1992 at Stoop Memorial Ground, Twickenham
POOL A: Richmond 29 v Harlequins O; Northampton 14 v Newport 35; Richmond 7 v Northampton 29; Harlequins 21 v Newport 33; Richmond 12 v Newport 21; Harlequins 12 v Northampton 24; Final positions: Newport 6 pts., Northampton 4 pts., Richmond 2 pts., Harlequins O pts.,
POOL B: Zebre (Italy) 7 v England 26; Cardiff 14 v Lord's Taverners 17; Cardiff 26 v Zebre (Italy) 14; England 26 v Lord's Taverners 14; Zebre 12 v Lord's Taverners 26; Engand 17 v Cardiff 21. Final positions: England 4 pts. (win pool on tries difference), Lord's Taverners 4 pts., Cardiff 4 pts., Zebre (Italy) O pts.

FINAL
NEWPORT 14   ENGLAND 38

WOMEN'S RUGBY 1992-93

MAIN RESULTS

WRFU NATIONAL CUP

QUARTER FINALS

Saracens 18   Richomd I 3
Wasps 56   Richmond II 0
Bury 0   Old Leamingtonians 0
Waterloo   Blackheath
(Waterloo win)

SEMI-FINALS

Wasps 5   Saracens 11
Old Leamingtonians 0   Waterloo 46

FINAL

Saracens 70   Waterloo 0

OTHER RESULTS

League Championship
Saracens

UAU Final
Cardiff IHE 0   Loughborouh University 46

England 10   Nomads 0

INTERNATIONALS

Scotland 10   Ireland 0
England 23   Wales 5

WORTHINGTON NATIONAL TENS

1st Round

Wasps 26	Newcastle Gosforth 5
Bristol 31	London Scottish 14
Gloucester 24	West Hartlepool 0
Wakefield 36	Northampton 5
Bath 26	Orrell 14
London Irish 0	Saracens 29
Orrell 35	Rugby 7
Nottingham 5	Harlequins 38
Wasps 17	Bristol 14
Gloucester 14	Wakefield 5
Bath 12	Saracens 21
Orrel 12	Harlequins 35

SEMI-FINALS

Gloucester 21	Wasps 19
Harlequins 26	Saracens 12

FINAL

Gloucester 29   Harlequins 0

SUPER TEN COMPETITION RESULTS

POOL A

	P	W	D	L	F	A	Pts
Auckland	4	4	0	0	125	59	16
Natal	4	3	1	0	129	63	12
Western Samoa	4	2	2	0	80	113	8
Queensland	4	1	3	1	75	89	5
Otago	4	0	4	0	63	148	0

POOL B

	P	W	D	L	F	A	Pts
Transvaal	4	4	0	0	121	53	16
New South Wales	4	2	2	1	57	84	9
Northern Transvaal	4	2	2	0	109	109	8
North Harbour	4	1	3	2	82	99	6
Waikato	4	1	3	1	75	99	5

FINAL

Saturday, 22nd May 1993 in Johannesburg.

Transvaal 20   Auckland 17

Transvaal: Pienaar (1T), Schmidt (1T), van Rensburg (2P 2C)

Auckland: Tuigamala (1T), Stensness (1T), Fox (1P 2C).

NOTES

NOTES

NOTES

NOTES

NOTES

NOTES

CLUB INDEX

CLUB INDEX

CLUB INDEX

CLUB INDEX

CLUB INDEX

567

CLUB INDEX

CLUB INDEX

CLUB INDEX

CLUB INDEX

CLUB INDEX

LEAGUE
STRUCTURE

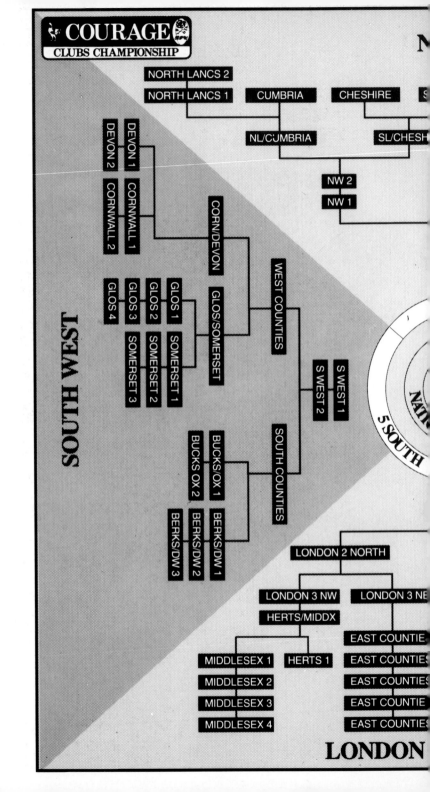

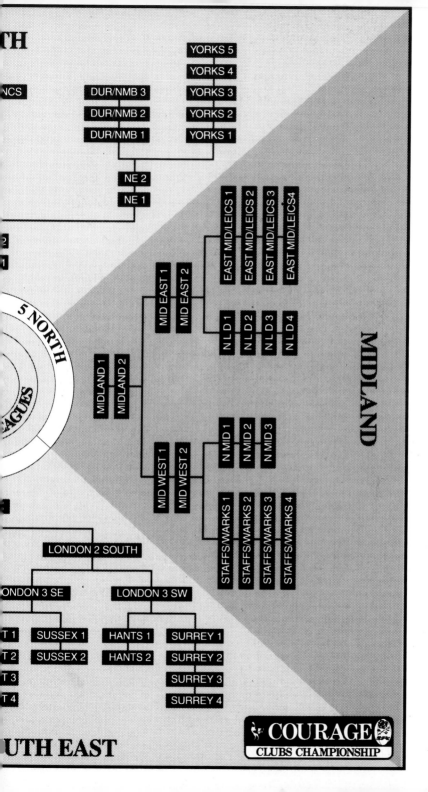

TH

NCS

DUR/NMB 3
DUR/NMB 2
DUR/NMB 1

YORKS 5
YORKS 4
YORKS 3
YORKS 2
YORKS 1

NE 2
NE 1

EAST MID/LEICS 1
EAST MID/LEICS 2
EAST MID/LEICS 3
EAST MID/LEICS4

MID EAST 1
MID EAST 2

N L D 1
N L D 2
N L D 3
N L D 4

MIDLAND 1
MIDLAND 2

5 NORTH
LEAGUES

MID WEST 1
MID WEST 2

N MID 1
N MID 2
N MID 3

STAFFS/WARKS 1
STAFFS/WARKS 2
STAFFS/WARKS 3
STAFFS/WARKS 4

MIDLAND

LONDON 2 SOUTH

ONDON 3 SE
LONDON 3 SW

T 1
SUSSEX 1
HANTS 1
SURREY 1

T 2
SUSSEX 2
HANTS 2
SURREY 2

T 3
SURREY 3

T 4
SURREY 4

UTH EAST

COURAGE
CLUBS CHAMPIONSHIP